D1571854

Physics of Electrolytes

Physics of Electrolytes

Volume 1

Transport Processes in
Solid Electrolytes and
in Electrodes

edited by

J. HLADIK

*Department of Physics,
University of Dakar,
Senegal, Africa*

1972

ACADEMIC PRESS · London · New York

CHEMISTRY

ACADEMIC PRESS INC. (LONDON) LTD.
24/28 Oval Road,
London NW1

United States Edition published by
ACADEMIC PRESS INC.
111 Fifth Avenue
New York, New York 10003

Library of Congress Catalog Card Number: 70–170742
ISBN: 0–12–349801–5

PRINTED IN GREAT BRITAIN BY
ROYSTAN PRINTERS LIMITED
Spencer Court, 7 Chalcot Road
London NW1

CONTRIBUTORS

G. Amsel, *Groupe de Physique des Solides, Ecole Normale Supérieure, Tour 23, 9 quai Saint Bernard, Paris 5, France.*

F. Bénière, *Laboratoire d'Electrochimie, Bat F, Faculté des Sciences, 9 quai Saint Bernard, Paris 5, France.*

F. K. Fong, *Department of Chemistry, Purdue University, Lafayette, Indiana 47907, USA.*

R. J. Friauf, *Département of Physics and Astronomy, University of Kansas, Lawrence, Kansas 66044, USA.*

E. Hartmann, *Technical University, Budapest, Hungary.*

J. Hladik, *Département de Physique, Faculté des Sciences, Université de Dakar, Sénégal, West Africa.*

K. Hughes, *Webb Corbett Limited, Stourbridge, Worcestershire, England.*

J. O. Isard, *Department of Glass Technology, University of Sheffield, England.*

A. Kvist, *Department of Physics, Chalmers University of Technology, Göteberg, Sweden.*

E. Riande,* *Instituto de Plásticos y Caucho, Madrid, Spain.*

*Present address *Mellon Institute, 4400 Fifth Avenue, Pittsburgh, Pennsylvania 15213, USA.*

FOREWORD

Electrochemistry deals with chemical reactions in response to electrical phenomena and vice versa. It has always been based on a mutual interaction between people studying the phenomenological laws of electricity and those concerned with the atomistic concepts of matter. The basis of the introduction of electrochemistry as a scientific discipline was the discovery of electrolytes. For a long period only liquid electrolytes were known, the reason for this being that the the mobility of ions in liquid systems are by and large several orders of magnitude higher than in solids.

Electrical potential differences in electrochemical systems amount to several volts and reflect the magnitude of the chemical affinities. In order to build up and keep stable these differences in electrical potential by a separation of electrical charges in a finite time, at least a minimum electrical conductivity is necessary for the system under consideration. In solid systems this minimum conductivity is in general obtained only at elevated temperatures. Thus, much of solid state electrochemistry turns out also to be high temperature electro-chemistry. Generally both ionic and electronic conductivity occurs in solids. Since by definition solid electrolytes must have ionic transference numbers close to unity, one may state that solid electrolytes occur only among those ionic compounds of which the components differ in Pauling's electronegativity scale by two or more. This rule of thumb is in line with experimental facts; by and large only halides and oxides exhibit component activity regions in which the transference number of ionic species comes close to unity, and there seems to be little chance of finding sulphides, nitrides or carbides sufficiently stable to permit their use as solid electrolytes.

Historically, the application of solid electrolytes is much newer than the application of salt melts or aqueous ionic solutions as electrolytes. Nevertheless, at the beginning of this century such physical chemists as Nernst, Warburg, Haber and Tubandt knew of the electrolytic nature of certain ceramics or glasses. A systematic approach towards ionic conductivity in solids, however, was not possible before the advent of point defect thermodynamics in crystals, which must be regarded as a prerequisite for the understanding of transport properties in solids. This field was investigated in principle in the late twenties and early thirties by Frenkel, Wagner, Schottky and Jost, among others, and has the same importance for solid state electrochemistry as has the field of electrolyte structure and ion interactions for the electrochemistry of aqueous or liquid systems.

During the following years C. Wagner presented his classical work on the oxidation of metals and solid state reactions in which he assumed that these heterogeneous reactions are electrochemical in character. This meant that he postulated an independent transport of ions and electrons (and/or holes) through the reaction product layer to find the reactants at the phase boundary. It is well known today that the formulation of the transport equations in the reaction product layer and their integration, taking into account the proper boundary conditions, lead directly to the parabolic rate law of tarnishing and solid state reactions. Integration of the same transport equations, taking into account the boundary conditions of an open circuit galvanic cell, yields the electromotive force of the galvanic cell, in which the Gibbs free energy of the virtual cell reaction is the essential term beside the transference numbers. In view of this it becomes clear why research in the fields of solid state electrochemistry and solid state reactions is so mutually beneficial.

In the last decade there were two main stimuli for solid state electrochemistry at elevated temperatures. Firstly, there appeared a paper by Kiukkola and Wagner in the *Journal of the American Electrochemical Society* of 1957 which pointed out the potentialities of solid electrolytes for thermodynamic investigations at moderate and high temperatures and which reintroduced doped zirconia as a solid electrolyte. This and similar electrolytes have subsequently gained great popularity among chemists and physical chemists for thermodynamic and kinetic investigations. Secondly, modern techniques in space and in reactor plants require new methods for the conversion of different sorts of energy into electrical energy, a subject right within the province of solid state electrochemists. Here the interest has been stimulated also by the discovery of the ionic solids Ag_3SI, $RbAg_4I_5$ and related compounds, which conduct anomalously well at room temperature. Research on fuel cells and new batteries for smogless propulsion should also be mentioned in this context.

Where are the main activities in solid state electrochemistry nowadays, and in which direction can the future research in this field be expected to go? Looking through journals for original publications, it is still the application of the traditional solid electrolytes for thermodynamic investigations including coulometric titrations which seems to have priority. Moreover, solid electrolytes have recently been used extensively to determine transport coefficients of condensed systems without introducing new principles. Another point worth mentioning is the search for new solid electrolytes or a testing of new combinations of known electrolytes in order to extend the range of applicability in high temperature electrochemistry.

What is the future direction then for solid state electrochemistry? Regarding the analogy with electrochemical research on liquid systems, one may expect considerable efforts from solid state electrochemists in the field of electrodes, which is concerned with the structure and the kinetic aspects of solid/liquid and solid/solid interfaces. The state of knowledge in this area is still deficient, however by improving it, not only will interfaces be understood much better, but also the application of electrochemical probes for various questions in solid state kinetics will be promoted. In any case, solid state electrochemistry will prove to be an exciting scientific field in the years to come, and its influence on technology can hardly be overrated.

June, 1972.

H. SCHMALZRIED

Institute for Theoretical Metallurgy, Technical University, Clausthal, West Germany.

CONTENTS OF VOLUME 2

CONTENTS

A. SOLID ELECTROLYTES AND ELECTRODES

1. THE SOLID STATE

J. Hladik

Université de Dakar, Senegal, West Africa

I. Classification of Solids

A. Types of Solids

1. Crystalline and Amorphous States

The solids may be classified as crystalline or amorphous substances.

A crystal is a discontinuous medium with a triply periodic distribution of matter. The three-dimensional pattern may be obtained by a three-dimensional repetition of a certain pattern unit. Crystals may be formed from solution, by cooling the molten material or by deposition from the vapour. According to the conditions, single crystals or polycrystalline material may be obtained.

Since there will, in general, be random orientation of the individual crystallite in a polycrystalline mass, the properties of the material in bulk may resemble those of an amorphous rather than a crystalline substance.

When the size of the crystallite becomes comparable with the size of the pattern unit, one can no longer speak of crystals, since the essential feature of

1

a crystal is its periodicity of structure. One then speaks of amorphous solids. Typical examples of amorphous substances are glasses, charcoal, and polymers. Glasses are alternatively described as supercooled melts, the rate of cooling and the viscosity having been too great to permit rearrangement of the ordered state of crystal. Polymers are composed of very large and irregular molecules and in such cases a crystalline packing is not easily obtained.

Between the two extreme cases of crystalline and amorphous states, it is possible to find intermediate substances which are very difficult to classify. For simplicity we shall not discuss the mixed types here.

2. Molecular and Macromolecular Compounds

When the molecules of a compound keep their individuality in a solid, one then speaks of a molecular compound. One can identify the H_2O molecules in ice by means of X-ray diffraction; this solid is therefore a molecular crystal.

The molecules in the crystal structures of almost all organic compounds are bound within themselves by strong covalent bonds whereas they are bound one to another only by much weaker forces, usually of the van der Waals type. Structures in which discrete molecules can be clearly recognized are said to be molecular. Although they are most common among organic compounds we shall in fact find that there are many inorganic compounds, and even elements, whose structure is molecular in this sense.

The great majority of inorganic compounds are non-molecular in that no molecule can be discerned in the crystal structure. For example, in the structure of sodium chloride no one sodium atom is associated with one chlorine atom to form the molecule NaCl.

3. Metals and Non-metals

Since electrons play such an important part in determining physical and chemical properties, it is appropriate to divide all solids into two basic groups —metals and non-metals—the principal difference being the form of their electron energy spectra.

We consider as non-metals those substances which have a finite value for the activation energy of the valence electrons, $\Delta E > 0$, and as metals those substances for which $\Delta E = 0$. Metals are good electrical conductors and their electrical conductivity falls as the temperature rises.

In non-metals the valence band is full and the conduction band is completely empty, so that at low temperatures the substance behaves as an insulator. As the temperature rises, thermal activation takes places and some of the valence electrons make the transition into the conduction band, producing electron conductivity. The electrical conductivity increases rapidly with temperature according to an exponential law.

In non-metals ionic conductivity may occur; this is a possible method of charge transfer in heteropolar substances at high temperatures, when the velocity of diffusion is sufficiently large. The electrical conductivity in this case increases exponentially with the temperature.

The electrical conductivity of solids depends on their physical and chemical nature and the conditions of the experiments. The electrical conductivity varies within wide limits (Table I). Some metals at low temperatures pass into the superconducting state and their resistivity is zero. The best insulators attain the value of 10^{20}–10^{30} ohm. cm at low temperatures.

TABLE I. Specific resistivity of some solids (25°C)

Insulators and semiconductors	ρ(ohm. cm)	Metals	ρ(ohm. cm)
Paraffin wax	3×10^{18}		
Quartz	$1\cdot2 \times 10^{14}$	Bismuth	$1\cdot2 \times 10^{-4}$
Silicon	10^2	Lead	2×10^{-5}
		Zinc	6×10^{-6}
		Silver	$1\cdot49 \times 10^{-6}$
Germanium	$8\cdot9 \times 10^{-1}$		
Graphite	3×10^{-3}	Superconductors 0 (0°K)	

B. Types of Binding

Other aspects of crystals required attention concerning the communal effects. Most important of these, perhaps, is the nature of the bonding which exists between the molecules, atoms or ions, holding these particles in their crystal position.

The forces that hold non-metallic crystal particles together can be classified into four main types. In a given crystal, although one of these forces might predominate, there will probably be contributions from forces of some of the other types. In spite of this overlapping, the classification of crystals, in terms of the predominant force type, is very useful.

(1). *Ionic forces.* The predominant force operating in ionic crystals is the electrostatic, or ionic, force between the charged ions. A smaller contribution results from the interaction of the charge of a given particle with the polarizability of the neighbouring ions.

(2). *Covalent bonding.* A few rather important crystals are made up of atoms joined together throughout the crystal by covalent forces. A number of no less important crystals depend on covalent forces in one or two dimensions and on van der Waals forces in the remaining dimension.

The classic example of the first type is that of the diamond. The most important representatives of the class of crystals which have a two-dimensional array of covalent bonds are graphite and mica; the layers of graphite are held together by the relatively weak van der Waals forces.

(3). *Van der Waals forces.* Most organic crystals fall into the crystal type in which van der Waals forces predominate. The source of these forces can be broken down to dipole–dipole, induction and London dispersion forces. Those forces are relatively weak and the typical organic crystal, which is usually held together by such forces, is soft and has a low melting point.

(4). *Hydrogen bonds.* The effect of hydrogen bonds on the form and strength of crystals is both important and widespread. The typical hydrogen-bond energy of 6 kcal puts the strength of this bond between that of the covalent bond and the van der Waals effect. Ice is the classical example of this type of bond. Many organic compounds with hydroxyl groups, such as alcohols, phenols and carboxylic acids, crystallize in a manner at least partly dictated by hydrogen-bond formation.

We emphasize that the distinction between the bond types is by no means absolute. In many crystals, the bonds are of an intermediate character, displaying some of the properties of two or more types. Initially, however, it is convenient to discuss these bond types in isolation.

C. Classification of Solids

The classification of crystals adopted by Seitz (1949) is based on the chemical, electric, magnetic and thermic properties of solids. He distinguishes five main types of crystal: metals, ionic crystals, covalent crystals, semiconductors and molecular crystals.

We can adopt a similar classification, but dividing it according to our previous considerations. Semiconductors are not a very unified class of solids as far as the type of binding is concerned and we shall not include them in our preliminary classification. A rough classification of solids is shown in Table II.

Subdivision of each type of solid in this classification may be made by considering other criteria: ionic or electronic conductivity, organic or inorganic compounds, type of structure.

Wells (1962) bases his classification of crystals on the distinction between structures containing infinite one- or two-dimensional complexes, or those consisting of three-dimensional complexes. It seems, however, that no attempted classification of crystalline structures will allow for all the possible types of structure which can be adopted, even by the elements and the simpler compounds. A structure like that of $HgBr_2$ may be regarded as intermediate between a purely molecular and a layer structure. The structures of elementary arsenic and bismuth illustrate the transition from two-dimensional to a three-dimensional complex.

TABLE II.   A classification of solids

State	Association	Type of binding
Crystalline	Macromolecular	Metals
		Ionic crystals Covalent crystals
	Molecular	Van der Waals bonds
		Hydrogen bonds
Amorphous	Macromolecular	
	Molecular	

Wells (1962) criticises a classification according to the types of bonds:

"At first sight it might appear that the most obvious way of classifying structures would be to group them according to the types of bonds between the atoms, recognising the four extreme types, ionic, covalent, metallic and van der Waals. However, bonds approximating to pure types are rare, and in most crystals these are bonds of several different types. Numerous intermediate classes have to be recognised and it is found that classifications based on bond type become complicated without being comprehensive. They also have the disadvantage that they over-emphasise the importance of "pure" bond types, bonds of intermediate character being treated as a departure from these extremes. It would seem preferable to be able to discuss the nature of the bonds in a particular crystal without having prejudged the issue by classifying the crystal."

We can add that all the types of interatomic binding forces to which we have referred above are primarily electronic in nature, their differences only arising from differences in the electronic structures of the particles concerned. Thus, wave-mechanically speaking, the distinctions are quite artificial, the electron density distribution being the only "reality".

It seems that no classification is perfect, Nature being too complicated for the logical dreams of the human mind. "God is sophisticated, but He is not malevolent" (A. Einstein).

II. The Band Theory

A. One-electron Approximation

1. General Assumptions

The quantum theory of solids is well developed for crystalline solids. We shall only give a survey of some quantum properties of crystalline solids, even though electrochemists do not consider their domain limited to the crystalline state. The quantum theory has also been extended to liquid and solid amorpohus conductors (Gubanov, 1965).

In crystalline solids, the atoms are stacked in a regular manner, forming a three-dimensional pattern which may be obtained by a three-dimensional repetition of a certain pattern unit. When the periodicity of the pattern extends throughout a certain piece of material one speaks of a single crystal.

Although we shall assume in this chapter that the crystals under consideration are "perfect", the reader will have ample opportunity in the remainder of this book to realise that a large number of properties of solids are determined by lattice imperfections, such as impurities, vacant lattice sites, and atoms in interstitial positions.

In a solid, the number of interacting particles is very large and the problem of calculating the electronic wave functions is very complicated. One must therefore introduce a number of simplifying assumptions. Firstly, one will assume that the nuclei in the crystalline solid are at rest. Even with this assumption, we are still left with a many-electron problem which can be solved only by approximative methods.

The most important approximation method which has been applied extensively to the problem of solids is the so-called one-electron approximation. In this approximation, the field seen by a given electron is assumed to be that of the fixed nuclei plus some average field produced by the charge distribution of all other electrons. Thus, the total wave function for the system is given by a combination of individual wave functions of each electron.

The discussion given below is essentially limited to the Bloch scheme where an electron is considered to belong to the crystal as a whole rather than to a particular atom.

2. The Bloch Theorem

We shall use the Bloch theorem: all one-electron wave functions for periodic potentials have the form

$$\Psi_k(\mathbf{r}) = \exp(i\mathbf{k}\mathbf{r})\, u_k(\mathbf{r})$$

where $u_k(\mathbf{r})$ is a periodic function whose periodicity is that of the crystal lattice.

We can note that the Bloch functions have the property

$$\Psi_k(x + na) = \exp[ik(x + na)]\, u_k(x + na) = \exp[ik(x + na)]\, u_k(x)$$
$$= \exp(ikna)\, \Psi(x)$$

where n is an integer.

The Bloch functions lead to the same probability density $\psi^* \psi$, in each unit cell of the crystal. In the nth unit cell we can write this probability density,

$$\Psi^*(x + na)\,\Psi(x + na) = \exp\,(-ikna)\,\Psi^*(x)\exp\,(ikna)\,\Psi(x) = \Psi^*(x)\,\Psi(x).$$

B. The Krönig–Penney Model

1. One-dimensional Model

It is possible to arrive at an exact solution of the Schrödinger equation, if we consider the infinite periodic, one-dimensional, square-well potential shown in Fig. 1. Although this periodic potential is only a crude approximation to that

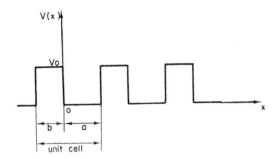

FIG. 1. The Krönig–Penney model. Infinite periodic one-dimensional potential.

found in the real crystal, it is, nevertheless, very useful to illustrate many of the important characteristic features of the quantum behaviour of electrons in periodic lattices.

The Schrödinger equation for a single electron in the periodic potential $V(x)$ is

$$\frac{\mathrm{d}^2 \Psi(x)}{\mathrm{d}x^2} + \frac{2m}{\hbar^2}\,[E - V(x)]\,\psi(x) = 0. \tag{1.1}$$

The wave functions associated with this model must have the Bloch form,

$$\Psi(x) = \exp\,(ikx)\,u_k(x)$$

where $u_k(x)$ is a periodic function whose periodicity is $(a + b)$. Substituting into the Schrödinger equation (1.1), $u_k(x)$ must satisfy the equation,

$$\frac{\mathrm{d}^2 u}{\mathrm{d}x^2} + 2ik\,\frac{\mathrm{d}u}{\mathrm{d}x} + \left(\alpha^2 - k^2 - \frac{2mV}{\hbar^2}\right)u(x) = 0 \tag{1.2}$$

where $\alpha = (2mE/\hbar^2)^{1/2}$. For the given potential we have the two equations,

$$\frac{d^2u_1}{dx^2} + 2ik\frac{du_1}{dx} + (\alpha^2 - k^2)u_1(x) = 0 \qquad 0 < x < a, \qquad (1.3)$$

$$\frac{d^2u_2}{dx^2} + 2ik\frac{du_2}{dx} + (\beta^2 - k^2)u_2(x) = 0 \qquad -b < x < 0, \qquad (1.4)$$

where $\beta = [2m(E - V_0)/\hbar^2]^{\frac{1}{2}}$. It is a purely imaginary quantity for $0 < E < V_0$.

The solutions $u_1(x)$ and $u_2(x)$ are:

$$u_1(x) = A\exp[i(\alpha - k)x] + B\exp[-i(\alpha + k)x] \qquad 0 < x < a, \qquad (1.5)$$

$$u_2(x) = C\exp[i(\beta - k)x] + D\exp[-i(\beta + k)x] \qquad -b < x < 0. \qquad (1.6)$$

The continuity of the wave function $\Psi(x)$ and its derivative at $x = a$ and $x = -b$, demands that the functions $u(x)$ satisfy these same conditions, since e^{ikx} is a well-behaved function. These boundary conditions give:

$A + B = C + D$

$i(\alpha - k)A - i(\alpha + k)B = i(\beta - k)C - i(\beta + k)D$

$A\exp[i(\alpha - k)a] + B\exp[-i(\alpha + k)a] = C\exp[-i(\beta - k)b]$
$$+ D\exp[i(\beta + k)b]$$

$i(\alpha - k)A\exp[i(\alpha - k)a] - i(\alpha + k)B\exp[-i(\alpha + k)a]$
$$= i(\beta - k)C\exp[-i(\beta - k)b] - i(\beta + k)D\exp[i(\beta + k)b].$$

There is no solution other than $A = B = C = D = 0$, unless the determinant of these equations vanishes. Expanding this determinant, one can show that it can be expressed as:

$$-\frac{\alpha^2\beta^2}{2\alpha\beta}\sin\alpha a\sin\beta b + \cos\alpha a\cos\beta b - \cos k(a + b) = 0. \qquad (1.7)$$

In the energy range $0 < E < V_0$, β is imaginary, and the determinant can be expressed in a slightly different form. Letting $\beta = i\gamma$, and noting that $\cos ix = \cosh x$ and $\sin ix = i\sinh x$, the preceding equation can be written:

$$\frac{\gamma^2 - \alpha^2}{2\alpha\gamma}\sinh\gamma b\sin\alpha a + \cosh\gamma b\cos\alpha a - \cos k(a + b) = 0. \qquad (1.8)$$

The two expressions of the determinant are useful; the first when $V_0 < E < \infty$ and the second when $0 < E < V_0$.

The equations (1.7) and (1.8) can be still written in the form:

$$\left[1 + \frac{(\alpha^2 - \beta^2)^2}{4\alpha^2\beta^2} \sin^2 \beta b\right]^{\frac{1}{2}} \cos(\alpha a - \delta) = \cos k(a + b) \qquad (1.9)$$

where

$$\tan \delta = \frac{-\alpha^2 + \beta^2}{2\alpha\beta} \tan \beta b; \qquad V_0 < E < \infty$$

and

$$\left[1 + \frac{(\alpha + \gamma^2)^2}{4\alpha^2\gamma^2} \sinh^2 \gamma b\right]^{\frac{1}{2}} \cos(\alpha a - \delta) = \cos k(a + b) \qquad (1.10)$$

where

$$\tan \delta = \frac{\alpha^2 + \gamma^2}{2\alpha\gamma} \tanh \gamma b; \qquad 0 < E < V_0.$$

The wave functions, $\Psi(x) = e^{ikx} u_k(x)$, must have finite values when x tends towards $\pm\infty$. Since $u(x)$ is a periodic function whose values are the same in each unit cell, it is a well-behaved function as x approaches $\pm\infty$. But e^{ikx} is well behaved at $\pm\infty$, only if k is real. If k were imaginary, e^{ikx} would diverge towards infinity, either at $+\infty$ or $-\infty$. We must, therefore, accept only Bloch functions with real values for k.

From the preceding expressions, (1.9) and (1.10), we can see that in both cases the left-hand side has the form of a cosine function modulate by a factor whose amplitude is always greater than unity. The value of this factor is a maximum for $\alpha = 0$, and tends towards unity in the limit of large energies, where $\alpha \simeq \beta$.

Therefore, for a given value of energy, the function on the left-hand side of these equations will have a value in the range between $+1$ and -1. Then the value for $\cos k(a + b)$ is obtained with a real value for the argument $k(a + b)$. On the other hand, when the value of the function on the left-hand side of the above expressions, (1.9) and (1.10), lies outside the range, ± 1, it means that $\cos k(a + b)$ will have an imaginary argument. Under these last circumstances, the Bloch solutions $\Psi(x)$ will not behave properly at infinity, and the energies associated with such values of k will be forbidden to the electron.

2. Results

The results are illustrated in Fig. 2. The left-hand side of the preceding equations is plotted as a function of energy. The shaded regions show forbidden energy bands, where the value of k is complex. The unshaded regions correspond to the real values of k of the permissible energy bands.

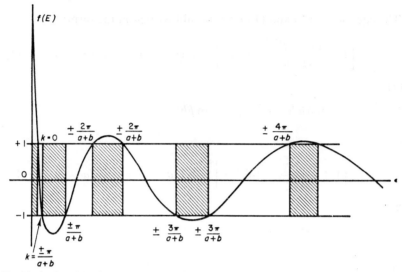

FIG. 2. A plot of the functions on the left-hand side of eqns (1.9) and (1.10) versus energy.

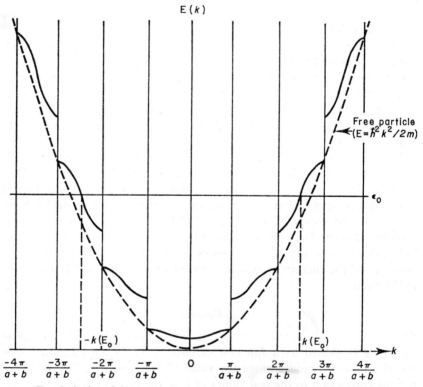

FIG. 3. A plot of the energy E versus k, according to eqns (1.9) and (1.10).

It is possible to plot a curve showing energy E as a function of k as shown in Fig. 3. For large energies, it is evident that the function approaches the free-electron relation $E = \hbar^2 k^2 / 2m$. Therefore, the following conclusions may be drawn:

—the energy spectrum of the electrons consists of a number of allowed energy bands, separated by forbidden regions.

—the width of the permissible energy bands increases with increasing energy.

—the discontinuities in the energy E versus k curve, occur for $k = \pm n\pi/(a + b)$, where n is an integer.

These k-values define the boundaries of the first, second, etc. Brillouin zones.

3. Number of Possible Wave Functions per Band

For a linear crystal of length L, the boundary condition may be taken as:

$$\Psi(x + L) = \Psi(x).$$

Making use of the fact that we are dealing with Bloch functions, this boundary condition can be written:

$$\exp\left[ik(x + L)\right] u_k(x + L) = \exp(ikx)\, u_k(x).$$

u_k being a periodical function, we have $u_k(x + L) = u_k(x)$, and the boundary condition thus requires:

$$k = 2\pi n/L \qquad n = \pm 1, \pm 2, \pm 3, \ldots .$$

The number of possible wave functions in the range dk is, therefore:

$$dn = \frac{L}{2\pi}\, dk. \tag{1.11}$$

If N is the number of unit cells, we have $L\,a = N$. This is the maximum value of n in the relation $k = 2\pi n/L$. This leads to the conclusion that the total number of possible wave functions in any energy band is equal to the number of unit cells N.

According to the Pauli exclusion principle for electrons, each wave function can be "occupied" by at most two electrons. Thus each energy band provides a place for a maximum number of $2N$ electrons.

C. Metals and Non-metals

1. The Motion of Electrons

Although the Krönig–Penney model is a simplified approximation of the potential encountered in real crystals, it will be useful to consider the consequences of the results obtained so far for the motion of electrons.

According to the wave mechanical theory, the particle velocity is equal to the group velocity of the waves representing the particle, i.e.

$$v = \frac{dw}{dk} \tag{1.12}$$

where w is the angular frequency of the Broglie waves. The energy of the particle can be expressed by:

$$E = \hbar w. \tag{1.13}$$

Therefore, the velocity of the particle is written:

$$v = \frac{1}{\hbar} \frac{dE}{dk}. \tag{1.14}$$

When an external electric field F is applied and has acted on the electron for a short period of time dt, the electron has gained the energy:

$$dE = eFv\,dt = (eF/\hbar)(dE/dk)dt. \tag{1.15}$$

Since $dE = (dE/dk)dk$, the rate of change of the wave vector is:

$$\frac{dk}{dt} = \frac{eF}{\hbar}. \tag{1.16}$$

The acceleration of the electron is obtained by differentiating v with respect to t; this gives:

$$\frac{dv}{dt} = \frac{1}{\hbar} \frac{d^2E}{dk^2} \frac{dk}{dt} = \frac{eF}{\hbar^2} \frac{d^2E}{dk^2}. \tag{1.17}$$

The acceleration of a free electron of mass m is:

$$\frac{dv}{dt} = \frac{eF}{m}. \tag{1.18}$$

It follows that the electron in a crystal behaves as if it had an effective mass m equal to

$$m^* = \hbar^2 \left/ \frac{d^2E}{dk^2} \right. . \tag{1.19}$$

Introducing the factor,

$$a_k = m/m^* = (m/\hbar^2)(\mathrm{d}^2E/\mathrm{d}k^2) \tag{1.20}$$

we can see that a_k is a measure for the extent to which an electron in state k is "free".

2. Metals, Intrinsic Semi-conductors and Insulators

The distinction between metals, insulators and intrinsic semi-conductors can be discussed by the preceding band theory, although a proper distinction between these three groups is only possible by considering the theory of a three-dimensional model.

Consider a particular energy band filled with electrons up to a certain value k_1, as shown in Fig. 4.

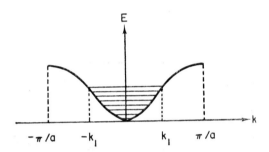

FIG. 4. Energy band filled up to state k_1.

To draw conclusions about the conductivity associated with this band, it is necessary to know the effective number of "free" electrons in the band.

The number of states in an interval $\mathrm{d}k$ (excluding the spin) for a one-dimensional lattice of length L, is (see eqn 1.11):

$$\mathrm{d}n = \frac{L}{2\pi}\,\mathrm{d}k.$$

According to the Pauli exclusion principle, only two electrons occupy each of these states and their number in an interval $\mathrm{d}k$ is L/π. The effective number of "free" electron in this interval can thus be written:

$$\mathrm{d}n_{\mathrm{eff}} = a_k \frac{L}{\pi}\,\mathrm{d}k. \tag{1.21}$$

Extending the summation over all occupied states in the band, we may write, according to eqn. (1.20):

$$N_{\text{eff}} = \int_{-k_1}^{k_1} dn_{\text{eff}} = (L/\pi) \int_{-k_1}^{k_1} a_k \, dk = \frac{2Lm}{\pi\hbar^2} \int_0^{k_1} \frac{d^2E}{dk^2} \, dk. \qquad (1.22)$$

Therefore, the effective number of electrons in the band filled up to state k_1 is:

$$N_{\text{eff}} = (2mL/\pi\hbar^2)[dE/dk]_{k=k_1}. \qquad (1.23)$$

When the band is completely filled, the value $(dE/dk)_{k=k_1}$ is equal to zero and the effective number of electrons vanishes. From this result, it follows that a solid for which a certain number of energy bands are completely filled, the other bands being entirely empty, is an insulator (Fig. 5). When a solid contains an incomplete energy band, the effective number of "free" electrons is different from zero and the solid has a metallic character (Fig. 5).

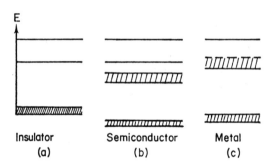

FIG. 5. Electron distribution at $T = 0$. The shaded regions are occupied by electrons.

The theoretical situation depicted by Fig. 5 can occur only at absolute zero. At this temperature, the crystal is in its lowest energy state. When the temperature increases, some electrons from the upper, filled band, are excited into the next empty band and electronic conduction becomes possible. When the forbidden energy gap is of the order of several electron volts, the solid practically remains an "insulator". If the forbidden energy gap is small, about 1 eV, the number of thermally excited electrons may become appreciable. In this case, the solid is an intrinsic semiconductor.

The distinction between insulator and intrinsic semiconductors is thus only a quantitative one. At absolute zero, all intrinsic semiconductors are insulators. When the temperature increases, all insulators may be considered semiconductors.

If a certain number of electrons are excited thermally from the upper, filled band into the conduction band, some of the states in the normally filled bands are unoccupied. These unoccupied states lie essentially near the top of the filled band. We can speak of a "hole" in the filled band.

III. The Tight-binding Approximation

A. The Energy Levels of an Electron

1. The Approximations

In actual crystals, the potential function which is used must be somehow related to the actual potential experienced by an electron, due to the ion cores and all the other electrons of the crystal. An exact solution of this problem, even in the one-electron approximation, is impossible. It is, therefore, customary to approach the problem from two viewpoints: the free-electron approximation and the tight-binding approximation.

In the free-electron approximation, the total energy of the electron is assumed to be always large compared to the periodic potential energy. The circumstances are never perfectly realised in any actual crystal, but for the outermost electrons in many simple metals, including the alkali metals, the requirements are met fairly well over most of the volume of the crystal. Under these conditions the forbidden energy regions will be quite narrow, and the allowed bands broad.

In the tight-binding approximation, the potential energy of the electron accounts for nearly all of the total energy. In this instance, the allowed energy bands are narrow in comparison with the forbidden bands. The tight-binding approximation is based on the assumption that the atoms of the crystals are so far apart that the wave functions for electrons associated with neighbouring atoms overlap only to a small extent. The interaction between neighbouring atoms will, in this case, be relatively weak. The wave functions and allowed energy levels of the crystal as a whole will be closely related to the wave functions and energy levels of isolated atoms.

The question of which of the two approximations is correct in any given situations, of course, depends upon the particular material at hand. In some substances the tight-binding approximation is quite good, while for others, the free-electron approximation is more nearly correct. There are also crystals where neither is very good because the situation is intermediate between the two extreme cases.

2. The Tight-binding Approximations

(a) *LCAO method*: Let us now consider the limit of binding in which the valence electrons are bound sufficiently tightly to their parent ions that all knowledge of their origin is not lost. This is the tight-binding approximation.

This approximation is valid whenever the notion of the valence electron is influenced to a much greater extent by the Coulomb potential of its parent ion than by all other neighbouring ions. We shall see that there are allowed and forbidden energy regions for the valence electrons.

This approximation uses the wave function for an electron in a free atom for constructing the crystal orbital and is based on a linear combination of atomic orbitals (LCAO). We consider an electron in a free atom with the wave function, $\phi(z)$, where z represents the distance from the nucleus. This electron is placed in a central potential $V(\mathbf{r})$, due to the nucleus and the other electrons.

(b) *The s band*: Let us now consider the solution of the Schrödinger wave equations,

$$\Delta \Psi_0 + \frac{2m}{\hbar^2} (E_0 - V)\Psi = 0 \tag{1.24}$$

which corresponds to the spherically symmetric, nondegenerate, s wave. $V(\mathbf{r})$ is the lattice potential.

If $\mathbf{r}_i$ denotes the position of the nucleus of the ith atom, then, in view of the assumption that neighbouring atoms have a very small effect on the electrons of the ith atom, the valence-electron wave function near the ith atom is approximately independent of the other atoms and is, therefore, a function of $\mathbf{r} - \mathbf{r}_i$. The crystal orbital Ψ_0 may then be expressed in the form of a superposition of atomic wave functions,

$$\Psi_0(\mathbf{r}) = \sum_{i=1}^{N} c_i \Phi_0(\mathbf{r} - \mathbf{r}_i) \tag{1.25}$$

where N is the number of lattice ions and $\Phi_0(\mathbf{r} - \mathbf{r}_i)$ is an atomic s-state wave function (the same for each atom of the crystal).

Since we are dealing with an electron in a periodic potential, the function $\Psi_0(\mathbf{r})$ must be a Bloch function. If we take the expression,

$$\Psi_0(\mathbf{r}) = \sum_i \exp(i\mathbf{k} \cdot \mathbf{r}_i) \, \Phi_0(\mathbf{r} - \mathbf{r}_i) \tag{1.26}$$

we can verify that the properties of a Bloch function are satisfied. We have:

$$\Psi_0(\mathbf{r} + \mathbf{r}_j) = \sum_i \exp(i\mathbf{k} \cdot \mathbf{r}_i) \, \Phi_0[\mathbf{r} - (\mathbf{r}_i - \mathbf{r}_j)]$$

$$= \exp(i\mathbf{k} \cdot \mathbf{r}_j) \sum_i \exp[ik(\mathbf{r}_i - \mathbf{r}_j)] \, \Phi_0[\mathbf{r} - (\mathbf{r}_i - \mathbf{r}_j)].$$

The sum in the last expression is equal to $\Psi_0(\mathbf{r})$ and its expression is a Bloch function.

The calculus of the energy of an electron, with wave vector $\mathbf{k}$ in the crystal, is based on the expression

$$E_0(\mathbf{k}) = \frac{\int \Psi_0{}^* \hat{H} \Psi_0 \, d\mathbf{r}}{\int \Psi_0{}^* \Psi_0 \, d\mathbf{r}}. \tag{1.27}$$

where

$$\hat{H} \Psi_0 = \left(\frac{-\hbar^2}{2m} \Delta + V_0 \right) \Psi_0 = \sum_{i=1}^{N} \exp{(i\mathbf{k} \cdot \mathbf{r}_i)} \hat{H} \Phi_0(\mathbf{r} - \mathbf{r}_i). \tag{1.28}$$

The denominator is:

$$\int \Psi_0{}^* \Psi_0 \, d\mathbf{r} = \sum_i \sum_j \exp{[i\mathbf{k}(\mathbf{r}_i - \mathbf{r}_j)]} \int \Phi_0{}^*(\mathbf{r} - \mathbf{r}_j) \Phi_0(\mathbf{r} - \mathbf{r}_i) \, d\mathbf{r}. \tag{1.29}$$

We can only retain the terms $i = j$ of the summation because $\Phi_0(\mathbf{r} - \mathbf{r}_j)$ and $\Phi_0(\mathbf{r} - \mathbf{r}_i)$ have appreciable values only when the end point of the vector $\mathbf{r}$ lies, respectively, in the vicinity of atoms j and i. If the atomic wave functions are normalised, we have:

$$\int \Psi_0{}^* \Psi_0 \, d\mathbf{r} = \sum_i \int \Phi_0{}^*(\mathbf{r} - \mathbf{r}_i) \Phi_0(\mathbf{r} - \mathbf{r}_i) \, d\mathbf{r} = N. \tag{1.30}$$

The numerator will be calculated as follows. Observing that the parent ions have the greatest influence on the valence electrons, it becomes convenient to separate $\hat{H}$ into a large part $\Sigma \hat{H}_i$, and the small part, $\hat{H} - \Sigma \hat{H}_i$, where H_i is the free-atom Hamiltonian

$$\hat{H}_i = \frac{-\hbar^2}{2m} \Delta_i + V_0(\mathbf{r} - \mathbf{r}_i). \tag{1.31}$$

Since

$$\hat{H}_i \Phi_0(\mathbf{r} - \mathbf{r}_i) = E_0{}^{(0)} \Phi_0(\mathbf{r} - \mathbf{r}_i) \tag{1.32}$$

where $E_0{}^{(0)}$ is the unperturbed energy level, it follows that,

$$\hat{H} \Psi_0 = E_0{}^{(0)} \Psi_0 + \sum_i \exp{(i\mathbf{k} \cdot \mathbf{r}_i)} (\hat{H} - \hat{H}_i) \Phi_0(\mathbf{r} - \mathbf{r}_i). \tag{1.33}$$

Thus the energy of an electron with wave vector $\mathbf{k}$ becomes:

$$E_0 = E_0{}^{(0)} + \frac{1}{N} \sum_{i=1}^{N} \exp{(i\mathbf{k} \cdot \mathbf{r}_i)} \int \Psi_0{}^*(\hat{H} - \hat{H}_i) \Phi_0(\mathbf{r} - \mathbf{r}_i) \, d\mathbf{r}. \tag{1.34}$$

Substituting for Ψ_0^* (eqn 1.26), we then have:

$$E_0 = E_0^{(0)} + \frac{1}{N} \sum_i \sum_j \exp\left(i\mathbf{k}\cdot\mathbf{r}_i\right) \int \Phi_0^*(\mathbf{r} - \mathbf{r}_j)(\hat{H} - \hat{H}_i)\,\Phi_0(\mathbf{r} - \mathbf{r}_i)\,d\mathbf{r}. \quad (1.35)$$

Since the terms in the summation over i are identical because of the periodicity of the lattice potential, we need consider only one term, and multiply by N. On the other hand, we can notice that:

$$\hat{H} - \hat{H}_i = V(\mathbf{r}) - V_0(\mathbf{r} - \mathbf{r}_i) \qquad (1.36)$$

and, substituting in the preceding expression, (1.35), we have,

$$E_0 = E_0^{(0)} + \sum_j \exp\left(-i\mathbf{k}\cdot\boldsymbol{\rho}_j\right) \int \Phi_0^*(\mathbf{r} - \boldsymbol{\rho}_j)[V(\mathbf{r}) - V_0(\mathbf{r})]\,\Phi_0(\mathbf{r})\,d\mathbf{r} \qquad (1.37)$$

where $\boldsymbol{\rho}_j = \mathbf{r}_j - \mathbf{r}_i$; $\mathbf{r}_i$ is taken to be the origin.

Taking into account the effect of nearest neighbours on the electronic energy levels and calling

$$\int \Phi_0^*(\mathbf{r})[V(\mathbf{r}) - V_0(\mathbf{r})]\,\Phi_0(\mathbf{r}),\,d\mathbf{r} = -\alpha \qquad (1.38)$$

$$\int \Phi_0^*(\mathbf{r} + \boldsymbol{\rho})[V(\mathbf{r}) - V_0(\mathbf{r})]\,\Phi_0(\mathbf{r})\,d\mathbf{r} = -\beta \qquad (1.39)$$

the expression of E_0 becomes

$$E_0(\mathbf{k}) = E_0^{(0)} - \alpha - \beta \sum_j \exp\left[i\mathbf{k}\cdot(\mathbf{r}_i - \mathbf{r}_j)\right]. \qquad (1.40)$$

Since the free-ion potential V_0 is more binding, i.e. more negative, than is the lattice potential $V(\mathbf{r})$, $V - V_0$ is always negative (α and β are thus always positive). Therefore, $E_0 < E_0^{(0)}$.

(c) *Application to a simple cubic lattice*: In this lattice a given atom has six nearest neighbours, located such that,

$$\boldsymbol{\rho}_j = (\pm a, 0, 0); \quad (0, \pm a, 0); \quad (0, 0, \pm a).$$

Evaluation of the sum $E_0(\mathbf{k})$ then yields for the energy of an s electron in the crystal,

$$E_0(\mathbf{k}) = E_0^{(0)} - \alpha - 2\beta(\cos k_x a + \cos k_y a + \cos k_z a). \qquad (1.41)$$

In the first place, it is observed that the part of $E_0(\mathbf{k})$ is periodic with $\mathbf{k}$. The first Brillouin zone in this case is evidently a cube of edge $2\pi/a$ in $\mathbf{k}$-space, the origin of the $\mathbf{k}$-space being located at the centre of the cube.

Furthermore, since the cosine terms vary between ± 1, the energy levels are contained within an energy band of a total width, 12β. The bottom of the energy band is:

$$(E_0)_{bottom} = E_0^{(0)} - \alpha - 6\beta,$$

and the top:

$$(E_0)_{top} = E_0^{(0)} - \alpha + 6\beta.$$

As long as $\mathbf{k}$ is small, the cosine terms may be expanded. Retaining only the first approximation of this expansion, one obtains:

$$E_0(\mathbf{k}) = E_0^{(0)} - \alpha - 6\beta + \beta\, a^2\, \mathbf{k}^2 \tag{1.42}$$

where $\mathbf{k}^2 = k_x^2 + k_y^2 + k_z^2$. With reference to the bottom of the band, the energy of the electron is proportional to $\mathbf{k}^2$, as in the case of free electrons. Thus in this region the electrons may be considered free electrons with an effective mass m^* determined by:

$$m^* = \frac{\hbar^2}{2\beta\, a^2}.$$

As the band width decreases (decreasing β), the effective mass of the electrons near the bottom of the band increases. This is consistent with the qualitative notion that strongly bound electrons do not move readily from one atom to another. They have a high effective mass and the acceleration produced by an electric field will be relatively small.

(d) The p band: The calculation of the p band is complicated because of the inherent degeneracy that is present. The three degenerate p states are characterised by the functions:

$$\Phi_1(\mathbf{r}); \quad \Phi_2(\mathbf{r}); \quad \Phi_3(\mathbf{r}).$$

In order to avoid excessive mathematical details, we shall consider only the simple-cubic lattice. In this case,

$$\mathbf{r}_j = \mathbf{m}a$$

where $\mathbf{m} = (m_1, m_2, m_3)$ is a set of integers and a is the lattice constant.

The extension of the Bloch function to the p-like orbitals is accomplished by treating each of the three degenerate wave function $\Phi_n(\mathbf{r})$ separately. We have:

$$\Psi_n = \sum_{m_1\, m_2\, m_3} \exp\left[ia(\mathbf{m}\cdot\mathbf{k})\right] \Phi_n(\mathbf{r} - \mathbf{m}a); \qquad n = 1, 2, 3. \tag{1.43}$$

A crystal potential, characterised by the transformations of a cubic group, leaves the atomic p state triply degenerate. Thus the three wave functions, Φ_1, Φ_2, Φ_3, all correspond to the same energy level and we need consider only one of them in calculating the electron energy. If we call this energy E_1, then, in a fashion completely analogous to the derivation of $E_0(\mathbf{k})$ for the s-band, we arrive at the following expression for the p-band energy.

$$E_1(\mathbf{k}) = E_1^{(0)} - \alpha_1 + 2\beta_1 \cos k_x a + 2\beta_1' (\cos k_y a + \cos k_z a) \quad (1.44)$$

where:

$$\alpha_1 = -\int \Phi_1^*(\mathbf{r})(V - V_1)\,\Phi_1(\mathbf{r})\,d\mathbf{r}$$

$$\beta_1 = \int \Phi_1^*(x \pm a, y, z)(V - V_1)\,\Phi_1(x, y, z)\,d\mathbf{r}$$

$$\beta_1' = \int \Phi_1^*(x, y \pm a, z)(V - V_1)\,\Phi_1(x, y, z)\,d\mathbf{r}$$

$$= \int \Phi_1^*(x, y, z \pm a)(V - V_1)\,\Phi_1(x, y, z)\,d\mathbf{r}.$$

If we now invoke the inequality,

$$ka \ll 1$$

inherent in the tight-binding approximation, $E_1(\mathbf{k})$ takes the form

$$E_1(\mathbf{k}) = (E_1^{(0)} - \alpha_1 + 2\beta_1 + 4\beta_1') - \beta_1 a^2 k_x^2 - \beta_1' a^2 (k_y^2 + k_z^2). \quad (1.45)$$

3. Constant Energy Surfaces

For the simple cubic crystal of the preceding section, for values $ka \ll 1$, the energy may be written in the form (eqn 1.42).

$$E(\mathbf{k}) = E_0 - \alpha - 6\beta + \beta a^2 (k_x^2 + k_y^2 + k_z^2).$$

Let us now investigate the form of the surfaces of constant energy in $\mathbf{k}$-space for the simple cubic crystal discussed in the tight-binding approximation. The equation of these surfaces is simply the latter expression with $E(\mathbf{k})$ being regarded as a parametric constant. We can slightly rearrange this expression,

$$k_x^2 + k_y^2 + k_z^2 = \frac{E(\mathbf{k})}{\beta a^2} - \frac{E_0 - \alpha - 6\beta}{\beta a^2} = \text{constant}. \quad (1.46)$$

This is the equation of a sphere in **k**-space. The spherical form of the surfaces of constant energy is indicative of the fact that electrons in this region of **k**-space behave like free electrons. As the value of $E(\mathbf{k})$ increases, the radius of the spherical constant energy surface increases, until the values of **k** associated with points on the surface become so great that the approximation $ka \ll 1$ is no longer valid.

The more general equation (1.41):

$$E(\mathbf{k}) = E_0 - \alpha - 2\beta(\cos k_x a + \cos k_y a + \cos k_z a)$$

must then be used to plot the constant energy surface. As $E(\mathbf{k})$ increases the surfaces which are thus obtained are illustrated in Fig. 6.

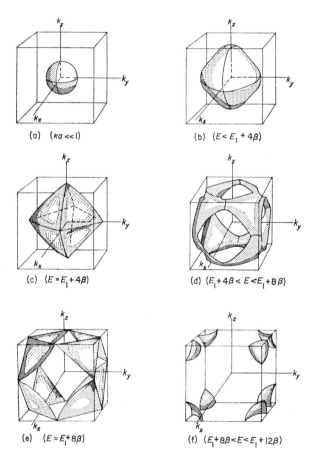

(a) $(ka \ll 1)$

(b) $(E < E_1 + 4\beta)$

(c) $(E = E_1 + 4\beta)$

(d) $(E_1 + 4\beta < E < E_1 + 8\beta)$

(e) $(E = E_1 + 8\beta)$

(f) $(E_1 + 8\beta < E < E_1 + 12\beta)$

FIG. 6. Fermi surface for a simple cubic crystal with spherically symmetric wave functions. Variation of the electron population in the band.

It is clear, from the preceding expression of $E(\mathbf{k})$, that all states within the band must have energy between E_1 and $E_1 + 12\beta$ and that all possible states within this energy range are represented by values of k_x, k_y, k_z lying between the limits, $(\pm \pi/a, \pm \pi/a \pm \pi/a)$.

If there are a given number of electrons belonging to this energy band, and if the temperature is at absolute zero, the electronic energy states will all be occupied up to given Fermi energy, in accord with the Pauli exclusion principle. The electron distribution will, therefore, lie within a volume in **k**-space, which is enclosed by a surface of constant energy, the value of the energy on this surface being the Fermi energy. This surface is often referred to as the Fermi surface. For electrons in a periodic crystal potential, the Fermi surface may also be approximately spherical if the band is nearly empty or nearly full.

At temperatures in excess of absolute zero, some of the electrons will be excited to states of energy higher than the Fermi energy, lying outside the Fermi surface. Thus, there will be some unoccupied states within the Fermi surface. The transition between full and empty states will then no longer be a sharp one; nevertheless, if the difference in temperature is small compared to the Fermi temperature, the region of transition will be quite thin and the essential validity of the Fermi surface picture will be unimpaired.

The intersections of constant energy surfaces with the $k_x k_y$-plane are shown in Fig. 7. These curves can also be regarded as the curves of constant energy for a two-dimensional crystal with a square lattice whose interatomic spacing is a.

4. The Lowest Energy Band

Let us now examine what happens at a point on the surface of the limiting cube enclosing the volume of **k**-space which the electronic states, belonging to this band, may occupy. For simplicity, we shall initially confine our attention to the $k_x k_y$-plane. Let us consider a point on the upper (or lower) edge of the square region shown in Fig. 7. The k_y coordinate of such a point is π/a, while the k_x coordinate may have any arbitrary value, say k_{x_0}. The electron wavelength λ will then be given by:

$$\lambda = \frac{2\pi}{k} = \frac{2\pi}{\sqrt{k_{x_0}^2 + (\pi^2/a^2)}} \tag{1.47}$$

while the sine of the glancing angle θ, related to a set of crystal planes parallel to the x-axis, will be

$$\sin \theta = \frac{k_y}{\sqrt{k_x^2 + k_y^2}} = \frac{\pi}{a\sqrt{k_{x_0}^2 + (\pi^2/a^2)}}. \tag{1.48}$$

We know that the use of X-ray diffraction as a technique for crystal structure analysis is based on the Bragg relation,

$$n\lambda = 2d \sin \theta \qquad (1.49)$$

where n is an integer; d is the spacing between adjacent atomic planes, and θ is the glancing angle between the atomic plane and the incident beam.

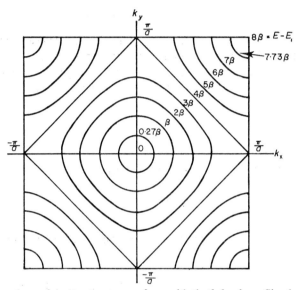

FIG. 7. Intersections of constant energy surfaces with the $k_x k_y$-plane. Simple cubic crystal.

From the preceding value (1.47) of λ, the Bragg relation becomes, with $n = 1$ and $d = a$,

$$\sin \theta = \frac{\lambda}{2a} = \frac{2\pi}{2a\sqrt{k_{x_0}^2 + (\pi^2/a^2)}} \frac{\pi}{a\sqrt{k_{x_0}^2 + (\pi^2/a^2)}} . \qquad (1.50)$$

Thus, the Bragg condition is satisfied by the electron wave function at all points on this part of the boundary. In the same way, it is easy to verify that the Bragg condition, related now to a glancing angle referred to an equivalent set of planes parallel to the y axis, is satisfied at all points on the right-hand (or left-hand) edge of the bounding square. The electron, regarded as a wave, is internally diffracted by the lattice whenever its momentum vector touches this square boundary. Points in **k**-space, beyond the limits of this boundary, correspond to points outside the lowest energy band, belonging to other bands which arise from atomic states of higher energy than the ground state.

There is always an energy gap between the bands. For example, whenever one crosses the edge of the square region enclosed by the lines $k_x = \pm \pi/a$, $k_y = \pm \pi/a$, then a discontinuity in energy accompanied by internal Bragg reflection must occur. The interior of the region contains the totality of states belonging to the lowest energy band.

5. The Two-Dimensional Brillouin Zones

The Bragg condition can be expressed as a relation between vectors in the reciprocal lattice. If $\mathbf{G}$ is 2π times a vector from the origin to a lattice point of the reciprocal lattice, and $\mathbf{k}$ is a vector of magnitude $2\pi/\lambda$ along the direction of the incident X-ray beam, the Bragg condition must imply that (Ewald, 1921):

$$(\mathbf{k} + \mathbf{G})^2 = (\mathbf{k} + \mathbf{G}) \cdot (\mathbf{k} + \mathbf{G}) = k^2 \qquad (1.51)$$

or, expanding the dot product and simplifying:

$$2\mathbf{k} \cdot \mathbf{G} + G^2 = 0. \qquad (1.52)$$

This equation is the vector form of the Bragg equation and we can write this relation:

$$2(k_x G_x + k_y G_y + k_z G_z) + G_x^2 + G_y^2 + G_z^2 = 0. \qquad (1.53)$$

For a two-dimensional square lattice, whose lattice spacing is a, the reciprocal lattice is a square lattice of lattice spacing $1/a$. If the origin is taken for simplicity at a lattice point, then the vectors $\mathbf{G}$ have the form:

$$\mathbf{G}_{mn} = \frac{2\pi}{a}(m\mathbf{i}_x + n\mathbf{i}_y) \qquad (1.54)$$

where m and n are integers and $\mathbf{i}_x$ and $\mathbf{i}_y$ are unit vectors in the k_x and k_y directions respectively. Using this form for the vector $\mathbf{G}$, the preceding equation (1.53) becomes:

$$mk_x + nk_y + \frac{\pi}{a}(m^2 + n^2) = 0. \qquad (1.55)$$

This equation represents a family of straight lines in the $k_x k_y$-plane. Their k_x-intercepts and k_y-intercepts are:

$$k_x\text{-intercepts:} \quad -\frac{\pi}{a}\frac{m^2 + n^2}{m}$$

$$k_y\text{-intercepts:} \quad -\frac{\pi}{a}\frac{m^2 + n^2}{n}.$$

Each of these lines represents a boundary along which a Bragg reflection takes place, and which may form the boundary between states belonging to different energy bands.

If we take $m = 0$, $n = \pm 1$, and $m = \pm 1$, $n = 0$ in k_x- and k_y-intercepts, we obtain the four lines $k_x = \pm \pi/a$ and $k_y = \pm \pi/a$, which bound the region in Fig. 8a, whose interior contains all the states in the lowest energy band of the crystal. This region of k-space is called the first Brillouin zone.

If we now take $m = \pm 1$, we obtain the four lines $k_x \pm k_y = 2\pi/a$ and $k_x \pm k_y = -2\pi/a$.

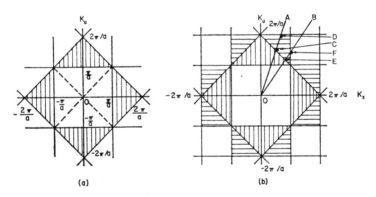

(a)   (b)

FIG. 8. Brillouin zones for a two-dimensional square lattice.
(a) First and second zones.   (b) First three zones.

These four lines are plotted in Fig. 8a. On these boundaries the Bragg condition is satisfied with the order of reflection n, equal to 2. This region is enclosed between the first Brillouin zone and these four intersecting lines, containing all the states in the second energy band. It is referred to as the second Brillouin zone, and has the same area as the first.

The higher zones may be constructed by an extension of the procedure used to arrive at the form of the first and second zones. If we take $m = 0$, $n = \pm 2$, or $m = \pm 2$, $n = 0$, the four lines $k_x = \pm 2\pi/a$, $k_y = \pm 2\pi/a$ are obtained, as shown in Fig. 8b. This method of calculating can be extended to find as many zones as desired.

6. The Three-dimensional Brillouin Zone

The extension of these results to three-dimensional lattices is quite straight-forward. In this instance, of course, the Brillouin zones are three-dimensional regions of k-spaces bounded by planes along which the Bragg condition is satisfied.

The equation of these plane boundaries are obtained from the same equation (1.53):

$$2(k_x G_x + k_y G_y + k_z G_z) + G_x^2 + G_y^2 + G_z^2 = 0.$$

Again, each zone is of equal volume. It is obvious that the first Brillouin zone, for a simple cubic lattice, is a cube of side $2\pi/a$.

The form of the first Brillouin zone for the face-centred and body-centred cubic lattices, and for the hexagonal structure, are shown in Fig. 9. For the b.c.c. lattice, the zone is a rhombic dodecahedron, all of whose faces are {110} planes in k-space. The zone for the f.c.c. lattice is a Tetrakaidecahedron, a polyhedron of 14 faces having the {100} and {111} orientations.

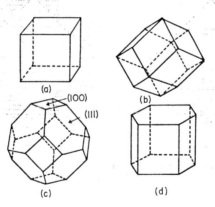

(a)

(100)
(111)

(b)

(c)   (d)

FIG. 9. First Brillouin zones.
(a) Simple cubic lattice,   (b) body-centred cubic lattice,
(c) face-centred cubic lattice,   (d) hexagonal lattice.

B. The Density of States

1. Electronic States within an Energy Band

The density of states is the number of electron states per unit energy interval. This density may be obtained by considering Bloch functions.

Firstly, we shall show that for a finite crystal the number of possible reduced k-values within a single energy band is equal to the number of unit cells contained in the crystal. This statement is the analogue of the conclusion on the number of possible wave functions per band for the Krönig–Penney model.

Let us consider a crystal in the form of a parallelepiped, with edges $N_1\mathbf{a}_1$, $N_2\mathbf{a}_2$, $N_3\mathbf{a}_3$, where N_1, N_2, N_3 are large integers. Employing cyclic boundary conditions, the wave functions should satisfy the conditions,

$$\Psi(\mathbf{r}) = \Psi(\mathbf{r} + N_1\mathbf{a}_1 + N_2\mathbf{a}_2 + N_3\mathbf{a}_3). \tag{1.56}$$

Since $\Psi(\mathbf{r})$ is a Bloch function, this condition is equivalent to the requirement,

$$\mathbf{k} \cdot (N_1\mathbf{a}_1 + N_2\mathbf{a}_2 + N_2\mathbf{a}_3) = 2\pi \text{ times an integer.}$$

This implies that the possible $\mathbf{k}$-values are given by

$$\mathbf{k} = 2\pi[(n_1/N_1)\mathbf{b}_1 + (n_2/N_2)\mathbf{b}_2 + (n_3/N_3)\mathbf{b}_3] \tag{1.57}$$

where n_1, n_2, n_3 are integers and $\mathbf{b}_1, \mathbf{b}_2, \mathbf{b}_3$ are the reciprocal lattice vectors. Now, the components of $\mathbf{k}$ along the reciprocal lattice vector directions, are restricted in accordance with:

$$-\pi b_1 \leqslant k_1 \leqslant \pi b_1,$$

$$-\pi b_2 \leqslant k_2 \leqslant \pi b_2,$$

$$-\pi b_3 \leqslant k_3 \leqslant \pi b_3.$$

From this and from the preceding expression (1.57) of $\mathbf{k}$, it follows that n_1, n_2, and n_3 can accept a total of, respectively, N_1, N_2, N_3 different values. In other words, the total number of $\mathbf{k}$-values within an energy band is given by the product N_1, N_2, N_3 which is equal to the number of unit cells in the crystal.

Each $\mathbf{k}$-value corresponds to one wave function if we exclude the two possible spin directions. Including the spin, the number of possible electronic states within an energy band is, therefore, equal to twice the number of unit cells in the crystal.

2. The Density of States

The result obtained here may be expressed also in the following way. Let us consider a crystal of unit volume, the volume of the unit cell being:

$$\mathbf{a}_1 \cdot (\mathbf{a}_2 \wedge \mathbf{a}_3) = \Omega. \tag{1.58}$$

The crystal then contains $N = 1\Omega$ unit cells. Since the whole reduced zone contains N possible k-values, and since these values are uniformly distributed in the k-space, the number of electronic states dn_s corresponding to a volume element $d\Omega_k$ in k-space is, per unit volume of the crystal:

$$dn_s = \frac{2}{(2\pi)^3}\, d\Omega_k. \tag{1.59}$$

The factor 2 arises from the spin. The quantity dn_s is referred to as the density of states corresponding to the element $d\Omega_k$ in k-space. It will frequently be desirable to introduce the number of states per unit volume of the crystal, per unit energy interval.

Thus, let us consider in the k-space two surfaces of constant energy, one of E and the other of $E + dE$. The volume element $d\Omega_k$ in k-space, corresponding to a differential area dS and bounded by the constant energy surfaces, is:

$$d\Omega_k = dS{\cdot}dk = dS{\cdot}\frac{dk}{dE}\cdot dE. \tag{1.60}$$

Since $(dk/dE) = |\nabla_k E(\mathbf{k})|^{-1}$, we have:

$$dn_s = \frac{2}{(2\pi)^3}\, d\Omega_k = \frac{2ds}{(2\pi)^3}\,\frac{dE}{|\nabla_k E(\mathbf{k})|}. \tag{1.61}$$

Thus, the density of states for the energy band may be obtained by integrating over the entire surface of the reduced zone, so that:

$$Z(E) = \frac{dn_s}{dE} = \frac{2}{(2\pi)^3}\int_S \frac{dS}{|\nabla_k E(\mathbf{k})|} \tag{1.62}$$

where the integration is carried out over a constant energy E. The equation (1.62) represents a general expression for the density of electron states in a three-dimensional crystal.

3. The Density of States for the Simple-Cubic Lattice

If the function $E(\mathbf{k})$ is known, the density of states can, in principle, be calculated from the preceding formula. Unfortunately, however, the mathematical form of $E(\mathbf{k})$ is, in most cases of practical interest, so complex that the integration can be done only by numerical methods.

For the simple cubic lattice in the tight-binding approximation, the $E(\mathbf{k})$ function for an s-band has been given previously and the corresponding density of states function is illustrated in Fig. 10.

Near the bottom of the energy band for this particular example, the form of $E(\mathbf{k})$ is given by equation (1.42).

$$E_0(\mathbf{k}) = E_0^{(0)} - \alpha - 6\beta + \beta a^2 (k_x^2 + k_y^2 + k_z^2)$$
$$= E_1 + \beta a^2 k^2$$

and thus:

$$\frac{dE_0}{dk} = 2\beta a^2 k$$

where $k^2 = k_x^2 + k_y^2 + k_z^2$. The density of states is then, according to equation (1.62)

$$Z(E) = \frac{dn_s}{dE} = \frac{\sqrt{E_0 - E_1}}{2\pi^2 (\beta a^2)^{3/2}}. \tag{1.63}$$

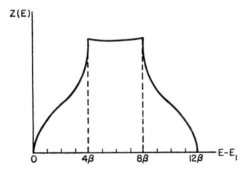

FIG. 10. Density of states curve for the simple cubic lattice in the tight-binding approximation.

Expressing βa^2 in terms of the effective mass, this can be written as:

$$Z(E) = \frac{8\sqrt{2\pi}}{\hbar^3} m^{*3/2} \sqrt{E_0 - E_1} \ (E_0 - E_1 \ll 12\beta) \tag{1.64}$$

which, provided that the origin of energy is taken at the bottom of the band, is the usual parabolic free-electron density states of expression with the inertial mass replaced by the effective mass m^*.

In a similar manner, it can be shown that for energies near the top of the band, where the constant energy surfaces are again spherical in shape, we may write:

$$Z(E) = \frac{8\sqrt{2\pi}}{\hbar^3} m^{*3/2} \sqrt{E + 12\beta - E_0} \tag{1.65}$$

with $E_1 + 12\beta - E_0 \ll 12\beta$. This density of states function vanishes at the top of the band, where $E_0 = E_1 + 12\beta$, and increases parabolically for decreasing energies. It may thus be regarded as a free-particle density of states function for hole-conduction, in a nearly filled band.

C. The Electron Distribution

In any electronic system in thermal equilibrium, the number of electrons per unit volume occupying states in the energy range between E and $E + dE$ is:

$$n(E)\, dE = Z(E)\, F(E)\, dE \tag{1.66}$$

where $Z(E)$ represents the number of possible states per unit volume (including the spin) and $F(E)$ is the Fermi–Dirac distribution:

$$F(E) = 1/[\exp (E - E_F)/kT + 1]. \tag{1.67}$$

E_F is called Fermi level and corresponds to the level which has a probability of $1/2$ of being occupied.

In the case of insulators and semi-conductors, E_F is usually located somewhere between the valence and conduction bands. Therefore, E_F is not a level which can actually be occupied by an electron. If N is the total number of electrons per unit volume, the position of the Fermi level may be determined from the equation,

$$N = \int n(E)\, dE = \int Z(E)\, F(E)\, dE. \tag{1.68}$$

E_F being determined, one can calculate $n(E)$ for a given temperature and function $Z(E)$.

At a temperature other than zero, the density of electrons in the conduction band is:

$$n_c = \int_{E_o}^{top} Z(E)\, F(E)\, dE. \tag{1.69}$$

E_c represents the bottom of the conduction band and $Z(E)$ is the density of states represented in Fig. 11.

Near the bottom of the conduction band. one has, according to the preceding section (eqn 1.64).

$$Z(E) = (4\pi/h^3)(2m_e^*)^{3/2} (E - E_c)^{1/2}, \tag{1.70}$$

m_e^* being the effective mass of an electron near E_c.

If E_f lies roughly halfway between E_v and E_c (Fig. 12), the Fermi–Dirac distribution $F(E)$ decreases rapidly as one moves up in the conduction band. Therefore, we may write, using (1.67), (1.69) and (1.70):

$$n_c = \frac{4\pi}{h^3} (2m_e^*)^{3/2} \int_{E_c}^{\infty} \frac{(E - E_c)^{1/2} \, \mathrm{d}E}{\exp \left[(E - E_F)/kT \right] + 1} . \tag{1.71}$$

One may integrate from E_c to ∞ because $F(E)$ decreases rapidly.

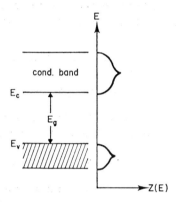

FIG. 11. Scheme of the density of states in an insulator.

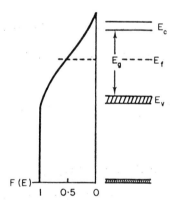

FIG. 12. Fermi distribution function and electron distribution in an insulator.

The term unity in the denominator may be neglected to a close approximation if we assume that $(E_c - E_c) \gtrsim 4kT$. In that case, the integral may be reduced to the form:

$$\int_0^{\infty} y^{1/2} \exp \left(-y \right) \mathrm{d}y = \frac{\pi^{1/2}}{2}.$$

Thus we obtain:

$$n_c = 2(2\pi m_e^* kT/h^2)^{3/2} \exp\left[(E_F - E_c)/kT\right]. \qquad (1.72)$$

The number of holes n_h in the valence band must be equal to the number of electrons n_c. This fact can be used to calculate the unknown quantity E_F by the direct calculation of n_h.

The probability for a state of energy E to be unoccupied is $[1 - F(E)]$. The number of holes per unit volume may thus be written:

$$n_k = \int_{\text{bottom}}^{E_v} Z(E)[1 - F(E)]\,dE$$

where E_v represents the top of the valence band.

$[1 - F(E)]$ decreases rapidly as one goes below the top of the valence band. Near the top, one has, according to the preceding section (eqn 1.65),

$$Z(E) = (4\pi/h^3)(2m_h^*)^{3/2}(E_v - E)^{1/2} \qquad (1.74)$$

where m_h^* represents the effective mass of a hole near the top of the valence band. If the Fermi level lies more than about $4kT$ above E_v, one may use the approximation,

$$1 - F(E) \simeq \exp\left[(E - E_F)/kT\right]. \qquad (1.75)$$

Therefore the density of holes in the valence band is, using (1.73), (1.74) and (1.75),

$$n_k = \frac{4\pi}{h^3}(2m_h^*)^{3/2}\int_{-\infty}^{E_v}(E_v - E)^{1/2}\exp\left[(E - EF)/kT\right]dE. \qquad (1.76)$$

One obtains:

$$n_h = 2(2\pi m_h^* kT/h^2)^{3/2}\exp\left[(E_v - E_f)/kT\right]. \qquad (1.77)$$

Using the fact that $n_h = n_c$, we have, from eqns (1.72) and (1.77):

$$E_F = (E_c + E_v)/2 + \frac{3kT}{4}\log(m_k^*/m_e^*). \qquad (1.78)$$

In general $m_h^* > m_e^*$ and the Fermi level is raised slightly as T increases. If $m_k^* = m_e^*$, the Fermi level lies halfway between E_c and E_v.

From the expression (1.78) of E_F, the densities n_c and n_h are:

$$n_c = n_h = 2(2\pi kT)/h^2)^{3/2}(m_e^* m_h^*)^{3/4}\exp\left[(E_v - E_c)/2kT\right]. \qquad (1.79)$$

References

Bragg, W. L. (1968). "The Crystalline State". Bell, London.

Clark, H. (1968). "Solid State Physics; An Introduction to its Theory". McMillan, Toronto.

Dekker, A. J. (1963). "Solid State Physics". Prentice-Hall, Englewoods Cliffs.

Ewald, P. P. (1921). Z. Kristal. **56,** 129

Ferraro, J. R. (1969). "Introductory Group Theory and its Application to Molecular Structure". Plenum Press, New York.

Fox, D. (1963). "Physics and Chemistry of the Organic Solid State". Interscience, New York.

Gray, T. J. (1957). "The Defect Solid State". Interscience, New York.

Greenaway, D. L. (1968). "Optical Properties and Band Structure of Semiconductors". Pergamon Press, Toronto.

Gubanov, A. I. (1965). "Quantum Electron Theory of Amorphous Conductors". Consultants Bureau, New York.

Hladik. J. (1970). "Eléments de chimie quantique". Dunod, Paris.

Ioffe, A. F. (1960). "Physics of Semiconductors". Academic Press, New York.

Kittel, C. (1970). "Introduction à la physique de l'état solide". Dunod, Paris.

McKelvey, J. P. (1966). "Solid State and Semiconductor Physics". Harper and Row, New York.

Pauling, L. C. (1960). "The Nature of the Chemical Bond and the Structure of Molecules and Crystals". Cornell University Press, Ithaca.

Seitz, F. (1949). "Théorie moderne des solides". Masson, Paris.

Sheehan, W. F. (1962). "Physical Chemistry". Allyn and Bacon, Boston.

Slater, J. C. (1965). "Quantum Theory of Molecules and Solids". McGraw-Hill Book, New York.

Smith, R. A. (1969). "Wave Mechanics of Crystalline Solids". Chapman and Hall, London.

Van Gool, W. (1966). "Principles of Defect Chemistry of Crystalline Solids". Academic Press, New York.

Wells, A. F. (1962). "Structural Inorganic Chemistry". Clarendon Press, Oxford.

2. THE SOLID ELECTROLYTE

J. Hladik

Université de Dakar, Senegal, West Africa

I. Classification of Solid Electrolytes

A. Definitions

Solid electrolytes are solid state materials which possess an electric conductivity partly or wholly due to ionic displacements.

35

This definition is not very precise. Firstly, the magnitude of the conductivities is not mentioned, and secondly, the ratio between the electronic and ionic contributions is not specified. The imprecision of this definition seems inevitable, since the solid electrolyte domain is still not very well defined. A more accurate definition, with quantitative precisions, leads to a restriction concerning the variety of materials to which it would be possible to apply electrochemical techniques.

The range of conductivity of solid ionic conductors is very large. For example, we have the following values at 25°C (Table I):

TABLE I.   Conductivity of some solid electrolytes

Electrolyte	Conductivity Mho-cm^{-1}	Electrolyte	Conductivity Mho-cm^{-1}
$RbAg_4I_5$	$2 \cdot 4 \times 10^{-1}$	AgCl	3×10^{-8}
KAg_4I_5	$2 \cdot 4 \times 10^{-1}$	AgBr	4×10^{-9}
Ag_3SI	1×10^{-2}	commercial glasses	10^{-10} to 10^{-17}
AgI	2×10^{-6}	NaCl	10^{-20}
Cu_2HgI_4	$7 \cdot 6 \times 10^{-8}$	commercial plastics	10^{-20}

The range of the conductivity from 10^{-1} to 10^{-20} Mho cm^{-1}, at 25°C, is only approximate for the ionic conductivity of solid electrolytes. Furthermore, it is possible that ionic conductors with lower and higher values than these given could be studied.

When solid electrolytes possess a conductivity due to both ionic and electronic transport, it is necessary to distinguish between solids which are relevant only to the domain of semi-conductors and those which deal more particularly with the electrochemical studies. This distinction however is neither easy nor clear to establish.

Thus, the electronic contribution to the total conductivity changes both with temperature and with current. In some electrolytes, the ionic conductivity can disappear at lower temperatures and the electronic conductivity may disappear at higher temperatures. For example, the partial ionic conductivity in γ–CuBr changes with temperature (Table II).

In other cases, the partial ionic conductivity increases with temperature. For example, the partial electronic conductivity in β–Ag_2S changes with temperature, at constant current (Table III):

In general, electrochemical experiments will be performed in the temperature range where the conductivity is almost entirely ionic. However, when the electronic contribution is sufficiently weak in relation to the ionic conductivity, such solids can be considered as belonging to the electrochemical domain. For example, zirconia exhibits an electronic contribution in the high temperature range where many experiments have been performed.

TABLE II. Conductivity of mixed ionic and electronic conductors (Friauf, 1963)

$T°C$	t_{cation}	$T°C$	t_{cation}
27	0·00	272	0·39
153	0·02	299	0·87
191	0·08	335	0·97
223	0·14	390	1·00

TABLE III. Conductivity of β-Ag$_2$S

$T°C$	$t_{electronic}$
20	1·5
60	7·0
100	10·1
150	16·1
170	18·8

The temperature range, however, where the magnitudes of the ionic and electronic conductivity are the same, should not be neglected. This is a complicated field where electrochemical and semi-conductor properties interfere with each other. The mixed conductors belong to two fields of study which have already tried to merge their specific knowledge. The diffusion in semi-conductors (Boltaks, 1963) has, for example, been treated by different authors using electrochemical concepts.

B. Classification

The general scheme of the classification of solids, given in the preceding chapter, may be used for a classification of the solid electrolytes. Thus we obtain the following scheme (Table IV).

Each type of electrolyte may be subdivided according to numerous criteria, for example, unipolar or bipolar conductivity, pure or mixed conductivity, and so on.

The ionic crystals constitute the greater part of the crystalline solid electrolytes studied at the present time. They may have a pure ionic conductivity or be partially semiconductor, depending on the temperature range.

They may be unipolar or bipolar conductors. The transfer numbers for the cations, n_c, and the anions, n_a, determine the kind of conductivity; in unipolar cations conductors $n_c = 1$ and in unipolar anions conductors, $n_a = 1$; in a bipolar conductor $n_a \neq 1$, $n_c \neq 1$ and $n_a + n_c = 1$. The ratio of anionic and cationic conductivity may change with temperature. Thus, an electrolyte like PbI_2, is a unipolar anionic conductor at lower temperatures, gradually changing into a bipolar conductor with increasing temperature, and, finally, into a unipolar cationic conductor.

Covalent crystals do not constitute, in principle, solid electrolytes. The covalent bonds form a stable structure in which the constituent particles do not migrate under the influence of an electric field. However, these crystals may have a structure such that foreign ions can diffuse within the crystal. Thus quartz, SiO_2, can contain interstitial foreign ions whose diffusion coefficients have been measured. We can therefore classify in this category the crystals of which the main structure is covalent and which have foreign ions diffusing through the structure.

It does not seem that the electrochemical properties of the molecular crystals have been extensively studied. These compounds may possess an ionic conductivity due to their own constituent particles or to foreign ions which can diffuse throughout their structure. For example, ordinary ice has a rather open hexagonal crystalline structure in which every oxygen atom is

TABLE IV.   Classification of solid electrolytes

State	Association	Type of electrolyte
Crystalline	Macromolecular	Ionic crystals
		Covalent crystals
	Molecular	Van der Waals bonds Hydrogen bonds
Amorphous		Glasses Ions exchange resins Polymers

surrounded by a tetrahedron of oxygen atoms. Many foreign molecules or ions can diffuse into this structure.

In general, the amorphous compounds do not seem to have been classified; we shall therefore give only a few examples from among these substances. Their number and importance is, however, no less than that of the crystalline electrolytes. For example, the practical importance of glasses has led to many studies of their electrochemical properties. The ion-exchanges also have increasing importance because of their numerous industrial applications.

We shall now illustrate some of the crystalline and amorphous structures adopted by some typical solid electrolytes.

II. Crystalline Electrolytes

A. Pure Ionic Crystals

1. Halite and Sylvine

The structure of halite was the first crystal structure to be analysed by X-rays (Bragg, 1914). It is shown in Fig. 1.

The sodium and chlorine atoms are arranged alternately at the corners of a set of cubes, the atoms of either kind alone forming a face-centred cubic lattice. Each sodium atom is surrounded by six chlorine atoms and vice versa.

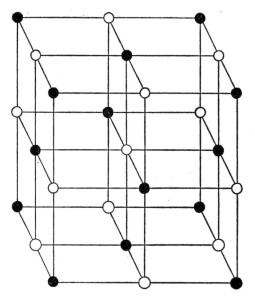

FIG. 1. The structure of halite, NaCl, and sylvine, KCl.

Sylvine, KCl, has a similar cubic structure of alternating potassium and chlorine atoms.

A very large number of compounds with the formula AB crystallise like NaCl. Among them are the fluorides, chlorides, bromides and iodides of Li, Na, K and Rb.

2. Fluorite

The structure of fluorite, CaF_2, is shown in Fig. 2. The calcium atoms lie on a face-centred cubic lattice. Each fluorine atom is at the centre of one of the smaller cubes obtained by dividing the unit cube into eight parts. It is surrounded by four calcium atoms, and each calcium atom is surrounded by eight fluorine atoms (Bragg, 1914).

Fluorite is the simplest structure assumed by compounds with the formula AB_2 and is characteristic of a large number of substances including some minerals: SrF_2, $SrCl_2$, BaF_2, CdF_2, PbF_2, ZrO_2, CeO_2, ThO_2, Li_2O, Li_2S.

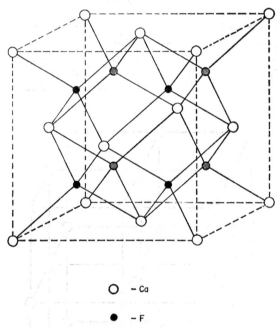

$\bigcirc$ $-$ Ca

$\bullet$ $-$ F

FIG. 2. The structure of fluorite, CaF_2.

3. High-Conductivity Solid Electrolytes: MAg₃I₄

Solid electrolytes at ambient temperatures generally have extremely low ionic conductivities. However, solid electrolytes MAg_4I_5, where M may be potassium, rubidium, ammonium, or to a limited extent Cs, have an ionic conductivity of $0.2 \, (\Omega . cm)^{-1}$ at 20°C. Owens and Argue (1967) have investigated the electrical conductivity of the MAg_4I_5 group. These authors prepared the MAg_4I_6 compounds by combining stoichiometric amounts of AgI and the alkali iodide, melting the mixture, and then quenching it. This intermediate product was ground, made into pellets, and then annealed at 165°C for 16 h. The products obtained in this manner were shown to be single-phase by X-ray powder analysis. Figure 3 shows their conductivity results for KAg_4I_5, $RbAg_4I_5$, and the solid solution $(K_3Rb)_{1/4} Ag_4I_5$ (this can be written $K_{3/4} Rb_{1/4} Ag_4I_5$) and also those of Bradley and Greene (1966, 1967). These authors reported that the solid electrolyte KAg_4I_5 is thermodynamically unstable below 38°C with respect to a disproportionation reaction to form K_2AgI_3 and AgI. However, the disproportionation reaction is quite sluggish; no difficulty was encountered in the low-temperature measurements.

The compound which appeared to be the best suited for determining the structure of MAg_4I_5 is that in which M is Rb, because it is the most stable against moisture. The X-ray data, on which the structure reported here was based, were obtained from a single crystal, ground to a sphere of 0.22 mm diameter.

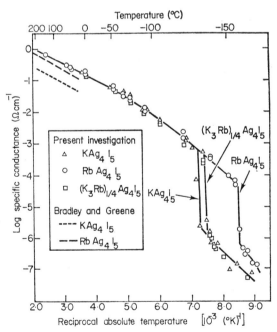

FIG. 3. Ionic conductivity of KAg_4I_5, $RbAg_4I_5$ and $(K_3Rb)_{1/4}Ag_4I_5$. The temperature range is from 150° to 160°C (after Owens and Argue, 1967).

Crystals of $RbAg_4I_5$ are optically isotropic, therefore cubic, with a equal to 11.24 ± 0.02 Å and cell content of four $RbAg_4I_5$. The X-ray density is 5.384 g/cm^3, in good agreement with the density, 5.30 g/cm^3, measured by Owens. The crystals have diffraction symmetry $m3m$; the only systematic absences are those for $h00$ with $h \neq 4n$. On the assumption that intensities of such reflections are identically zero, the crystal bleongs to one of the enantiomorphous space groups, $P4_33(O^6)$ or $P4_13(O^7)$.

With the knowledge of the properties of the crystal, it was apparent that the Ag^+ ions would not be ordered. Disorder of the I^- and Rb^+ ions appeared to be precluded by their sizes. Thus, the iodide ions were probably in sets 8(c) and 12(d) of the space group. The combination of these two sets allows only moderate variation on one logical arrangement of these ions in the unit cell: the arrangement is that of the Mn atoms in β-Mn (β-Manganese and some isostructural intermetallic compounds are the only other crystals known to belong to the space group). The Rb^+ ions are in the 4(a) sites, which are surrounded by distorted octahedra of iodide ions.

4. Complex Ions

In some ionic crystals it is convenient to regard as structural units certain compact groups of atoms termed complex ions. Common examples are CO_3^{--}, NO_3^-, and SO_4^{--}. It is useful to have some idea of the general shapes of the common complex ions and we have summarized some in Table V.

TABLE V.   The shapes of some complex ions.

A_3, AX_2, AXY	Linear	N_3^-, CNO^-, CNS^-, I_3^-, $Ag(CN)_2^-$
	Angular	ClO_2^-, NO_2^-
AX_3	Planar	CO_3^{2-}, NO_3^-
	Trigonal	PO_3^{3-}, SO_3^{2-}, SeO_3^{2-}
	Pyramidal	ClO_3^-, BRO_3^-, IO_3^-
AX_4	Tetrahedral	BF_4^-, PO_4^{3-}, SO_4^{2-}, ClO_4^-
	Planar	$Ni(CN)_4^{2-}$, $PdCl_4^{2-}$, $PtCl_4^{2-}$
AX_6	Octahedral	SiF_6^{2-}, $SnCl_6^{2-}$, $PtCl_6^{2-}$

The study of crystals containing complex ions has shown that the internal structure of a complex ion is remarkably constant in crystals of different salts. Moreover, the way in which the ions, complex or otherwise, pack together in a crystal is determined by geometrical consideration (Wells, 1962).

Pauling (1960) has summarised the principles determining the structures of complex ionic crystals in a set of "rules" based on the knowledge gained from the early studies of the structures of complex oxides and silicates.

5. Ionic Organic Crystals

The metal salts of organic acids, and certain other compounds such as the substituted ammonium halides, form essentially ionic structures with the components held together by electrostatic forces.

Monomethylammonium iodide, NH_3CH_3I, has an arrangement of $NH_3CH_3{}^+$ and I^- ions which may be regarded as a distorted sodium chloride structure. Tetramethylammonium chloride, $N(CH_3)_4Cl$, resembles that of caesium chloride.

Sodium oxalate, $(COO)_2Na_2$, has a relatively simple structure in which each sodium ion is octahedrally coordinated by six oxygen atoms of adjacent planar $(COO)_2{}^{--}$ ions. In this salt, and many others of carboxylic acids, it is found that no distinction can be made between the two oxygen atoms of the carboxylate ion; both are at the same distance ($1.23Å$) from the carbon atom and both are similarly co-ordinated to the sodium ions.

Closely similar interatomic distances within the oxalate ion have been observed in other oxalate structures. The ion, however, is not always planar, and in the strongly hydrogen-bonded structure of ammonium oxalate monohydrate, $(COO)_2(NH_4)_2H_2O$, the hydrogen bonds have the effect of twisting the ion about the C–C bond. This illustrates the important point that the structure of a molecule in an organic crystal is determined not only by the intermolecular bonds but also by the forces between the molecules.

B. Mixed Ionic Crystals

1. Acanthite

Acanthite, Ag_2S, has a comparatively simple structure which has been analysed by Frueh (1958).

Though the structure has monoclinic symmetry, it is based on an arrangement of sulphur atoms very nearly in the positions of a simple, body-centred cubic lattice. The silver atoms have two positions. $Ag_{(I)}$ lies nearly in the sulphur sheets, each Ag being between three sulphur atoms, at an average distance of 2.7 Å. $Ag_{(II)}$ lies approximately halfway between two sulphur atoms of successive sheets at an average distance of 2.5 Å, so linking the sheets together.

The form of Ag_2S, stable above 173°C, is a body-centred cubic structure in which the sulphur atoms have the same arrangement as in acanthite, but the silver atoms are differently distributed.

2. Rutile

The three forms, rutile, anatase and brookite, of T_iO_2 constitute a well-known case of polymorphism.

The structure of rutile, shown in Fig. 4 was first analysed by Vegard (1916).

It is a structure of $6:3$ coordination. Every titanium atom is surrounded by six oxygen atoms, approximately at the corners of a regular octahedron, and every oxygen atom by three titanium atoms approximately at the corners of an equilateral triangle. The rutile structure played an important part in demonstrating the importance of the coordination principle.

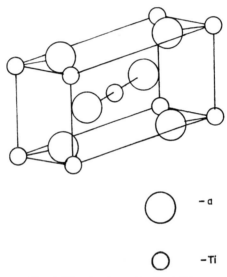

FIG. 4. The structure of rutile, TiO_2.

C. Covalent Crystals

1. Quartz

Silica crystallizes commonly in three low-pressure forms as quartz, tridymite and cristobalite. Each of these minerals has high- and low-temperature modification. In quartz, the low temperature α modification changes into the β modification at 573°C.

The first complete determinations of the simpler β-quartz structure were made by Bragg and Gibbs (1925).

Each silicon atom is surrounded by four oxygen atoms, two of which are somewhat above and two below each Si. The tetrahedral groups lie on three layers at different heights.

Figure 5 illustrates the relations between α- and β-quartz, according to Gibbs (1926). Only the silicon atoms are shown and the oxygen must be pictured as lying between each pair of silicon atoms.

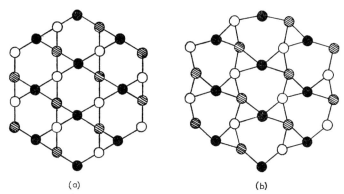

(a)   (b)

FIG. 5. The structure of quartz. Silicon atoms only are shown, and heights are indicated by shading.   (a) β—quartz,   (b) α—quartz.

D. Molecular Crystals

1. Ordinary Ice

There are nine known crystalline forms of ice, but most of these are stable only at high pressure.

Our most complete structural information is for ordinary ice Ih (hexagonal), both because it has been extensively studied, and because it has been the subject of a precision neutron diffraction investigation.

Ice Ih has a rather open, hexagonal, crystalline structure, in which every oxygen atom is surrounded by a tetrahedron of oxygen atom at a distance of 2·75 Å.

In most ice crystals, the two hydrogen atoms are directed at random along two of the four possible 0 ... 0 vectors from a given oxygen position.

2. Copper Sulphate Pentahydrate

The structure of $CuSO_4$–$5H_2O$ has been accurately determined by neutron diffraction (Bacon and Curry, 1962).

There are five crystallographically distinct water molecules. Four of these are in the coordination sphere of the copper ion. Each of the coordinated water molcules forms two hydrogen bonds and the free molecule forms four: two accepted and two donated.

The smallest H—O—H angle is associated with the free water molecule and the mean of the H—O—H angles, for the four molecules coordinated to copper, is somewhat larger than for water vapour.

3. Ion Exchange Materials

The structure of several minerals are such that a large fraction of the cations in the structure may be replaced by cations of an electrolyte solution without grinding. The zeolite minerals and several clays are examples of such structures.

The structure must be porous enough to permit an exchanging ion to diffuse into the lattice. Dense structures such as feldspars and micas will not permit the exchange of ions unless they are in a fine state of subdivision, whereas less dense structures, such as the zeolites and ultramarines, will permit ion exchange without a prior reduction to a fine state of subdivision.

The zeolites such as chabazite ($CaAl_2Si_6O_{16}$. $8H_2O$), heulandite (CaO. Al_2O_3. $6SiO_2$. $5H_2O$), analcite (Na_2O. Al_2O_3. $4SiO_2$. $2H_2O$) are highly porous, chain-like silicate structures in which the sodium and calcium ions are readily accessible by means of these fine pores. Ions small enough to diffuse through these pores may then exchange with the sodium and calcium of the crystal. These exchangeable ions occupy essential lattice sites.

III. Imperfect Crystalline Electrolytes

A. Stoichiometric Crystals

1. Defect Structures

A crystal consists of an extended array of atoms arranged with regular periodicity in all directions. We may refer to such a crystal as an ideal crystal, for real crystals do not have such a perfectly regular internal structure.

Measurements of the intensity of reflection of X-rays from particular planes in crystals, usually give results different from those expected for ideal crystals.

Apart from the X-ray crystallographic evidence, there are other properties which suggest the presence of imperfections in crystals. The study of diffusion in solids, of electrical properties (electronic and photoconductivity), and of luminescence, emphasized the importance of defects in solids.

In any crystal in thermodynamic equilibrium, at a temperature above $0°K$, there is a finite probability that some atoms will be displaced from their positions of minimum potential energy. The two simplest types of defect, named after those who postulated their existence, are:

Schottky defect, a vacant site from which the atom has migrated to the surface of the crystal, and

Frenkel defect, an interstitial atom and somewhere in the vicinity, the vacant site from which the atom originated.

2. Radiation Defects

Structure imperfections of the Frenkel type can arise when crystals are irradiated with fast particles (neutrons, electrons, ...). Unlike thermal defects, radiation defects are not in thermodynamic equilibrium with the crystal, and tend to disappear when irradiation is discontinued. The process is facilitated by annealing at high temperatures to accelerate the diffusion and recombination of defects.

The passage of fast particles through crystals involves a number of complex processes, such as:

elastic collisions between the fast particles and the nuclei of the crystal atoms,

excitation and ionization by fast particles of the electrons bounds to the crystal atoms,

nuclear transmutations.

In general, all three processes will occur together, but any of them may predominate according to the bond character, other properties of the irradiated crystal, and also according to the nature and energy of the fast particles. Thus, the excitation and ionization of valence electrons is the most significant effect with insulating or semiconducting crystals, whereas with metals this effect is entirely absent.

3. Disordered Crystals

If the atoms A and B in a molecule $A–B$ are similar in size, it may be relatively easy for some molecules to become incorporated in the growing crystal with the wrong orientation ($B–A$ instead of $A–B$). Corresponding to orientational disorder in a crystal consisting of finite molecule, "mistakes" can arise during the growth of a layer structure if there are two or more ways of stacking one layer on the previous one which are approximately equivalent energetically.

The decrease with rising temperature of the intensity of monochromatic X-rays reflected by a plane of atoms in a crystal, is satisfactorily interpreted as being due to the increased amplitude of vibration of the atoms about their mean positions. There is also the possibility that a group of atoms can rotate one or more axes.

Another type of defect solids is the statistical distribution of atoms of more than one kind, in one set of equivalent positions. Examples for this include all stoichiometric compounds with statistical structures, such as complex halides with the random CaF_2 or LaF_3 structures, and inverse spinels in which atoms of two elements (or ions of the same elements with different charges) occupy statistically a set of equivalent positions.

A number of iodides, sulphides, selenides and tellurides are remarkable for forming high-temperature modifications with properties strikingly different from those of the ordinary low-temperature forms. There is a complete disorder of atoms of one kind.

For example, at a temperature just below 145·8°C, silver iodide forms hexagonal crystals (β–AgI) with the wurtzite structure, in which the iodine atoms are closely-packed each being equidistant from twelve others. At 145°8, these crystals transform, sharply and reversibly, into the high-temperature (α) modification in which the coordination number of the large iodine ions has fallen to 8. This form has an exceptionally high ionic conductivity, and the silver ions move freely between the easily deformed iodine ions.

We can list the five types of disordered stoichiometric crystal which we have discussed:

	Examples
1. Orientational disorder	CO, $B_{10}H_4$
2. Stacking faults in layer and close-packed structures	Cd halides, Co
3. Rotation or random orientation of molecules or complex ions	$CaCo_3$, $NaNO_3$
4. Statistical distribution of atoms of more than one kind in one set of equivalent positions	Random CaF_2 structure
5. Complete disorder of cations	α–AgI, α–Ag$_2$S

4. Dislocations

Dislocations are still another type of imperfection frequently encountered in a crystal structure. The term describes a particular kind of disturbance of a crystalline lattice, caused by relative motion of parts of the crystal during growth or as a result of plastic deformation.

Two distinct types of dislocation are usually considered: linear (or edge) dislocations and screw dislocations.

Edge dislocations are due to a relative displacement of two regions of the crystal, such that the numbers of atomic layers in two regions differ by one. The most highly disturbed region of the crystal, in the slip plane, is the centre of the dislocation. Edge dislocations lie perpendicular to the slip vector (Fig. 6).

Screw dislocations appear in a plane parallel to the slip vector. Slip, in the direction of the slip vector, occurs over the whole thickness of the crystal so that, instead of a stack of parallel atomic layers, there is one continuous spiralling plane, very similar to a spiral staircase.

Dislocations can move through the crystal, either in the slip plane or at right angles to it. When a dislocation moves in the slip plane, the slipped region grows and plastic deformation occurs. Motion of a dislocation at right angles to the slip plane involves matter transport, i.e. diffusion.

Dislocations affect the electrical as well as the mechanical properties of crystals.

Diffusion processes, and the solubility of impurities in crystals, are also very sensitive to the presence of dislocations.

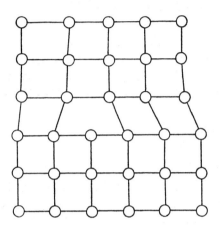

FIG. 6. Model of an edge dislocation.

B. Non-Stoichiometric Crystals

1. Small Amount of Impurities

Non-stoichiometric compounds are solid phases which are stable over a range of composition which is in some cases narrow, and in other wide.

(a) *Colour centres.* A number of alkali halides become coloured when heated in the vapour of the metal or halogen owing to the absorption of a stoichiometric excess of one of the constituents.

Thus, NaCl becomes yellow when heated in sodium vapour, the stoichiometric excess of metal being of the order of 1 in 10^4. Similar coloration is produced by electron bombardments of the crystals. The optical absorption giving rise to the term colour centre (or F-centre) is due to the presence of electrons trapped in vacant halogen ion sites.

(b) *Phosphors.* If zinc sulphide is heated with a small amount of copper to about 1100°C, this is absorbed into the lattice and the crystals will fluoresce a brilliant yellow-green when exposed to ultra-violet light or cathode rays. Moreover, they continue to emit light after irradiation has ceased (phosphorescence). Phosphorescence of solids is caused by the return to their original ground states of electrons trapped in localized energy levels, just below the conduction levels.

(c) *Semi-conductors.* The coloured alkali halides and phosphors are examples of a large group of compounds which are insulators in the pure state, but which conduct electricity either when they contain a small amount of certain impurities or when they have become non-stoichiometric as a result of being heated under appropriate conditions.

2. Solid Solutions

An element can be introduced into the crystal lattice of another, up to some limiting concentration, without any loss of homogeneity. These homogeneous regions are called solid solutions, of which there are three distinct types:

Substitutional solid solutions

Interstitial solid solutions

Defect solid solutions

Of special interest are substitutional solid solutions in which the atoms have different valences. For example, lithium may be introduced into NiO to form solid solutions which are p-type semiconductors.

These substitutional solid solutions are examples of defect solids. since all the crystallographically equivalent positions are occupied, but by atoms of different kinds. Similar to these are the mixed alkali halides, for example (K, Na) Cl, in which the K and Na ions are distributed at random over the Na positions in a sodium chloride lattice.

There are also solid solutions in which there is not only random arrangement of different kinds of atoms in equivalent positions but, in addition, some of these positions are unoccupied. In solid solutions of compounds of different formula type, of which $MgCl_2$–LiCl is an example, there must be either vacant sites or additional interstitial ions. If a small amount of $MgCl_2$ dissolves in LiCl, then, since the packing of large Cl^- ions determines the structure, there will be one vacant lithium position for every Mg^{2+} ion which enters the structure. At the $MgCl_2$ end of the series, on the other hand, two Li^+ will enter for every two Cl^- in order to maintain electrical neutrality and there will be an excess of positive ions in the crystal.

There are examples of the formation of solid solutions by compounds of similar formula-type, but different crystal structures, for example AgBr and AgI. This case is complicated by the fact that while AgBr has the NaCl structure, AgI appears to be capable of crystallizing at atmospheric pressure in a number of different forms, and only adopting the NaCl structure under a pressure of some 3000 atmospheres.

3. Structures with Interstices

We group together all crystals in which there are holes large enough to accommodate foreign atoms or molecules. The resulting non-stoichiometric crystals could be classified in various ways.

(a) *Layer and framework structure.* Some crystals with layer structures can take up material between the layers. Examples include the lamellar compound of graphite and of clay minerals.

When interstitial material is accommodated in tunnels or in a series of connected holes which are accessible from the surface of the crystals, the foreign atoms (ions, molecules) can enter or leave the crystal without disturbing the structure. A group of minerals called zeolites exhibit this type of behaviour with certain gases (CO_2, NH_3), water and foreign ions. The term zeolitic is conveniently applied to crystals of this general type.

Some crystals, on the other hand, take in foreign molecules during growth, but they are enclosed in cavities from which they cannot escape until the crystal is dissolved or vaporized. These crystals have been termed clathrate compounds.

An example of a 3-dimensional clathrate structure is that of β-quinol. The frameworks are electrically neutral and the included molecules are held in the structure only by van der Waals forces. The crystals are usually non-stoichiometric because the structure is stable, provided that a certain minimum proportion of the interstices is filled.

The zeolites provide examples of charged frameworks. The substitution of Al for Si in SiO_2 must be accompanied by the introduction of cations to balance the charge of the $(Si, Al)O_2$ anion. Corresponding to alumino-silicate frameworks built of SiO_4 and AlO_4 tetrahedra, there are frameworks built of $Mn(IV)O_6$ octahedra in which some $Mn(IV)$ has been replaced by ions of lower charge. Some of these compounds exhibit ion-exchange like the zeolites.

(b) *Crystals built of finite ions or molecules.* The arrangement of the atoms in certain crystals is such as to leave open tunnels wide enough to accommodate atoms or molecules of certain gases or liquids.

For example. in the mineral beryl, the large cyclic ions are packed in columns, and helium is sometimes found occluded in the tunnels which extend throughout the crystal.

IV. Amorphous Electrolytes

A. Glasses

1. Definition

Numerous definitions of glass can be given. Mackenzie's (1960) opinion is that any isotropic material, whether it be inorganic or organic, in which three-dimensional atomic periodicity is absent and the viscosity of which is greater than about 10^{14} poise, may be described as a glass.

The difference between a glass, the corresponding liquid or supercooled liquid, and a crystal may be conveniently demonstrated by a volume–temperature relationship (Fig. 7). On cooling a liquid which normally does not form a glass, path I will be followed. However, in the absence of crystallization, the volume–temperature relationship may be described by path II to give a supercooled liquid. On further cooling to a temperature region denoted by T_g, when the viscosity of the supercooled liquid has reached about 10^{13}–10^{14} poise, a break occurs. This is the so-called glass transition temperature below which the non-crystalline material is termed a glass and path III is followed.

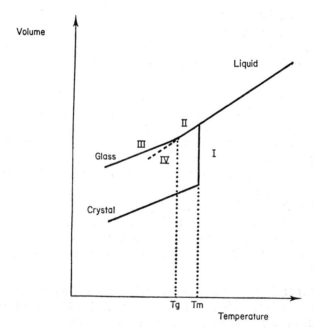

FIG. 7. Difference between a glass, the corresponding liquid of super-cooled liquid, and a crystal.

At extremely slow cooling rate, contraction may occur via path IV but in practice the length is limited by the increasing slower rate which becomes necessary.

The glass transition is essentially caused by a relaxation effect which prevents the ready attainment of internal equilibrium, and not the result of intramolecular transformation. Thus, we can consider that the types of molecular units and forces present in a liquid are unchanged in the glass. For example, in molten and glassy $KNO_3Ca(NO_3)_2$ the entities are probably K^+, Ca^{2+} and NO_3^- ions; we may regard the forces between the K^+, Ca^{2+} and NO_3^- to be ionic and those within the NO_3^- ion to be covalent.

Although the crystalline phase of most pure substances is thermodynamically more stable than the corresponding glass, most glasses remain for very long periods without appreciable crystallization.

What determines whether a liquid, when undercooled, crystallizes or forms a glass? The information on the relation between molecular constitution and glass-forming tendency seems to be consistent with the following generalization: at a given level of cohesive energy, the glass-forming tendency of a substance in a particular glass is greater the smaller the ratio of the energy of crystallization to the entropy of crystallization (Turnbull and Cohen, 1960).

2. Structure of Silicate Glasses

Zachariasen (1932) postulated a number of important empirical rules for glass formation in inorganic oxide systems. According to his concept, the

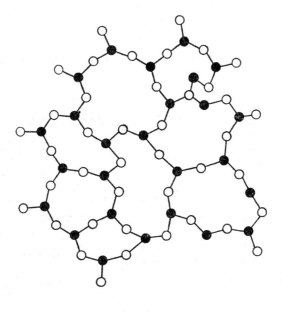

● – SILICON

○ – OXYGEN

FIG. 8. Glass network.

atoms in a glass are linked together by forces essentially the same as in the corresponding crystal, the principle difference between a crystal and a glass network being the presence of symmetry and periodicity on the former, and their absence in the latter.

Zachariasen wrote in his paper on the atomic arrangements in glass (1932), "the network in vitreous silica according to our argument is built up of oxygen tetrahedra which surround the silicon atoms. The oxygen tetrahedra share corners with each other in such a manner that any oxygen atom is linked with two silicon atoms. In the crystalline forms of silica the relative orientation of two tetrahedra with a common corner will be the same throughout the entire attice. That is not the case in vitreous silica where the relative orientation may vary within rather wide limits" (Fig. 8).

Westman (1960) asks the question, "What is the structure of glass?" and answers that glasses can have many structures. Thus, the question resolves into "How many of the conceivable structures of glass can we produce experimentally?"

What is needed is a method for introducing some randomness. So far all attempts to produce glasses of unusual structure have depended largely on rapid cooling from a melt; rapid heating to a high temperature followed by quenching may be equally important. Another approach is the use of a large number of cations of different sizes and charges, in order to introduce some randomness into the structure which is difficult to remove by devitrification.

B. Ion Exchange Resins

1. Cations and Anions Exchange Resins

Though lacking in crystallinity, the mechanism of ion exchange in ion exchange resins is fully analogous with the exchange of crystal lattice ions. The various cation and anion exchange resins may be considered as insoluble, high molecular weight, polymeric electrolytes.

The various cation exchange resins are high-polymeric and tightly crosslinked structures containing polar anionic groups whose negative charges are balanced by cations. We may consider these cation exchange resins to be, essentially, highly insoluble electrolytes consisting of an enormous nondiffusible anion and a simple diffusible cation.

The cation exchange resins owe their capacity for exchanging ions to such functional groups as the sulphonic carboxylic and the phenolic groups. It is more interesting to note that the capacity of the various sulphonic acid cation exchange resins may be quite accurately accounted for by the sulphur content of the resins. This indicates quite strongly that the exchange of ions with these resins takes place throughout the whole gel structure of the resin, and is not limited merely to surface effects. Similarly, we may account for the exchange capacity of the carboxylic and phenolic cation exchange resins.

The exchange of anions in ion exchange resins has been mainly limited to the amine-type resin. As in the case of the cation exchange resin, practically all the amine content of the anion exchange resins may be accounted for by the exchange capacity. The preparation of quaternary type resinous exchangers has furnished the necessary evidence that these polyamine-type exchangers function as true anion exchangers.

2. Structure of Cation Exchange Resins

Let us consider the synthesis of a specific cation exchange resin, the phenol-formaldehyde polymer containing nuclear sulphonic acid groups. For simplicity, it is assumed that this polymer is being formed by condensing m-phenosulphonic acid,

with formaldehyde CH_2O.

The first stage of this condensation is the reaction of two molecules of phenolsulphonic acid with one molecule of formaldehyde, with the elimination of water, and the formation of a methylene ($-CH_2-$) bridge. With more formaldehyde the condensation continues with the formation of the chain.

Such long chain compounds are still completely soluble in water. At about the proportion of one mole of CH_2O per mole of phenosulphonic acid, a very significant change takes place. This is the proportion of CH_2O required for the formation of one long straight chain. With more formaldehyde, we begin to form methylene bridges between chains.

Physically, a gelation of the mass sets in. The cross linking has tied up the structure into a vast network. The final exchange resin is formed by still further addition of formaldehyde with a progressive tightening of the network as more cross-links are formed. Physically the weak jelly becomes more and more firm, until finally it is a hard and tough particle containing as little as 30–50% water, in the completely swollen state.

In summary, then, the essential features of a spherical cation exchange particle are shown in Fig. 9. The skeleton network is shown by wavy lines, to which are affixed the $-SO_3^-$ (or other anionic) groups indicated merely by short dashes. The H^+ cations are then shown in the vicinity of each anion.

In a strong acid resin, such as a sulphonic acid resin, the H^+ cations are completely dissociated from the $-SO_3^-$ groups and wander freely within the particle, controlled only by the overall requirement of electrical neutrality. In a weak acid resin, such as a carboxylic acid resin, the majority of these H^+ cations will be associated with the $-COO^-$ anions.

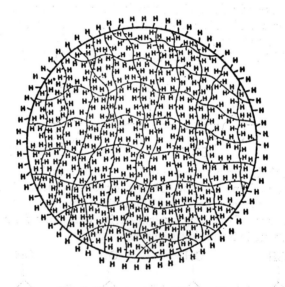

Fig. 9. Basic structure of Dowex 50.

C. Polymers

Except at high voltages, and in semiconductor polymers, conduction in polymers is ionic. The level of this conduction depends on the number of charge carriers, their charge and their mobility (Miller, 1966).

Polyelectrolytes, such as polyacrylic acid, which contain many ions, conduct well as solids and in aqueous solutions.

Generally, however, most common polymers conduct poorly because they contain only a few ions, and because the mobility of these ions, especially in glassy polymers, is low. The very low conductance which polymers such as polystyrene and polymethyl methacrylate exhibit, is primarily a result of the presence of ions supplied by initiators, inhibitors and by chance impurities, either present in the monomer or produced by a reaction with oxygen or water. The amount of these impurities is purposely kept low in commercial plastics and, therefore, the conductance of commercial plastic is ordinarily low, of the order of $10^{-20} \, \Omega^{-1} \, cm^{-1}$.

In spite of the polarization phenomenon, the conductance of numerous polymers measured at a fixed time after application of a field shows only small deviations from Ohm's law, provided that the voltage is not too high (up to at least 1000 V) and that only small amounts of plasticizer are present.

In polypropylene, in which an increase in field strength produces new carriers, the conductance does not follow Ohm's law (after the initial transient current has died out), but instead the conductance increases linearly with field strength.

The apparent energy of activation for conductance is high in polymers (34·6 kcal per base mole in polypropylene and 21·7 kcal in polyvinyl chloride) and varies with field strength, temperature and percentage of plasticization.

Polymers can conduct electronically. Typical of polymers which conduct elecrtonically are polyacetylene polymers of phthalocyanine and polymers that are charge transfer complexes. Polyanilines are representative materials of the organic protolytic polyconjugated macromolecular semiconductors (De Surville et al., 1968).

Polyanilines are also ion exchangers, as is shown by the fixation of their "inner acidity" by means of the exchange of strong acids (sulphonic or hydrochloric) with aqueous solutions (Hefferich, 1962). Consequently, ionic conductivity is superimposed on electronic.

V. Interatomic Distances

A. Electron Density Distribution

1. Free-ion and Ionic Crystals

We must distinguish between the radius of a free-ion and the radius of an ion that is a constituent part of an ionic crystal.

The radius of the ion could be described, quantum-mechanically, in terms of the radius at which the absolute value of the square of the wave function for the outermost electronic orbital state has its maximum value. This wave function is, in turn, a solution of the Schrödinger wave equation. The calculation of the radii of ions may be carried out by solving the one-electron Schrödinger equation by the Hartree–Fock self-consistent field method.

In the free-ion case, the solution must be made self-consistent with the field of the constituent ionic electrons. In the crystal case, the solution must be made self-consistent with the field of the constituent electrons, plus the electronic clouds of the surrounding ions.

For metals, one defines the atomic radius as half the distance between nearest neighbours. For ionic crystals one might try a similar approach, but is immediately faced with the difficulty that these compounds consist of at least two types of ions, so that the lattice constant provides information only about the sum of two radii.

The effective radii in crystals are not calculated theoretically; they are determined from observed interionic distances. In crystals, the ions do not approach closer together than the equilibrium distance. By X-ray methods, we can determine the distance which may be regarded as the sums of the radii of pairs of positive and negative ions.

2. Ionic Radii from Minima in the Electron Density Distribution

Distributions of valency electrons in certain crystals can apparently be determined reliably. Where this information is available for an ionic crystal, radii may be assigned to the constituent ions by dividing up the internuclear distance at the minimum electron density (Morris, 1968).

Electron distribution in sodium chloride has been ascertained by Witte and Wölfel (1955) and by Schoknecht (1957).

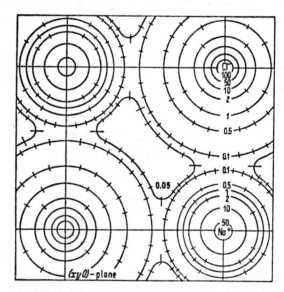

Fig. 10. Electron density distribution of NaCl at 290° K in $(x, y, 0)$ plane (After Schoknecht, 1957).

An electron density map in the (100) plane is shown in Fig. 10. The essentially ionic character of the crystal is confirmed, and the density along the line Na–Cl drops to a low value. From the electron distribution, Witte and Wölfel derived radii of 1·17 Å for Na^+ and 1·64 Å for Cl^- (the Pauling radii are $R_{Na^+} = 0·95$ Å and $R_{Cl^-} = 1·81$ Å).

The electron distribution in LiF has been elucidated by Krug et al. (1955) and a map of the (100) plane is illustrated in Fig. 11. It will be noted that the ions in this compound show a greater deviation from spherical symmetry than those in sodium chloride and that overlap of the electron clouds is greater. However, an electron count shows that the binding is essentially ionic, and radii deduced from the position of minimum density between the oppositely charged ions are 0·91 Å for Li^+ and 1·09 Å for F^-. These are not the traditional radii of Pauling ($R_{Li^+} : 0·60$ Å, $R_{F^-} = 1·36$ Å).

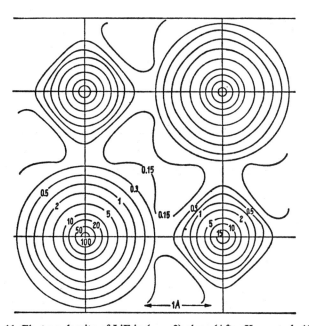

FIG. 11. Electron density of LiF in (x, y, 0) plane (After Krug et al., 1955).

It is of interest to consider the experimental radial electron density distribution in the ions Na^+ and Cl^- in sodium chloride in relation to corresponding results for the free ions calculated by the self-consistent field method.

In Fig. 12 data from the experimental study of Schoknecht (1967) are plotted together with theoretical results obtained by Hartree and Hartree (1936, 1948).

The distances between the experimental and theoretical distributions may arise in part from uncertainties in the correction for temperature and from errors of measurement. However, a comparison of the distributions shows that there is some tightening of the outer electron cloud of the chloride ion, and some "loosening" of that of the sodium ion in passing from the free ion state to the crystal. This phenomenon, which may be regarded as arising from the mutual polarization of ions, has been emphasized in papers by Fajans (1941), Fajans and Bauer (1942), and Fajans and Joo (1924) on molar refraction.

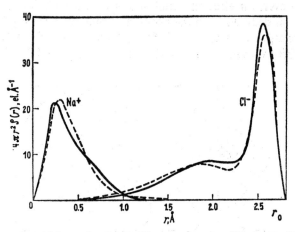

FIG. 12. Comparison of the results obtained from the theories of Hartree and Debye (broken curves) with the radial electron density distribution of Na$^+$ and Cl$^-$ obtained fron experimental results of Schoknecht (solid curves) (afetr Morris, 1968).

Moreover, Petrashen *et al.* (1958, 1960) have shown wave mechanically, on the basis of the Hartree–Fock method and the central ion model, that generally, in ionic crystals, the anions suffer tightening and the cations loosening.

It would appear that the radii for alkaline and halide ions based on experimental electron distribution results for NaCl provide the most realistic set currently available. The values agree well with crystal radii of ions determined by Fumi and Tosi (1964a, b).

The definition of crystal radii from the location of the minimum of the experimental electron density between neighbouring ions appears to be physically satisfactory when the individual ions approximate to spherical shape and show little overlap, as in the case in sodium chloride. Where deviations from spherical symmetry become more significant and the zone of electron cloud overlap is appreciable, the concept of ionic radius becomes dubious.

B. Slater's Atomic Radii

Slater (1965) has returned to Bragg's simple idea that the observed inter-atomic distances in a crystal between two atoms which are forming a bond can be approximately written as the sum of atomic radii for the two atoms, these radii being determined empirically by study of the experimental measurements. Slater will point out the advantage of returning to Bragg's simple scheme of having a unique radius for each type of atom, to be used in every sort of compound.

In Table VI, Slater gives the radii which he will use, close to Bragg's values, but somewhat refined as a result of using a much larger amount of empirical material than was available at the time of Bragg's work.

TABLE VI.   Slater's atomic radii

H	0·25	Ti	1·40	Nb	1·45	Nd	1·85	Pt	1·35
Li	1·45	V	1·35	Mo	1·45	Pm	1·85	Au	1·35
Be	1·05	Cr	1·40	Tc	1·35	Sm	1·85	Hg	1·50
B	0·85	Mn	1.40	Ru	1.30	Eu	1.85	Tl	1·90
C	0·70	Fe	1·40	Rh	1·35	Gd	1·80	Pb	1·80
N	0·65	Co	1·35	Pd	1·40	Tb	1·75	Bi	1·60
O	0·60	Ni	1·35	Ag	1·60	Dy	1·75	Po	1·90
F	0·50	Cu	1·35	Cd	1·55	Ho	1·75	At	
Na	1·80	Zn	1·35	In	1·55	Er	1·75	Fr	
Mg	1·50	Ga	1·30	Sn	1·45	Tu	1·75	Ra	2·15
Al	1·25	Ge	1·25	Sb	1·45	Yb	1·75	Ac	1·95
Si	1·10	As	1·15	Te	1·40	Lu	1·75	Th	1·80
P	1·00	Se	1·15	I	1·40	Hf	1·55	Pa	1·80
S	1·00	Br	1·15	Cs	2·60	Ta	1·45	U	1·75
Cl	1·00	Rb	2·35	Ba	2·15	W	1·35	Np	1·75
K	2·20	Sr	2·00	La	1·95	Re	1·35	Pu	1·75
Ca	1·80	Y	1·80	Ce	1·85	Os	1·30	Am	1·75
Sc	1·60	Zr	1·55	Pr	1·85	Ir	1·35		

C. Semi-Empirical Ionic Radii

Semi-empirical methods of calculating radii of ions in crystals have been proposed by several authors. The form of the potential indicates that the distance between neighbouring ions in the crystal (which is refered to as the lattice constant r_0) should be approximately equal to the sum of the radii of the neighbouring ions. This is referred to as the additivity rule.

The lattice constants of crystals are measured by X-ray techniques, and thus it remains merely to determine the ratio of the radii of the two ions

A^+ and B^- in order to determine the ratio of the radii of all other ions which occur in crystals with the ions A^+ and B^-. Wasastjerna (1923) measured the ratio of molar refractions of ions. Goldschmidt (1926, 1927) then took Wasastjerna's results and, combining them with the measured lattice constants and the assumption of the additivity rule, calculated the radii of many ions in ionic crystals. These radii are referred to as Goldschmidt radii.

Pauling (1927) pointed out particularly the fact that a given atomic or ionic radius must not be assumed to be a constant, but must in fact be a function of the coordination number (the number of ions of the opposite sign surrounding a given ion), the radius ratio (ratio of radius of positive to negative ion) and the charge on the ion. He worked out so-called univalent radii, radii which would hypothetically be found if ions with different charges were artificially assumed to have a standard charge of one unit.

Zachariasen (1931) proceeded along much the same lines as Pauling, but made use of somewhat more experimental materials, and followed Goldschmidt's empirical radii whenever possible.

VI. Electronic Energy Bands

A. Alkali Halide Crystals

In Section I, we have given some indication of the methods for calculating energy bands in crystals, and especially the tight-binding method.

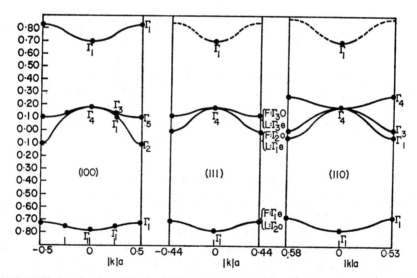

FIG. 13. Electronic energy bands of LiF . $E(k)$ plots for three prominent crystallographic directions. The ordinates are Rydberg units. (After Ewing and Seitz, 1936)

TABLE VII. $E(k)$ for particular points in LiF

Band	I	II	III	IV	V
$k = 0$	−0·77	+0·18	0·18	0·18	0·7
(100) Limit	−0·73	0·10	0·10	−0·11	0·82
(100) Midpoint	−0·75	0·15	0·15	0·12	
(111) Limit	−0·75	0·12	0·12	0·03	
(110) Limit	−0·68	0·01	0·05	0·07	

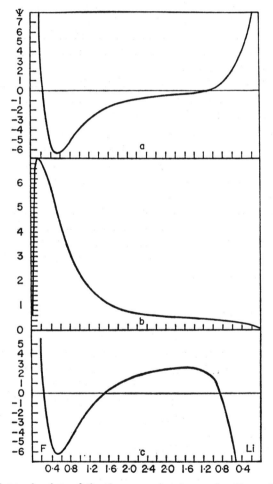

FIG. 14. Relative scale plots of the three prominent wave functions of LiF, for $k = a$. a and b go with the second filled band and c goes with the first unfilled one (After Ewing and Seitz, 1936).

Slater and Shockley (1936) gave an estimate regarding the dependence of the energy bands of NaCl on internuclear separation.

An early calculation of the energy bands of LiF and LiH by the cellular method give the wave functions as well as the energy bands (Ewing and Seitz, 1936). A self-consistent solution of the Hartree–Fock system of equations for the ionic crystals is attempted by using approximation methods previously employed in metals. The energies going with the various wave functions are tabulated in Table VII for LiF, and the probable positions of the bands are shown in Fig. 13. The wave functions for $k = 0$ going with the first three bands are shown in Fig. 14. The difference in energy between centre points of the second (filled band) and the upper band correspond to the long wave-length limit of the absorption band of LiF and is found here to be about 1500 Å, as compared (Melvin, 1931; Schneider, 1936) with the observed value of about 1200 Å.

It is to be observed that the wave function going with the unfilled band is much more like that for a free electron than are the other functions.

The Wigner and Seitz method of cellular potentials has been applied to the calculation of wave functions in NaCl by Shockley (1936).

Sodium chloride has been studied by many other workers, either by the cellular method (Tibbs, 1939) or by the tight-binding method (Casella, 1956; Kucher, 1958a, b; Tolpygo and Tomasevich, 1968, 1960; Kucher and Tolpygo, 1960; Evseev and Tolpygo, 1962; Evseev, 1963).

On account of the large internuclear separations in the alkali halide crystals, the energy bands have no resemblance at all to the free-electron case which is used in describing the energy bands of metallic crystals and of the substances held by covalent bonds; they are much more like the energy levels of the separated atoms.

B. Band Structure of Potassium Chloride

1. Introduction

The band structure of crystalline KCl has been calculated by Howland (1958) in an LCAO approximation. Interactions between free-ion Hartree–Fock functions are calculated directly from molecular-type integrals without reducing exchange interactions to an exchange potential. The structure of the filled bands of KCl is obtained by solving secular equations on a cubic mesh of points in k-space.

According to the results of X-ray measurements, crystalline KCl has a cubic lattice with K^+ and Cl^- ions occupying alternate lattice sites. The electronic structure of the crystal is expected to be closely related to that of the free ions. Both of these ions are isoelectronic with neutral argon, and both have ^1S, closed-shell electronic wave functions in their ground states.

The KCl crystal is expected to have a ground-state wave function which also is closed-shell, being a singlet and having the full symmetry of the nuclei. This closed-shell structure is expected because of the large first excitation energy of about 7·65 eV which is observed for KCl. In view of these features a Hartree–Fock procedure probably would give a reasonably good approximation to the ground-state wave function and total energy of the crystal. In addition, the array of the resulting Hartree–Fock one-electron energy parameters probably would give a fairly good representation of the structure of the filled energy bands of KCl.

2. Band Structure as a Function of Inter-ionic Distance

To provide some information about density-dependent effects in KCl as well as about band structure in general, the band structure of KCl was calculated as a function of the inter-ionic distance. For this the matrix elements of energy and overlap between free-ion functions were taken to vary in simple analytical ways as functions of the distance.

The upper and lower limits of all the bands as functions of inter-ionic distance have been obtained, and they are plotted in Fig. 15. This plot shows many similarities to the plot of the NaCl energy bands which was constructed

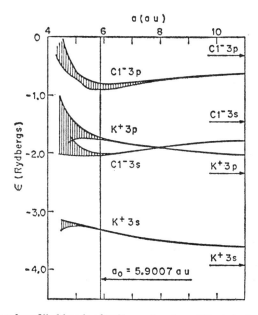

Fig. 15. The upper four filled bands of KCl as a function of the inter-ionic distance a. The values of the free-ion Hartree–Fock energy parameters are given at the right on the figure; the bands approach these parameters in the limit as the inter-ionic distance approaches infinity (After Howland, 1958).

by Slater and Shockley (1936). The reasons for the behaviour of the bands in Fig. 15 may be understood by a consideration of the analytic forms of the elements of energy and overlap. As the inter-ionic distance a decreases from 7·0 to 4·5 a.u. the two-centre elements all increase essentially exponentially, and this increase is responsible for the observed broadening of the bands. At the same time, each Cl^- band first falls because of the negative Madelung energy in the Cl^- one-centre energy elements, and then it rises rapidly as the positive, exponentially-increasing, overlap-dependent contributions to the one-centre elements come to over-weigh the Madelung energy. The K^+3p band first rises due to the positive Madelung energy in the K^+ one-centre energy elements and then rises much more rapidly as the positive overlap-dependent contributions become predominant. The K^+3s band probably should behave in the same general way as the K^+3p band, but owing to calculation inaccuracies the small overlap-dependent contributions to its normal one-centre energy element turn out to be negative; the magnitudes of these contributions are, however, less than their uncertainties.

The rapid rise of the three upper bands in Fig. 15 at small distances outweighs the band broadening. This is because the overlap-dependent contributions to the one-centre energy elements vary roughly as the square of the largest overlaps while the two-centre elements, which cause broadening, vary only as the overlaps themselves. Orthogonality requirements probably account for the particularly rapid rise of the Cl^-3p band.

VII. Cohesive Energy of Ionic Crystals

A. Coulomb Interaction

1. Pure Ionic Crystals

The calculation of the binding energy of a crystal is one of the fundamental problems in the theory of solids. The cohesive energy of the ionic crystals was calculated in 1910 by Born and Madelung. The basic assumption in this theory is that the solid may be considered as a system of positive and negative ions.

For example, in sodium chloride it is assumed that these units are the Na^+ ion and the Cl^- ion. The free alkali atom sodium has the electronic configuration $1s^2\,2s^22p^6\,3s^1$ and the free halogen atom chlorine $1s^2\,2s^2\,2p^6\,3s^2\,3p^6$. As a single sodium atom is brought into very close proximity with a single chlorine atom, the affinity of the chlorine atom for one extra electron to complete its $3p$ shell becomes large enough to ionize the sodium atom and transfer the $3s$ electron of Na to its own $3p$ shell. The result is an ionic bond of the ionized sodium atom Na^+, with an electron configuration $1s^22s^2\,2p^0$, and the ionized chlorine atom Cl^-, with the electron configuration

$1s^2\,2s^2\,2p^6\,3s^2\,3p^6$. The ionic bond is thus due to the electrostatic attraction of the positively charged sodium ion and the negatively charged chlorine ion.

In this section we shall confine ourselves to the properties of an ideally purely ionic NaCl-type crystal. We assume throughout this chapter that the anion and cation nuclei are fixed in their lattice positions. Although the nuclei are in reality oscillating about their fixed lattice positions, with amplitudes dependent upon the crystal temperature, the assumption of a rigid lattice will not materially alter the general results which we shall obtain.

The symmetry of the NaCl crystal may be described by the interpenetration of the two face-centred-cubic crystals, one for each type of ion, Na^+ and Cl^-. We shall denote the shortest inter-ionic distance as a. A given sodium ion is surrounded by $6Cl^-$ at a distance a, $12Na^+$ ions at a distance $a\sqrt{2}$, $8Cl^-$ ions at a distance $a\sqrt{3}$, and so on.

2. The Classical Coulomb Potential

Let us consider a NaCl crystal which is made up of $N\,Na^+$ ions and $N\,Cl^-$ ions, N being the Avogadro number. The total number of ions is $2N$ and the electrostatic potential, neglecting for the moment the overlap potential, felt by one of the constituent ions in the presence of the remaining ions, is:

$$E_i = \sum_{j=1}^{2N-1} v_{ij}$$

$$v_{ij} = \pm \frac{e^2}{|r_{ij}|},$$

$r_{ij} = r_i - r_j$, is the electrostatic potential between any two ions in the lattice. The total electrostatic potential energy of the lattice is:

$$E = N\,E_i.$$

Let us take the origin of our coordinate system to be at one of the positive ions. All other ions in the lattice may now be located in terms of three integers, n_1, n_2, n_3, signifying the number of lattice constants that the given ion is from the origin in the x, y, and z directions, respectively. Thus:

$$r_{ij} = (in_1 + jn_2 + kn_3)\,a$$

$$|r_{ij}| = (n_1{}^2 + n_2{}^2 + n_3{}^2)^{1/2}\,a.$$

With a positive ion at the origin, any negative ion will be at a location $(n_1, n_2, n_3)\,a$ where the sum $(n_1 + n_2 + n_3)$ is an odd integer; any positive ion will be at a location $(n_1, n_2, n_3)\,a$, where the sum $(n_1 + n_2 + n_3)$ is an even integer. The electrostatic energy between the ion at the origin and any other given ion at $\mathbf{r}_j$ may be expressed in the form:

$$v_{ij} = \frac{(-1)^{n_1 + n_2 + n_3}}{(n_1{}^2 + n_2{}^2 + n_3{}^2)^{1/2}} \frac{e^2}{a} .$$

The total potential energy which acts on the ion at the origin is:

$$E_i = \frac{Ae^2}{a} .$$

The constant:

$$A = \sum_{n_1=0}^{2N-1} \sum_{n_2=0}^{2N-1} \sum_{n_3=0}^{2N-1} (-1)^{n_1 + n_2 + n_3}(n_1{}^2 + n_2{}^2 + n_3{}^2)^{-1/2}; \, (n_1, n_2, n_3) \neq (0,0,0)$$

is called the Madelung constant. Generally, the constant A depends on the type of the lattice structure considered.

The preceding series is an alternating series with very slow convergence properties. The value which is obtained for A for NaCl structure is 1·747558. Using the value just obtained for the Madelung constant for NaCl, we have:

$$E_i = -1 \cdot 7476 \frac{e^2}{a}$$

and the total electrostatic energy becomes:

$$E = NE_i = -1 \cdot 7476 \frac{e^2 N}{a} .$$

The Madelung constants for some typical ionic crystals are as follows (Table VIII).

TABLE VIII.   Madelung constants for some ionic crystals

Formula	Lattice type	$-A$
ZnS	Wurtzite	1·641
ZnS	Zinc blende	1·6381
NaCl	Sodium Chloride	1·7476
TiO_2	Aratose	4·800
TiO_2	Rutile	4·816
CuF_2	Fluorite	5·039
Al_2O_3	Corundum	25·031

B. Repulsive Overlap Potential

Let us suppose that the only forces present are those due to the classical electrostatic interactions between the array of charged ions. Since the Coulomb force acting between any pair of ions is inversely proportional to the distance between the ions, we can see that, because of the lack of a minimum value for the electrostatic potential as a function of the inter-ionic spacing, the supposition of the existence of electrostatic forces alone leads to the result that there will be no equilibrium value for the inter-ionic spacing. In this case, the entire crystal will collapse in toward the origin.

There must, therefore, be a repulsive force, which has an origin other than the classical electrostatic field, that compensates for the effects of the Coulomb force. The repulsive potential required must necessarily be short range and must have a magnitude of sufficient strength to compensate for the attractive electrostatic potential thereby producing a minimum in the total potential at the equilibrium inter-ionic spacing.

1. The Interaction b/r^n

These forces, as other overlap forces, can best be discussed on the basis of wave mechanics, because they are of a non-classical nature. Born, in his early work, made the simple assumption that the repulsive energy between two ions as a function of their separation could be expressed by a power law of the type b'/r^n, where b' and n are as yet undetermined constants characteristic of the ions in the solid under consideration.

Focussing our attention on one particular ion, we may thus write for the repulsive energy of this ion due to the presence of all other ions:

$$E_{rep} = \frac{b}{r^n}$$

where b is related to b' by a numerical factor.

The total energy of one ion due to the presence of all others is then:

$$E(r) = \frac{-Ae^2}{r} + \frac{b}{r^n}.$$

If we consider the crystal at absolute zero, the equilibrium conditions require $E(r)$ to be a minimum, which will be the case for the equillibrium $r = a$, where a represents the smallest inter-ionic distance in the crystal at $T = 0$. For this minimum,

$$\left(\frac{dE}{dr}\right)_{r=a} = 0.$$

From the last two expressions we thus obtain the following relation between b and n:

$$b = \frac{Ae^2}{n} a^{n-1}.$$

From the total binding energy of a crystal containing N positive and N negative ion:

$$E(r) = N\left(\frac{-Ae^2}{r} + \frac{b}{r^n}\right)$$

and the last expression of b, we obtain:

$$E(a) = -N\frac{Ae^2}{a}\left(1 - \frac{1}{n}\right).$$

The inter-ionic distance can be obtained from X-ray diffraction data. If the repulsive exponent n is known, the lattice energy can thus be calculated.

The unknown repulsive exponent n can be obtained from measurements of the compressibility K_0 of the crystal which is given by

$$1/K_0 V_0 = \left(\frac{d^2E}{dV^2}\right)_{V=V_0}$$

at absolute zero; V_0 being the volume of the crystal corresponding to an inter-ionic distance a; V corresponding to the variable r.

The relation between interionic distance and volume is:

$$V = \alpha N r^3$$

where α is a constant determined only by the type of lattice. Hence, we have:

$$\frac{dE}{dV} = \frac{1}{3\alpha N r^3}\frac{dE}{dr}$$

and

$$\frac{d^2E}{dV^2} = \frac{1}{9\alpha^2 N^2 r^2}\frac{d}{dr}\left(\frac{1}{r^2}\frac{dE}{dr}\right).$$

From the preceding expression of $E(r)$, we obtain:

$$\frac{1}{K_0 \alpha N a^3} = \left(\frac{d^2E}{dV^2}\right)_{r=a} = \frac{1}{9\alpha^2 N a^2}\left[\frac{-4Ae^2}{a^5} + \frac{n(n+3)b}{a^{n+4}}\right].$$

Substituting the value of b, we have:

$$n = 1 + 9\alpha a^4 / K_0 e^2 A.$$

Some experimental values obtained by extrapolation of compressibility measurements to $T = 0$ are given below (Table IX).

TABLE IX.   Experimental values of n for the interaction b/r^n

Substance	n	Substance	n	Substance	n
LiF	6·0	LiCl	7·0	LiI	8·5
NaF	7·0	NaCl	8·0	NaI	9·5
KF	8·0	KCl	9·0	KI	10·5
RbF	8·5	RbCl	9·5	RbI	11·0
CsF	9·5	CsCl	10·5	CsI	12·0

Although there is a marked variation from one crystal to another, an appreciable error in n leads to a relatively small error in the lattice energy which is proportional to $(1 - 1/n)$. Thus $E(a)$ changes by only 1 or 2% if we change n by unity.

2. The Interaction $\lambda e^{-|r|/\rho}$

Although the necessity for a repulsive potential to maintain a stable crystal was recognized long before the discovery of quantum mechanics, the source of a repulsive potential was not discovered until the advent of this theory and the requirements of the Pauli exclusion principle.

As adjacent atoms approach each other their electronic clouds tend to overlap. The Pauli principle would then predict that the only way that an electron associated with one ion may occupy the location in space occupied by an equivalent electron of the adjacent ion would be to excite that electron to a higher energy state. On the other hand, the energy that is required to excite the neighbouring ion is generally much greater in magnitude than is available to the ion under consideration. Consequently, the outermost electronic clouds of adjacent ions tend to repel their further motion toward each other after they have come into very close proximity.

The repulsive potential between a pair of ions in a crystal is represented by the following approximate form:

$$(v_{ij})_{\text{rep}} = \lambda_{ij}\, e^{-|r_{ij}|/\rho}.$$

$|r_{ij}| = |r_i - r_j|$, λ_{ij} and ρ depend, in general, on the nature of the ions i and j but are independent of the distance r_{ij}. This form of the repulsive potential allows a more accurate calculus of the lattice energy than the expression b/r^n.

C. Experimental Cohesive Energy

An experimental check on the calculated values of the lattice energies may be obtained from what is known as a Born–Haber cycle. Let us consider, for example, one gram atom of solid solium reacting with half a gram molecule of Cl_2 gas. As a result of the reaction, solid NaCl is formed and a certain amount of heat, the heat of formation, is given off. The change in energy due to such a reaction may be calculated by considering the following steps:

$$Na_{solid} + S_{Na} \longrightarrow Na_{vapour}$$

$$Na_{vapour} + I_{Na} \longrightarrow Na^+ + electron$$

$$1/2\ Cl_2 + (1/2)D_{Cl_2} \longrightarrow Cl$$

$$Cl + electron \longrightarrow Cl^- + A_{Cl}$$

$$(Na^+ + Cl^-)_{gas} \longrightarrow NaCl_{solid} + E_L$$

$$Na_{solid} + 1/2\ Cl_2 + S_{Na} + I_{Na} + (1/2)D_{Cl} \longrightarrow NaCl_{solid} + A_{Cl} + E_L$$

The quantities introduced all refer to the formation of one ion pair of solid NaCl. The sublimation energy S_{Na} can be determined experimentally by direct caloric measurements or from measurements of the vapour pressure as a function of temperature. The ionization energy I_{Na} can be obtained experimentally from optical measurements. The dissociation energy D_{Cl_2}, required to separate the two Cl atoms in a Cl_2 molecule, can be obtained by determining the dissociation constant as a fucntion of temperature. The electron affinity A_{Cl} can be determined by measuring the ionization energy of the negative ions, or by measuring the density of halide ions in alkali halide vapour.

We also know the heat of formation:

$$Na_{solid} + 1/2\ Cl_2 \longrightarrow NaCl_{solid} + Q$$

per "molecule" NaCl formed. Substracting this equation from the one obtained above, we find for the latter energy per ion pair,

$$E_L = S_{Na} + I_{Na} + (1/2)D_{Cl2} - A_{Cl} + Q.$$

Generally, all quantities on the right-hand side can be obtained from experimental measurements. For NaCl we find,

$$E_L = 184 \cdot 7\ kcal/mol$$

and we see that theory and experiment agree within a few per cent (Table X), indicating that the relatively simple approach is essentially correct.

Values of the cohesive energy obtained by theoretical equations are given in Table X. The two approximations with the repulsive potential b/r^n and $\lambda e^{-a/\rho}$ are used and compared to the experimental results.

TABLE X.   Experimental and theoretical values of the lattice energy

Substances	a (Å)	n	Cohesive energy, kcal/mol		Experimental
			with b/r^n	with $\lambda e^{-a/\rho}$	
LiF	2·010	6·0	240·1	254	...
LiCl	2·572	7·0	193·3	196	201·5
LiBr	2·745	7·5	183·1	184	191·5
LiI	3·000	8·5	170·7	169	180·0
NaF	2·310	7·0	215·0	220	...
NaCl	2·814	8·0	180·4	182	184·7
NaBr	2·981	8·5	171·7	173	175·9
NaI	3·231	9·5	160·8	159	166·3
KF	2·665	8·0	190·4	193	...
KCl	3·639	9·0	164·4	166	167·8
KBr	3·293	9·5	157·8	158	161·2
KI	3·526	10·5	149·0	148	152·8
RbF	2·815	8·5	181·8	183	...
RbCl	3·270	9·5	158·9	159	163·3
RbBr	3·427	10·0	152·5	152	158·0
RbI	3·663	11·0	144·2	143	149·7

D. Multipole Interaction and the Zero-point Energy

1. The van der Waals Forces

In the third place, the van der Waals attraction between the ions must be taken into account. This makes a contribution of 2–3% to the total lattice energy of the alkali-halides and about 10% for the silver halides. For example, for AgBr it is about 14%; this is a consequence of the relatively high polarizability of the silver ion. We should note that the van der Waals energy sometimes plays an important role in the discussion of the stability of different lattice structures.

According to the work of London (1930, 1937) and Margenau (1931, 1939), the van der Waals attraction between any two atoms of ions gives rise to an energy:

$$V(r) = \frac{-C}{r^6}.$$

Once the constants C are determined for the various ion pairs, the contribution to the crystal energy may be found by summing over all ion pairs. The summations may be carried out by using the results of Jones and Ingham (1925).

If C_{++}, C_{--}, C_{+-} are the values of the constants for ions of like and unlike signs, the constant C is:

$$C = 6{\cdot}5952\, C_{+-} + 1{\cdot}8067 \frac{C_{++} + C_{--}}{2}.$$

Using these methods Mayer and his co-workers have estimated the van der Waals energy in the halkali-halides (Mayer, 1933a), silver and thallium halides (Mayer, 1933b) and for the cuprons halides (Mayer and Levy, 1933). Some results are given in Table XI according to Mayer's works.

TABLE XI.   Constant of the van der Waals forces

Substances	C
LiF	18
LiBr	183
NaCl	180
NaI	482
RbCl	691
CsBr	2,070

In fact, the energy C/r^6 is only part of the van der Waals energy and there is an infinite series of rapidly converging terms. The next one corresponds to dipole–quadrupole interaction and varies as r^{-8}.

2. The Zero-point Energy

The zero-point energy of the crystal is a consequence of quantum mechanics. The possible energy levels of a harmonic oscillator are given by:

$$E = (n + \tfrac{1}{2})h\nu$$

where v is the frequency and n an integer. Thus, even at absolute zero an oscillator has a zero point energy of $hv/2$.

TABLE XII. Theoretical values of the cohesive energy

	Madelung	Overlap	Dipole–Dipole	Dipole–Quadripole	Zero-point	Total
LiF	285·5	−44·1	3·9	0·6	−3·9	242·0
LiCl	223·5	−26·8	5·8	0·1	−2·4	200·2
LiBr	207·8	−22·5	5·9	0·1	−1·6	189·7
LiI	188·8	−18.3	6·8	0·1	−1·2	176·2
NaF	248·1	−35·3	4·5	0·1	−2·9	214·5
NaCl	204·3	−23·4	5·2	0·1	−1·7	184·4
NaBr	192·9	−20·6	5·5	0·1	−1·4	176·5
NaI	178·0	−17·1	6·3	0·1	−1·2	166·1
KF	215·1	−28·1	6·9	0·1	−2·2	191·8
KCl	183·2	−21·5	7·1	0·1	−1·4	167·5
KBr	174·5	−18·6	6·9	0·1	−1·2	161·7
KI	162·8	−15·9	7·1	0·1	−1·0	153·1
RbF	203·8	−26·2	7·9	0·1	−1·4	184·2
RbCl	175·8	−19·9	7·9	0·1	−1·2	162·7
RbBr	167·2	−17·6	7·9	0·1	−0·9	156·7
RbI	156·5	−15·4	7·9	0·1	−0·7	148·4
CsF	191·1	−23·9	9·7	0·1	−1·2	175·8
CsCl	162·5	−17·7	11·7	0·1	−1·0	155·6
CsBr	155·8	−16·4	11·4	0·1	−0·9	150·0
CsI	146·8	−14·6	11·1	0·1	−0·7	142·7

In the Debye theory of the specific heat of solids, a crystal is represented formally by a system of harmonic oscillators with a frequency spectrum given by:

$$F(v)\, dv = 4\pi V \left(\frac{2}{v_t^2} + \frac{1}{v_l^2} \right) v^2\, dv$$

where V is the volume of the crystal, v_t and v_l are, respectively, the velocities of propagation of transverse and longitudinal elastic waves. Using the definition of the Debye frequency v_D, we may write:

$$F(v)\,\mathrm{d}v = (9N/v_D{}^3)v^2\,\mathrm{d}v$$

with N standing for the total number of atoms or ions in the crystal. Hence, at absolute zero, the contribution of the zero-point energy is:

$$\tfrac{1}{2}\int_0^{v_D} F(v)\,hv\,\mathrm{d}v = \tfrac{9}{8}Nh\,v_D.$$

As the correction to the lattice energy, the zero point energy thus contributes about 1%. The zero-point energy must be substracted. In general, the Van der Waals correction is more important for heavy elements (large polarizabilities) and the zero-point energy for light elements (high Debye frequency).

The contributions of the different terms for the cohesive energy of alkalihalides are given in Table XII.

References

Bacon, G. E. and Curry, N. A. (1962). *Proc. Roy. Soc.* **A266**, 95.

Boltaks, B. (1963). "Diffusion in Semiconductors". Academic Press, London.

Bradley, J. N. and Greene, P. D. (1966). *Trans. Faraday. Soc.* **62**, 2069.

Bradley, J. N. and Greene, P. D. (1967). *Trans. Faraday. Soc.* **63**, 424.

Bragg, W, L. (1914). *Proc. Roy. Soc.* **A89**, 468.

Bragg, W. L. (1968). "The Crystalline State". Bell, London.

Bragg, W. L. and Gibbs, R. E. (1925). *Proc. Roy. Soc.* **A109**, 405.

Casella, R. C. (1956). *Phys. Rev.* **104**, 1260.

Clark, H. (1968). "Solid State Physics; An Introduction to Its Theory" Mc.Millan, Toronto.

De Surville, R. Josefowicz, M., Yu, L. T., Perichon, J. and Buvet, R. (1968). *Electrochimica Acta.* **13**, 1451.

Dekker, A. J. (1963). "Solid State Physics". Prentice Hall, Englewoods Cliffs.

Dent. L. S. and Smith, J. V. (1958). *Nature.* **181**, 1794.

Evseev, Z. Ya. (1963). *Fiz. Tverd. Tela.* **5**, 2345.

Evseev, Z. Ya and Tolpygo, K. B. (1962). *Fix. Tverd. Tela.* **4**, 3644.

Ewing, D. H. and Seitz, F. (1936). *Phys. Rev.* **50**, 76.

Fajans, K. (1941). *J. Chem. Phy.* **9**, 281.

Fajans, K. and Bauer, N. (1942). *J. Am. Chem. Soc.* **64**, 3023.

Fajans, K. and Joo, G. (1924). *Z. Physik.* **23**, 1.

Fox, D. (1963). "Physics and Chemistry of the Organic Solid State". Interscience, New York.

Friauf, R. J. (1963). *In* "American Institute of Physics Handbook", Mc Graw-Hill, New York.

Frueh, A. J. (1958). *Z. Krist.* **110**, 136.

Fumi, F. G. and Tosi, M. P. (1964a). *J. Phys. Chem. Solids.* **25**, 31.

Fumi, F. G. and Tosi, M. P. (1964b). *J. Phys. Chem. Solids.* **25**, 45.

Geller, S. (1967). *Science.* **157**, 310.

Gibbs, R. E. (1926). *Proc. Roy. Soc.* **A110**, 443.

Goldschmidt, V. M. (1926). *Skrifter Norske Videnskaps.* no. 2.

Goldschmidt, V. M. (1927). *Skrifter Norske Videnskaps.* no. 8.

Gray, T. J. (1957). "The Defect Solid State". Interscience, New York.

Gubanov, A. I. (1965). "Quantum Electron Theory of Amorphous Conductors". Consultants Bureau, New York.

Hamilton, W. C. and Ibers, J. A. (1968). "Hydrogen Bonding in Solids". Benjamin Inc., New York.

Hannay, N. B. (1967). "Solid State Chemistry". Prentice-Hall, New York.

Hartree, D. R. and Hartree, W. (1936). *Proc. Roy. Soc.* **A156**, 45.

Hartree, D. R. and Hartree, W. (1948). *Proc. Roy. Soc.* **A193**, 299.

Helfferich, F. (1962). "Ion Exchanges", McGraw-Hill, New York.

Herman, F. and Skillman, S. (1963). "Atomic Structure Calculation". Prentice Hall, Englewoods Cliffs.

Hosemann, R. and Bagchi, S. N. (1962). "Direct Analysis of Diffraction by Matter". North-Holland Publishing Co., Amsterdam.

Howland, L. P. (1958). *Phys. Rev.* **109**, 1927.

Huggins, M. L. (1926). *Phys. Rev.* **28**, 1086.

Jones, J. E. and Ingham, A. E. (1925). *Proc. Roy. Soc.* **107**, 636.

Jost, W. (1960). "Diffusion in Solids Liquids, Gases". Academic Press, New York.

Kittel, C. (1970). "Introduction à la Physique de l'état Solide". Dunod, Paris.

Koopmans, T. (1933). *Physica.* **1**, 104.

Kröger, F. A. (1964). "The Chemistry of Imperfect Crystals". Wiley, New York.

Krug, J., Witte, H. and Wölfel, E. (1955). *Z. Physik Chem.* **4**, 36.

Kucher, T. I. (1958a). *Zh. Sksperim. i Teor. Fiz.* **34**, 394 (1958b) *Ibid.* **35**, 1049.

Kucher, T. I. and Tolpygo, K. B. (1960). *Fiz. Tverd. Tela.* **2**, 2301.

London, F. (1930). *Z. für. Phys. Chem.* **11**, 222. (1937) *Trans. Faraday Soc.* **33**, 8.

McKelvey, J. P. (1966). "Solid State and Semi-conductor Physics". Harper and Row, New York.

Mackenzie, J. D. (1960). "Modern Aspects of the Vitreous State". Butterworths, London.

Margenau, H. (1931). *Phys. Rev.* **38**, 747. (1939) *Rev. Mod. Phys.* **11**, 1.

Mayer, J. E. (1933a). *J. Chem. Phys.* **1**, 270. (1933b) *Ibid.* **1**, 327.

Mayer, J. E. and Levy, R. B. (1933). *J. Chem. Phys.* **1**, 647.

Meckler, A. (1953). *J. Chem. Phys.* **21**, 1750.

Melvin, F. H. (1931). *Phys. Rev.* **37**, 1230.

Miller, M. L. (1966). "The Structure of polymers". Reinhold Publ. Corp.

Morris, D. F. C. (1968). *In* "Structure and Bonding". Vol. 4, p. 63, Springer-Verlag, New York.

Osborn, G. H. (1955). "Synthetic Ions-exchangers". Chapman and Hall, London.

Owens, B. B. and Argue, G. R. (1967). *Science.* **157**, 308.

Pauling, L. (1927). *Proc. Roy. Soc.* **A114**, 181.

Pauling, L. (1960). "The Nature of the Chemical Bond and the Structure of Molecules and Crystals". Cornell University Press, Ithaca.

Petrashen, M. I., Gutman, T. L. and Balarin, M. (1958). *Nachr. Leningrad Univ.* **22**, 28.

Petrashen, M. I., Arbarenkov, V. and Kristofel, N. N. (1960), *Opt. Spectry. USSR,* (English transl.) **9**, 276.

Pratt, G. W. Jr. (1952). *Phys. Rev.* **88,** 1217.
Seitz, F. (1949). "Theorie moderne des solides". Masson, Paris.
Schneider, E. G. (1936). *Phys. Rev.* **49,** 341.
Shockley. W, (1936). *Phys. Rev.* **50,** 754.
Schoknecht, G. (1957). *Z. Naturforsh.* **12a,** 983.
Slater, J. C. (1965). "Quantum Theory of Molecules and Solids". McGraw-Hill, New York.
Slater, J. C. and Shockley, W. (1936). *Phys. Rev.* **50,** 705.
Smith, R. A. (1969). "Wave Mechanics of Crystalline Solids". Chapman and Hall, London.
Tibbs, S. R. (1939). *Trans. Faraday. Soc.* **35,** 1471.
Tolpygo, K. B. and Tomasevich, O. F. (1958). *Ukr. Fiz. Zh.* **3,** 145; (1960) *Fiz. Tverd. Trla.* **2,** 3110.
Turnbull, D. and Cohen, M. H. (1960). *In* "Modern Aspects of the Vitreous State". (J. P. Mackenzie, Eds). Vol. 1, p. 38. Butterworths. London.
Van Gool, W. (1966). "Principles of defect Chemistry of Crystalline Solids". Academic Press, New York.
Vegard, L. (1916). *Phil. Mag.* **32,** 65.
Warren, B. E. (1941). *J. Amer. Ceram. Soc.* **24,** 256.
Wasastjerna, J. A. (1923). *Soc. Sci. Fennica. Commentationes. Phys. Math.* **38,** 1.
Wells, A. F. (1962). "Structural Inorganic Chemistry". Clarendon Press, Oxford.
Westman, A. E. R. (1960). *In* "Modern Aspects of the Virtreous State". (J. D. Mackenzie, Ed). vol. 1, p. 63. Butterworths.
Weyl, W. A. (1949). *J. Am. Ceram. Soc.* **32,** 367.
Witte, H. and Wölfel, E. (1955). *Z. Physik. Chem.* **3,** 296.
Wyckoff, R. W. (1960). "Crystal Structures". Interscience, New York.
Zachariasen, W. H. (1931). *Z. Krist.* **80,** 137. (1932). *J. Amer. Chem. Soc.* **54,** 384.

3. THEORY OF CRYSTALLINE SOLID ELECTROLYTE SOLUTIONS†

Francis K. Fong

Department of Chemistry, Purdue University, Lafayette, Indiana, U.S.A.

I. Introduction

In thermodynamic equilibrium, the free energy

$$F = E - TS,$$

of a crystal, where E, T, and S are the energy, temperature, and entropy respectively, is at a minimum. Although energy is expended to form a defect against the cohesive forces of the crystal, the increase in entropy resulting from the defect formation causes the free energy to be minimized at some

† This work was supported under the sponsorship of the Advanced Research Project Agency.

given temperature. For vanishing values of temperature T, the entropy term becomes negligibly small, and an ideal crystal may approach a perfect state in which no imperfections or lattice defects exist. As the temperature of a crystal is raised, the mean amplitude of the thermal vibrations of the atoms about their mean positions increases. These vibrations cause a certain departure from periodicity in a crystal lattice. In addition to this, there exists in a normal crystal a number of vacant lattice sites and interstitials. An interstitial is an ion situated at an interlattice position between the normal lattice sites, as indicated by point b in Fig. 1. The representation of an interstitial in CaF_2 is shown in Fig. 2. The ideas of lattice defects involving lattice vacancies and interstitials were developed mainly by Frenkel (1926), Wagner and Schottky (1930), and Jost (1933, 1938).

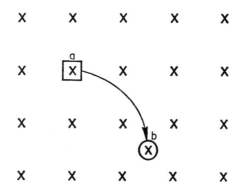

FIG. 1. Schematic representation of a Frenkel (interstitial) defect.

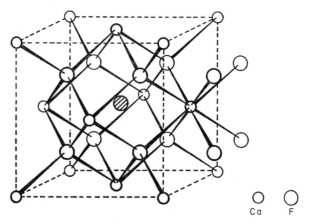

FIG. 2. Schematic representation of an interstitial F^- ion (shaded circle in the centre) in CaF_2.

Two major types of defects may arise from lattice vacancies and inter-stitials: Schottky defects and Frenkel defects. The Frenkel disorder is illu-strated in Fig. 1. An atom of the crystal leaves its normal position (a) and migrates to an interstitial position (b). Alkaline earth fluorides are known to exhibit the so-called anti-Frenkel disorder. At thermal equilibrium there are equal numbers of F^- vacancies and F^- interstitials. The Schottky defect is illustrated in Fig. 3. An atom vacates its normal lattice site to move to the surface of the crystal, adding to the outermost layers of the normal crystal lattice. Because of the vacancies that result from the Schottky lattice defect formation, the volume of the crystal increases as the density of the crystal decreases, without necessarily affecting the crystal lattice constant. At thermal equilibrium, there are equal numbers of metal ion and halide ion vacancies in alkali halides. The alkali halides are thus characterized by the Schottky-type disorder.

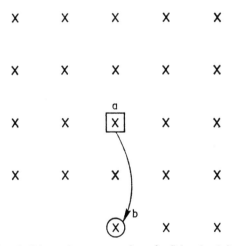

FIG. 3. Schematic representation of a Schottky defect.

The presence of intrinsic lattice defects, which gives rise to ionic conduc-tivity in alkali halides and alkaline earth halides owing to defect mobility at elevated temperatures, has been dealt with in earlier review articles (Mott and Gurney, 1948; Lidiard, 1957; Fong, 1966). The major concern of the present work shall instead be to consider the problem of interactions between impurity ions and lattice defects in ionic crystals and the interesting pheno-mena which arise from these interactions. Perhaps the most important ion defect interactions in crystalline lattices are exemplified by those found in crystals doped with aliovalent ions of valencies ± 1 different from that of the corresponding host ions. For example, since the disorder in CaF_2 is of the *anti*-Frenkel type, the solution of substitutional trivalent cations is usually accompanied by the creation of an equal number of F^- interstitials which neutralize the additional positive charges on the impurity ions. The following representations of charge compensation in CaF_2 are often encountered in the literature (Fong, 1966):

$$M^{1+} + F_v^- \overset{K_1}{\rightleftharpoons} M^{1+} : F_v^-$$

and
$$M^{3+} + F_i^- \overset{K_2}{\rightleftharpoons} M^{3+} : F_i^-$$

where M^{1+} and M^{3+} represent the aliovalent impurity cations which may be compensated respectively by F^- vacanices, F_v^-, and F^- interstitials, F_i^-. The subscripts v and i denote vacancy and interstitial, respectively. Here, the equilibrium constants K_1 and K_2 have been usually taken to signify the thermal equilibrium condition under which the impurity defect pairs may either be dissociated (left hand side of (1) and (2)) or be associated as complexes. This notion of a two state association–dissociation phenomenon, as we shall see in the following sections, is quite misleading.

In Schottky-type disordered alkali halide lattices, divalent cations M^{2+} that enter the crystal substitutionally are charge compensated by metal ion vacancies. On the other hand, dinegative ions (such as the O^{2-} ion) can enter the lattice substitutionally into the halide ion sublattice with the creation of an equal number of halide ion vacancies. Clearly, in the first approximation, the aliovalent ions and their associated compensation defects in the above examples can be thought of as mutually interacting ions of opposite charges with the remainder of the lattice being considered as a continuous dielectric medium. The problem is quite similar to that of an aqueous solution of a binary salt such as NaCl, except that the interacting entities lie on points in a periodic lattice. As such, we have in our possession a unique handle, which is not available in the case of an aqueous electrolyte solution, in treating the statistical mechanics of the crystalline electrolyte. In the following, we shall develop the theoretical concepts of crystalline solid electrolyte solutions, and describe some of the experiments which have been designed in the characterization of these materials.

II. Statistical Mechanics of Crystalline Electrolytes

In the discussion of the crystalline electrolyte in this section, we shall employ, as prototypes of our discussion, the (alkali–halide): M^{2+} and the (alkaline–earth–fluoride): M^{3+} systems, in which the aliovalent cations are compensated by metal ion vacancies (Lidiard, 1957) and halide ion interstitials (Fong, 1966), respectively (see also Fong, 1969; Heist and Fong, 1970; Fong *et al.*, 1970).

A. The Configuration Partition Function of Ion-defect Interactions in a Periodic Lattice

For a given temperature, there exists in alkali halide crystals an equilibrium law which governs the presence of cationic and anionic vacancies. The introduction of M^{2+} impurity ions into the cation sublattice increases the number of the cationic vacancies, such that electroneutrality is maintained. If the concentration of the M^{2+} ions, N_i, is much greater than the equilibrium concentration of the intrinsic lattice defects, one can assume equal numbers of vacancies and M^{2+} ions. In general, N_i unipositive (i.e., M^{2+}) ions and N_i uninegative ions (i.e., cation vacancies) give rise to a total interaction energy, for a given configuration,

$$U(\hat{R}_1, \hat{R}_2, ..., \hat{R}_{2N_i}) = \sum_{1 \leqslant i < j \leqslant N_i} \cdots \sum {}^+u(\hat{R}_{ij}) + \sum_{(N_i+1) \leqslant m < l \leqslant 2N_i} \cdots \sum {}^+u(\hat{R}_{lm})$$

$$+ \sum_{\substack{1 \leqslant k \leqslant N_i \\ N_i+1 \leqslant p \leqslant 2N_i}} \cdots \sum {}^-u(\hat{R}_{kp}) \tag{1}$$

where $\hat{R}_1, \hat{R}_2, ..., \hat{R}_{2N_i}$ are the position vectors of the N_i cations and N_i anions, and ${}^+u$ and ${}^-u$ denote repulsive and attractive interaction energies, respectively.

If we take into account all the pairwise interactions ${}^+u$ and ${}^-u$ in eqn (1), the longer range interactions will be purely Coulombic, and the evaluation of the configuration partition function

$$Z_{\text{configuration}} = \sum_{\substack{\text{all} \\ \text{configurations}}} \exp[-U(\hat{R}_1, \hat{R}_2, ..., \hat{R}_{2N_i})/kT] \tag{2}$$

can be attempted, for example, in terms of the Mayer cluster theory (Mayer and Mayer, 1940) which has been previously applied (Mayer, 1950) to fluid electrolytic solutions. Conceptually, it is easier at the outset to visualize the interactions between two charged particles in a dielectric medium. The assumption of long range Coulomb interactions in this case leads to apparent divergences (Pines and Nozières, 1966). In reality, the effective interaction between two charges is actually limited in its range due to the screening arising from the polarization of the ionic atmosphere in the vicinity of a given charge (Debye and Hückel, 1923). The distant interaction energy between two charged particles of unit charges in a dielectric medium is

$$\pm u(R) = \pm e\phi(R) = \pm \frac{e^2}{\varepsilon R} \exp(-bR) \tag{3}$$

where

$$b = \left(\frac{8\pi N_i e^2}{\varepsilon V k T} \right)^{\frac{1}{2}},$$

V being the volume of the system and ε the dielectric constant of the medium.

Due to the exponential screen, the effective number of interacting neighbours is finite. Instead of eqn (1), the total pairwise interaction energy of a given configuration can thus be expressed:

$$U(\hat{R}_1, \hat{R}_2, ..., \hat{R}_{2N_i}) = \sum_{1 \leqslant i < j \leqslant 2N_i} \cdots \sum {}^{\pm}u(R_{ij}) = \tfrac{1}{2} \sum_{i=1}^{2N_i} \cdots \sum_{j=1}^{z_i} \pm e\phi(R_{ij}) \qquad (4)$$

where z_i is the actual effective number of interacting neighbours of the ith charge. The factor $\tfrac{1}{2}$ corrects for the over-counting incurred in the double sum. The configuration partition function can now be written:

$$Z_{\text{configuration}} = \sum_n \exp[-U_n(R_{ij})/kT] = \sum_n \exp\left[-\frac{1}{2kT} \sum_{i=1}^{2N_i} \sum_{j=1}^{z_i} \pm e\phi(R_{ij}) \right] \quad (5)$$

where the sum is carried over all the n possible configurations. If we now assume that at sufficiently low temperatures, the attractive terms will predominate as opposite charges tend to pair formation, eqn (5) can be rewritten:

$$Z_{\text{configuration}} = \sum_n \exp\left[-\frac{1}{kT} \sum_{i=1}^{N_i} -e\phi(R_{il}) \right] = \Omega_p \left\{ \sum_{R_l} g_l \exp\left[\frac{e\phi(R_l)}{kT} \right] \right\}^{N_i} \quad (6)$$

where Ω_p is the number of ways of placing N_i ion-defect pairs in the lattice. The sum after the first equal sign is carried over all possible values of R_{il}, the distance of separation of the ith charge from its nearest opposite charge. Only the attractive terms are retained in eqn (6). The sum over j of eqn (5) is set equal to $-e\phi(R_{il})$, the attractive energy of the ith charge with its close-by opposite charge. In effect, these simplifications are equivalent to neglecting the dipolar interactions between the charge pairs. The second equal sign in eqn (6) reduces the configuration partition function to a product of "molecular" partition functions of N_i *pairs* of opposite charges. Here, R_l is the distance of separation of a specified pair, and g_l is the number of equivalent ways in which such a pair can be formed. The conditions under which the separation of the variables of the charge pairs is valid will be given in Section II. D.

B. The Low Temperature Case—Site Symmetry Distributions in (alkali–halide): M^{2+} and (alkaline–earth–halide): M^{3+} Systems

A typical alkali halide is KCl. The cation sub-lattice is face-centered cubic. The $K^+ - Cl^-$ separation, a, is $3\cdot14$ Å. When a divalent cation M^{2+} enters the lattice substitutionally, a K^+ vacancy is created so that charge neutrality is maintained. Neglecting the dipolar interactions between the M^{2+} vacancy pairs, as in eqn (6), we assume that at sufficiently low temperatures and concentrations, each M^{2+} ion is associated with a K^+ vacancy with an energy which varies as R^{-1}. Since the vacancy can only occupy discrete positions, R can assume only discrete values, with the consequence that the Coulomb energy of association, u_l, is also discrete:

$$u_l = \frac{-e^2}{\varepsilon R_l},$$

where $\varepsilon = 5{\cdot}03$. Here, we have assumed that the quantity b in eqn (3) is vanishingly small at high dilution.

Taking the structural properties of the f.c.c. lattice into consideration, one observes that R_1 for the n.n. (nearest neighbour) pair is $\sqrt{2}\,a$, and that there are twelve distinguishable but equivalent n.n. sites whose C_2 symmetry axes point in the directions of the [110], [101], [011], [$\bar{1}$10], [$\bar{1}$01], [0$\bar{1}$1], [1$\bar{1}$0], [10$\bar{1}$], [01$\bar{1}$], [$\bar{1}\bar{1}$0], [$\bar{1}$0$\bar{1}$], and [0$\bar{1}\bar{1}$] crystal axes. For the n.n.n. (next nearest neighbour) pair, R_2 is $\sqrt{4}\,a$ with six possible equivalent sites with the vacancy occupying one of the six equivalent $(2, 0, 0)$ lattice points. The C_{2v} n.n. site, the C_{4v} n.n.n. site and the C_s third n.n. site are shown in Fig. 4. In general, if the M^{2+} ion is taken as the origin and the lattice point occupied by the associated vacancy is given by (i, j, k), $(i + j + k)$ must be even in order for the vacancy to be in the K^+ sublattice. The value for R_l is simply $\sqrt{i^2 + j^2 + k^2}\,a$. R_l can be written as $\sqrt{2l}\,a$, where $l = 1, 2, 3, \ldots$. The various site symmetries (and corresponding values of the g_l number of distinguishable but equivalent lattice points in parenthesis) are: $C_{2v}(12)$ when $i = j \neq 0$, $k = 0$; $C_{4v}(6)$ when $i \neq 0$, $j = k = 0$; $C_s(24)$ when $i \neq j = k$ $(i, j, k \neq 0)$; $C_s(24)$ when $i \neq j$, $k = 0$ and $i, j \neq 0$; $C_1(48)$ when all i, j, k are unequal and unequal to zero; and $C_{3v}(8)$ when $i = j = k \neq 0$. At $l = 9$, 13, 17, 18, 19, 25, 27 and 31 more than one site symmetry can occur.

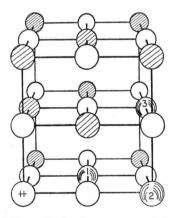

FIG. 4. The C_{2v} nearest neighbour (1), the C_{4v} next nearest neighbour (2), and the C_s third nearest neighbour (3) M^{2+}–K^+ vacancy sites.

The energy of pairing can now be written as

$$u_1 = -0.39 \text{ eV},$$

$$u_l = -\frac{e^2}{\varepsilon\sqrt{2l}a} = -k\Theta_p l^{-\frac{1}{2}}, \quad l = 2, 3, 4, \ldots. \tag{7}$$

The value u_1 for the n.n. $M^{2+}:K^+$ vacancy is assumed to be the same as that for the n.n. pair energy in $KCl:Sr^{2+}$ as calculated by Bassani and Fumi (1954), namely -0.39 eV. This has been confirmed experimentally by Watkins in $KCl:Mn^{2+}$ system (Watkins, 1959). The pairing energies for $l > 1$ are estimated by using the simple homogeneous dielectric shielding model. This is a fairly good approximation. The calculated value for u_2 is -0.50 eV ($KCl:Sr^{2+}$) (Tosi and Airokli, 1958). The experimental value ~ -0.42 eV ($KCl:Mn^{2+}$) was obtained by Watkins (1959). The Coulombic value -0.46 eV lies in between the two values quoted above.† For KCl, $\Theta_p = e^2/\varepsilon\sqrt{2}ak = 7497$ K.

Assuming the conditions for the canonical ensemble configuration partition function of eqn (6), we now write the distribution numbers n_l^* associated with the energy level u_l:

$$n_l^* = \frac{N_i g_l \exp(-u_l/kT)}{\sum_{l'} g_{l'} \exp(-u_l/kT)} = N_i q_p^{-1} g_l \exp(-u_l/kT) \tag{8}$$

where the crystal contains N_i impurity atom/cm^3, and q_p is the molecular partition function for the pair formation. Equation (8) holds subject to the restrictive conditions

$$u_p = \sum_l n_l^* u_l,$$

and

$$N_i = \sum_l n_l^*,$$

where u_p is the total energy of the crystal due to pairing, and is actually the most probable configuration energy U^* if eqn (6) is valid. To obtain n_l^*, we substitute the appropriate values for g_l and u_l (Fong, 1969) into eqn (8). When $u_l \gg kT$, only the ground level u_2 is populated, and $q_p = g_2 \exp(-u_2/kT)$ leading to the result that $n_2^* = N_i$, i.e., all the M^{2+} ions and K^+

---

† The uncertainty in the values of the pairing energies presents the one and only problem in the prediction of low temperature distribution of M^{2+}-vacancy pairs in alkali halides. The comparison of Mn^{2+} with Sr^{2+} in KCl is only qualitative in nature due to the difference in their respective ionic sizes. In Section II.C, the value -0.50 eV calculated by Tosi and Airokli (1958) for ε_2 in $KCl:Sr^{2+}$ is assumed. In either case, however, the main arguments remain unaffected.

vacancies are associated as n.n.n. pairs. As T increases, the excited levels become populated. The partition function must now be summed over successively increasing values of l to obtain accurate results. At 300 and 500 K the value for q_p does not change significantly when the sum is carried beyond $l' = 13$, whereas at 700 and 900 K, the terms in q_p beyond $l' = 13$ become increasingly significant, and q_p apparently does not converge readily (Fong, 1969). There are several causes for this difficulty. First of all, as the distant sites become populated, the Coulombic interaction tends to be screened, and eqn (7) is no longer valid. More significantly, the assumptions underlying eqn (6) are no longer valid at high temperatures since the repulsive terms and the terms other than the first in the sum over j in eqn (5) can no longer be neglected. To do justice to the problem, we must employ the configuration energy of eqn (1) or eqn (4) in our calculations, which is unfortunately a rather difficult task. An approach to the high temperature (> 900 K) case will be attempted in Section II.C. In using the molecular approach, however, we have meaningful values of q_p at temperatures less than 500 K. Calculations of q_p at higher temperatures are subject to serious errors. Nevertheless, even at 900 K, the largest terms in q_p are still those characterized by the smallest l values, i.e., those corresponding to the low-lying bound states. In Section IV, a theoretical treatment of the intermediate temperature region (500–900 K), in which ion–defect pairs begin to dissociate, will be given.

The calculated values of n_l^*/N_i are plotted against T in Fig. 5 for the first three bound states and in Fig. 6, for the next five higher bound states. For temperatures up to 600 K, the $C_{4v}(2, 0, 0)$ n.n.n. pairs are the predominant species. This result has been known to be the case in view of the fact that $u_1 > u_2$ according to the lattice theory (Bassani and Fumi, 1954). The result that the $C_s(2, 1, 1)$ pairs ($l = 3$) are more predominant than the $C_{2v}(1, 1, 0)$ n.n. pairs at all temperatures is somewhat unexpected. Upon reflection, however, the result is quite reasonable, for although $u_1 = -0.39$ eV is slightly lower than $u_3 = -0.38$ eV, the number of equivalent sites, g, is 24 for the $C_s(2, 1, 1)$ pair as compared with 12 for the $C_{2v}(1, 1, 0)$ pair. At concentrations an order of magnitude lower and at temperatures below 500 K, we find the group of three different types of pairs, namely the $C_{2v}(2, 2, 0)$, $C_s(3, 1, 0)$ and $C_1(3, 2, 1)$ pairs (Fig. 6). At still a lower order of magnitude in concentration, we find the group of two pairs identified as $C_{3v}(2, 2, 2)$ and $C_{4v}(4, 0, 0)$.

The alkaline–earth–fluorides are typified by CaF_2. The cation sublattice is face-centered cubic. When a M^{3+} ion enters the cation sublattice substitutionally, a F^- interstitial is created so that charge neutrality is maintained. Under the conditions specified above, we can, as a first approximation, assume that each M^{3+} ion is paired with a F^- interstitial, and that the energy of association varies as R_l^{-1}, where R_l is the distance of separation and l denotes an interstitial in the lth n.n. position. Since the F^- interstitial can only occupy discrete positions, R_l can only take on discrete values, with the consequence that the Coulombic energy of association is also discrete:

$$u_l = - e^2/\varepsilon R_l,$$

where $\varepsilon = 6\cdot7$ for CaF_2. If the point occupied by the interstitial F^- in a given pair is denoted by (i, j, k), $(i + j + k)$ must be odd. The value for R_l is simply $(i^2 + j^2 + k^2)^{\frac{1}{2}}a$, where $a = 2\cdot726$ Å is half the distance between two neighbouring Ca^{2+} ions. R_l can be written as $(2l - 1)^{\frac{1}{2}}a$, where $l = 1$, $2, 3, \ldots$. The various site symmetries (and corresponding values of the num-

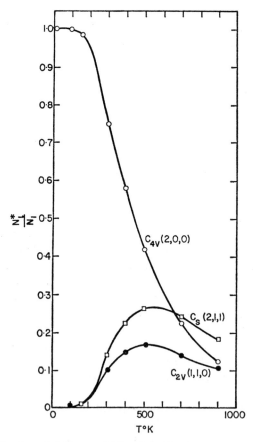

FIG. 5. The calculated probabilities, n_i^*/N_l, of finding the $C_{4v}(2, 0, 0)$, $C_s(2, 1, 1)$, and $C_{2v}(1, 1, 0)$ M^{2+}–K^+ vacancy pairs assuming the homogeneous dielectric shielding model for $u_l(l \geqslant 2)$ with $u_1 = -0\cdot39$ eV.

ber of distinguishable but equivalent lattice points, g_l, in parenthesis) are: $C_{4v}(6)$ when $i \neq 0$, $j = k = 0$; $C_s(24)$ when $i \neq j = k$ $(i, j, k \neq 0)$; $C_s(24)$ when $i \neq j$, $k = 0$ and $i, j \neq 0$; $C_1(48)$ when all i, j, k are unequal and unequal to zero; and $C_{3v}(8)$ when $i = j = k \neq 0$. At $l = 5, 9, 13, 17, 21, 25, 29,$ and 33 more than one site summetry can occur.

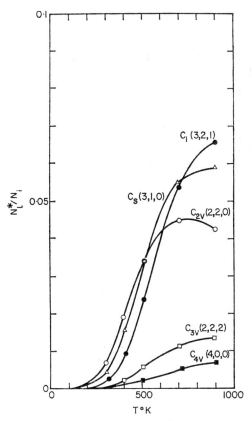

FIG. 6. The calculated probabilities, $n_l{}^*/N_l$, of finding the $C_s(3, 1, 0)$, $C_1(3, 2, 1)$, $C_{2v}(2, 2, 0)$, $C_{3v}(2, 2, 2)$, and $C_{4v}(4, 0, 0)$ M^{2+}–K^+ vacancy pairs assuming the homogeneous dielectric shielding model for $u_l(l \geqslant 2)$ with $u_1 = -0.39$ eV.

From a best fit (Heist and Fong, 1970) of literature data (Rossing, 1966; Rector et al., 1966), the energy of pairing can be written

$$u_1 = -0.48 \text{ eV},$$
$$u_2 = -0.30 \text{ eV},$$
$$u_l = e^2/[\varepsilon(2l - 1)^{\frac{1}{2}}a],$$

where $l = 3, 4, \ldots$.

The values of (n_i*/N_i) calculated through eqn (8) are plotted against T in Fig. 7 for the first three bound states. In Fig. 8, the next four higher bound states are shown. At $T < 700$ K the value for q_p does not change significantly when the sum is carried beyond $l = 16$, whereas at higher temperatures, the terms in q_p beyond $l = 16$ become increasingly significant, and q_p apparently does not converge readily. This of course, is the same difficulty as that previously encountered in the KCl : M^{2+} case.

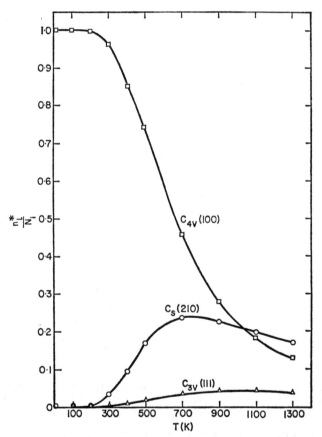

FIG. 7. The calculated probabilities, n_i*/N_i, of finding the $C_{4v}(1, 0, 0)$, $C_{3v}(1, 1, 1)$, and $C_s(2, 1, 0)$ M^{3+}–F^- interstitial pairs assuming the homogeneous dielectric shielding model for $u_l(l \geqslant 3)$ with $u_1 = -0.48$ eV and $u_2 = -0.30$ eV.

An inspection of Fig. 7 indicates that for the temperature range in which the calculations of q_p are valid, practically all the trivalent impurity cations are in close association up to the third nearest neighbour with the associated

F^- interstitials, which is of considerable prominence. The situation here is quite similar to that observed for the alkali halide: M^{2+} system, in which the third-nearest-neighbour $C_s(2, 1, 1)$ site has been shown to be the second most probable site (Fig. 5). The spectroscopic confirmation of these observations will be described in Section III.

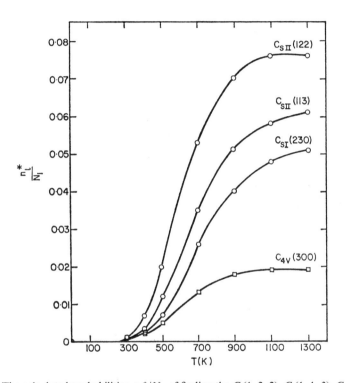

FIG. 8. The calculated probabilities, n_l^*/N_i, of finding the $C_s(1, 2, 2)$, $C_s(1, 1, 3)$, $C_s(2, 3, 0)$, and $C_{4v}(3, 0, 0)$ M^{3+}–F^- interstitial pairs assuming the homogeneous dielectric shielding model for $u_l(l \geqslant 3)$ with $u_1 = -0.48$ eV and $u_2 = -0.30$ eV.

C. High Temperature Partition Function and Pair Correlation Functions

At elevated temperatures, the assumptions on which eqn (6) is based are no longer valid. The ion-defect pairs undergo dissociation, and the separation of the variables of the charge pairs becomes meaningless. We must therefore begin our treatment with the inclusion of the repulsive as well as the attractive terms in the evaluation of the configuration partition function. We define the following quantities as a measure of departure from ideality (i.e., the absence of interactions between the ions):

$$^+f_{ij} = \exp[-\,^+u(\hat{R}_{ij})/kT] - 1$$
$$^+f_{lm} = \exp[-\,^+u(\hat{R}_{lm})/kT] - 1$$

and
$$^-f_{kp} = \exp[-\,^-u(\hat{R}_{kp})/kT] - 1 \tag{9}$$

such that

$$Z = \sum_{\text{a.c.}} (1 + \,^+f_{ij})(1 + \,^+f_{lm})(1 + \,^-f_{kp}) \tag{10}$$

where a.c. denotes all configurations.

For a given configuration,

$$
\begin{aligned}
\exp[-U(\hat{R}_1, \hat{R}_2, ..., \hat{R}_{2N_i})] &= (1 + \,^+f_{ij})(1 + \,^+f_{lm})(1 + \,^-f_{kp}) \\
&= 1 + \Sigma \,^+f_{ij} + \Sigma \,^+f_{lm} + \Sigma \,^-f_{kp} + \Sigma \,^+f_{ij}\,^+f_{i'j'} \\
&+ \Sigma \,^+f_{lm}\,^+f_{l'm'} + \Sigma \,^-f_{kp}\,^-f_{k'p'} + \Sigma \,^+f_{ij}\,^-f_{kp} \\
&+ \Sigma \,^+f_{lm}\,^-f_{kp} + \Sigma \,^+f_{ij}\,^+f_{lm} + \text{higher terms} \quad (11)
\end{aligned}
$$

where there are $\tfrac{1}{2}N_i(N_i - 1)$ identical terms in $\Sigma \,^+f_{ij}$ which is identical to $\Sigma \,^+f_{lm}$,

$$N_i^2 \quad \text{in} \quad \Sigma \,^-f_{kp},$$

$$\frac{N_i^4}{8} \quad \text{in} \quad \Sigma \,^+f_{ij}\,^+f_{i'j'}$$

which is identical to $\Sigma \,^+f_{lm}\,^+f_{l'm'}$,

$$\frac{N_i^4}{2} \quad \text{in} \quad \Sigma \,^-f_{kp}\,^-f_{k'p'},$$

$$\frac{N_i^4}{2} \quad \text{in} \quad \Sigma \,^+f_{ij}\,^-f_{kp}$$

which is identical to $\Sigma \,^+f_{lm}\,^-f_{kp}$, and

$$\frac{N_i^4}{4} \quad \text{in} \quad \Sigma \,^+f_{ij}\,^+f_{lm}.$$

The meaning of the sum of $^+f_{ij}$ over all configurations:

$$\sum_{\text{a.c.}} \,^+f_{ij} = \sum_{\text{a.c.}} \{\exp[-\,^+u(\hat{R}_{ij})/kT] - 1\} \tag{12}$$

can be examined in the following manner. For a given fixed $\hat{R}_{ij}$, there are

Ω' ways of arriving at all possible ways of arranging the remaining $2(N_i - 1)$ ions, such that,

$$\sum_{a.c.} {}^+f_{ij} = \Omega' \sum_{R_{ij}} \{\exp[-{}^+u(\hat{R}_{ij})/kT] - 1\} \tag{13}$$

where the sum is carried over all possible values for R_{ij}. Fixing the position of the ith as the centre of our new coordinate system, we have $R_{ij} = R_j$, the distance of separation of the jth ion measured from the origin:

$$\sum_{a.c.} {}^+f_{ij} = \Omega \sum_{R_j} g_j \{\exp[-{}^+u(R_j)/kT] - 1\} \tag{14}$$

where g_j is the number of equivalent positions about the ith ion (i.e., the origin) at R_j. The prime on Ω has been dropped because of the coordinate transformation. The determination of Ω can be made by realizing the fact that

$$\Omega \sum_j g_j = \Omega_0(2N_i, N) \tag{15}$$

where $\Omega_0(2N_i, N)$ is the total number of configurations for the random mixing of $2N_i$ ions on N available lattice sites

$$\Omega_0(2N_i, N) = \frac{N!}{(N_i!)^2(N - 2N_i)!}. \tag{16}$$

Since $\sum_j g_j = N - 1$, we obtain

$$\Omega = \frac{N!}{(N_i!)^2(N - 2N_i)!(N - 1)}. \tag{17}$$

Further analysis of the terms in eqn (10) in terms of Ω, g_j, N_i, ${}^+u$ and ${}^-u$, readily leads (Davidson, 1962) to the following expression for the configuration partition function in the case $N_i/N \ll 1$:

$$Z = \Omega_0(2N_i, N) \left\{ 1 + \frac{N_i}{(N-1)} \left[\sum_j g_j \{\exp[-{}^+u(R_j)/kT] - 1\} \right. \right.$$

$$\left. \left. + \sum_p g_p \{\exp[-{}^-u(R_p)/kT] - 1\} \right] \right\}^{N_i} + \text{"other terms"} \tag{18}$$

where the contribution of the "other terms" becomes negligibly small for a dilute system in which $N_i/N \ll 1$. Neglecting the "other terms" in eqn (18), we write for the internal energy due to configuration interaction:

$$\bar{U} = kT^2 \frac{\partial \ln Z}{\partial T} = \frac{N_i^2}{zN} \sum_l g_l \left(\exp[-u_l/kT] - \exp(u_l/kT) \right) \left(u_l - T \frac{\partial u_l}{\partial T} \right) \tag{19}$$

where

$$z = 1 + \frac{N_i}{N}\left\{2\sum_l g_l\left[\cosh(u_l/kT) - 1\right]\right\} = 1 + \frac{N_i}{N}S \qquad (20)$$

and $u_l = {}^+u(R_l) = - {}^-u(R_l)$. From eqn (2), we obtain

$$\bar{U} = \frac{kT^2}{Z}\frac{\partial}{\partial T}\sum_{\text{a.c.}}\exp[-U(\hat{R}_1, \hat{R}_2, ..., \hat{R}_{2N_i})/kT]$$

$$= \frac{1}{Z}\Sigma\left(U - T\frac{\partial U}{\partial T}\right)\exp(-U/kT). \qquad (21)$$

Upon substitution of eqn (1) in eqn (21),

$$\bar{U} = \frac{1}{Z}\sum_{\text{a.c.}}\left\{\left[2\sum_i\sum_j {}^+u(\hat{R}_{ij})\exp(-U/kT) + \sum_k\sum_p {}^-u(\hat{R}_{kp})\exp(-U/kT)\right]\right.$$

$$\left. - T\left[2\sum_i\sum_j\frac{\partial {}^+u(\hat{R}_{ij})}{\partial T}\exp(-U/kT) + \sum_k\sum_p\frac{\partial {}^-u(\hat{R}_{kp})}{\partial T}\exp(-U/kT)\right]\right\}. \quad (22)$$

Since there are $N_i(N_i - 1) \sim N_i^2$ identical terms in

$$\sum_i\sum_j {}^+u(\hat{R}_{ij})\exp(-U/kT)$$

and N_i^2 identical terms in

$$\sum_k\sum_p {}^-u(\hat{R}_{kp})\exp(-U/kT),$$

we rewrite eqn (22) in the equivalent form (replacing $\hat{R}_{ij}$ by $\hat{R}_{12}$ and $\hat{R}_{kp}$ by $\hat{R}_{1(N_i+1)}$):

$$\bar{U} = \frac{N_i^2}{Z}\left[\left(\sum_{\hat{R}_1\hat{R}_2} {}^+u(\hat{R}_{12})\sum_{\hat{R}_3,\hat{R}_4...\hat{R}_{2N_i}}\exp[-U(\hat{R}_1, \hat{R}_2, ..., \hat{R}_{2N_i})/kT]\right.\right.$$

$$+ \sum_{\hat{R}_1\hat{R}_{(N_i+1)}} {}^-u(\hat{R}_{1(N_i+1)})\sum_{\substack{\hat{R}_2,\hat{R}_3,...,\hat{R}_{N_i}\\\hat{R}_{(N_i+2)},...,\hat{R}_{2N_i}}}\exp[-U(\hat{R}_1, \hat{R}_2, ..., \hat{R}_{2N_i})/kT]$$

$$- T\left(\sum_{\hat{R}_1\hat{R}_2}\frac{\partial {}^+u(\hat{R}_{12})}{\partial T}\sum_{\hat{R}_3,\hat{R}_4,...,\hat{R}_{2N_i}}\exp[-U(\hat{R}_1, \hat{R}_2, ..., \hat{R}_{2N_i})/kT]\right.$$

$$\left.\left.+ \sum_{\hat{R}_1\hat{R}_{(N_i+1)}}\frac{\partial {}^-u(\hat{R}_{1(N_i+1)})}{\partial T}\sum_{\substack{\hat{R}_2,\hat{R}_3,...,\hat{R}_{N_i}\\\hat{R}_{(N_i+1)},...,\hat{R}_{2N_i}}}\exp[-U(\hat{R}_1, \hat{R}_2, ..., \hat{R}_{2N_i})/kT]\right)\right]. \quad (23)$$

We now define the generic distribution functions $\rho^{(2)}$:

$$^+\rho^{(2)}(\hat{R}_{12}) = N_i^2 \, {}^+p^{(2)}(\hat{R}_{12}) = \frac{N_i^2}{Z} \sum_{R_3, R_4, ..., R_{2N_i}} \cdots \sum \exp[-U(\hat{R}_1, \hat{R}_2, ..., \hat{R}_{2N_i})/kT]$$

(24a)

$$^-\rho^{(2)}(\hat{R}_{1(N+1)}) = N_i^2 \, {}^-p^{(2)}(\hat{R}_{1(N+1)}) = \frac{N_i^2}{Z} \sum_{\substack{R_2, R_3, ..., R_{N_i} \\ R_{(N_i+2)}, ..., R_{2N_i}}} \cdots \sum$$

$$\exp[-U(\hat{R}_1, \hat{R}_2, ..., \hat{R}_{2N_i})/kT] \qquad (24b)$$

where $^+p^{(2)}(\hat{R}_{12})$ is the specific distribution function giving the probability of finding the second like ion at $\hat{R}_2$ with the first at $\hat{R}_1$, the sum being carried over all possible position vectors for the remaining $(2N_i - 2)$ ions, and $^-p^{(2)}(\hat{R}_{1(N+1)})$ has the same meaning for two ions of opposite charges. The pair correlation function, or the radial distribution function is given as:

$$G(\hat{R}_{12}) = \left(\frac{N}{N_i}\right)^2 \rho^{(2)}(\hat{R}_{12}). \qquad (25)$$

Performing a coordinate transformation fixing a cation as the centre of origin, we write

$$^\pm G(R_l) = \left(\frac{N}{N_i}\right)^2 {}^\pm\rho^{(2)}(R_l) \qquad (26)$$

where the $+$ and $-$ signs denote the charge of the second ion that is R_l away from the origin. Upon substitution of eqn (26) in eqn (23), we obtain

$$\bar{U} = \frac{N_i^2}{N} \Sigma \left(u_l - T \frac{\partial u_l}{\partial T}\right) [^+G(R_l) - {}^-G(R_l)] \qquad (27)$$

having made use of the identity

$$\sum_{R_1, R_2} \equiv N \sum_l .$$

Comparison of eqns (19) and (27) yields

$$^\pm G(R_l) = z^{-1} g_l \exp(\mp u_l/kT) \qquad (28)$$

which gives a measure of the probability of finding a $+$ or $-$ ion at a distance R_l from the centre or origin.

There is the probability

$$\frac{N_i}{N-1} {}^\pm G(R_l)$$

of placing one of the N_i + or − ions at a distance R_l from the central positive ion. Since there are N_i positive ions, the total number $^\pm n_i^*$ of pair interactions at R_l is given by

$$\pm n_i^* = \frac{N_i^2}{N-1} {}^\pm G(R_l) = \frac{N_i^2}{(N-1)z} g_l \exp(\mp U_l/kT). \tag{29}$$

The total number of attractive interactions at all values of R_l is N_i^2, i.e., from eqn (29).

$$\sum_l {}^- n_i^* = N_i^2 = \frac{N_i^2}{(N-1)z} \sum_l g_l \exp(-u_l/kT) \tag{30}$$

such that

$$\sum_l g \exp(-u_l/kT) = (N-1)z = q. \tag{31}$$

This is true only when $u_l < kT$ for most important values of R_l, when $q \sim (N-1)$ and $z \sim 1$. The resulting condition from the definition of z in eqn (20) is

$$S = 2 \sum_l g_l[\cosh (u_l/kT) - 1] \ll \frac{N}{N_i}. \tag{32}$$

In the evaluation of Z in eqn (20), we have $^\pm u_l = \pm e^2/\varepsilon R_l$ (except for the nearest neighbour interactions which are briefly described in Section II.D) where e is the electrostatic unit and ε is the macroscopic dielectric constant of the crystalline lattice. In neglecting the "other terms" in eqn (18) in arriving at eqn (29), however, we have in essence overlooked the presence of all the other ions in our consideration of the interactions between given pairs of ions. As a result of this, S in eqn (32) diverges unless a screen $\exp(-bR_l)$ is invoked for Coulombic interactions at large R_l as in the Debye–Hückel theory, where $b = (8\pi N_i e^2/\varepsilon V kT)^{\frac{1}{2}}$, V being the volume of the system. That S diverges if we assume purely Coulombic interactions can be shown as follows. For the (alkali–halide): (divalent cation) system (Section II.B),

$$\sum_l g_l R_l^{-2} = \frac{1}{2a^2} \sum \frac{g_l}{l}. \tag{33}$$

Here, $l = \frac{1}{2}(i^2 + j^2 + k^2)$, where (i, j, k) denotes a lattice point in the metal sublattice with the M^{2+} ion at the origin. We have seen earlier that g_l is a noncontinuous function of i, j, k, and can only assume the values 0, 6, 8, 12, 24, 24, and 48. Equation (33) can thus be written as seven independent sums, of which the four sums involving $g_l = 0, 6, 8,$ and 12 are readily shown to converge. The remaining three sums involving $g_l = 24$, 24 and 48 do not converge. For example, for $g_l = 24$, $i \neq j = k$ $(i, j, k \neq 0)$, and i is even,

$$\sum_l \frac{g_l}{l} = 24 \sum_i \sum_j \frac{1}{(2i^2 + j^2)} = 24 \left(\sum_i \frac{\pi}{i} \coth \pi i + \frac{\pi}{2} \sum_i \frac{1}{i^2} \right). \tag{34}$$

The second term

$$\frac{\pi}{2} \sum_i \frac{1}{i^2}$$

is a well-known convergent series. However, for

$$0 \leqslant \pi i \leqslant \infty, \quad \infty \geqslant \coth \pi i \geqslant 1; \quad \sum_i \frac{\pi}{i} \coth \pi i$$

clearly diverges since every term in the sum is larger than the corresponding term in the harmonic series

$$\sum_i \frac{1}{i},$$

which diverges. Z in eqn (18), therefore, diverges, if $^\pm u_i$ is purely Coulombic. It is thus necessary to invoke the screen $\exp(-bR_l)$ at large R_l as in the Debye–Hückel theory, in which case Z readily converges.

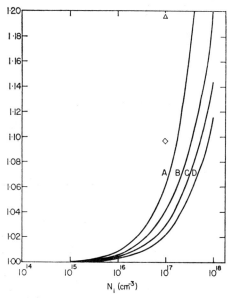

FIG. 9. The variation of z with N_i at 1100 K (A), 1300 K (B), 1500 K (C), and 1700 K (D) for CaF_2:RE^{3+}. The symbols $\lozenge$ and $\triangle$ represent calculations for the CaF_2:RE^{3+} and KCl:Sr^{2+} systems at 900 K, respectively.

In the numerical evaluation of Z, we need to define u_l for all values of R_l. We assume that when $u_l/kT < 0.1$,

$$u_l = \frac{e}{\varepsilon R_l} \exp(-bR_l).$$

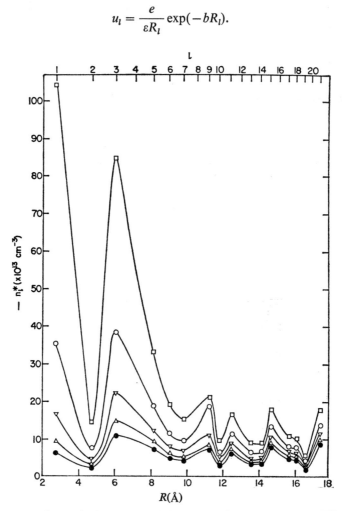

Fig. 10. The number $^-n_l^*$ of attractive pair interactions for $l \leqslant 21$ at 900 K ($\square$), 1100 K (○), 1300 K ($\triangledown$), 1500 K ($\triangle$), and 1700 K (●). The curves connecting the points are shown as a visual guide and are not to be taken as part of the calculations.

At $l = 1$ and 2, polarization effects as well as Coulombic interactions must be taken into consideration in the evaluation of u_1 and u_2 (Bassani and Fumi, 1954; Tosi and Airokli, 1958). At $l = 3$, we assume purely Coulombic interaction as in Section II.B. In the intermediate region $R_3 \leqslant R_l \leqslant R_m$, where R_m is the value of R_l at which $u_m/kT \sim 0.1$, u_l is assumed to have the following form

$$u_l = \frac{e^2}{\varepsilon R_l} \exp\{-bR_l \exp[-(R_m - R_l)(R_l - R_3)^{-1}]\} \qquad (35)$$

which provides a smooth interpolation from the screened Coulombic interaction at $R_l \geqslant R_m$ to the pure Coulombic interaction at R_3. By employing the appropriate lattice descriptions for g_l as a function of l, the configuration

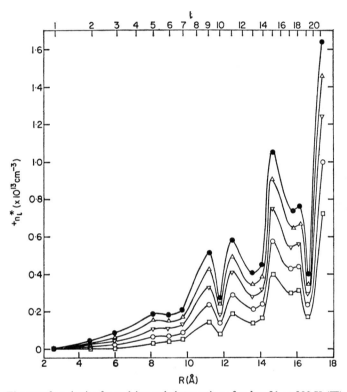

FIG. 11. The number $^+n_l^*$ of repulsive pair interactions for $l \leqslant 21$ at 900 K ($\square$), 1100 K ($\bigcirc$), 1300 K ($\triangledown$), 1500 K ($\triangle$), and 1700 K ($\bullet$).

partition function Z in eqn (18) has been evaluated (Fong et al., 1970) in sum up to $l = 1350(R_{1350} = 163.16$ Å) with a CDC 6500 computer for the $CaF_2 : RE^{3+}$ ($\varepsilon = 6.7$, $u_1 = -0.477$ eV, and $u_2 = -0.300$ eV) (Heist and Fong, 1970) and the $KCl : Sr^{2+}$ ($\varepsilon = 5.03$, $u_1 = -0.39$ eV (Bassani and Fumi, 1954) and $u_2 = -0.50$ eV (Tosi and Airokli, 1958) systems. The dependence of

$$z = [\Omega_0^{-1}(2N_i, N)Z]^{1/N_i} \qquad (36)$$

on N_i and T is given in Fig. 9 in the region for $1 \leqslant z \leqslant 1 \cdot 2$. From eqn (29), $n^{\pm}_i{}^*$ has been calculated for $CaF_2 : RE^{3+}$ at $T = 900, 1100, 1300, 1500$, and $1700 \, K$ with $N_i = 10^{17} cm^{-3}$. The results of this calculation are shown in Figs 10 and 11 for $l \leqslant 21$. In sharp contrast with the low temperature distribution curves (Figs 5–8), in which practically *all* the cations are paired with associated compensation defect anions, we observe from Fig. 10 that in the high temperature case under conditions specified above, only a small fraction $(10^{-3}–10^{-2})$ of the cations are in close association with the compensation defects. $^+n_i{}^*$ is several orders of magnitude lower than $^-n_i{}^*$ at small l, which is to be expected. Clearly, $^+n_i{}^*/^-n_i{}^*$ increases exponentially with T, approaching unity as $Z \to \Omega_0(2N_i, N)$. Moreover, at $R_l \gg R_m$,

$$^-n_l{}^* \cong {}^+n_l{}^* \cong \frac{N_i{}^2}{(N-1)z} g_l \qquad (37)$$

which follows from eqn (29) since

$$\frac{u_l}{kT} \sim 0 \quad \text{at} \quad R_l \gg R_m.$$

For $N_i = 10^{17} cm^{-3}$, $^-n_l{}^* \sim {}^+n_l{}^* \sim 10^{12}g_l$.

D. Comparison of the High Temperature Treatment and the Low Temperature Pair Distribution Treatment

The results of the high temperature treatment given in Section II.C differ in a fundamental manner from those of the low temperature treatment given in Section II.B. From the high temperature treatment, the concept of pair correlation functions evolves which leads to the total number $^{\pm}n_i{}^*$, of pair interactions at a distance R_l between the interacting ions (eqn (29) and Figs 10 and 11). The effect of the presence of other ions about a given cation in the high temperature treatment thus, in essence, averages out isotropically so that the cubic environment of the host lattice becomes the dominant perturbation for the crystal field symmetry. In the low temperature limit, however, the picture is one of cation-defect pairs, and the cubicity about the cation is lowered to some symmetry prescribed by the position of the defect relative to the cation. In this section we shall first extend the low temperature distribution calculation to several cyrstalline ionic solutions in order to observe certain trends. The fundamental differences between the high temperature and low temperature treatments will then be discussed.

At low temperature and high dilution, screening due to other impurity-defect pairs may be neglected (Fong, 1969), and the interaction energy u_l may be regarded as purely Coulombic for all but the first and second n.n. (nearest neighbour) pairs (Bassani and Fumi, 1954; Tosi and Airokli, 1958).

The departure from a purely Coulombic potential at small values of l is due to the repulsive interaction from electron overlap and to the polarization of the lattice about the impurity-defect pair. Values for u_1 and u_2, the first and second n.n. interaction energies, have been calculated or measured for the following systems: $NaCl : Sr^{2+}$ ($u_1 = -0.45$ eV, $u_2 = -0.41$ eV) (Bassani and Fumi, 1954), $NaCl : Mn^{2+}$ ($u_1 = -0.39$ eV, $u_2 = -0.35$ eV) (Watkins, 1959) and $LiCl : Mn^{2+}$ ($u_1 = -0.3$ eV, $u_2 = -0.26$ eV) (Watkins, 1959). Using these values and eqn (8), we have calculated site symmetry distributions with q_p summed to $l' = 200$ in the manner described in Section II.B. The results are shown in Figs 12, 13 and 14.

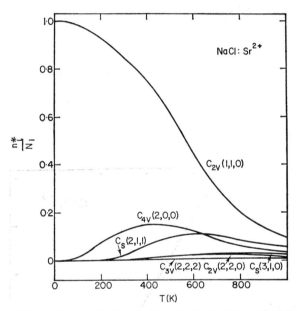

FIG. 12. Probabilities n_i^*/N_i of finding $C_{2v}(1, 1, 0)$, $C_{4v}(2, 0, 0)$, $C_s(2, 1, 1)$, $C_{2v}(2, 2, 0)$, $C_s(3, 1, 0)$, and $C_{3v}(2, 2, 2)$ sites in $NaCl:Sr^{2+}$ (Sr^{2+} ionic radius $= 1.13$ Å; Na^+ ionic radius $= 0.95$ Å). The symmetry notations have been explained in Section II.B.

From Figs 12–14 and the distribution curves (Figs 5 and 6) determined for the $KCl : Sr^{2+}$ system, we observe that as the size of the impurity ion decreases, or conversely as the lattice spacing of the host increases, the second n.n. compensation becomes increasingly more probable. Although the unavailability of u_1 and u_2 for alkaline–earth–halides: RE^{3+} (where RE denotes rare earth) systems other than CaF_2 deprives us of detailed calculations of site symmetry distributions, EPR (electron paramagnetic resonance) investigations have revealed a similar trend in these systems (Ranon and Yariv, 1964; Sierro, 1963). For example, first n.n. compensation was not observed for the $BaF_2:Yb^{3+}$ (Ranon and Yariv, 1964) and $BaF_2:Gd^{3+}$ (Sierro, 1963) systems, while the probability for the first n.n. compensation in $CaF_2:RE^{3+}$ systems is found to be predominant (Fig. 7). An explanation of this trend can be given by considering one of the terms contributing to the binding energies of the first and second n.n. pairs. This term, introduced by Brauer (1951), considers the effect of the size of the impurity ion on the binding energy of the pair. It accounts for the fact that the perturbing impurity ion is not only a source of electrostatic polarization, but, as its ionic radius may be quite different from that of the cation it has replaced, it may also be a source of displacement polarization. Each ion on the surrounding lattice undergoes a purely elastic displacement and consequently produces a displacement dipole which has the net effect of altering the binding energies of the impurity-defect pairs. When the impurity ion decreases in size, the n.n. shell of host anions, in particular, will be displaced inward. These displacement dipoles will have the effect of increasing the shielding between the impurity ion and its first n.n. defect compensations, thus reducing u_1. The quantity u_2, on the other hand, will increase as the second n.n. defect moves closer to the impurity ion due to the inward displacement of these n.n. host anions, thus accounting for the observed charges in the relative abundance of the first two n.n. pairs.

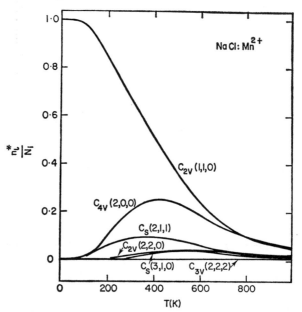

FIG. 13. Probabilities n_i^*/N_i of finding $C_{2v}(1, 1, 0)$, $C_{4v}(2, 0, 0)$, $C_s(2, 1, 1)$, $C_{2v}(2, 2, 0)$, $C_s(3, 1, 0)$, and $C_{3v}(2, 2, 2)$ sites in $NaCl:Mn^{2+}$ (Mn^{2+} ionic radius $= 0.8$ Å; Na^+ ionic radius $= 0.95$ Å).

The high temperature treatment given in this work is valid under the condition eqn (32), which will be satisfied at high temperature and high dilution. In the Debye–Hückel theory, the basic assumption is that $^{\pm}G(R) = \exp\left[\mp u(R)/kT\right]$ which is, in essence, the same statement as eqn (28) derived from the configuration partition function eqn (18) and the definition of the pair correlation function $G(R_{12})$ in eqn (25). Our high temperature treatment thus lends itself to comparisons with the Debye theory, except that the discreteness of the crystalline lattice provides us with a unique handle on the evaluation of the pair correlation functions $^{\pm}G(R_l)$ and $^{\pm}n_i^*$.

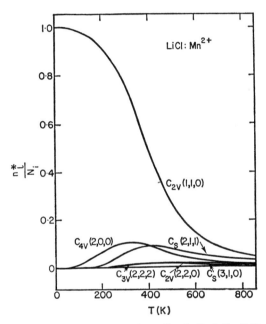

FIG. 14. Probabilities n_i^*/N_i of finding $C_{2v}(1, 1, 0)$, $C_{4v}(2, 0, 0)$, $C_s(2, 1, 1)$, $C_{2v}(2, 2, 0)$, $C_s(3, 1, 0)$, and $C_{3v}(2, 2, 2)$ sites in LiCl:Mn^{2+} (Mn^{2+} ionic radius $= 0.8$ Å; Li^+ ionic radius $= 0.60$ Å).

The low temperature treatment leading to eqn (6), on the other hand, is completely different in nature. If equilibrium conditions are attained at finite ionic concentrations, ions of opposite charges will pair as temperature decreases through attractive Coulombic interactions. At sufficiently low temperatures these ion pairs will cluster through higher-polar interactions such that precipitation eventually results. This is the case, for example, in an aqueous solution of KCl. In crystalline ionic solutions of the type described in the present paper, however, true equilibrium is not readily attainable at low temperatures due to the very low mobilities of the aliovalent cations. These cations are in fact "frozen" in a metastable equilibrium characteristic of some higher temperature, in which they are well dispersed throughout the entire lattice. The associated defects (i.e., the anions), on the other hand, possess much greater mobilities so that they can equilibrate through attractive Coulombic forces in pair formation with the cations. For example the K^+ vacancy has a migrational activation energy of 0·63 eV (Watkins, 1959). Assuming the value 10^{14} given (Dreyfus and Nowick, 1962) for the pre-exponential frequency factor for the jump of a K^+ vacancy from one lattice position to an adjacent one, the time required for thermal equilibration of the vacancy about a divalent cation will be in the order of 10^{-3} sec at 300 K.† We thus visualize the formation of cation-defect pairs which cannot aggregate through higher polar attractions at low temperatures. In some proper temperature range, therefore, we have N_i pairs whose mutual interactions are negligibly small (at sufficiently high dilution), and eqn (6) results. The conceptual model depicted in eqn (6) requires that the ensemble of ions is divided into N_i cells, each of which contains one ion-defect pair. The "molecular" pair partition function q_p must be summed over all

$$\left(\frac{N}{N_i} - 1\right)$$

lattice points per cell. The model will be valid if the occupation probability is significant only for the first few n.n. positions, i.e.,

$$q_p = \sum_{l=1}^{l=l'} g_i \exp(-u_l/kT) \gg \frac{N}{N_i}. \tag{38}$$

For example, $q_p \sim 10^8$ and 10^5 at 300 and 500 K, respectively for $KCl : M^{2+}$ for

$$N_i = 10^{17} cm^{-3}, \frac{N}{N_i} \sim 10^3,$$

and eqn (6) is thus valid for $T \lesssim 500$ K if pair formation equilibrium is

---

† There is some question in this estimate due to the uncertainty in the migrational barrier for the K^+ vacancy migration. The value 0·63 eV given by Watkins corresponds to the migration of a K^+ vacancy in the close proximity of the divalent cation. In an ionic conductivity experiment, Etzel and Maurer reported the value 0·85 eV for the migrational barrier of a Na^+ vacancy in NaCl. The higher value reported by these authors probably corresponds to free vacancy migration. Employing the value 0·65 eV in our estimate, the time required for thermal equilibrium of the vacancy about a divalent cation will be on the order of 2 sec at 300 K. The main argument in the text thus remains unaffected.

attained. (At $T \ll 300$ K even the K^+ vacancy mobility will be too low for thermal equilibration.) At higher dilution, eqn (6) will be valid at lower temperatures.

Finally, we return to the high temperature results in an assessment of their applicability to real systems. The calculations have been made at sufficiently high dilution (10^{17}–10^{18}cm^{-3}) and temperatures ($T \geqslant 900$ K) in order to ascertain the condition stated in eqn (32). The concentrations of intrinsic defects were ignored in all our calculations for the sake of simplicity. In reality, however, these concentrations are by no means negligible at $T \geqslant 900$ K. In KCl and CaF$_2$, for example, the intrinsic defect concentrations are on the order of 10^{16} cm^{-3} (Dreyfus and Nowick, 1962) and 10^{17} cm^{-3} (Ure, 1957; Fong, 1966) at 900 K, respectively. It is therefore necessary to extend our treatment to include the interactions due to the presence of intrinsic defects in the evaluation of Z, which presents no serious difficulties. At $T > 900$ K, however, the intrinsic defect concentrations in CaF$_2$ exceed the range in which eqn (32) is valid, being as high as $\sim 10^{20}$ at $T = 1300$ K. An adequate treatment of such a situation would require an inclusion of the "other terms" in eqn (18). The results described here nevertheless represent a quantitative, albeit idealized, *approach* to the fairly complex problem of interacting dissociated ions in a periodic crystalline lattice. The spectroscopic observation of the predominance of "cubic" sites in CaF$_2$: RE^{3+} systems (Section IV) when they are quenched from elevated temperatures is, in fact, experimental evidence of the results shown in Figs 10 and 11. At $T = 900$ K and $N_i = 10^{17}$ cm^{-3}, only $\sim 2 \times 10^{15}$ cm^{-3} ion-defect pairs are within $l \leqslant 21$ (Fig. 10). Since the compensation crystal field potential varies as $R_l^{-(k+1)}$ where $k > 0$ is the rank of the spherical harmonic in the corresponding crystal-field potential expansion, the crystal field effect of the more distant compensation sites would be negligibly small as the cubic environment of the RE^{3+} ion becomes the dominant factor in the spectroscopic observations. The predominance of cubic sites in CaF$_2$ (which is not observed in the KCl : M^{2+} system† as we shall see in Section III) arises from the high migrational activation energy 1·51 eV (Fong and Hiller, 1967) of the compensation F$^-$ interstitials. At 600 K, the time required for thermal equilibration of the site distribution characteristic of the low temperature range is ~ 1 sec. At room temperature (~ 300 K), however, the time required for thermal equilibration is in the order of 10^7 years if a pre-exponential "jump" frequency factor 10^{14} is assumed. Rapid quenching to room temperature, therefore, would cause freezing of the high temperature equilibrium depicted in Figs 10 and 11 in a metastable equilibrium. In view of the present discussion, it appears certain that quenching from elevated temperatures of alkali halide: M^{2+} systems to $T \ll 300$ K should also give rise to a predominance in cubic sites, which characterize the high temperature equilibria.

† See, however, Fenn, Cox and Fong (1971).

III. Experimental Characterization of Ion-defect Pair Formation

A. Historical Development

The problem of a multiplicity of sites in (alkali halide): M^{2+} systems has long been suggested by a large number of investigations. Numerous studies on the broadening of the Debye loss curve observed for the dielectric relaxation of M^{2+}-vacancy pairs indicate the presence of inequivalent dipolar pairs (Breckenridge, 1948, 1959; Lidiard, 1954a; Haven and van Santen, 1954, 1958; Franklin, 1963; Franklin et al., 1964). Franklin and co-workers, in particular, have considered the contribution of the $C_{2v}(1, 1, 0)$, $C_{4v}(2, 0, 0)$, and $C_3(2, 1, 1)$ pairs to dielectric relaxation. Although current theories (Lidiard, 1954b; Etzel and Maurer, 1950; Fuller et al., 1968) on the conductivity of (alkali halide): M^{2+} crystals have been formulated on the assumption that only the nearest neighbour pairs are bound, the very notion of the association and dissociation of the bound pairs in ionic conductivity explicitly calls for the varying degree of association of the vacancies with the divalent cations. In fact, Lidiard (1954) and more recently Fuller et al., (1968) have considered the effect of neglecting the higher bound states on the consistent failure of the conductivity theories. In an electron spin resonance (ESR) experiment. Watkins (1959) observed for several (alkali halide): Mn^{2+} systems signals corresponding to the $C_{2v}(1, 1, 0)$, $C_{4v}(2, 0, 0)$, a more distant pair which he called "cubic", and a second C_{4v} site which is most probably due to compensation of the Mn^{2+} ion by a dinegative impurity anion. The $C_{2v}(1, 1, 0)$ and $C_{4v}(2, 0, 0)$ sites in the Watkins investigation alternate in their relative importance, depending upon the relative sizes of the Mn^{2+} ion and the host ion which it replaces.

The ESR observations of the "cubic" sites gave apparently irrefutable support to the view that the M^{2+}-vacancy pairs are either associated in complex formation or dissociated according to a law of mass action. The cubicity of the M^{2+} ion site implies that the compensation defect is far beyond the detection limit of the ESR spectroscopic experiments. In reality, however, if one observes the $C_{2v}(1, 1, 0)$ and the $C_{4v}(2, 0, 0)$ pairs, one must be also be expected to observe the $C_s(2, 1, 1)$ pair by virtue of the results given in the preceding statistical mechanical calculations. The problem is then a matter of *experimental technique* in the verification of the mathematical formulations given above. In recent years, a new spectroscopic technique, the Zeeman anisotropy fluorescence (ZAF) method, has been shown (Fong, 1970; Fong and Wong, 1967; Fong and Bellows, 1970; Fong et al., 1970, 1971) to be particularly useful in the investigations into the site symmetry problem in compensated lattices. This method exploits the specific Zeeman splitting behaviour of narrow fluorescence lines of rare earth ions in a crystalline host, and is described in some detail in the following paragraphs with

KCl : Sm^{2+} as the prototype system whose site distribution at low temperatures should be approximately depicted by the results given in Fig. 5.

B. Zeeman Anisotropy Fluorescence Patterns of Allowed Sm^{2+} Site Symmetries in Alkali Halides

The ground configuration of Sm^{2+} is $4f^6$. Narrow-line fluorescence transitions of Sm^{2+} in ionic crystals are readily observed at cryogenic temperatures by "pumping" into the $4f^{n-1}5d$ bands of the Sm^{2+} ion which usually lie above the ^5D multiplet of the $4f^6$ configuration. The narrow-line fluorescence originates from transitions between the ^5D and ^7F multiplets. In KCl : Sm^{2+} they arise from $^5D_0 \rightarrow {}^7F_J$ ($0 \rightarrow J$, where $J = 0$, 1, ..., 6) transition.

In the free ion state, the LS coupling scheme is usually considered as a good approximation for the Sm^{2+} ion. The ($f^6\alpha LSJM$) free ion states, where α denotes all other quantum numbers not specified, are employed as the zeroth order wavefunctions in our problem. In a crystalline lattice the crystal field potential contributes a term to the total Hamiltonian of the Sm^{2+} ion. The term is usually expanded as a series of spherical harmonics

$$\mathscr{H}_{c.f.} = \sum_{l,m,i} A_l^m r_i^l Y_l^m(\theta_i, \phi_i) \qquad (39)$$

where the expansion coefficients A_l^m are determined by the position of the charge compensation in a complex of a given site symmetry. In terms of the Wigner–Eckart theorem, a typical matrix element of the crystal field perturbation matrix can be written (Judd, 1963)

$$(f^6\alpha LSJM \,|\mathscr{H}_{c.f.}|\, f^6\alpha SLJM') = B_l^m C_{MmM'}^{JlJ} (\alpha SLJ \,||\, Y_l \,||\, \alpha SLJ) \qquad (40)$$

$$B_l^m = \langle r^l \rangle A_l^m$$

where $C_{MmM'}^{JlJ}$, is a Wigner coefficient and $(\alpha SLJ \,||\, Y_l \,||\, \alpha SLJ)$ a reduced matrix element. The diagonalization of the crystal field perturbation matrix results in the crystal field states, provided that coefficients B_l^m are known.

If one assumes the point charge model, the crystal field expansion coefficients, A_l^m, are

$$A_l^m = \frac{4\pi}{2l+1} \sum_j \frac{q_j e^2}{R_j^{l+1}} Y_l^{*m}(\theta_j, \phi_j) \qquad (41)$$

where R_j is the distance between the jth ion and the central ion, the sum extends over all the ions of the lattice, and q_j is the effective charge of the jth ion. The point charge model, however, ignores effects arising from charge overlap, covalency, polarization of the lattice about the central ion, as well as the lattice distortion about the divalent cation-compensation pair. Equation (41) is thus often invalid, and the coefficients B_l^m are best treated as experimental parameters. When only one site symmetry exists or is assumed for the rare earth ion, it is possible to identify the representation origin of a given transition through conventional spectroscopic techniques such as polarization and group theoretical selection rules, and diagonalization of the $\mathscr{H}_{c.f.}$ matrix can be readily achieved by parameter fitting of the B_l^m coefficients.

In compensated lattices such as $KCl : Sm^{2+}$ in which the fluorescence is made up of a superposition of Sm^{2+} fluorescence lines arising from various sites, the above procedure is not possible unless the site origin of each line is determined. The polarized excitation technique employed by Bron and Heller (1964) in the determination of dipole origin, representation origin, and site origin is unique only for the $0 \rightarrow 0$ transition. For all the other transitions, it is necessary to assume the site origin or the polarization of the excitation, which is not justified in $KCl : Sm^{2+}$. One unique method for the determination of symmetry origin is the ZAF technique in which characteristic patterns of the angular dependence of energy shifts of the Zeeman components are readily recognizable for each of the site symmetries allowed for the Sm^{2+} ion due to geometric restrictions of the f.c.c. KCl lattice.

Under an external magnetic field, an additional term must be added to the total Hamiltonian of the central Sm^{2+} ion in the form

$$\mathscr{H}_m = g_\lambda \mu_B H_0 \{\cos \theta_H J_Z + \tfrac{1}{2} \sin \theta_H [\exp(i\phi_{H_{J_-}}) + \exp(-i\phi_{H_{J_+}})]\} \quad (42)$$

where μ_B is the Bohr magneton, g_λ the Landè g factor, H_0 the effective magnetic field strength, θ_H the angle between the H field and the Z axis, and ϕ_H the corresponding azimuthal angle. In axial symmetries such as C_{2v}, C_{3v} and C_{4v}, Z is taken to be the rotational C axis. In C_s symmetries Z is taken to be the axis perpendicular to the reflection (XY) plane. In $KCl : Sm^{2+}$ there are six types of site symmetries in K^+ vacancy compensation: C_{2v}, C_{3v}, C_{4v}, $C_s(I)$, $C_s(II)$, and C_1 which are typified by the $C_{2v}(1, 1, 0)$, C_{3v} $(2, 2, 2)$, $C_{4v}(2, 0, 0)$, $C_s(2, 1, 1)$, $C_s(3, 1, 0)$, and $C_1(3, 2, 1)$ $Sm^{2+}-K^+$ vacancy pairs, respectively. Here, we shall consider the theoretical patterns of the C_{3v} and $C_s(II)$ sites, which are shown in Fig. 15 along with the schematic ZAF patterns for C_{2v}, C_{4v}, $C_s(I)$, and C_1 sites.

For $C_{3v}(2, 2, 2)$ $Sm^{2+}-K^+$ vacancy pairs there are 8 equivalent sites, four of which are shown in Fig. 16 at the corners of a face of a cube whose centre is occupied by the Sm^{2+} ion. Each side of the cube measures $4a$, where $a = 3 \cdot 15$ Å is the K^+–Cl^- distance of separation. Since the magnetic field is invariant upon inversion, the $[l, m, n]$ and $[\bar{l}, \bar{m}, \bar{n}]$ crystal axes are equivalent, and the 4 remaining sites are indistinguishable from the four sites shown through an inversion of coordinates. With $H\|[100]$ all the sites are equivalent, and only one line will arise from them. As H is rotated toward [010] in the (001) plane, two lines arise due to the two sets of equivalent sites: (i) a, a'; (ii) b, b'. These two lines will reach a maximum separation when H is in the [110] direction and will merge back together with H in the [010] direction. (See anisotropy pattern in Fig. 15C.)

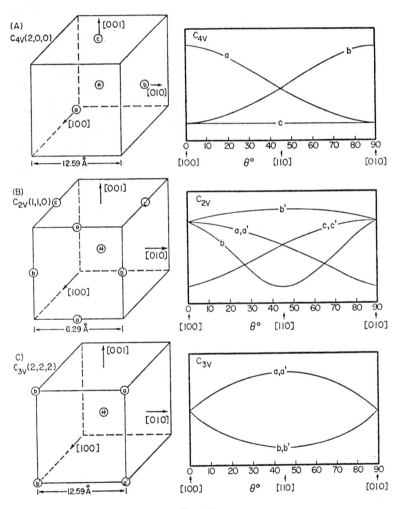

FIG. 15.

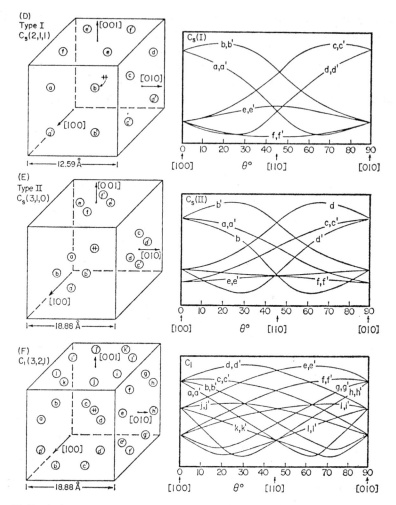

Fig. 15. Equivalent magnetically distinguishable vacancy sites and corresponding schematic ZAF patterns [with H rotating in (001) plane] for the six typical Sm^{2+} site symmetries allowed for K^+ vacancy compensation as exemplified by: (A) 3 equivalent $C_{4v}(2, 0, 0)$ sites, (B) 6 equivalent $C_{2v}(1, 1, 0)$ sites, (C) 4 equivalent $C_{3v}(2, 2, 2)$ sites, (D) 12 equivalent Type I $C_s(2, 1, 1)$ sites, (E) 12 equivalent Type II $C_s(3, 1, 0)$ sites, and (F) 24 equivalent $C_1(3, 2, 1)$ sites. The ZAF patterns are deduced on the basis of a transition between two non-degenerate levels.

For the Type II $C_s(3, 1, 0)$ site there are 24 equivalent sites. In Fig. 15E, 12 of there sites are shown lying on three faces of a cube of $(6a)^3$. Each site lies $+a$ or $-a$ away form the centre of a cube face in one of the six major crystal planes, {100}. Again, the remaining 12 sites are obtained through a coordinate inversion. With **H** in the [100] direction, there are three sets of equivalent sites: (i) a, a', b, b'; (ii) d, d', f, f'; and (iii) c, c', e, e' which give rise to three lines. As **H** is rotated toward [010] in the (001) plane, there is splitting of the above three lines into eight lines corresponding to the eight sets of equivalent sites: (i) b'; (ii) a, a'; (iii) b; (iv) d; (v) f, f'; (vi) d'; (vii) c, c'; and (viii) e, e'. When **H**∥[110] the pattern will merge into three lines according to the groups: (i) b', d; (ii) a, a', c, c'; and (iii) b, d', e, e', f, f'. As **H** rotates away from [110], eight lines appear due to the same eight sets of equivalent sites as previously mentioned. Finally, when **H** reaches [010], the eight lines merge into three corresponding to the following sets of equivalent sites: (i) c, c', d, d'; (ii) b, b', e, e'; and (iii) a, a', f, f'.

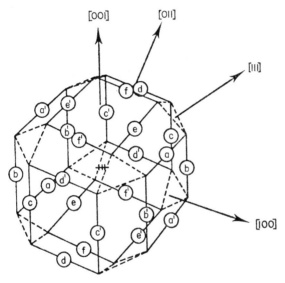

FIG. 16. The 12 magnetically distinguishable $C_s(2, 1, 0)$ M^{3+}–F^- interstitial sites: a, a', $b, b', c, c', d, d', e, e', f$, and f'.

It is important to realize that it is possible to identify experimental ZAF patterns according to the schematic patterns shown in Fig. 15 without ever having to solve the matrix equations involving the perturbation Hamiltonians of eqns (39) and (42). When the no-field line is intense and its Zeeman components well resolved, it is possible to determine its symmetry origin beyond any doubt. Difficulties arise when the ZAF patterns of two no-field lines of comparable intensities overlap, particularly when a lower symmetry (and thus more complicated) pattern is involved. Such difficulties are encountered in the case of the overlapping ZAF patterns of the 7693·5 and

7694·5 Å no-field lines in $0 \to 3$. Although the $C_s(2, 1, 1)$ origin of the 7694·5 Å line was apparent (Fong, 1970), the additional ZAF pattern due to the 7693·5 Å line was not easily accounted for until a field dependence investigation (which traces the two ZAF patterns to their respective no-field origins) was carried out (Fong et al., 1971). The analytical details of the ZAF patterns are given elsewhere (Fong, 1970; Fong and Wong, 1967; Fong and Bellows, 1970; Fong et al., 1970, 1971; Ford and Fong, 1972; Heist et al., 1972). Here, we shall only summarize the results: all the dominant 4·2 K narrow-line flourescence lines in $KCl:Sm^{2+}$ spanning the wavelength region 6891–9440 Å, as well as weaker flourescence lines of $KCl:Sm^{2+}$ show Zeeman effects under external magnetic fields up to 93·5 kG. Through ZAF (Zeeman anisotropy flourescence) determinations, the no-field lines at 7014·7 Å $(0 \to 1)$ 7031·7 Å $(0 \to 1)$, 7264·4 Å $(0 \to 2)$, 7304·6 Å $(0 \to 2)$, 7693·5 Å $(0 \to 3)$, 8204·9 Å $(0 \to 4)$ and 8778·4 Å $(0 \to 5)$ have been attributed to C_{2v} symmetry origin, the no-field lines at 8132·6 Å $(0 \to 4)$, 8194·7 Å $(0 \to 4)$, 9439·1 and 9440·0 Å $(0 \to 6)$ have been attributed to C_{4v} symmetry origin, the no-field lines at 7282·8 Å $(0 \to 2)$ and 7694·5 Å $(0 \to 3)$ have been attributed to $C_s(I)$ site symmetry origin and the very weak line at ˙8742·8 Å $(0 \to 5)$ have been attributed to C_{3v} symmetry origin, and a very weak ZAF pattern occurring in the 7696–7700 Å $(0 \to 3)$ region has been identified to originate from a $C_s(II)$ site. The $0 \to 0$ line at 6891·9 Å $(0 \to 2)$ show Zeeman shifts at high fields, but they unfortunately do not give rise to resolvable Zeeman splitting, and no discernable ZAF patterns are available even at 92·9 kG. The important point here is that no "cubic" sites have been observed, and the low temperature distribution of M^{2+} sites in alkali halides undoubtedly exists. The site distribution in $KCl:Sm^{2+}$ is currently being determined from fluorescence intensity measurements in the writer's laboratory, and will be compared with the corresponding distribution calculated (Section II.B) for the $KCl:Sr^{2+}$ system.

C. Spectroscopic Observation of the Third-Nearest-Neighbour $C_s(2, 1, 0)$ M^{3+}–F^- Interstitial Pair in CaF_2

Although Fig. 7 indicates that for the temperature range in which the calculations of q_p are valid, practically all the trivalent impurity cations are in close association up to the third nearest neighbour with the associated F^- interstitials in CaF_2, the observation of "cubic" sites has been frequently reported (Mahlab et al., 1963; Ranon and Low, 1963; Sierro, 1963; Ranon and Yariv, 1964; Weber and Bierig, 1964; Rector et al., 1966). In light of the discussions in Section II, many of the so-called cubic sites must correspond to the third-nearest-neighbour $C_s(2, 1, 0)$ M^{3+}–F^- interstitial pair, the significant presence of which is a dominant feature of the distribution data shown in Fig. 7. The situation with which we are faced is thus similar to that encountered in the case of the (alkali halide): M^{2+} system.

In the search for the $C_s(2, 1, 0)$ site, the EPR observation (Mahlab et al., 1963) of an "orthorhombic" site in $CaF_2 : U^{3+}$ reported by Mahlab, Volterra, Low, and Yariv (MVLY) became an interesting suspect. In addition to the usual observation of the tetragonal site corresponding to the $C_{4v}(1, 0, 0)$ site, a group of EPR lines gave rise to a novel anisotropy pattern which MVLY attributed to the fifth-nearest-neighbour U^{3+}–F^- interstitial pair†. Since no trigonal sites corresponding to the presence of oxygen were observed, MVLY were probably correct in concluding that their observation was due to a new F^- interstitial site. From our present distribution calculations (Section II.B), the probability of finding the fifth-nearest-neighbour pair is vanishingly small. If our calculations are at least qualitatively correct, the MVLY EPR spectral lines are most probably due to the third-nearest-neighbour $C_s(2, 1, 0)$ site. We shall show in detail in the following that this is indeed the case.

The effective spin Hamiltonian for the U^{3+} ion in an external magnetic field $\hat{H}$ is

$$\mathscr{H} = \beta H_0 \{ g_z \cos\theta S_z + \tfrac{1}{2}\sin\theta[g_x \cos\phi(S_+ + S_-) - ig_y \sin\phi(S_+ - S_-)]\},$$

(43)

where β is the Bohr magneton, g_x, g_y, and g_z are the projections of the g tensor along the x, y, z directions, respectively, H_0 is the effective magnetic field strength, θ_H the angle between the $\hat{H}$ field and the Z axis, and ϕ_H the corresponding azimuthal angle. In C_s symmetry, Z is taken to be the axis perpendicular to the reflection plane, while ϕ_H is measured from the U^{3+}–F^- interstitial axis in the reflection plane. There are altogether 24 equivalent $C_s(2, 1, 0)$ sites, which are shown in Fig. 16 bisecting the edges of the six squares normal to the [100], [010], [001], [$\bar{1}$00], [0$\bar{1}$0], and [00$\bar{1}$] crystal axes. The 12 sites associated with the [100], [010] and [001] axes are denoted by a, a', b, b'; c, c', d, d'; and e, e', f, f'; respectively. Since the magnetic field is invariant upon inversion, the [lmn] and [$\bar{l}\bar{m}\bar{n}$] crystal axes are equivalent, and the 12 remaining sites associated with the [$\bar{1}$00], [0$\bar{1}$0], and [00$\bar{1}$] axes are indistinguishable from the 12 above-mentioned sites through an inversion of coordinates in the magnetic field. A group of sites will be magnetically equivalent if and only if their orientations with respect to the magnetic-field direction are identical in terms of the angles θ_H and ϕ_H, and of α, the angle between $\hat{H}$ and the U^{3+}–F^- interstitial axis. The general features of

† The fifth n.n. M^{3+}–F^- interstitial pair [$C_s (2, 2, 1)$] actually gives rise to a monoclinic site instead of the "orthorhombic" designation made by MVLY.

the angular dependence of the Zeeman shifts for the twelve sites with $\hat{H}$ rotating in the $(01\bar{1})$ plane can be ascertained as follows. When $\hat{H}$ is in the [100] direction, there are three identical groups of sites: (i) a, a', b, b' ($\alpha = 26°34'$, $\theta_H = 90°$, $\phi_H = 26°34'$), (ii) c, c', e, e' ($\alpha = 63°26'$, $\theta_H = 90°$, $\phi_H = 63°26'$), and (iii) d, d', f, f' ($\alpha = 90°, \theta_H = 0°, \phi_H = 0°$). As $\hat{H}$ is rotated away from the [100] direction in the $(01\bar{1})$ plane, there are six groups of equivalent sites: a, b; $a'b'$; c, e; $c'e'$; d, f; and $d'f'$, which should give rise to a maximum of six lines. With $\hat{H}$ in the [211] direction, the resulting spectrum should consist of six lines due to the six different sets of equivalent sites. (i) a, b ($\alpha = 24°06', \theta_H = 65°54', \phi_H = 0°$); (ii) a', b' ($\alpha = 56°47', \theta_H = 65°54', \phi_H = 53°08'$); (iii) e, c ($\alpha = 43°05', \theta_H = 65°54', \phi_H = 36°52'$); (iv) e', c' ($\alpha = 90°, \theta_H = 65°54', \phi_H = 90°)'$; (v) f, d ($\alpha = 56°47', \theta_H = 35°16', \phi_H = 18°26'$); and (vi) f', d' ($\alpha = 79°29', \theta_H = 35°16', \phi_H = 71°34'$). As $\hat{H}$ is rotated to the [111] direction, the six sets of lines merge into two due to the two sets of equivalent sites, (i) a, b, c, d, e, f ($\alpha = 39°14', \theta_H = 54°44', \phi_H = 18°26'$); and (ii) a', b', c', d', e', f' ($\alpha = 75°02', \theta_H = 54°44', \phi_H = 71°34'$). Finally, with $\hat{H}$ in the [011] direction, the spectrum should consist of four lines arising from the four different sets of equivalent sites a, b, a', b' ($\alpha = 71°34', \theta_H = 45°, \phi_H = 63°26'$); c, e, c', e' ($\alpha = 50°46', \theta_H = 45°, \phi_H = 26°34'$); f, d ($\alpha = 18°26', \theta_H = 90°, \phi_H = 18°26$) and f', d' ($\alpha = 71°34', \theta_H = 90°, \phi_H = 71°34'$).

Since $U^{3+}(f^3)$ is a Kramer's salt, the $S = \frac{1}{2}$ representation for the C_s spin Hamiltonian is a valid representation in view of the twofold degeneracy due to time-reversal symmetry. The parameters g_x, g_y, and g_z are evaluated from the experimental g factors reported by MVLY through the equation

$$g(\theta, \phi) = (g_x{}^2 \cos^2\phi \sin^2\theta + g_y{}^2 \sin^2\phi \sin^2\theta + g_z{}^2 \cos^2\theta)^{\frac{1}{2}}. \qquad (44)$$

For a reasonably good fit of the experimental data, the parameters g_x and g_y can be accurately determined, while g_z is a fractional number lying in the range $0 \leqslant g_z \leqslant 0.8$. The anisotropy pattern of the observed ESR lines with $\hat{H}$ rotating in the $(01\bar{1})$ plane for $S = \frac{1}{2}$, $g_x = 3.01$, $g_y = 1.63$, and $g_z = 0.69$ is calculated employing eqn (43). It is plotted and compared with MVLY's data in Fig. 17. The excellent agreement between theory and the experiment leaves little doubt as to the $C_s(2, 1, 0)$ site origin of MVLY's spectroscopic observations.

IV. Intermediate Temperature Region: Dissociation of Ion-defect Pairs and Ionic Conductivity

In Section II, the problem of compensated lattices is viewed from two opposite situations. At low temperatures for which eqn (6) is valid, the description is one of complete association in which the impurity cations and their accompanying lattice defects are paired in a Boltzmann distribution consistent with the geometric restrictions of the host lattice. At high temperatures for which eqn (18) is valid, the description is essentially one of weakly interacting ions in a more or less random distribution. The question which remains to be answered is: how can we best describe the intermediate temperature region in which neither of the above descriptions is valid? In this intermediate temperature, we must deal with equally important species of ions in close proximity of their charge compensating defects and of weakly interacting ions

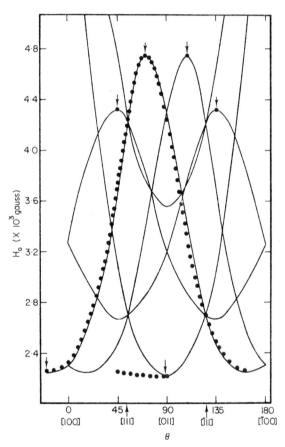

FIG. 17. Angular dependence with **H** rotating in the $(01\bar{1})$ plane of 3-cm EPR lines arising from 12 magnetically distinguishable $C_s(2, 1, 0)$ sites (Fig. 16) for $CaF_2:U^{3+}$. θ is the angle between **H** and the [100] axis. The solid lines are theoretical calculations employing eqn (43) with $g_x = 3\cdot01$, $g_y = 1\cdot63$, and $g_z = 0\cdot69$. The dotted lines as well as the arrows at maxima and minima of the pattern are the experimental observations made by MVLY. The only and rather minor discrepancy between theory and experiment appears at the incomplete dotted line given in the vicinity of 2·3 kG between 45° and 90°.

in nearly random distribution. This is the temperature region in which the condition specified in eqn (38) for the convergence of q_p no longer holds. This is also the temperature region in which the condition specified in eqn (32) for the application of the high temperature treatment is no longer valid. Here, ion-defect interactions vary in the range $u_l/kT \lesssim 1$. The notion of an equilibrium mixture of a distribution of ion-defect pairs (for which $1 < u_l/kT$) and ions and defects in approximate random distribution (for which $u_l/kT < 1$) becomes a useful conceptual mode. Consider a lattice of N points at which N_i impurity cations and N_i compensation defects can be placed. At the outset, let us assume that of the N_i impurity cations, there are n ion-defect pairs. The criterion for the formation of an ion-defect pair will be given later. The configuration partition function for the n pairs can be written after eqn (6):

$$Z_p = \frac{1}{n!} \prod_{s=0}^{n-1} (N - s') \left[\sum_{l=1}^{l=l'} g_l \exp(-\,^-u_l/kT) \right]^n ; \; s' = \tfrac{27}{16}s \sum_{l=1}^{l=l'} g_l \quad (45)$$

where l' is determined by the criterion for the formation of an ion-defect pair. The configuration partition function for the dissociated $(N_i - n)$ ions and $(N_i - n)$ compensation defects can be written after eqn (18):

$$Z(N_i - n, N_i - n, N - n') = \frac{(N - n')!}{(N - 2N_i)!(N_i - n)!^2} \left\{ 1 + \frac{N_i - n}{(N - n' - 1)} \right.$$

$$\times \left[\sum_j g_j[\exp(-\,^+u_j/kT) - 1] + \sum_k g_k[\exp(-\,^-u_k/kT) - 1] \right] \Bigg\}^{N_i - n}$$

$$= \Omega_0(2N_i - 2n, N - 2n')z^{N_i - n}; \; n' = \tfrac{27}{16}n \sum_{l=1}^{l=l'} g_l. \quad (46)$$

The free energy due to configuration interaction of the entire assembly can accordingly be written:

$$F = - kT \ln Z_p Z(N_i - n, N_i - n, N - n')$$

$$= - kT \left[\ln(q_p^{l'})^n \prod_{s=0}^{n-1} (N - s')/n! + \ln Z(N_i - n, N_i - n, N - n') \right] \quad (47)$$

where

$$q_p^{l'} = \sum_{l=1}^{l=l'} g_l \exp(-\,^-u_l/kT) \quad (48)$$

The average potential energy of an unassociated defect in its surrounding Debye–Hückel charge cloud (Bjerrum, 1926; Flower and Guggenheim, 1939; Lidiard, 1954b) has been accounted for in eqn (46). Using Stirling's approximation, we obtain the equilibrium number n of pairs by minimizing F_c with respect to n

$$\bar{n}\left(N - \tfrac{27}{16}\bar{n}\sum_{l=1}^{l'}g_l\right)^{(\Sigma_{l=1}^{l'}gl - 1)} \Bigg/ \left[N - \left(\tfrac{27}{16}\sum_{l=1}^{l'}g_l - 2\right)\bar{n} - 2N_i\right]^{(\Sigma_{l=1}^{l'}gl - 2)}$$

$$\times (N_i - \bar{n})^2 = q_{l'}z^{-1}\,e^{\beta(z-1)/z}$$

$$\beta = -\left(N + N_i\sum_{l=1}^{l'}g_l + 1\right)\Bigg/\left(N - \tfrac{27}{16}\bar{n}\sum_{l=1}^{l'}g_l - 1\right), \tag{49}$$

where

$$\frac{nN}{(N_i - n)^2} = q_p^{l'}z^{-1}\exp[(z-1)/z]\exp(-\omega/kT). \tag{50}$$

In order to appreciate the meaning of l', we must seek the answer to the question: At which value of R_l, the distance of pair separation, can we consider the cation-defect pair as dissociated? Since the transition of a pair into dissociation must be a gradual process, there is no clear-cut answer to this question.† The expression for n given by Lidiard (1954), who essentially assumed the case in which $l' = 1$ and $z = 1$, takes on the simple form:

$$\frac{nN}{(N_i - n)^2} = g_1 \exp(-\omega/kT) \tag{51}$$

where ω is the binding energy of the lowest bound pair. In light of our present discussion, however, we see immediately the incompatibility of these two assumed conditions. For in order that $z \sim 1$, we must have $|u_{l'}|/kT \ll 1$ for most important values of $R_l > R_{l'}$. For the temperature region under consideration, in which both pairs and dissociated ions are important, clearly $u_l/kT > 1$ for several l values other than $l = 1$. A reasonable (although still imperfect) approach to this problem has been made by Fuoss (1934), who in an extension of Bjerrum's (1926) treatment of electrolyte solutions, categorized the ions into pairs and dissociated species with the condition

$$R_{l'} = e^2/2\varepsilon kT. \tag{52}$$

Thus we have $2 \cdot 72 (2l' - 1)^{\frac{1}{2}} = e^2/12 \cdot 4\,kT$ for CaF_2 and $3 \cdot 14 (2l)^{\frac{1}{2}} = e^2/10 \cdot 06\,kT$ for KCl. It can be readily shown that in the region given by eqn (52), the solution for n is quite insensitive to the exact choice of l'. The choice of $l' = 1$ by Lidiard, on the other hand, is quite unjustified for the intermediate temperature region in which the dissociation of ion-defect pairs begins to contribute to ionic conductivity. A second improvement over the Lidiard treatment is given by the present treatment in the inclusion of z, which modifies the random distribution combinatorial factor by taking into consideration all the attractive and repulsive interactions between the dissociated ions and defects. The inclusion of z should be particularly im-

† An operational criterion, however, has been given by Ford and Fong (1971).

portant in the high temperature region in which n is vanishingly small and practically all the ions are dissociated. It may be noted here that in a detailed comparison of the Lidiard theory with experiment, Fuller and co-workers (1968), have found a consistent discrepency in the high temperature region. It remains to be seen whether the present treatment is in fact an improvement over the Lidiard theory in the interpretation of experimental data.

The ionic conductivity, σ, is directly related to the number $(N_i - n)$ of dissociated defects through the expression

$$\sigma = \frac{N_i - n}{V} e.\mu. \tag{53}$$

where μ is the mobility of the unassociated defects. In the absence of inter-actions between the dissociated ions and the defects, μ is independent of concentration and may be calculated in the manner given by Mott and Gurney (1948). For the face-centered cubic lattice, we write (Lidiard, 1954b)

$$\mu = 4a^2 e\omega_0 / kT \tag{54}$$

where

$$\omega_0 = v \exp(-E/kT) \tag{55}$$

is the field free probability of a defect jumping to a neighbouring position per unit time. Here E is the barrier height for the jump migration. In reality the defects migrate in the force field of the other unassociated defects and ions. It is therefore necessary to multiply eqn (55) by a factor $f < 1$ which corrects for the tendency of a defect being held back by its "ionic atmosphere". The theory of Onsager (1927) as extended by Pitts (1953) gives

$$f = 1 - \frac{e^2 b}{3\varepsilon kT(\sqrt{2} + 1)(1 + bR_{l'})(\sqrt{2} + bR_{l'})} \tag{56}$$

where, as before, b is the Debye–Hückel screening constant. Detailed numerical calculations based on the concepts outlined herein have been presented by Ford and Fong (1971).

V. Reactions in Crystalline Lattices

Alkaline–earth halides and alkali halides are two major classes of ionic crystals which show promise as appropriate host media for redox reactions of the lanthanide (RE) ions. Several detailed investigations into the reduc-tion of RE^{3+} ions to the divalent state in CaF_2 (Hayes and Twidell, 1961; Wood and Kaiser, 1962; McClure and Kiss, 1963; Fong, 1964a, b, c, 1965; Saleisky, 1965; Kiss and Yocom, 1964; Guggenheim and Kane, 1964; Fong and Hiller, 1967; Fong et al., 1970) and RE^{2+} ions to the monovalent state in KCl (Fong et al., 1966, 1970) have been made in the last decade. In both hosts, we are dealing with compensated lattices in which the RE ions are associated with lattice defects characteristic of the hosts. In CaF_2, RE^{3+} ions are charge compensated by F^- interstitials, while in KCl, RE^{2+} ions are accompanied by K^+ vacancies. The various processes of reduction may be broadly described in terms of two categories: (a) valence reduction by ionizing radiation and (b) valence reduction by chemical means. In the former case, the reduction process is characterized (Fong, 1964a) by: (1) the concentration of the reduced ions attainable in the sample of a given total rare-earth saturates with the radiation dosage; (2) the attainable concentration of reduced rare-earth ions saturates as the total rare-earth content increases; and (3) the reduced ions thus obtained are relatively unstable. The reconversion of these ions to the original oxidation state occurs readily with brilliant thermoluminescence when the samples are heated above the irradiation temperature (Fong, 1964a). These observations have been considered to be consistent with the postulate that only rare-earth ions unassociated with charge compensation can trap electrons to give reduced rare-earth ions (Fong, 1966). The instability of the divalent rare-earth ions is ascribed to the fact that trapped hole centres are produced simultaneously with the trapping of electrons on the RE impurities. In case (b) the RE ions are reduced when the samples are heated in the vapour or liquid of the corresponding metal of the host cation at elevated temperatures (Fong and Hiller, 1967; Fong et al., 1970). Alternatively, when the samples are subjected to an electric field at elevated temperatures, the RE impurities are electrochemically reduced (Fong, 1964a, b). In both cases the reduced species appear to be stable thermally and optically. The stability of the chemically or electrochemically reduced species is attributable to the fact that the compensation defects are removed from the crystal lattice during the reduction process.

The concepts outlined above represent generalized current interpretations of the reduction phenomena in compensated lattices. While they give plausible explanations to many of the observations, they are somewhat vague in several important details. The postulate that only RE ions in dissociation from compensation defects are reduced in radiation experiments implies the association dissociation equilibrium involving the RE ion and the compensation defect (Fong, 1966; Fong and Hiller, 1967),

   RE ion − compensation defect complex $\leftrightarrows$

                    RE ion + compensation defect.

Just what is meant by a RE ion in dissociation from its charge compensation? In view of the discussion in the preceeding sections, we observe that RE ions and lattice defects in compensated lattices are virtually all paired within the first few nearest-neighbour positions at appropriately low temperatures.

The association–dissociation hypothesis of radiation-induced reduction of RE ions to lower valence states is thus incorrect. Instead, we must take into consideration the presence of a distribution in RE ion-defect pairs. Take the example of a $CaF_2 : RE^{3+}$ system. The binding energies of the first three nearest-neighbour (n.n.) RE^{3+}–F^- interstitial pairs are (Heist and Fong, 1970) -0.48, -0.30, and -0.35 eV, respectively. If the RE^{3+} is reduced to the divalent state through trapping of an electron, the RE ion would lose the stabilization energy owing to the attraction of the trivalent cation to the F^- interstitial. From this point of view, it is clear that the n.n. $C_{4v}(1, 0, 0)$ RE^{3+}–F^- interstitial pair, having the greatest stabilization energy due to pairing, would be the most resistant to reduction. On this basis, too, we would expect that the radiation-reduced RE^{2+} ions would exist in several site symmetries in so far as they arise from RE^{3+} ions in a multiplicity of sites. Experimental verification of this point has been explored recently (Fong et al., 1970) in terms of thermoluminescence glow peaks.

When an alkaline–earth halide (MX_2) crystal containing trivalent rare-earth ions is heated in the corresponding alkaline–earth metal vapour at sufficiently high temperatures (>1050 K), the rare-earth ions are readily reduced to the divalent state as the charge compensation anion interstitials are removed from the crystalline lattice to form additional MX_2 layers on the crystal surface. Valence reduction of this type may be described by a reaction cycle similar to that outlined previously (Fong, 1966). The energy U required or gained by the additive reduction process can be empirically determined from simple equilibrium considerations (Fong, 1966). The free energy of a monatomic vapour of M containing n_1 atoms per unit volume may be written as

$$F_v = -n_1 kT \{\log [2\pi mkT/h^2)]^{3/2} + \log(n_1)^{-1} + 1\}. \tag{57}$$

The change in free energy caused by the removal of one atom from the vapour is

$$\Delta F_v = kT \{\log [2\pi mkT/h^2)]^{3/2} + \log(n_1)^{-1} + 1\}. \tag{58}$$

At high temperatures at which $kT \gg \pm u_l$ for most important values of l, we can neglect the configuration interaction energy described in Section II. Since for every M atom that settles on the crystal, two R^{3+} ions are reduced according to the equation,

$$M + 2R^{3+} = M^{2+} + 2R^{2+},$$

we have $\frac{1}{2}n_2$ excess M^{2+} ions if there exists n_2 R^{2+} ions in the crystal. The entropy of the system is, if there are n_3 R^{3+} ions,

$$S = k \log\{[(N + \tfrac{1}{2}n_2) + n_2 + n_3]!/(N + \tfrac{1}{2}n_2)! n_2! n_3!\} \tag{59}$$

where N is the original number of MX_2 molecules. When the number of excess M^{2+} ions increases by one, the charge in entropy is

$$\Delta S = k \log\{[(N + \tfrac{1}{2}n_2) + n_2 + n_3]n_3^2/(N + \tfrac{1}{2}n_2)n_2^2\}. \tag{60}$$

The increase in free energy in the crystal is thus

$$\Delta F_s = U - kT \log\{[(N + \tfrac{1}{2}n_2) + n_2 + n_3]n_3^2/(N + \tfrac{1}{2}n_2)n_2^2\}. \tag{61}$$

At equilibrium

$$\Delta F_v + \Delta F_s = 0, \tag{62}$$

and we obtain

$$\frac{(N + \tfrac{1}{2}n_2)n_2^2}{[(N + \tfrac{1}{2}n_2) + n_2 + n_3]n_3^2} = n_1 \left(\frac{2\pi mkT}{h^2}\right)^{-3/2} \exp\left(-\frac{U}{kT}\right). \tag{63}$$

For $N \gg n_2$, and setting $n_2 + n_3 = n_0$, which is constant,

$$\kappa = \frac{n_2}{n_1 n_3^2} = \frac{(N + n_0)}{N} \left(\frac{2\pi mkT}{h^2}\right)^{-3/2} \exp\left(-\frac{U}{kT}\right), \tag{64}$$

where κ is the equilibrium constant for the reduction process, and n_1, n_2, and n_3 are measurable quantities.

The basic features of the additive reduction process are thus different in a fundamental way from those of the radiation-induced reduction process in which practically all the RE ions undergoing valence reduction are in close proximity of the compensation defects. In an additive reduction process, however, the influence of the compensation defects on the RE ions involved is in fact quite unimportant.

A variation on the valence reduction of RE^{3+} ions by chemical means is the solid state electrolytic reduction procedure independently discovered by Guggenheim and Kane (1964), and Fong (1964b, c). By raising the temperature of the crystals containing RE^{3+} ions to some temperature at which the mobility of the compensation defects is appreciable, reduction to the divalent state has been achieved for Tm, Dy, and Ho in CaF_2, $SrCl_2$ and $BaBr_2$ (Fong, 1964c). The experimental arrangement for the electrolytic reduction process simply consists of an assembly of the sample crystal cut or cleaved in a given crystal plane with oppositely charged electrodes snugly fitted at both ends. The reduction is carried out in an inert or slightly reducing atmosphere. A variety of metals can be suitably employed as electrodes: W, Au and Ca have actually been employed (Fong 1964b, c; Guggenheim and Kane, 1964). From a theoretical point of view the reduction of RE^{3+} ions in CaF_2 with Ca electrodes is most readily understandable. The cathodic reaction is

$$RE^{3+} + e^- \rightleftarrows RE^{2+}.$$

The anodic reaction is

$$Ca + 2F^- \rightleftarrows CaF_2 + 2e^-.$$

The total net reaction is simply

$$Ca + 2RE^{3+} \rightleftarrows Ca^{2+} + 2RE^{2+}$$

which resembles the net reaction for the additive reduction process previously described. The differences arise from the fact that whereas the sources of the reducing matter in the additive process is a monatomic vapour, that of the reducing matter in the electrolytic process is a monatomic solid. The entropy of a monatomic crystal of Ca containing n_1 atoms and n_v vacancies per unit volume is

$$S = k \log \frac{(n_1 + n_v)!}{n_1! \, n_v!}. \tag{65}$$

When a Ca atom leaves the electrode to form a new CaF_2 molecule in the reduction of $2RE^{3+}$ ions, an additional vacancy is created in the solid electrode. The change in entropy caused by this process is

$$\Delta S = k \log \frac{n_1}{n_v}. \tag{66}$$

The corresponding change in energy, assuming the Einstein model for a monatomic crystal, is

$$\Delta U_e = -\varepsilon - 3h\nu \left(\tfrac{1}{2} + \frac{1}{\exp(h\nu/kT) - 1} \right) \tag{67}$$

where ε is the binding energy of one Ca atom to the remainder of the Ca lattice at $T = 0$ K, and ν is the fundamental harmonic oscillator frequency of the crystal. When $kT \gg h\nu$,

$$\Delta U_e = -\varepsilon - 3\left(\frac{h\nu}{2} + kT \right). \tag{68}$$

Combining eqns (66) and (68), we obtain

$$\Delta F_e = -\left(\varepsilon + 3\frac{h\nu}{2} \right) - kT \log \frac{20 \cdot 09 n_1}{n_v}. \tag{69}$$

The increase in free energy in the crystal when $2RE^{3+}$ ions are reduced to the divalent state with the number of excess Ca^{2+} ions increasing by one is given by the expression for ΔF_s in eqn (61). At equilibrium, the total change in Gibbs free energy of the reversible electrolytic process in which $2RE^{3+}$ ions are reduced to the divalent state is given by

$$\Delta F = \Delta F_s + \Delta F_e = -\frac{2FE}{N_0} \tag{70}$$

where E is the potential difference in volts through which $2F/N_0$ of electrical charge is transported. Here F is the faraday, and N_0 the Avogadro's number. Substituting eqns (61) and (69) into eqn (70), we write for the equilibrium constant κ for the electrolytic reduction process when $N \gg n_2$

$$\kappa = \frac{n_v n_2{}^2}{n_1 n_3{}^2} = \frac{20 \cdot 09(N + n_0)}{N} \exp\left(-\frac{U'}{kT}\right) \tag{71}$$

where

$$U' = U - \varepsilon - \frac{3h\nu}{2} + \frac{2FE}{N_0}. \tag{72}$$

The quantity U in eqns (61), (64), and (72) can be calculated by means of a Bron–Haber-type cycle, with (Fong, 1967)

$$U = A - \tfrac{1}{2}H - (I - M) - E_0{}^i - W \tag{73}$$

where $E_0{}^i$ is the amount of work required to remove one F^- interstitial from the crystal lattice to set it at rest at infinity, A is the energy required for the removal of one electron from the F^- ion to yield a neutral F atom, which is equal to the electron affinity of the F atom, $\tfrac{1}{2}H$ is the heat of formation of $\tfrac{1}{2}F_2$ molecule from F, I is the third ionization potential of the RE atom, M is the loss or gain of electrostatic energy in the Madelung potential due to the change in the valence of RE, and W is the gain in energy attributed to the role played by the reducing agent, which is in the present case, the heat of formation of CaF_2 from Ca and F_2. The standard-state value ("Handbook of Chemistry and Physics", 1964) for W is $-290 \cdot 3$ kcal/mole. For CaF_2: Dy^{3+}, U has been determined to be $68 \cdot 5$ kcal/mole in the Ca vapour additive reduction process (Fong and Hiller, 1967).

Although the theory of reactions in cyrstalline lattices described in the present section is given for specific examples, it can be readily extended to analogous systems of rare earth ions or, indeed, any cations which can exist in multiple valence states, in other ionic hosts. By virtue of the stabilizing influence of the host lattice, low valence states of lanthanide ions have been shown to occur. It should be quite possible to extend the theory and experimental techniques described herein to ions in the transition and the actinide series. Thus new chapters in the chemistry of the crystalline state are yet to be written.

The present chapter has given a somewhat idealized description of impurity cation-defect interactions in periodic crystalline lattices. In reality, the situation is often complicated by the presence of unintentional impurity ions, such as O^{2-} ions, which complete with intrinsic lattice defects in the charge compensation of the aliovalent cations (Chilver and Fong, 1970; Fong et al., 1971; Heist et al., 1972). Moreover, the possibility of ion-defect pair clustering has not been included in the low temperature treatment given in Section II. This is reasonable when the samples are rapidly quenched from elevated temperatures. If the cooling of the samples from elevated temperatures is allowed to occur slowly, it is quite possible that ion-defect pairs may acquire sufficient mobility to aggregate through higher polar attractive forces (Naberhuis and Fong, 1972). Such a possibility must be examined individually as the mobility of ion-defect pairs may differ from one host to another. The aggregation of two ion-defect pairs to form a four-centre cluster at ordinary temperatures can be readily treated (Chilver and Fong, 1970) by means of an extension of the method detailed in Section IV for the pairing of two dissociated oppositely charged ions. Although the detailed treatments of these complications are not given in the present work, it may be stated in conclusion that most of the problems encountered in crystalline electrolyte solutions can be tackled within the framework of the straightforward theory described above.

Acknowledgments

The writer gratefully acknowledges the collaboration and numerous enlightening discussions with many of his colleagues, co-workers, and students throughout the years during which most of the ideas in the present work were formulated. Thanks are particularly due to Professors H. Reiss, D. S. McClure, D. Diestler, C. R. Mueller, Drs. R. L. Ford and R. H. Heist. It is a pleasure to acknowledge the painstaking efforts of Mrs. Nancy Gottschalk in the preparation of the manuscript.

References

Bassani, F. and Fumi, F. G. (1954). Nuovo Cim. 11, 274.
Bjerrum, N. (1926). K. danske Vidensk, Selsk. Skr. 7, No. 9.
Brauer, P. (1951). Z. Naturforsch. 6A, 255.
Breckenridge, R. G. (1948). J. chem. Phys. 16, 959.
Breckenridge, R. G. (1959). J. chem. Phys. 18, 913.
Bron, W. E. and Heller, W. R. (1964). Phys. Rev. 136, A1433.

Chilver, C. R. and Fong, F. K. (1970). *Chem. phys. Letters* **7**, 229.
Davidson, N. (1962). "Statistical Mechanics", Chap. 15, McGraw-Hill, New York.
Debye, P. P. and Hückel, F. (1923). *Phys. Z.* **24**, 185.
Dreyfus, R. W. and Nowick, A. S. (1962). *Phys. Rev.* **33**, 473.
Etzel, H. W. and Maurer, R. J. (1950). *J. chem. Phys.* **18**, 1003.
Fenn, J. B. Jr., Cox, D. E. and Fong, F. K. (1971). *J. chem. Phys.* **56**, 188.
Fong, F. K. (1964a). *J. chem. Phys.* **41**, 245.
Fong, F. K. (1964b). *RCA Rev.* **25**, 303.
Fong, F. K. (1964c). *J. chem. Phys.* **41**, 2291.
Fong, F. K. (1965). "Proceedings of the Fourth Rare Earth Conference" (L. Eyring, ed.) Phoenix, Ariz., 22–25 April, 1964. pp. 373–392. Gordon and Breach, New York.
Fong, F. K. (1966). "Progress in Solid State Chemistry". (H. Reiss, ed), Vol. 3, Chap. 4. Pergamon, New York.
Fong, F. K. (1969). *Phys. Rev.* **187**, 1099.
Fong, F. K. (1970). *Phys. Rev.* **B1**, 4157.
Fong, F. K. and Bellows, J. C. (1970). *Phys. Rev.* **B1**, 4240.
Fong, F. K. and Hiller, M. A. (1967). *J. phys. Chem.* **71**, 2854.
Fong, F. K. and Wong, E. Y. (1967). *Phys. Rev.* **162**, 348.
Fong, F. K., Cape, J. A. and Wong, E. Y. (1966). *Phys. Rev.* **151**, 299.
Fong, F. K., Fenn, J. B. Jr., and McCaldin, J. O. (1970). *J. chem. Phys.* **53**, 1559.
Fong, F. K., Heist, R. H., Chilver, C. R., Bellows, J. C. and Ford, R. L. (1970). *J. Luminescence* **2**, 823.
Fong, F. K., Sundberg, M. N., Heist, R. H. and Chilver, C. R. (1971). *Phys. Rev.* **B3**, 50.
Ford, R. L. and Fong, F. K. (1971). *J. chem. Phys.* **55**, 2532.
Ford, R. L. and Fong, F. K. (1972). *J. chem. Phys.* Feb. 15.
Fowler, R. H. and Guggenheim, E. A. (1939). "Statistical Thermodynamics". eqn. (911, 10). Cambridge University Press.
Franklin, A. D. (1963). *J. Res. NBS* **67A**, 291.
Franklin, A. D., Shorb, A. and Wachtman, J. B. Jr. (1964). *J. Res. NBS* **68A**, 425.
Frenkel, J. (1926). *Z. Physik* **35**, 652.
Fuller, R. G., Marquardt, C. L., Reilly, M. H. and Wells, J. C. Jr. (1968). *Phys. Rev.* **176**, 1036.
Fuoss, R. M. (1934). *Trans. Faraday Soc.* **30**, 967.
Guggenheim, H. and Kane, J. V. (1964). *Appl. Phys. Letters* **4**, 172.
"Handbook of Chemistry and Physics", (1964). 45th Ed., Chemical Rubber Co., Cleveland, Ohio.
Haven, Y. and van Santen, J. H. (1954). *J. chem. Phys.* **22**, 1146.
Haven, Y. and van Santen, J. H. (1958). Suppl. *Nuovo Cim.* **7**, 605.
Hayes, W. and Twidell, J. W. (1961). *J. chem. Phys.* **35**, 1521.
Heist, R. H. and Fong, F. K. (1970). *Phys. Rev.* **B1**, 2970.
Heist, R. H., Chilver, C. R. and Fong, F. K. (1971). *Phys. Rev.* **B1**.
Jost, W. (1933). *J. chem. Phys.* **1**, 466.
Jost, W. (1938). *Trans. Faraday Soc.* **34**, 860.
Judd, B. R. (1963). "Operator Techniques in Atomic Spectroscopy", Chap. 2. McGraw-Hill, New York.
Kiss, Z. J. and Yocom, P. N. (1964). *J. chem. Phys.* **41**, 1511.
Lidiard, A. B. (1954a). *In* "Report on the Conference on Defects in Crystalline Solids" (The Physical Society, London, 1954). p. 283.

Lidiard, A. B. (1954b). *Phys. Rev.* **94**, 29.
Lidiard, A. B. (1957). "Handbuch der Physik" **20**, p. 245. Springer Verlag, Berlin.
McClure, D. S. and Kiss, Z. J. (1963). *J. chem. Phys.* **39**, 3251.
Mahlab, E., Volterra, V., Low, W. and Yariv, A. (1163). *Phys. Rev.* **131**, 920.
Mayer, J. E. (1950). *J. chem. Phys.* **18**, 1426.
Mayer, J. E. and Mayer, M. G. (1940). "Statistical Mechanics", Chap. 13. John Wiley, New York.
Mott, N. F. and Gurney, R. W. (1948). "Electronic Processes in Ionic Crystals", Oxford University Press, London, 2nd edition.
Naberhuis, S. L. and Fong, F. K. (1972). *J. chem. Phys.* Feb. 1.
Onsager, L. (1927). *Z. Phys.* **28**, 286, eqn (45).
Pines, D. and Nozières, P. (1966). "The Theory of Quantum Liquids", Vol. 1, p. 149. W. A. Benjamin, New York.
Pitts, E. (1953). *Proc. R. Soc. Lond.* A.**217**, 43.
Ranon, U. and Low, W. (1963). *Phys. Rev.* 132, 1609.
Ranon, U. and Yariv, A. (1964). *Phys. Letters* **9**, 17.
Rector, C. W., Pandey, B. C. and Moos, H. W. (1966). *J. chem. Phys.* **45**, 171.
Rossing, B. R. (1966). Unpublished Ph.D. thesis, Massachusetts Institute of Technology, Boston.
Sabisky, E. (1965). *J. appl. Phys.* **36**, 802.
Sierro, J. (1963). *Phys. Letters* **4**, 178.
Tosi, M. P. and Airokli, G. (1958). *Nuovo Cim.* **8**, 584.
Ure, R. W. Jr. (1957). *J. chem. Phys.* **26**, 1363.
Wagner, C. and Schottky, W. (1930). *Z. phys. Chem.* (B) **11**, 163.
Watkins, G. D. (1959). *Phys. Rev.* **113**, 79 and 91.
Weber, M. J. and Bierig, R. W. (1964). *Phys. Rev.* **134**, A1492.
Wood, D. L. and Kaiser, W. (1962). *Phys. Rev.* **126**, 2079.

4. NUCLEAR MICROANALYSIS

Georges Amsel

Groupe de Physique des Solides de l'Ecole Normale Supérieure,
Paris, France.

The study of physical and chemical phenomena taking place on the surface of solids, which is fundamental in several fields of electrochemistry, requires quantitative determination and localization of very small amounts of elements. Tracer experiments with separated isotopes may give further insight into such phenomena as atomic transport, self-diffusion and surface exchange with external media. Conventional analytical techniques do not always allow such measurements, especially when high sensitivity as well as good depth resolution are required. The radioactive isotopes of most of the light elements are too short-lived to allow tracer experiments to be carried out. The merits of the electron probe, the ion probe, infrared and NMR techniques have been discussed in detail (Amsel and Samuel, 1967; Amsel *et al.*, 1971a). Low energy electron diffraction and Auger electron spectroscopy are invaluable for the study of the first atomic layers of solids but give little

127

information on layers thicker than some 10 Å; moreover they do not allow tracer experiments to be performed.

Recently ellipsometry has been developed to study surface phenomena (Barret, 1964). This method allows the determination *in situ* of the thickness and refractive index of thin films formed at the surface of solids in electrolytes, provided some assumptions are made concerning their nature. Although absolute calibration may present problems and isotopic analysis is precluded, ellipsometry is a particularly valuable complement to any other analytical method as its possible use *in situ* is irreplaceable in electrochemistry (see also special issue of *Surf. Sci.* **16**, August 1969).

Nuclear techniques provide an alternative for the determination of small amounts of nuclei. Activation analysis by neutrons, γ-rays or charged particles may be used with advantage in many experiments, especially to measure trace impurities in the bulk of the samples (see discussion in Amsel et al., 1971a). The direct observation of nuclear reactions induced by charged particles bombarding the samples is, on the other hand, particularly suitable for the study of surface phenomena. The presence and amount of many light elements and of their stable isotopes (as well as of heavy elements in favourable cases) may be determined by this method with a very high sensitivity; universal absolute calibration, independent of the matrix in which the element is embedded, is achieved and the location of the nuclei as a function of depth is possible with submicron resolution. In what follows we shall present the use of these methods to the determination or tracing of nuclei like D, Li^6, Li^7, C^{12}, N^{14}, O^{16}, O^{18}, and F^{19} and typical applications in various fields of electrochemistry, like oxidation processes, metal passivity, etc.

I. Method

The analytical method itself will be described here only briefly; details may be found in Amsel and Samuel (1967), Amsel et al. (1968) and Amsel and David (1969). Full technical details and a discussion of its use by other authors are presented in Amsel et al. (1971a). Charged particles (protons, deutrons, etc.) in the 600–1500 keV energy range, from a low energy accelerator (a 2 MeV Van de Graaff) are directed on the sample; the beam diameter is typically 1 mm. The charged particles (protons, alphas, etc.) produced by the nuclear reactions induced on the light nuclei located near the surface of the sample are detected by means of semiconductor detectors and their energy spectrum is analysed by conventional nuclear electronics. Well chosen Mylar films may stop the elastically backscattered incoming patricles, providing practically background-free detection. Nuclear reactions lead to monoenergetic particles and the resulting peaks in the energy spectrum are characteristic of the nuclei under study. Figure 1 shows a typical spectrum so obtained. Interfering parasitic reactions may arise only from low Z substrata ($Z < 15$); a correct choice of the bombarding energy may minimise such effects. In some cases it may be useful to detect γ-rays or neutrons instead of charged particles. In other cases elastically backscattered particles are observed, usually from He^4 or C^{12} beams.

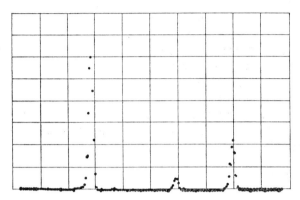

FIG. 1. A typical proton energy spectrum from the deuteron bombardment of an 800 Å thick Ta_2O_5 target on tantalum backing. The p_1 and p_0 peaks of $O^{16}(d, p)O^{17}$ (corresponding to the first excited and the fundamental states of O^{17}) are seen and the p_0 peak of $C^{12}(d, p)C^{13}$ (on the right, from carbon contamination). $E_0 = 830$ keV, 19μ Mylar; energy of p_1 at detection: 950 keV; 15 keV/channel. The p_1 peak is generally used to measure O^{16}, owing to the high cross section of the corresponding reaction.

A. The Measurement of the Total Amount of Nuclei in Surface Regions

If the bombarding energy E_0 is in the vicinity of a plateau of the differential cross section curve $\sigma_\theta(E_0)$, for a direction of observation θ, the counting rate $N(E_0)$ will be:

$$N(E_0) = Ki\sigma_\theta(E_0)\Omega \int C(x)\,dx \qquad (1)$$

where K is a constant, i is the beam current, Ω the solid angle of detection and $C(x)$ the number of reacting nuclei per cm^3 at depth x. $q = \int C(x)\,dx$ is the total amount of nuclei in the surface region of the sample; q is expressed in atom/cm^2 or mg/cm^2, etc. Absolute quantities q may be obtained by comparison to reference standards (see below) and the results are independent of the shape of the distribution profile $C(x)$.

The yield of the nuclear reactions depends only on the reaction cross-section and hence the matrix containing the nuclei has no influence on the results, provided that the nuclei are contained in a thin enough region near the sample surface (except for channeling effects in single crystals, see

Amsel *et al.*, 1971a). The analysis is non-destructive. However, adsorbed elements may be desorbed under vacuum or by the ionization of the beam. This is a limitation of the method shared by practically all other analytical techniques, except radiotracing which is of little use for elements like oxygen and nitrogen. *In situ* measurements with ellipsometry may help to establish the significance of nuclear measurements in doubtful cases.

Table I gives typical conditions for the analysis of some nuclei often measured as well as the corresponding counting rates for films containing 10^{16} atom/cm^2. Let us recall that the relative statistical precision for N counts is $1/\sqrt{N}$, so that 10^4 counts should be accumulated for a 1% precision. Such a precision is usually achieved within some minutes of measurement time.

The construction of reliable reference standards is one of the fundamental problems of nuclear microanalysis. For oxygen, both O^{16} and O^{18}, anodic oxidation of tantalum provides an easy way to obtain thin films of high uniformly and of well-known oxygen content (Amsel *et al.*, 1969a). Nitrogen standards may be obtained by reactive sputtering of tantalum (Amsel and David, 1969), whereas LiF and CaF$_2$ targets are used for lithium and fluorine (Maurel *et al.*, 1971).

B. Determination of Concentration Profiles

Concentration profiles $C(x)$ may be determined by two methods. For depths of the order of some microns the broadened energy spectrum of the emitted particles is analysed, yielding a concentration profile with a depth resolution of the order of 0·2 microns. This method is fully described in Amsel *et al.* (1971a) and will be illustrated below.

In the particular case where there exists a strong narrow resonance in the cross section curve $\sigma_\theta(E)$, the measurement of the yield curve $N(E_0)$ of all the emitted particles as a *function of the energy* E_0 in the vicinity of the resonance energy E_R may give valuable information on the concentration profile $C(x)$. Much qualitative information may be gained from the yield curve $N(E_0)$ even without deep mathematical analysis. More details on these techniques are presented in Amsel *et al.* (1971a, 1971b). A typical case is that of O^{18}, in the vinicity of the 1165 keV or 629 keV resonances of the $O^{18}(p, \alpha)N^{15}$ reaction (Amsel and Samuel, 1962; Amsel *et al.*, 1971a). The $F^{19}(p, \alpha\gamma)O^{16}$ reaction also presents such resonances (Maurel *et al.*, 1971). Using the resonance method the profile may be calculated, with a depth resolution of the order of from 30 to 300 Å, depending on experimental conditions.

C. Analysis by Elastic Backscattering

When a sample is bombarded by charged particles of mass m, with a bom-

TABLE 1. Typical experimental conditions for nuclear microanalysis

Nucleus	Reaction	Bombarding energy (KeV)	Energy of emitted particles (MeV)	Thickness of Mylar absorber (μ)	Counting Rate[a]
O^{16}	$O^{16}(d, p_1)\,O^{17*d}$	830	1·52	19	1600
O^{18}	$O^{18}(p, \alpha)\,N^{15}$	730	3·38	12	4600
N^{14}	$N^{14}(d, \alpha_1)\,C^{12*d}$	1300	6·76	19	470
F^{19}	$F^{19}(p, \alpha)\,O^{16}$	1260	6·93	26	265
	$F^{19}(p, \alpha)\,O^{16}$	1340[c]	6·97	31	1410
	$F^{19}(p, \alpha\gamma)\,O^{16}$	870[c]	$\left.\begin{matrix}7{\cdot}12\\6{\cdot}92\\6{\cdot}13\end{matrix}\right\}\gamma$	—	13800[b]
C^{12}	$C^{12}(d, p)\,C^{13}$	1000	3·01	19	20000
H^2	$D(d, p)\,T$	550	2·45	6	2000
Li^6	$Li^6(d, \alpha)\,He^4$	1560	9·25	26	930
Li^7	$Li^7(p, \alpha)\,He^4$	1000	7·84	19	400

[a] for a film containing 10^{16} atom/cm^2, a 1 μA beam, per min. The solid angle is 0·12 steradian, at 150° detection angle. The counting rates may be multiplied by 3, using three identical detectors, when necessary.

[b] 3 in. × 3 in. NaI(Tl) scintillation detector at 7 cm.

[c] for films of equivalent thickness <10 KeV.

[d] reaction leading to the first excited state (O^{17*} or C^{12*}) of the residual nucleus.

barding energy E_0, the energy E of the particles backscattered by nuclei of mass M is given, at an angle of 180°, by:

$$E = E_0 \left[\frac{M - m}{M + m} \right]^2.$$ (2)

The energy spectrum of the backscattered particles depends hence on the masses of the nuclei present in the target. The analysis method based on this principle is of special interest when observing traces of high Z elements in a low Z matrix. The yield of Coulomb scattering being enhanced in proportion of Z^2, a high sensitivity results in this case. He^4 or C^{12} beams are generally used for such a work as illustrated below. Details on this method may be found in Turos and Wilhelmi (1968, 1969).

II. Elemental Analysis

By elemental analysis, we mean all measurements which do not resort to tracing techniques. Here samples of natural isotopic composition are usually examined. Elements having several isotopes are determined by measuring the isotope of the highest natural abundance: Li^7 for lithium (92·43%), C^{12} for carbon (98·89%), N^{14} for nitrogen (99·63%) and O^{16} for oxygen (99·76%).

A. Measurement of Equivalent Thicknesses

For thin films of fixed and homogeneous composition it is possible to introduce an equivalent geometric thickness X deduced from the value q of the number of nuclei per cm^2 for one of the constituents, by assigning known values to the stoichiometry and the density of the chemical compound considered, as well as to the roughness factor of the underlying surface. Under such assumptions we may write

$$X = \lambda q$$ (3)

where λ is constant. On the other hand one may express X as a weight per cm^2 of the compound; this does not require that a density is assigned to the thin film considered. Such measurements may be most useful to determine oxide thicknesses by determining the oxygen content of thin oxide films. In many cases knowledge of the absolute thickness is not required and q by itself gives sufficient information on the phenomenon under study. Let us consider some typical applications.

1. The Growth Laws of Anodic Oxide Films

Figure 2 shows a typical set of results (see Siejka *et al.*, 1971a) obtained on rolled aluminium samples at room temperature, in a neutral aqueous solution, relating the number q_O of oxygen atoms per cm^2 to the anode potential V_{ox} for various current densities J. This potential satisfies, according to Young (1961), the relation:

$$V_{ox} - V_{eq} = \eta_m + \eta_s + \eta_{ox} \tag{4}$$

throughtout the oxidation, where η_m is the overpotential at the metal–oxide interface, η_s that at the oxide-solution interface, and η_{ox} that in the oxide. V_{eq} is the anode equilibrium potential, which is equal to the thermodynamic potential V_{th} for the formation of the oxide for which the overall reaction can be written

$$M + H_2O \rightleftharpoons MO + 2H^+ + 2e^- \tag{5}$$

where M represents the metal,

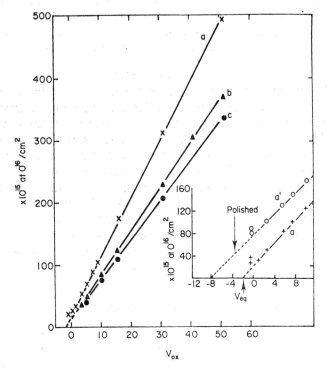

FIG. 2. Growth laws $q_0 = f(V_{ox})$ for unpolished aluminium. a: at constant potential for 50 minutes (current density $< 10\ \mu A/cm^2$). b and c: at constant currents of 1 mA/cm² and 10 mA/cm². The insert shows in detail the growth laws at constant potential for unpolished (a) and polished (a') aluminium. V_{ox} is in the hydrogen scale in volts.

If all the oxygen on the sample surface is contained in a highly insulating oxide film which behaves like an anodic barrier layer, we may write:

$$\eta_{ox} = \lambda E_{ox} q_O \qquad (6)$$

where E_{ox} is the electric field of formation of the oxide. If the film contains a region of high ionic conductivity, with oxygen content $q_O{}^c$, we have

$$\eta_{ox} = \lambda E_{ox}(q_O - q_O{}^c). \qquad (7)$$

It is clear from (7) that in the case when an initial layer of high ionic conductivity is present on the sample surface, the curve $q_O = f(V_{ox})$ is shifted towards the *negative* potentials. Moreover if $q_O{}^c = 0$ the curves $q_O = f(V_{ox})$ for various current densities J (hence various E_{ox}) intersect at one and the same point, the intercept $V_{ox}(0)$ yielding the sum $\eta_m + \eta_s$. The slope of the curves of Fig. 2 yields E_{ox} as a function of the oxidation current density J. From this figure is was concluded that (i) $\eta_m + \eta_s$ is statistically zero with standard deviation 170 mV, (ii) E_{ox} depends on J by a relation of logarithmic type. (iii) on electrochemically polished samples a layer of high ionic conductivity is present, shifting the growth law towards negative potentials. For a detailed analysis of this type of measurement see Siejka *et al.* (1971a).

2. Dissolution Rates

Chemical stripping of successive layers from thin films is often used to study the formation mechanisms of the latter. The dissolution rate in given experimental conditions may be measured by monitoring one of the constituents (oxygen for oxides) of the thin film by nuclear methods. As an example let us consider in Fig. 3 the case of silicon nitride films deposited on silicon wafers by reactive sputtering. Nuclear microanalysis showed (Croset *et al.*, 1971a) that these films contain both nitrogen and oxygen; the question arose whether the oxygen contaminates the bulk of the nitride film or whether it is located near the nitride–silicon interface. The dissolution of the nitride film was obtained in 50% HF. Figure 3 clearly shows that the second assumption holds, the oxygen probably being contained in a thin oxide layer on the silicon substrate; a dissolution rate of $1 \cdot 83 \times 10^{16}$ atoms of nitrogen per cm^2 per min is deduced from Fig. 3.

B. Determination of the Faradic Efficiency

The current efficiency of electrochemical film formation may be determined by associating nuclear microanalysis with coulometric measurements. We shall illustrate these techniques by the example of anodic oxidation processes. The current density J passing through the oxide may be decomposed according to

$$J = J_i + J_e \qquad (8)$$

where J_i is the ionic and J_e the electronic current density respectively. The ionic current density in equation (8) may in turn be decomposed at the oxide–solution interface according to

$$J_i = J_{ox} + J_{dis} \tag{9}$$

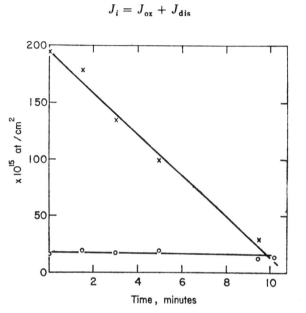

FIG. 3. Quantities of nitrogen and oxygen contained in a silicon nitride film deposited on silicon by reactive sputtering, as a function of dissolution time in 50% HF. × nitrogen; ○ oxygen.

where J_{ox} is the part of the current which contributes to the film growth and J_{dis} the dissolution current. J_e may be estimated either by the use of Redox systems in solution (see Amsel et al., 1969a) or by measuring oxygen evolution at the anode (Young, 1961). On the other hand J_{ox} is given directly by the nuclear measurements, from

$$q_O(t) - q_O(0) = k \int_0^t J_{ox}(\theta)\, d\theta \tag{10}$$

where the constant k is equal to $0\cdot312 \times 10^{19}$ atoms of oxygen per coulomb, if we assume that the oxygen is fixed in the film in the state O^{--}. The precise measurement of the number Q of coulombs per cm^2

$$Q = \int_0^t J(\theta)\, d\theta \tag{11}$$

consumed during oxidation allows the determination of the oxidation current efficiency from the following relation deduced from (10) and (11):

$$R = \frac{J_{ox}}{J} = \frac{1}{k}\frac{dq_o}{dQ}. \tag{12}$$

On Fig. 4 q_0 (minus the content of the initial layer) is plotted for aluminium samples, oxidized in conditions identical to those of Fig. 2, as a function of the number of coulombs per cm^2 used during the formation of the films (expressed in number of O^{--} per cm^2). The slope of the curves gives by definition the value of R. The oxidation of aluminium at constant current (1 to 10 mA/cm^2) in presence of a Redox system yielded an upper limit of the electronic component J_e: 2% for polished aluminium 5% for unpolished aluminium. By difference we obtained the minimum value of the ionic current density J_i. For polished aluminium the current efficiency appears independent of the current. For unpolished aluminium the decrease of the efficiency, as the layer thickness increases and the current density decreases,

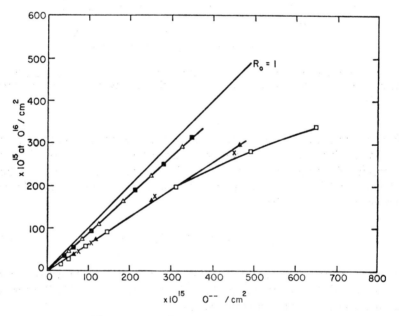

FIG. 4. Number of O^{16} atoms per cm^2 fixed on aluminium samples by anodic oxidation versus electric charge consumed, expressed as a number of O^{--} anions per cm^2. △ polished Al, 10 mA/cm^2 and ■ 1 mA/cm^2; ▲ unpolished Al, 10 mA/cm^2, × 6.6 mA/cm^2 and □ 1 mA/cm^2.

is due to an increase in the dissolution current, as the electronic current is less than 5% of the total. Moreover R is much smaller for unpolished than for polished aluminium. The large values of J_{dis} found for aluminium, raise the question whether the dissolution currents are of chemical or electrochemical nature. The equivalent chemical dissolution current density for aluminium oxide, without applied electric field, could also be measured by nuclear methods (this being proportional to $-dq_O/dt$); an estimated value of only 0·3 µA/cm^3 for both polished and unpolished aluminium was found. It would therefore appear that the dissolution current during oxidation is purely electrochemical. More details on this subject may be found in Siejka *et al.* (1971a).

C. Stoichiometry and Incorporations

In the preceding case the stoichiometry of the film under study was assumed to be well defined. When each of the constituents of the film can be determined independently, the stoichiometry may be measured to within the precision of the standards. When the substrate contains an element entering the composition of the film (as for aluminium oxide grown on aluminium, etc.) such a direct measurment is not possible. However, for thick enough films (500 Å to some thousands of Å according to the nature of the film) the analysis of the spectra obtained from nuclear reactions or elastic backscattering allows determination of the stoichiometry for binary and even tertiary coumpounds (Amsel *et al.*, 1971a). Thus the composition of silicon nitride films deposited on silicon by reactive sputtering in argon was studied with He^4 backscattering by Croset *et al.* (1971a). It was shown that argon is incorporated in the films. The argon/silicon ratio may reach 10 atom %; the nitrogen/silicon ratio steadily increaess with the partial pressure of nitrogen. Analoguous experiments were carried out by Gyulai *et al.* (1970) on silicon nitride films chemically deposited from $SiH_4 + NH_3$ mixtures using a slightly different analysis of the He^4 backscattering spectra.

When oxidizing anodically in concentrated acid solutions, large incorporations from the electrolyte are observed in many cases; the films obtained should then be termed "oxysalts" rather than "oxides". Figure 5 shows typical results for the incorporation of nitrogen in anodic films on tantalum and niobium formed in concentrated HNO_3 (93%), as a function of the oxygen content of the films. The slope of the straight lines yields an incorporation ratio of 8·8 ± 0·9 atoms of nitrogen per 100 atoms of oxygen for tantalum and 10·4 ± 1 for niobium. The errors indicated corresponds to that on the nitrogen standard used. A detailed account of these experiments was given by Amsel *et al.* (1969a) for tantalum and by Cherki (1971) for niobium.

D. Determination of Oxygen Yield and of Incorporation Mechanisms

When the amount of incorporated elements is large enough for them not to be considered as traces in the films the problem is to determine the mechanism of incorporation of these impurities. To that purpose it is convenient to measure the film formation oxygen R_O defined by

$$R_O = \frac{q_O{'}}{q_O{}^Q} \tag{13}$$

where $q_O{}^Q$ is the number of oxygen atoms per cm² deduced from the consumed charge density Q by assuming that the oxygen is incorporated in the form of divalent ions O^{2-}. $q_O{'}$ is the number of oxygen atoms fixed during the anodic treatment. An R_O greater than unity signifies an average charge per oxygen atom of less than two. This can only be explained if a fraction of the oxygen atoms is incorporated in the form of polyatomic anions, where the charge per oxygen atom is less than two. For example, this charge is equal to 1/3 in NO_3^-. On making a hypothesis on the nature of the oxygenated anion in question for a given electrolyte, the fraction of oxygen atoms incorporated in the form of polyatomic anions can be deduced from the value

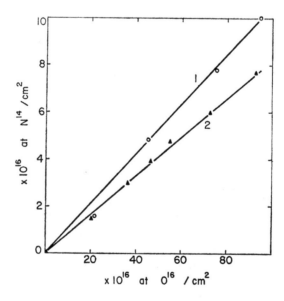

FIG. 5. Nitrogen content as a function of oxygen content of films formed in 93% NHO_3, at 23°C. (1) on niobium, at $J = 4$ mA/cm²; (2) on tantalum at various current densities 0.1 mA/cm² $< J < 10$ mA/cm².

of R_O provided the electronic losses are negligible. The values of R_O may be measured with an accuracy of the order of 1 %. This method and its application to the oxidation of tantalum in various electrolytes are analysed in detail by Amsel *et al.* (1969a).

In the case of tantalum oxidized in 93 % HNO_3 the observed value of R_O was 131 %. The quantitative results fully confirm that the hypothesis of incorporation in the form of polyatomic anions is valid. as the number of nitrogen atoms determined directly by nuclear reactions $((7 \cdot 7 \pm 0 \cdot 8) \times 10^{14}$ atoms/cm^2/V) is close to the number of nitrogen atoms calculated from R_O assuming incorporation of impurities from the solution in the form of NO_3^- $(7 \cdot 4 \times 10^{14}$ atoms/cm^2/V). Analogous results have been obtained by Cherki (1971) in the study of the influence of the electrolyte on the anodic oxidation of niobium.

E. Analysis of the State of the Surface of Samples

The state of the surface of solids may deeply influence their physicochemical properties. Thus the thickness and nature of the oxide films which may cover metallic or semiconductor electrodes play a fundamental role in determining their electrochemical behaviour. Contamination by traces of elements such a fluor may further modify the observed phenomena and may lead to irreproducible results. Careful surface preparation of the samples is therefore the first step in most of the experiments carried out in electrochemistry, semiconductor physics or technology, etc. Electron microscopy was used to study the effects of surface preparation (see Faust, 1969) by observing transmission micrographs of the stripped oxide layers from various semiconductors. As will be illustrated here, nuclear microanalysis may provide valuable information for evaluating the merits of various preparation procedures. The measurements may be carried out within a few minutes on the bulk samples.

1. Mechanical Perturbation of the Surface Region

The mechanical polishing of samples or the rolling of metallic foils may perturb the surface region up to depths of several microns. As any metallic surface exposed to air tends to be oxidized, the presence of cracks, scratches, etc., or other effects inducing surface roughness increase the quantity of oxygen in the surface region of samples which have a low bulk oxygen content. Hence the observation of the O^{16} (d, p) O^{17*} proton spectrum may give a first image of the state of the surface after mechanical treatment. Figure 6a shows a typical spectrum, recorded in conditions similar to those of Fig. 1, for a sample of nickel foil (Siejka *et al.*, 1971b). The foil was rolled from an ingot molten under high vacuum and was rated to have a purity of 99·99 %. The spectrum shows that the surface region up to several thousands of Å deep contains a high quantity of oxygen, of the order of several thousands of ppm. In this case the rolling procedure seems to have massively buried oxygen deep into the metal. Preliminary experiments on rolled high purity gold and platinum foils led to analogous results. Similar observations were made on mechanically polished zirconium samples (Amsel *et al.*, 1969b); in this case the use of abrasives like silicon carbide or diamond led to a massive inclusion, in addition to oxygen, of carbon and silicon. The only abrasive yielding a correct result was alumina.

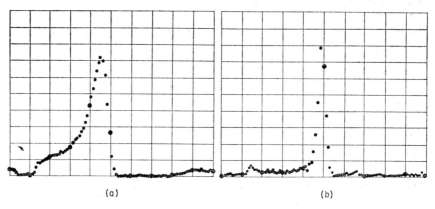

(a)   (b)

FIG. 6. Proton energy spectra for the reaction $O^{16}(d, p)O^{17*}$ observed on high purity nickel samples: (a) unpolished (b) polished. 17 keV/channel. Vertical scale: (a) 2000 counts/div; (b) 20 counts/div. Note that spectrum (a) is much broadened, indicating that the oxygen distribution penetrates several thousands of Angstrom deep; moreover polishing reduces the quantity of oxygen near the surface by a factor of over 100.

2. Oxide Layers Left by Chemical or Electrochemical Polishing

Figure 6b shows the $O^{16}(d, p)O^{17*}$ proton spectrum for a nickel sample similar to that of Fig. 6a, but electrochemically polished for 10 min in a H_2SO_4 solution at 400 mA/cm². The more than 100-fold decrease in the oxygen content of the surface region and the narrow peak obtained illustrate the effectiveness of the polishing procedure. The remaining oxygen, 4×10^{15} atom/cm², is most probably located on the surface and is equivalent to about 3 atomic layers. A systematic study of the oxide layer left by chemical or electrochemical polishing of various metals like zirconium (Amsel *et al.*, 1969b), niobium (Béranger *et al.*, 1970), tantalum and aluminium (Siejka *et al.*, 1971a) and silicon (see Fig. 3) showed that these layers have thicknesses ranging from about 30 Å to over 100 Å, according to experimental conditions. The smallest oxygen contaminations observed were on nickel (as shown above) and on monocrystalline gold.

3. Perturbations from Annealing

Annealing, under vacuum, of metals having a high affinity for oxygen may quickly lead to large oxygen contaminations up to several microns deep. Thus, when high purity, chemically polished zirconium was heated in a vacuum of 2×10^{-6} Torr at $800°$ C for 2 h, an oxygen penetration of more than 10μ was observed, with a surface concentration of 1200 ppm. The oxygen originated both directly from the residual gases and from the dissolution of the oxide layer left by the polishing (Amsel et al., 1968). Hence even annealing in ultra-high vacuum may lead to contamination. Similar results were observed on niobium (Béranger et al., 1970).

4. Trace Contaminations from Polishing

Fluor contamination of tantalum chemically polished in a $HF-HNO_3-H_2SO_4$ bath was studied by Maurel et al. (1971). As pointed out by Young (1961), traces of fluor may perturb the anodic oxidation of tantalum. It was shown using the $F^{19}(p, \alpha)O^{16}$ reaction that 5×10^{14} atom/cm^2 of fluor was left by the polishing procedure on the surface of the tantalum sample. Moreover, using a narrow resonance of the $F^{19}(p, \alpha\gamma)O^{16}$ reaction it could be shown that after anodic oxidation of the polished tantalum the traces of fluor remain near the metal–oxide interface, even when an anodic oxide as thick as 1500 Å is formed. The $F^{19}(p, \alpha\gamma)O^{16}$ reaction has been used by Möller and Starfelt (1967) to study fluorine contamination of zircaloy undergoing various treatments.

III. O^{18} Tracing

Nuclear microanalysis allows tracer experiments to be carried out with separated isotopes of light nuclei such as Li^6, C^{13}, N^{15} or O^{18}. Among these nuclei O^{18} has been extensively used for tracer studies of oxidation phenomena in solid state electrochemistry. Highly O^{18}-enriched compounds, up to 95% as compared with the 0.204% natural abundance, are available (from the Weizmann Institute, Rehovot, Israel). Typical labelled compounds are oxygen gas, water and salts like citric acid, KNO_3, etc. In addition, O^{18} depleted water (down to $0.003\% O^{18}$) may also be used in some experiments. The $O^{18}(p, \alpha)N^{13}$ reaction provides a highly sensitive and selective method of determining very small O^{18} isotopic concentrations in thin films, down to 10^{-5}, as the $O^{16}(p, \alpha)N^{13}$ reaction has a negative Q-value and does not contribute to the α particle emission at low bombarding energies. The O^{16} isotopic concentration C of an oxide film is determined by

$$C = \frac{q_{O^{18}}}{q_{O^{18}} + q_{O^{16}}} \qquad (14)$$

where $q_{O^{18}}$ is measured by the $O^{18}(p, \alpha)N^{15}$ reaction and $q_{O^{16}}$ by the $O^{16}(d, p)O^{17}*$ reaction.

A. The Source of Oxygen in Anodic Oxidation

When an electrolytic bath contains several oxygenated compounds, the question arises which of these compounds provide the oxygen in the anodic films formed. This can be elucidated by introducing O^{18} labelled compounds in the electrolyte. If preliminary experiments ascertain that the various components of the bath do not undergo isotopic exchange during the experiment, the proportion C of O^{18} in the film allows us to determine the relative contribution as an oxygen source of the labelled compound considered. In fact, if C_0 is the isotopic concentration of O^{18} in the compound, the normalized O^{18} concentration in the film

$$C* = C/C_0 \qquad (15)$$

gives directly the relative contribution to be determined.

Such experiments were carried out for the anodic oxidation of silicon and tantalum in N-methylacetamid (NMA) and glycol, containing 0.4% KNO$_3$ and from 0.1% to 1% water (by weight) by Croset et al. (1971b). By labelling in turn the water and KNO$_3$, it was shown that the main source of oxygen is the water; the organic bath does not contribute directly, whereas the contribution of the salt (of the order of 10%) decreases when the water content of the bath increases. This is illustrated in Fig. 7, which shows that $1/C*$ varies linearly with water content, silicon and tantalum leading to the same results. The KNO$_3$ was labelled to 77% O^{18}. As no nitrogen was found

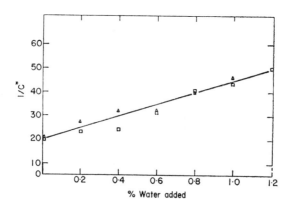

Fig. 7. Dependence of the normalised O^{18} content $C*$ of anodic oxide films formed in NMA solutions containing O^{18} labelled KNO$_3$, as a function of the amount of water added to the electrolyte. Films formed on silicon: □ and on tantalum: △.

in the films, incorporation of NO_3^- anions may be ruled out and the salt seems to act as a direct source of oxygen. Similar experiments were carried out by Ortega (1971) on the anodic oxidation of zirconium in aqueous solutions, using O^{18} labelled citric acid.

B. Passivity of Metals

The passivity of metals like nickel or iron could theoretically be studied in a similar way to that described above for anodic oxidation. However, the oxide films formed in the solutions are so thin that the subsequent oxidation of the samples in the air completely masks the phenomena to be observed. It was attempted to overcome this difficulty by using O^{18}-enriched water for the experiments. The passivity of nickel was studied by Siejka et al. (1971b) in 10% O^{18}-enriched 1 N water solutions of H_2SO_4 (H_2SO_4 non-labelled). The nickel samples, polished as described above, were first held under cathodic potential (400 mV for 4 min) and subsequently at various anodic potentials V_{ox} until the final current density decreased to $20 \mu A/cm^2$. The

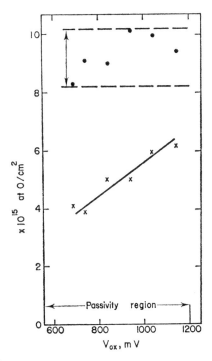

FIG. 8. Quantities of oxygen on the surface of polished nickel samples after anodic treatment at potentials V_{ox} in the passivity region. $\times : q_{O^{18}}^* = g^*(V_{ox})$ and $\bullet : q_O = q_{O^{16}} + q_{O^{18}} = f(V_{ox})$. V_{ox} in the hydrogen scale, millivolts.

samples were removed from the solution under potential. The normalized O^{18} content $q_{O^{18}}^* = q_{O^{18}}/C_0$ (see eqn 15) and the total oxygen content $q_O = q_{O^{16}} + q_{O^{18}}$ was then measured for various V_{ox}, yielding

$$q_{O^{18}}^* = g^*(V_{ox}); \quad q_O = f(V_{ox}) \tag{16}$$

$q_{O^{18}}^*$ gives the quantity of oxygen *coming from the solution* (assuming there is no isotopic exchange with the air). Figure 8 shows a typical result (the statistical errors were $<2\%$; spread is due to irreproducibility). From these experiments it was concluded: (i) no oxygen originates from the solution below the passivity region, (ii) $g^*(V_{ox})$ is linear in the passivity region, (iii) the maximal value of $g^*(V_{ox})$ is $(6 \cdot 3 \pm 0 \cdot 4) \times 10^{15}$ atom/cm^2, i.e. about 5 atomic layers. Assuming that the oxygen is in the form NiO, this is equivalent to about 10 Å, (iv) the total amount of oxygen on the samples is practically constant; it seems that no isotopic exchange occurs during further oxidation in the air. Analogous techniques were used by Carosella and Comas (1969) to study the oxidation of silicon in ultra high vacuum. They detected O^{18} by proton activation analysis using a large 5 MeV Van de Graaff.

C. Isotopic Exchange and Exchange Currents

Isotopic exchange phenomena have been studied chiefly by observing the change in isotopic concentration of an external, enriched medium, in contact with a sample which presents a very large surface. When the isotopic composition of the surface region of the sample can be directly measured, sensitivity may be enhanced by many orders of magnitude; the depth distribution of the exchanged atoms may yield further information of fundamental importance. The isotopic exchange of O^{18} between an oxide and a solution, assuming that no further growth of the oxide occurs, and that there is no dissolution of the oxide, is determined by the rate of the reversible anion transfer reaction at the interface:

$$(O^{--})_s \rightleftarrows (O^{--})_{ox} \tag{17}$$

where s and ox stand for solution and oxide. This rate is characterized by the exchange current J_{ex}. The net flux of O^{18} atoms into the oxide, $J_{O^{18}}$, is after an exchange time t:

$$J_{O^{18}}(t) = J_{ex}[C_s^0(t) - C_{ox}^0(t)] \tag{18}$$

where $C^0(t)$ is the isotopic O^{18} concentration at the interface. For a small sample and a large enough volume of solution $C_s^0(t) = C_s$ is constant. The net O^{18} uptake $q_{O^{18}}(t)$ is determined by the oxygen self-diffusion coefficient D in the oxide and may be calculated using the classical solution of the diffusion equation in the oxide, with the boundary condition (18). Full calculations may be found in Feuillade (1969). J_{ex} is proportional to the slope of $q^*_{O^{18}}(t)$ at $t = 0$ and D is proportional to the slope of $q^*_{O^{18}}(t)$ plotted in a $\sqrt{t}$ scale, for large t (provided the oxide is much thicker than $\sqrt{Dt}$).

1. Exchange Currents of Anodic Oxide Under Zero Field

Figure 9 shows typical results for isotopic exchange without any applied field of films formed in O^{18} depleted aqueous solutions on tantalum and aluminium ($0.007\% O^{18}$, constant current $10 \, mA/cm^2$ up to $V_{ox} = 20 \, V$, same solution as for Fig. 2) undergoing exchange in a similar solution enriched to $80\% O^{18}$. The use of O^{18}-depleted water greatly enhances sensitivity. The observed saturation value $q_{O^{18}}(\infty) = 7 \times 10^{14}$ atom/cm^2 for tantalum suggests that here D is negligible and the exchange is confined to the first (or first few) molecular layer; one gets $J_{ex} = 0.3 \, \mu A/cm^2$. The reversibility of the process was checked by again dipping the sample in a non-labelled solution: the observed disappearance of O^{18} proved the reversibility (dissolution being negligible). Similar results were found for aluminium. Full details are given by Siejka et al. (1971a).

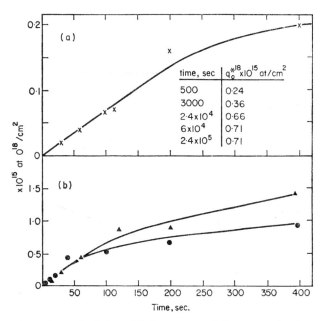

FIG. 9. Isotopic exchange in O^{18} enriched aqueous solutions as a function of time for oxides formed initially at 20 V, 10 mA/cm^2 in O^{18} depleted solutions. Films formed on tantalum (a) and aluminium (b). ▲ unpolished, ● polished samples.

Similar results were found by Feuillade and Jacoud (1969) on nickel hydroxides and by Cherki (1969) on tantalum oxysalts formed in concentrated H_2SO_4. In both cases D was large and could be determined in addition to J_{ex}.

2. Field-induced Exchange

Anodic silicon oxide films (formed in the same solutions as for Fig. 7) exhibit small spontaneous isotopic exchange when maintained for long periods of time in a bath similar to the formation bath but containing highly O^{18}-enriched water. However, it was observed that a fast isotopic exchange takes place when the sample is held under a potential. The O^{18} uptake after time t depends on the ratio F/F_f, where F is the field during exchange and F_f the field of formation. Figure 10 illustrates this phenomenon for a 300 Å thick film. $q^*_{O^{18}}(t)$ varies like $\sqrt{t}$ for times from some minutes to tens of hours, suggesting that J_{ex} is large. For $F = F_f$ saturation is reached after 100 h. The film is then completely labelled, as would be a film formed in the enriched solution. The growth of the film during this time is negligible. The rate of O^{18} uptake decreases exponentially with F/F_f as seen in Fig. 10 for $F = 0.9 F_f$. A detailed study of this phenomenon, as well as of the exchange properties of SiO_2 films at high temperatures in various atomspheres, may be found in Amsel and Croset (1969) and Croset et al. (1969).

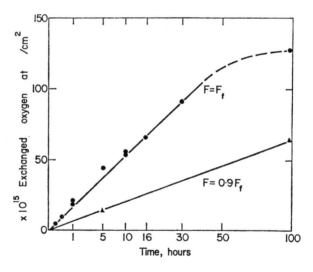

FIG. 10. Field-induced self-diffusion of oxygen in anodic films on silicon kept under a field F for times t in an organic bath containing O^{18} enriched water ($\sqrt{t}$ scale).

D. Film Growth Mechanisms and Atomic Transport Under High Fields

In considering the detailed mechanism of formation of oxide films the question arises as to what is the transport mechanism of the atoms across the oxide layer formed, so as to increase its thickness further. The transport may proceed by interstitial movements or by a vacancy-type mechanism (or a combination of both). In the former case the initial order of the atoms is inversed whereas in the latter their order is conversed; however a mixing of the atoms still occurs, unless the vacancy-type transport is highly correlated. A typical transport experiment consists of first forming a thin layer in a highly O^{18}-enriched bath and then further oxidizing the sample in a similar bath of natural or depleted O^{18} content (in some cases the reverse order is to be preferred). The O^{18} content of the O^{18}–O^{16} "sandwich" is then compared with that of a thin film formed in O^{18} alone: this indicates whether the O^{18} is conserved during the O^{16} treatment. By locating the O^{18} nuclei in the "sandwich" film it can be established further whether their order was conserved and to what extent. This may be achieved by the narrow resonance technique: if the O^{16} layer is facing the beam, the position of the observed resonance energy will be shifted towards higher bombarding energies, so as to allow for the energy loss in the O^{16} layer. In other cases stepwise dissolution of the oxide may allow to trace the O^{18} profile $C(x)$.

Figure 11 shows a typical result for aluminium. A 400 Å thick aluminium oxide film was formed in a 90% O^{18}-enriched aqueous solution of ammonium citrate at high current density. The film was further oxidized in the same conditions in a natural solution up to a total thickness of 2900 Å. The total amount of O^{18} was conserved during the second treatment. Figure 11a shows a shift of the resonance peak equivalent to the 2500 Å film thickness added in the natural bath. Figure 11b shows the result for a "sandwich" film which was stripped off from its aluminium backing and bombarded from the side originally in contact with the metal: no shift occurs here. The second experiment confirms, with a higher precision, that the order of the oxygen atoms is conserved during anodic growth of aluminium barrier layers. This means either that the oxygen sublattice is stationary or that the oxygen moves by a highly correlated vacancy mechanism. Full details on this experiment are given by Amsel and Samuel (1962). Similar results were obtained by Pringle (1969) on tantalum, using the direct observation of the neutrons from the reaction $O^{18}(p, n)F^{18}$ at 3 MeV.

A reversal of the order of the O^{18} atoms was observed in similar experiments by Cherki (1969) in studying oxysalts, by Ortega (1971) during anodic oxidation of zirconium in aqueous solutions and recently by Cherki and Siejka (1971) during porous oxidation of aluminium in H_2SO_4 solutions.

Another typical application of O^{18} tracing to film growth mechanisms is the study of the nature and intensity of the anion transfer which is the basis of the oxidation of bivalent nickel hydroxide, by Feuillade and Jacoud (1969). The results showed the importance of OH^- ion exchange and allowed to elucidate the nature of the reaction leading to trivalent nickel hydroxide.

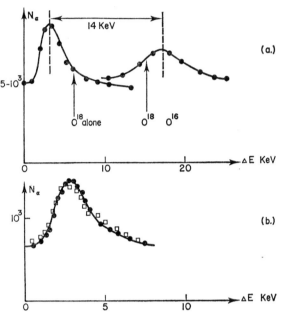

Fig. 11. Oxygen transport during anodic oxidation of aluminium at high current density. The excitation curve $N_\alpha(E_0)$ of the O^{18} (p, α) N^{15} reaction near the 1165 keV resonance is shown ($E_0 = 1163$ keV $+ \Delta E$) for samples oxidized in O^{18} alone and for samples oxidized in turn in O^{18} and O^{16}. (a) bombardment from electrolyte side, showing a 14 keV shift of $N_\alpha(E_0)$ (b) bombardment from the metal side showing no shift: ● O^{18} alone, □ $O^{18} + O^{16}$ treatment.

IV. Conclusion

The direct observation of nuclear reactions is a convenient analytical tool for studying numerous processes in electrochemistry. In some cases activation analysis by charged particles may also be used as indicated. The potential applications of these methods may be further extended by determining nuclei like C^{13} or N^{15} for tracer studies. These techniques have also been applied to other fields like metallurgy, high temperature oxidation processes, oxygen self-diffusion in bulk crystalline oxides, concentration profiles in oxygen-implanted semiconductors, etc. Their applications to catalysis and other domains like biological phenomena is being considered.

References

Amsel, G. and Croset, M. (1969). Proceedings Electrochem. Soc. Meeting (May 1969), New York, p. 24.

Amsel, G. and David, D. (1969). *Rev. Phys. Appl.* **4**, 383 and in Proc. *Internat. Conf. MIS Structures, Grenoble* (June 1969), p. 243.

Amsel, G. and Samuel, D. (1962). *J. Phys. Chem. Solids.* **23**, 1707.

Amsel, G. and Samuel, D. (1967). *Anal. Chem.* **39**, 1689.

Amsel, G., Béranger, B., de Gelas, B. and Lacombe, P. (1968). *J. Appl. Phys.* **39**, 2246.

Amsel, G., Cherki, C., Feuillade, G. and Nadai, J. P. (1969a). *J. Phys. Chem. Solids.* **30**, 2117.

Amsel, G., David, D., Béranger, G., Boisot, P., de Gelas, B. and Lacombe, P. (1969b). *J. Nucl. Matls.* **29**, 144.

Amsel, G., Nadai, J. P., d'Artemare, E., David, D., Girard, E. and Moulin, J. (1971a). *Nucl. Instr. Meths.* **92**, 481.

Amsel, G., d'Artemare, E. and Girard, E. (1971b) to be published.

Barret, M. A. (1964). "Ellipsometry in the measurements of surfaces and thin films". N.B.S. Publ. 856, Washington.

Béranger, G., Boisot, P., Lacombe, P., Amsel, G. and David, D. (1970). *Rev. Phys. Appl.* **5**, 383.

Carosella, C. A. and Comas, J. (1969). *Surf. Sci.* **15**, 303.

Cherki, C. (1969). Thesis, Paris University.

Cherki, C. (1971). *Electrochim. Acta.* **16**, 1727.

Cherki, C., and Siejka, J. (1971). to be published.

Croset, M., Rigo, S. and Amsel, G. (1969). *Proc. Internat. Conf. MIS Structures Grenoble*, (June 1969), p. 259.

Croset, M., Rigo, S. and Amsel, G. (1971a) *Appl. Phys. Letters* **19**, 33.

Croset, M., Petreanu, E., Samuel, D., Amsel, G. and Nadai, J. P. (1971b). *J. Electrochem. Soc.* **118**, 717.

Faust, J. W. Jr. (1969). *Surf. Sci.* **13**, 60.

Feuillade, G. (1969). *Electrochim. Acta.* **14**, 317.

Feuillade, G. and Jacoud, R. (1969). *Electrochim. Acta.* **14**, 1297.

Gyulai, J., Meyer, O., Mayer, J. W. and Rodriguez, V. (1970). *Appl. Phys. Letters* **16**, 232.

Maurel, B., Dieumegard, D. and Amsel, G. (1971). to be published.

Möller, E. and Starfelt, N. (1967). *Nucl. Instr. Meths.* **50**, 225.

Ortega, C. (1971). to be published.

Pringle, J. P. S. (1969). Proc. Electrochem. Soc. Meeting (May 1969), New York p. 17.

Siejka, J., Nadai, J. P. and Amsel, G. (1971a). *J. Electrochem. Soc.* **118**, 727.

Siejka, J., Cherki, C. and Yahalom, J. (1971b). *Electrochim. Acta.* (in press).

Turos, A. and Wilhelmi, Z. (1968). *Nukleonika.* **13**, 975.

Turos, A. and Wilhelmi, Z. (1969). *Nukleonika.* **14**, 319.

Young, J. (1961). "Anodic oxide films". Academic Press, New York and London.

B. TRANSPORT PROCESSES

5. BASIC THEORY OF IONIC TRANSPORT PROCESSES

R. J. Friauf

Department of Physics and Astronomy, University of Kansas, Lawrence, Kansas, U.S.A.

I. Introduction

Transport of charge and matter is readily observable in ionic crystals at elevated temperatures. Figs 1 and 2 display a representative portion of the extensive measurements of ionic conductivity and diffusion in these solids.

It should be noticed that the results cover many orders of magnitude and a wide range of both temperatures and materials. Diffusion occurs to some extent, of course, in all solids, but in ionic crystals the ions also carry electric charges in their displacements. This phenomenon allows the motion of ions to be studied by electrical as well as diffusion measurements, and we shall see later that such a possibility offers great advantages for determining the responsible mechanisms. Atomic transport processes also play a major role in many other properties of solids—sintering, tarnishing reactions, precipitation

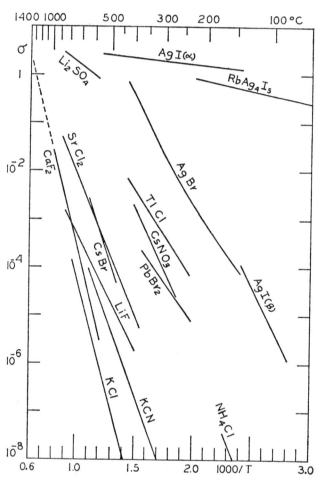

FIG. 1. Ionic conductivity. The conductivity in ohm^{-1} cm^{-1} is shown for a number of typical solid state ionic conductors. Values are taken from the tables in the Appendix (Volume 2), and the length of the solid line indicates the actual range of measurements. The upper end of the line marks the melting temperature.

of separate phases, electrolysis, fuel cells, dielectric loss, and the photographic process—and the development of fundamental understanding has been mutually beneficial to all of these fields.

How is it possible to have large scale displacements of atoms, when the

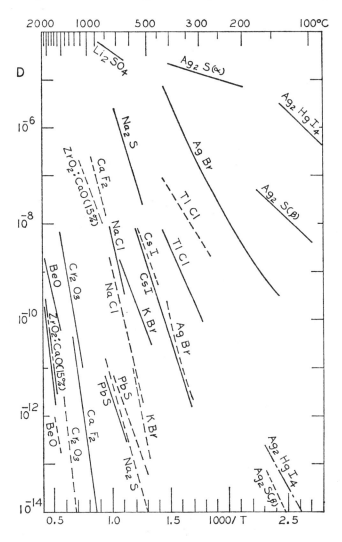

Fig. 2. Diffusion in ionic crystals. The diffusion coefficient in cm^2 sec^{-1} is shown for a number of typical ionic crystals. ——— cation, ——— — ——— second cation in mixed crystals, ------ anion. Values are taken from the tables in the Appendix (Volume 2), and the length of the solid line indicates the actual range of measurements. (In many instances the upper end of the line does *not* correspond to the melting temperature in this figure.)

usual picture of an ionic crystal is a close packed structure of only slightly deformable ions? The ions undergo thermal vibration about their equilibrium positions, but the root-mean-square amplitude is never more than a few tenths of the interatomic spacing, and the oscillatory nature of the motion does not lead to any net displacement. The answer is found in the presence of point defects in the structure of a real, rather than an ideal crystal—vacancies and interstitial ions that can move by successive jumps from one unit cell to the next and can thereby give rise to the transport of charge and mass through the crystal. These defects are present in amounts ranging from a few parts per million in a rather pure crystal at low temperatures up to anywhere from 0·01 to 1 mol % at temperatures near the melting point or in intentionally or unintentionally impure materials.

A number of possible types of point defects and atomic jump processes are shown in Fig. 3, which is a schematic representation of a crystal plane of the NaCl structure. Single vacancies may be present as Schottky defects, and one of the nearest neighbour (n.n.) ions can from time to time jump into the vacancy, giving contributions to both ionic conductivity and diffusion. Neutral vacancy pairs may also be present, and some of the n.n. ions (4 in the NaCl structure) can jump into the vacancy pair without causing it to dissociate; these jumps contribute to diffusion but not conductivity. The presence of impurity ions, such as the divalent cations shown in the figure, causes an excess concentration of cation vacancies, which make their usual contributions to the transport properties. There are also associated complexes of a divalent cation and cation vacancy; jumps of the cation vacancy around the impurity appear as dielectric loss, and jumps of the impurity ion are important for diffusion of the impurity. In some substances, notably the silver halides, interstitial cations are present as Frenkel defects along with cation vacancies, and the interstitial ions contribute to ionic conductivity and cation diffusion by either direct jumps or interstitialcy or dumb-bell motion. A final possibility is afforded by direct exchange of neighbouring ions or by a ring process. Such mechanisms could contribute to diffusion although not ionic conductivity, but no substantial experimental evidence has yet been offered for their occurrence.

In this Chapter we shall first describe in Section II the basic properties of point defects. Next we shall be concerned in Section III with their contribution to ionic conductivity and in Section IV with long range Coulomb interactions. Then in Section V we shall consider diffusion processes and their relation to ionic conductivity. Finally in Section VI we shall summarize the principal experimental methods that can be used to elucidate the nature of transport processes in crystalline solids and shall also provide a brief summary of the principal types of defects that are known to cause the results of Figs 1 and 2.

There is one important aspect of transport processes that can be illustrated by very simple considerations. Suppose that there is only one kind of mobile defect in a particular circumstance, such as NaCl doped with Ca^{2+}, where cation vacancies are predominant. As we shall show later in more detail, the ionic conductivity is then given by

$$\sigma = \sigma_+ = eN\mu_+ x_+,$$

where e is the charge on the electron, N is the number of molecules per unit volume, and x_+ is the mole fraction of cation vacancies. Furthermore the mobility μ_+ turns out to be directly proportional to the jump frequency ν_+ indicated in Fig. 3. Thus the conductivity, which is the directly observable quantity, depends on the product of two factors—the defect concentration and the jump frequency—and this result is found to hold true for all macroscopic transport properties. One implication is that we must therefore be concerned with the description of these two aspects of the microscopic properties of each kind of defect considered in the next section. Another consequence is that a great deal of experimental effort and ingenuity will always be involved in trying to separate these two characteristics of the defect.

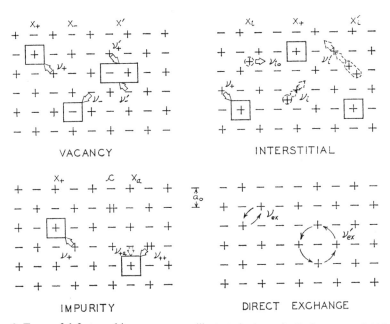

FIG. 3. Types of defects and jump processes, illustrated schematically for a crystal with the NaCl structure. The dotted circles indicate that the interstitial ions are $\frac{1}{2}a_0$ above the lattice plane shown here, and the dotted arrows indicate jumps that occur at an angle with respect to this plane.

II. Properties of Defects

A. Defect Concentrations in Pure Crystals

Let us consider first an ionic crystal of the type MX, such as NaCl or AgBr. The perfect crystal would have the lowest internal energy, but a real crystal must always contain a certain number of defects in thermodynamic equilibrium. The production of Schottky defects, for instance, can be envisaged as the removal of a cation and an anion from the interior to the surface of the crystal, leaving a cation and an anion vacancy, respectively, and can be represented by the reaction equation†

$$\text{crystal} \leftrightarrow V_M' + V_X^{\bullet}. \qquad (1A)$$

This process requires energy but also allows an increase in configurational entropy, so that the usual procedure for minimizing the free energy gives

$$x_{OS}^2 = x_+ \, x_- = \exp\left(-G_S/kT\right), \qquad (1B)$$

where x_+ and x_- are the mole fractions of cation and anion vacancies.‡ The Gibbs free energy G_S is usually written as

$$G_S = H_S - TS_S, \qquad (1C)$$

where H_S is the enthalpy of formation of a pair of separated Schottky defects. S_S is the corresponding entropy change (in addition to the configurational entropy, which has already been treated explicitly) and arises from changes in vibrational frequencies in the vicinity of the vacancies (Dekker, 1957, pp. 161–162). The Schottky product then becomes

$$x_{OS}^2 = x_+ \, x_- = \exp\left(S_S/k\right)\exp\left(-H_S/kT\right). \qquad (1D)$$

Thus the entropy S_S and enthalpy H_S of formation appear as parameters that determine respectively the pre-exponential factor and the temperature dependence.

It should be emphasized that the Schottky product expressed in eqn (1B) or (1D) must always be satisfied when the crystal is in thermodynamic equilibrium, no matter what impurities or other types of defects may be

† The notation is from Kröger (1964), who also gives a systematic treatment of the more extensive situation involving interactions among electronic defects (free or trapped electrons and holes) as well as ionic defects. The symbol shows the type of defect, the subscript the position in the lattice, and the superscript the excess charge: e.g. V_{Na}' means a cation vacancy (with a negative excess charge), $Ag_i^{\bullet}$ an interstitial Ag^+ ion, and $(V_{Na}V_{Cl})^{\times}$ a neutral vacancy pair.

‡ It is usually convenient to express defect concentrations as mole fractions, and this will be done uniformly throughout this Chapter. The actual volume concentrations are then Nx_+, for instance, where N is the number of molecules per unit volume.

present. For a pure crystal with only Schottky defects the condition of electric neutrality requires $x_+ = x_-$ in addition, giving immediately

$$x_+ = x_- = x_{OS} = \exp\left(S_S/2k\right)\exp\left(-H_S/2kT\right). \tag{1E}$$

Since the size of the product increases rapidly with temperature, this condition of *intrinsic* defect formation is found only at high temperatures in relatively pure crystals, as seen in Fig. 4 for NaCl.

It is also possible to form Frenkel defects, as in the silver halides, by removing a cation from a lattice site and inserting it into an interstitial position.

$$\text{crystal} \leftrightarrow V_M' + M_i^{\bullet} \tag{2A}$$

The corresponding Frenkel product is

$$x_{OF}{}^2 = x_+ x_i = z_i \exp\left(S_F/k\right)\exp\left(-H_F/kT\right), \tag{2B}$$

where z_i is the ratio of interstitial to lattice sites per unit cell ($z_i = 2$ for the NaCl structure). In a pure crystal with only Frenkel defects a simplification analogous to eqn (1E) occurs for the intrinsic concentrations. For a particular crystal the type of defect with the lowest formation enthalpy is usually predominant, but when several types are present together the concentrations are interrelated by the simultaneous operation of several of the mass action equations such as (1D) and (2B). For AgBr at high temperatures, for instance, where the Frenkel defect concentration is much larger than the Schottky, the concentration of bromine vacancies is suppressed even further by the large number of silver vacancies from the Frenkel defects.

$$x_- = x_{OS}{}^2/x_{OF} = C \exp\left[-(H_S - \tfrac{1}{2}H_F)/kT\right]. \tag{3}$$

Since $H_F < H_S$ the temperature dependence is also more extreme than it would be if only Schottky defects were present. These effects are seen for the diffusion of Br in AgBr in Fig. 2.

Whenever Schottky defects are present in an ionic crystal, it is clear from Fig. 3 that some of the single vacancies can be associated to form vacancy pairs. The most straightforward procedure is to regard the vacancy pairs as formed from the perfect crystal.

$$\text{crystal} \leftrightarrow (V_M V_X)^{\times} \tag{4A}$$

Since there are z' equivalent orientations for a vacancy pair ($z' = 6$ for the NaCl structure), the concentration is

$$x' = z' \exp\left(-G'/kT\right) = z' \exp\left(S'/k\right)\exp\left(-H'/kT\right), \tag{4B}$$

where $H' < H_S$ because less energy is required to remove an anion from a site adjacent to a cation vacancy than from a site in the perfect lattice. It must be emphasized that eqn (4B) indicates categorically that the vacancy pair

160   Robert J. Friauf

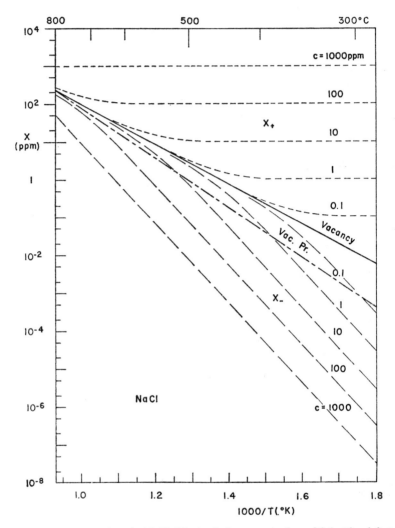

FIG. 4. Defect concentrations in NaCl. The intrinsic concentration of Schottky defects is taken from an analysis of conductivity measurements for doped crystals (Dreyfus and Nowick, 1962a). The concentration of vacancy pairs is estimated from diffusion experiments (Nelson and Friauf, 1970), with the assumption that $v_c'/v_a' = 10$ (see Section V.E) at all temperatures. The concentrations are expressed in mole parts per million (ppm), and the cation and anion vacancy concentrations are calculated from the simple theory without association.

concentration is independent of the impurity content of the crystal. Another point of view is sometimes useful, in which the formation of vacancy pairs is regarded as the coalescing of single vacancies,

$$V_M' + V_X^\bullet \leftrightarrow (V_M V_X)^\times, \tag{5A}$$

giving a mass action equation

$$x'/x_+ x_- = z' \exp(\Delta S'/k) \exp(-\Delta H'/kT). \tag{5B}$$

By comparison to eqns (1D) and (4B) the binding energy for a vacancy pair is found to be

$$-\Delta H' = H_S - H'; \tag{5C}$$

the binding occurs because of the Coulomb attraction between the oppositely charged single vacancies. The lack of dependence of x' on impurity content is confirmed by eqn (5B) since the Schottky product $x_+ x_-$ is also independent of the presence of impurities. The fractional concentration of vacancy pairs relative to single vacancies is

$$x'/x_{OS} = C \exp\left[-(H' - \tfrac{1}{2}H_S)/kT\right] = C \exp\left[-(\Delta H' + \tfrac{1}{2}H_S)/kT\right]. \tag{5D}$$

It is often found that $H' - \tfrac{1}{2}H_S > 0$, which means that the *relative* importance of vacancy pairs *increases* as the temperature is *raised*. At first thought it would seem that vacancy pairs should tend to dissociate at higher temperatures, and this would indeed be true if the single vacancy concentration were constant. But the Schottky product also increases with temperature, and when $\tfrac{1}{2}H_S > |\Delta H'|$ the increase is even more rapid than the tendency of vacancy pairs to dissociate, thereby driving the reaction in eqn (5A) to the right. This effect is shown in Fig. 4 for NaCl, where $H' = 1\cdot27$ eV (Tharmalingam and Lidiard, 1961), $H_S = 2\cdot18$ eV (Dreyfus and Nowick, 1962a), and $H' - \tfrac{1}{2}H_S = +0\cdot18$ eV (Nelson and Friauf, 1970).

B. Defect Concentrations in Impure Crystals

When an aliovalent impurity is introduced into an ionic crystal, e.g. Ca^{2+} in NaCl, the largest effect is produced by the difference in charge from the ions of the host crystal. This is compensated by the presence of additional defects, cation vacancies for example. (When the defects are strictly ionic the type of additional defect can also be seen on structural grounds, e.g. replacing two molecules of NaCl by one of $CaCl_2$.) For a mole fraction c of divalent impurity the equations governing the defect concentrations are

$$x_+ x_- = x_{OS}^2(T), \tag{6A}$$

$$x_+ = x_- + c, \tag{6B}$$

the first being simply the Schottky product and the second expressing the condition of electric neutrality. The concentrations are readily found to be

$$x_+ = \tfrac{1}{2}c\{[1 + (2x_{OS}/c)^2]^{\frac{1}{2}} + 1\}, \tag{6C}$$

$$x_- = \tfrac{1}{2}c\{[1 + (2x_{OS}/c)^2]^{\frac{1}{2}} - 1\}. \tag{6D}$$

When $c \ll x_{OS}$ the results reduce to $x_+ = x_- = x_{OS}$ as expected. When $c \gg x_{OS}$ expansion of the radical gives $x_+ = c$ and $x_- = x_{OS}^2/c$. (As soon as it is established that $x_+ = c$ the second result can also be obtained directly from the Schottky product.) Figure 5 illustrates the approach of x_+ to c at large c, and Fig. 4 shows the suppression of x_- at large c for typical impurity concentrations.

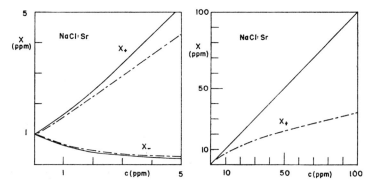

FIG. 5. Isothermal curves of defect concentrations. The curves are drawn for $T = 454°C$ where the intrinsic concentration is $x_{OS} = 10^{-6} = 1$ ppm in NaCl (Dreyfus and Nowick, 1962a). The solid curves are calculated from the simple theory of eqns (6) without association. The dash-dot curves are calculated from eqns (7) and (9) with association, for $S_a = 0$ and $-H_a = 0.53$ eV as suggested for Sr^{2+} in NaCl (Brown and Hoodless, 1967).

The extra charge of a divalent cation impurity Me^{2+} also tends to cause an association of the oppositely charged cation vacancies.

$$V_M' + Me_M^{\bullet} \leftrightarrow (V_M\, Me_M)^{\times} \tag{7A}$$

Hence some portion x of the total impurity concentration c is associated into impurity-vacancy complexes, leaving only an amount $c - x_a$ of free impurities to influence the defect concentrations through the electric neutrality condition. The corresponding mass action law is

$$\frac{x_a}{x_+\,(c - x_a)} = z_a \exp\left(\frac{S_a}{k}\right) \exp\left(-\frac{H_a}{kT}\right) = K_a(T), \tag{7B}$$

where z_a is the number of equivalent orientations of the complex ($z_a = 12$ in the NaCl structure) and $-H_a > 0$ is the binding energy for association. The totality of equations for the defect concentrations becomes

$$x_+ = x_- + (c - x_a),\qquad\text{(8A)}$$

$$x_+ x_- = x_{OS}^2(T),\qquad\text{(8B)}$$

$$x_a/x_+(c - x_a) = K_a(T).\qquad\text{(8C)}$$

With the definitions

$$\xi \equiv x_+/x_{OS},\quad P_a \equiv x_{OS} K_a,\qquad\text{(9A)}$$

substitution of the first two equations into the third gives

$$(c/x_{OS}) = (\xi - \xi^{-1})(1 + \xi P_a).\qquad\text{(9B)}$$

This cubic equation for ξ is most conveniently solved by iteration, after which

$$x_+ = x_{OS}\xi,\quad x_- = x_{OS}/\xi,\qquad\text{(9C)}$$

and the fractional degree of association of complexes is

$$p \equiv x_a/c = \xi P_a/(1 + \xi P_a).\qquad\text{(9D)}$$

When $c/x_{OS} \ll 1$, the solution reduces to $\xi = 1$, giving $x_+ = x_- = x_{OS}$ as expected. When $c/x_{OS} \gg 1$, we find also $\xi \gg 1$, and eventually when $\xi P_a \gg 1$, we have $\xi = \sqrt{c/x_{OS} P_a}$. The effectiveness of the impurity is, indeed, reduced by association, as seen in Figs 5 and 6, where the degree of association is appreciable because of the fairly low temperatures and rather large binding energies: in Fig. 5, $p = 19\%$ at $c = 5$ ppm, and 66% at 100 ppm; and in Fig. 6, $p = 70\%$ at 400°C for $c = 333$ ppm (Fuller, 1971). The tendency of x_+ to be proportional to the square root of c for large c is evident in Fig. 5 (see also Fig. 11b), but this extreme dependence is not usually observed in practice. The truth lies somewhere between the results with and without association, partly because of the influence of long range interactions as shown in Fig. 6 (see also Fig. 13).

When a large amount of impurity is incorporated into a crystal grown from the melt, it is quite likely that the solubility limit will be exceeded at lower temperatures, and this leads to a precipitation of the impurity

$$V_M' + Me_M^\bullet + 2X_X^x \leftrightarrow MeX_2 \text{ (ppt)}.\qquad\text{(10A)}$$

Since the anion mole fraction is unity and the precipitate is a condensed phase, the corresponding mass action law is

$$\frac{1}{x_+(c - x_a)} = \exp\left(\frac{S_p}{k}\right)\exp\left(-\frac{H_p}{kT}\right) = K_p(T),\qquad\text{(10B)}$$

where $-H_p > 0$ is the precipitation energy. Usually precipitation occurs at quite low temperatures where x_{OS} is very small, so that we may write, with eqn (8A), $c - x_a = x_+ - x_- \approx x_+$, and then find

$$x_+ = \exp\left(- S_p/2k\right) \exp\left(H_p/2kT\right) = [K_p(T)]^{\frac{1}{2}}. \tag{10C}$$

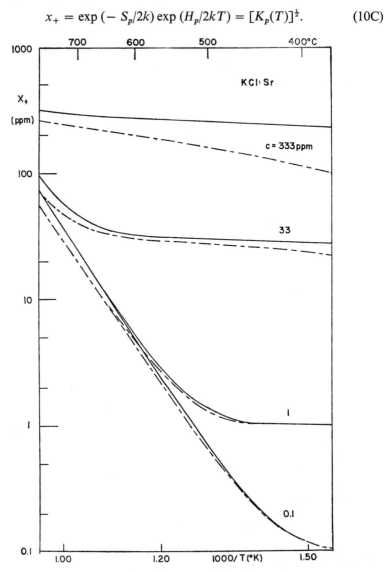

FIG. 6. Defect concentrations in KCl:Sr (Fuller, 1971). The dash-dot curves are calculated with association for $S_S = 5\cdot4k$, $H_S = 2\cdot26$ eV, $S_a = 0$, and $-H_a = 0\cdot42$ eV. The solid curves show the effect of long range interactions according to the Debye–Hückel–Lidiard theory discussed in Section IV.

C. Jump Frequencies

The ability of point defects to contribute to transport processes is determined by the frequency of jumping between neighbouring sites in the crystal lattice. Hence we introduce total jump frequencies v_+, v_-, v_i for cation vacancies, anion vacancies, and interstitial ions, respectively. The temperature dependence is given, for example, by

$$v_+ = z_+ v_0 \exp\left(-G_{m+}/kT\right), \tag{11A}$$

where z_+ is the number of cations that can jump into the vacancy ($z_+ = 12$ for NaCl), v_0 is an attempt frequency to be discussed shortly, and G_{m+} is the Gibbs free energy associated with the jump of a cation into a vacancy. The basic physical picture is a classical one since quantum effects are unimportant for the high temperatures and large masses usually involved in atomic transport processes.† A cation next to a vacancy usually bounces back and forth in its potential well with a frequency v_0, but occasionally it acquires enough excess energy from thermal fluctuations to surmount the barrier and jump into the vacancy. Thus G_{m+} may be identified with the saddle point through which the jumping ion passes. Usually G_{m+} is decomposed into an enthalpy and an entropy.

$$G_{m+} = H_{m+} - T S_{m+}, \tag{11B}$$

giving

$$v_+ = z_+ v_0 \exp\left(S_{m+}/k\right) \exp\left(-H_{m+}/kT\right). \tag{11C}$$

In a general sense S_{m+} is related to the number of possible paths through the saddle point configuration, but detailed interpretations differ. Furthermore there are no directly applicable theoretical calculations of either S_{m+} or the local vibration frequency v_0. Hence for practical purposes we may make a standard choice by setting v_0 equal to the Debye frequency, which is certainly the proper order of magnitude, and then regarding S_{m+} as an empirical parameter for the particular defect.

The treatment for anion vacancies is entirely analogous, with the expression for v_- involving z_- (which will be the same as z_+ for a simple MX structure), S_{m-}, and H_{m-}. No subscript is needed on v_0 since for convenience we have chosen the Debye frequency as the common attempt frequency for all types of defects, leaving local differences to be absorbed into S_{m-}, for instance. For interstitial ions we must distinguish in Fig. 3 between the direct interstitial jump with v_{i0} and the *interstitialcy*, or indirect interstitial, jump with v_i. For the interstitialcy jump the interstitial ion moves toward a lattice ion,

† The case of hydrogen might be an exception, where tunneling is sometimes possible because of the small mass.

knocks it into a neighbouring interstitial position, and then occupies the vacated lattice site. For the silver halides

$$v_i = z_i v_0 \exp(S_{mi}/k) \exp(-H_{mi}/kT), \tag{11D}$$

with $z_i = 4$, and it must be remembered that two ions participate in each jump. A vacancy pair can move through the lattice either by having a cation jump into it with

$$v_+' = z_+' v_0 \exp(S_{m+}'/k) \exp(-H_{m+}'/kT), \tag{11E}$$

where $z_+' = z_-' = 4$ for NaCl, or by having an anion jump into it with v_-'. It is to be emphasized that v_-' is not necessarily or usually equal to v_+' since in general S_{m-}' and H_{m-}' will differ from S_{m+}' and H_{m+}'. For an associated complex of a divalent cation impurity and a cation vacancy in Fig. 3 two jumps may occur without dissociation: v_{++} in which the divalent ion exchanges positions with the vacancy, and v_{+a} in which the vacancy moves around the divalent ion.† The temperature dependence is

$$v_{++} = z_{++} v_0 \exp(S_{m++}/k) \exp(-H_{m++}/kT), \tag{11F}$$

where $z_{++} = 1$ and $z_{+a} = 4$ for the NaCl structure. Finally there is the possibility indicated in Fig. 3 of a direct exchange or ring mechanism, which would have

$$v_{ex} = z_+ v_0 \exp(S_{ex}/k) \exp(-H_{ex}/kT), \tag{11G}$$

but there is no experimental evidence for these kinds of jumps.

D. Diffusion and Mobility of Defects

The measurement of transport properties in laboratory experiments is described in terms of continuum equations because the atomic scale is too small to be noticeable. The diffusion coefficient D, for instance, is defined by Fick's first law,

$$\mathbf{J} = -D\,\mathbf{grad}\,n, \tag{12A}$$

which relates the *particle* current density J to the gradient of the volume concentration $n = Nx$ of the diffusing particle. With the equation of conservation of particles (and assuming D to be independent of position and concentration), we find the diffusion equation

$$\frac{\partial n}{\partial t} = -\mathrm{div}\,\mathbf{J} = D\nabla^2 n. \tag{12B}$$

† The jump frequencies v_{+a} and v_{++} are often denoted by w_1 and w_2, respectively, in a widely used notation introduced by Lidiard (1955, 1957).

For a point source Q in an isotropic medium this has a solution (Jost, 1952, p. 18)

$$n(r, t) = Q(4\pi Dt)^{-3/2} \exp(-r^2/4Dt), \tag{12C}$$

which gives a mean square displacement in three dimensions of

$$\langle r^2 \rangle = 6 Dt \tag{12D}$$

Similarly the mobility is defined as the drift velocity per unit field when an electric field is present,

$$\mathbf{v}_{\text{drift}} = \mu\mathbf{E}, \tag{13A}$$

and this gives a total electric current density

$$\mathbf{J}_{\text{elec}} = q\mathbf{v}_{\text{drift}}\, n = q\mu n\mathbf{E} = \sigma\mathbf{E}, \tag{13B}$$

where q is the magnitude of the charge on the defect. The last form defines the conductivity σ for later use.

The easiest and most straightforward way of relating jump frequencies to defect transport properties is by regarding the thermally induced jumps of a defect through the lattice as a random walk problem in diffusion. We consider here only cubic lattices, for which the diffusion coefficient is isotropic.† For a sequence of N jumps the vector displacement is

$$\mathbf{r} = \mathbf{a}_1 + \mathbf{a}_2 + \dots \mathbf{a}_N = \sum_{i=1}^{N} \mathbf{a}_i, \tag{14A}$$

and the mean square displacement from the starting point is

$$\langle r^2 \rangle_{\text{av}} = \Sigma_i \langle a_i^2 \rangle_{\text{av}} + 2\Sigma_i\Sigma_j \langle \mathbf{a}_i \cdot \mathbf{a}_{i+j} \rangle_{\text{av}}, \tag{14B}$$

where the average is taken over a large number of possible jump sequences. The first term simply gives Na_+^2 since all jumps have the same length a_+ for a cation vacancy, and the average over the second term gives zero because the jumps have random directions. With $N = v_+ t$ we compare to eqn (12D),

$$6d_+ t = \langle r^2 \rangle_{\text{av}} = Na_+^2 = v_+ ta_+^2, \tag{14C}$$

† Other lattices can be treated in a similar way by calculating the displacements along three mutually perpendicular coordinate axes to obtain the principal values of the diffusion tensor.

and identify the *microscopic*† diffusion coefficient of a vacancy as

$$d_+ = \tfrac{1}{6}v_+\, a_+{}^2. \tag{14D}$$

This very simple and useful result is strictly correct for any isotropic diffusion mechanism, in either a cubic crystal or a liquid or gas, with v_+ as the *total* number of jumps per second and a_+ as the *actual* (or average, in case of a fluid) jump distance. For the NaCl structure $a_+ = \sqrt{2}a_0$, where a_0 is the cation–anion separation (a_0 = half the crystallographic unit cell edge), and in combination with eqn (11C) with $z_+ = 12$ we find

$$d_+ = \tfrac{1}{3}v_+\, a_0{}^2 = 4v_0\, a_0{}^2 \exp\,(S_{m+}/k)\exp\,(-H_{m+}/kT). \tag{14E}$$

When an electric field is applied there is a slight enhancement of the probability of a cation for jumping in the direction of the field, with a corresponding diminution for jumping in the opposite direction. Thus a slight drift along the field is superimposed on the random motion of the defect (the effect is slight because the fractional change in probability is much less than one for ordinary fields), and this gives the drift velocity in eqn (13A). As the physical picture indicates, there is a close relationship between mobility and diffusion, which is expressed by the *microscopic Einstein relation* (or Nernst–Einstein relation)

$$\mu_+ = (q/kT)\,d_+. \tag{15A}$$

This relation can be deduced on very general grounds of statistical mechanics (Mott and Gurney, 1948, p. 63) and must always be valid in its microscopic form. For the NaCl structure the expression obtained from eqn (14E) with $q = e$ is

$$\mu_+ = 4(e/kT)v_0\, a_0{}^2 \exp\,(S_{m+}/k)\exp\,(-H_{m+}/kT). \tag{15B}$$

It is also possible to obtain the above expressions for d_+ and μ_+ by considering the number of vacancies on each plane of the crystal lattice. The diffusion coefficient is then obtained from eqn (12A) by calculating the net flux of particles crossing between neighbouring planes when a concentration gradient exists, and the mobility is obtained in a similar fashion from eqn (13B) when an electric field is present (Dekker, 1957, Chapter 7 or Mott and Gurney, 1948, Chapter II). The chief advantage of this procedure is that it relates the atomic properties directly to the continuum equations, and it also

---

† It is convenient to use small letters for *microscopic* quantities and capital letters for the corresponding *macroscopic* quantities, viz. d_+ and D_+ for diffusion coefficients, μ_+ and M_+ for mobilities.

shows how the results should be modified if an extremely large concentration gradient or electric field exists. The results agree, of course, with eqns (14E) and (15B), and in particular give a detailed confirmation of the microscopic Einstein relation of eqn (15A).

III. Ionic Conductivity

A. General Expression

The motion of charged defects in an electric field gives rise to an ionic conductivity, which usually dominates the electrical behaviour of an ionic crystal because electronic conductivity is absent. The conductivity is obtained from the form of Ohm's law in eqn (13B) that says that the current density is proportional to the electric field,

$$\sigma_+ = q\mu_+ n_+ = qN\mu_+ x_+, \tag{16A}$$

where the concentration $n_+ = Nx_+$ is related to the mole fraction x_+ by the number of molecules per unit volume N. As emphasized in the introduction the macroscopic transport property represented by the conductivity depends on both the concentration and the mobility (or jump frequency) of the atomic defects. Furthermore σ_+ represents only the effect of cation vacancies; for an MX crystal with Schottky defects, for instance, the general expression for the total conductivity should also include the contribution from anion vacancies.

$$\sigma = \sigma_+ + \sigma_- = qN(\mu_+ x_+ + \mu_- x_-) \tag{16B}$$

B. Temperature Dependence for One Mobile Defect

One type of defect may often dominate the conductivity, either because its mobility is much larger in the intrinsic region where the defect concentrations are equal, or because its concentration is much larger in impurity controlled regions. This is the common situation, for instance, for many of the alkali halides with the NaCl structure, where cation vacancies usually have the larger mobility and where in addition their concentration is enhanced by divalent cation impurities, which are much more prevalent than the corresponding anion impurities. In such circumstances the simpler expression of eqn (16A) may be used, and the temperature dependence is determined directly by the product $\mu_+ x_+$.

$$\sigma_+ T = qN\mu_+ x_+ T = A \exp\left(-W/kT\right) \tag{17A}$$

The conductivity is multiplied by the absolute temperature in order to remove the pre-exponential factor of $1/T$ that appears explicitly in eqn (15B) for the mobility; a plot of log (σT) versus $1/T$ as in Figs 7–9 then gives W directly from the slope.†

$$SI = -\frac{d \log (\sigma T)}{d (1000/T)} = \frac{W}{k(\ln 10) \times 10^3} \qquad (17B)$$

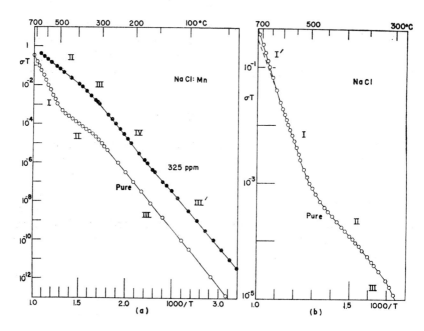

Fig. 7. Cation conductivity in NaCl (Kirk and Pratt, 1967). In (a) the curve for the pure crystal shows Stages I (intrinsic), II (extrinsic), and III (association), and the curve for the heavily doped crystal shows Stages II, III, IV (precipitation), and III′ (association with precipitation frozen). Part (b) for the pure crystal shows the additional rise in Stage I′ from the anion contribution to the conductivity. The conductivity is expressed in ohm^{-1} cm^{-1}.

† In a great deal of the earlier work the factor of $1/T$ was *not* considered explicitly, and an empirical plot was simply made of

$$\sigma = \sigma_0 \exp(-W'/kT).$$

There is no direct experimental distinction since a factor of $1/T$ causes only a very slight curvature on such a plot over a limited temperature range. There is an overall change in slope, however, such that

$$W = W' + kT,$$

where T is an average temperature for the plotted range. Even for 900°C the correction of kT is only 0·1 eV, but it should be kept in mind when comparing the work of different authors.

A convenient form of this result with W in eV is

$$W(\text{eV}) = Sl/5 \cdot 040, \tag{17C}$$

which is equally valid, of course, for plots of diffusion coefficients or other quantities with an Arrhenius type of temperature dependence.

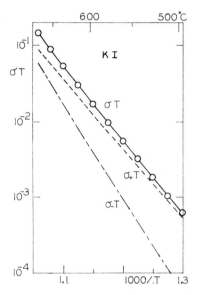

FIG. 8. Cation and anion vacancy contributions to the total conductivity of KI in the intrinsic region (Chandra and Rolfe, 1970). The conductivity is expressed in ohm^{-1} cm^{-1}.

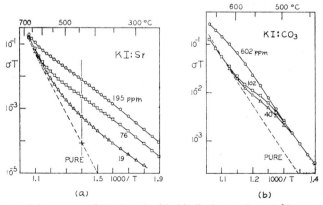

FIG. 9. Conductivity curves of KI doped with (a) divalent cations Sr^{2+} and (b) divalent anions CO_3^{2-} (Chandra and Rolfe, 1970). The conductivity is expressed in ohm^{-1} cm^{-1}.

In all temperature ranges the apparent activation energy W receives a contribution of H_{m+} from the mobility. The remaining portion of W is determined by the temperature dependence of the concentration, which varies according to the relative importance of intrinsic defects, impurities, association, and precipitation. At the highest temperatures the intrinsic defects are dominant and $x_+ = x_{OS}$, giving

$$\sigma_+ T = 4(Ne^2/k)v_0\, a_0{}^2 \exp\left[(S_{m+} + \tfrac{1}{2}S_S)/k\right] \exp\left[-(H_{m+} + \tfrac{1}{2}H_S)/kT\right].$$
(18A)

By comparison to eqn (17A) we find

$$A = 4(Ne^2/k)v_0\, a_0{}^2 \exp\left[(S_{m+} + \tfrac{1}{2}S_S/k\right]$$
(18B)

and

$$W_{\mathrm{I}} = H_{m+} + \tfrac{1}{2}H_S$$
(19A)

for intrinsic behaviour. This temperature range is denoted as Stage I in Fig. 7 (Kirk and Pratt, 1967) and may occur down to several hundred degrees below the melting point for reasonably pure crystals. At somewhat lower temperatures in Stage II it is supposed that the defect concentration is dominated by the divalent impurity without association, so that the large concentration limit of eqn (6C) gives $x_+ = c$ independent of temperature. Thus

$$W_{\mathrm{II}} = H_{m+},$$
(19B)

and it should be possible to determine both H_S and H_{m+} by combining measurements of W_{I} and W_{II}. This procedure has often been applied, but the appreciable scatter of results from different investigators and for various divalent impurities suggests that the actual picture is not quite so simple as suggested above. Complicating features occur because the transition from Stage I to Stage II does not occur abruptly, the slope in Stage I may be influenced by a non-negligible contribution from anion vacancies (see discussion of Stage I' below), and the slope at the lower end of Stage II may be altered by association (see Stage III below) or even precipitation (Stage IV). Hence although this simple method may be useful in giving preliminary estimates of H_S and H_{m+}, it cannot be relied upon in detail to give precise values.

At lower temperatures in Stage III the effects of association can no longer be neglected. For large impurity concentrations we have $c - x_a \approx x_+$ in eqn (8B) since $x_- \ll x_+$, and then eqn (7B) gives $x_+ \propto K_a{}^{-\frac{1}{2}}$. We find

$$W_{\mathrm{III}} = H_{m+} + (-\tfrac{1}{2}H_a);$$
(19C)

increasing the temperature not only causes the mobility to increase but also produces more free cation vacancies by causing complexes to dissociate. At still lower temperatures in Stage IV the impurity starts to precipitate out as a separate phase. Again we have $c - x_a \approx x_+$ and from eqn (10B) and (10C) obtain

$$W_{IV} = H_{m+} + (-\tfrac{1}{2}H_p), \tag{19D}$$

which gives an even steeper slope than Stage III (see Fig. 7). Increasing the temperature now provides more free vacancies by redissolving impurities from the precipitated phase. Finally at quite low temperatures Stage III' may occur with a slope nearly equal to that of Stage III. Presumably the precipitation of impurities, which requires impurity motion through appreciable distances in the crystal, can no longer occur during the time of the measurement. The amount of impurity dissolved in the crystal remains constant, instead, at a non-equilibrium value determined by the quenching history of the sample, but the formation of complexes can still occur through motion of cation vacancies. Below room temperature Stage V has even been observed (Dreyfus and Nowick, 1962b), where the complexing reaction is also frozen out, leaving some nearly constant, non-equilibrium concentration of cation vacancies present in the crystal. The slope should be

$$W_V = H_{m+} \tag{19E}$$

as in Stage II, and this result is indeed obtained after corrections have been made for the beginning of association at the higher temperature portion of this stage.

C. Temperature Dependence for Several Mobile Defects

Let us now return to the general situation where both cation and anion vacancies contribute to the conductivity as in eqn (16B). In the intrinsic region with $x_+ = x_- = x_{OS}$ we find with eqns (1E) and (15B)

$$\sigma T = 4(Ne^2/k)v_0 \, a_0{}^2 \, \{\exp[(\tfrac{1}{2}S_S + S_{m+})/k]\exp[-(\tfrac{1}{2}H_S + H_{m+})/kT]$$
$$+ \exp[(\tfrac{1}{2}S_S + S_{m-})/k]\exp[-(\tfrac{1}{2}H_S + H_{m-})/kT]\} \tag{20}$$
$$= A_+ \exp(-W_+/kT) + A_- \exp(-W_-/kT).$$

Thus a plot of $\log(\sigma T)$ versus $1/T$ should be a curved line representing the sum of two straight lines, as shown for KI in Fig. 9 (Chandra and Rolfe, 1970). Even when the experimental curve for the total conductivity can be decomposed into two lines, it is possible to obtain only the quantities $(\tfrac{1}{2}S_S + S_{m\pm})$ and $(\tfrac{1}{2}H_S + H_{m\pm})$, just because each term in eqn (16B) contains the product of a mobility and a concentration. In order to determine the actual concentration it is necessary to have another type of measurement, and this is usually provided by using doped crystals in which the impurity concentration is determined directly by chemical, neutron activation, or other types of trace analysis. Conductivity curves for Sr^{2+} and CO_3^{2-} in KI are shown in Fig. 9 (Chandra and Rolfe, 1970). Stages I, II, and III may be approximately identified in Fig. 9a, but it is clear that there really are not any appreciable segments of the curves with strictly constant slope, as was assumed in the qualitative discussion of eqn (19). The large precipitation region of Stage IV is especially evident in Fig. 9b because of the limited solubility of the CO_3^{2-} ion.

There should be enough information available in Figs 8 and 9 to determine the parameters S_S and H_S for the Schottky defect concentration, S_{m+} and H_{m+} for the motion of cation vacancies, and S_{m-} and H_{m-} for the motion of anion vacancies. Several procedures have been used for the necessary analysis. In some cases values of $(\frac{1}{2}H_S + H_{m\pm})$, etc., have been obtained by a least-squares fitting of eqn (20) to the intrinsic conductivity curve (Fuller and Reilly, 1967; Allnatt and Pantelis, 1968). It is usually possible to choose parameters that will give a good fit, (root-mean-square deviation of only a few per cent), especially if the long range interactions discussed in Section IV are taken into account, but the physical significance of the parameters is often doubtful, particularly for the less mobile carriers (Dawson and Barr, 1967). Completely outlandish values for the anion mobility parameters can give an apparently good fit, for example, in KI (Chandra and Rolfe, 1970) or NaCl (Nelson and Friauf, 1970). Hence, it is always desirable to use some additional information from conductivity in doped crystals or from diffusion measurements. The large solubility of divalent cation impurities often makes it possible to obtain situations where cation motion is predominant as in Fig. 9a. Then a fit of eqn (16A) with concentrations obtained from eqns (9) for association (including long range effects where appropriate) allows a good determination of the parameters for cation motion (Beaumont and Jacobs, 1966; Chandra and Rolfe, 1970). The much smaller solubility limit of divalent anion impurities requires the use of eqn (16B) for the fit, but may allow association to be neglected for these impurities (Chandra and Rolfe, 1970). When doping with divalent anion impurities is not possible, some information may be obtained from anion diffusion measurements, but this procedure may be complicated by contributions to diffusion from vacancy pairs (see Section V.E) or dislocations (see Fig. 15).

D. Conductivity Isotherms

Another way of analyzing the data is to plot isothermal curves of conductivity versus impurity concentration. This method has the disadvantage that the data must be obtained from a family of conductivity curves for a number of crystals with different impurity contents; the points indicated on the vertical line in Fig. 9 would suffice for one isotherm. The advantage is that the analysis can proceed without pre-assignment of the form of the temperature dependence of any of the pertinent quantities, such as the intrinsic defect concentration x_{OF} or the association constant K_a. We shall illustrate the procedure for AgBr, where interstitial cations are appreciably more mobile than cation vacancies. The mobility ratio

$$\phi = \mu_i/\mu_+ \tag{21A}$$

therefore is always greater than one. It is convenient to write the conductivity of the pure crystal from eqn (16B) as

$$\sigma_0 = eNx_{OF}\,\mu_+\,(1 + \phi) \tag{21B}$$

and to consider the conductivity of a doped crystal relative to that of a pure crystal at the same temperature.

$$\frac{\sigma(c)}{\sigma_0} = \frac{x_+ + \phi x_i}{x_{OF}\,(1 + \phi)} \tag{21C}$$

When association can be neglected substitution of x_+ and x_i from eqns (6) gives

$$\frac{\sigma}{\sigma_0} = \left[\left(\frac{c}{2x_{OF}}\right)^2 + 1\right]^{1/2} - \left(\frac{c}{2x_{OF}}\right)\frac{\phi - 1}{\phi + 1}, \tag{22A}$$

where c is positive for impurities with an excess positive charge and negative for an excess negative charge. The initial slope of a conductivity isotherm is found to be

$$\left[\frac{\partial(\sigma/\sigma_0)}{\partial c}\right]_{c=0} = -\frac{1}{2x_{OF}}\frac{\phi - 1}{\phi + 1}, \tag{22B}$$

and should be the same for positively or negatively charged impurities if association is not significant. This behaviour is illustrated for AgBr with Cd^{2+} and S^{2-} in Fig. 10 (Teltow, 1950a, b), where we see that the parabola of eqn (22A) does pass right through $c = 0$ with a slope that is essentially continuous to a first approximation. Thus addition of Cd^{2+} which introduces the less mobile cation vacancies according to

$$CdBr_2 \leftrightarrow Cd_{Ag}^{\bullet} + V_{Ag}' + 2Br_{Br}^{\times},$$

causes an initial decrease in conductivity because the more mobile interstitial ions are suppressed by the mass action law. In this case a minimum occurs at

$$\frac{c_1}{x_{OF}} = \frac{\phi - 1}{\phi^{1/2}}, \quad \frac{\sigma_1}{\sigma_0} = \frac{2\phi^{1/2}}{\phi + 1}. \tag{22C}$$

Hence, measurement of σ_1/σ_0 and the initial slope allows a calculation of ϕ and x_{OF}, after which μ_+ and μ_i are readily found from eqns (21B) and (21A). When c becomes much larger than x_{OF} the conductivity eventually increases because of the large number of cation vacancies,

$$\frac{\sigma}{\sigma_0} = \frac{1}{\phi + 1} \frac{c}{x_{OF}}, \tag{22D}$$

and the conductivity isotherm should be linear as seen for NaCl: Mn in Fig. 11a (Kirk and Pratt, 1967). Addition of S^{2-}, on the other hand, which introduces the more mobile interstitials according to

$$Ag_2S \leftrightarrow S'_{Br} + Ag^{\bullet}_i + Ag^{\times}_{Ag},$$

causes an immediate increase in conductivity as seen in Fig. 10. The negative curvature at larger concentrations of S^{2-} probably is caused by precipitation of some of the impurity.

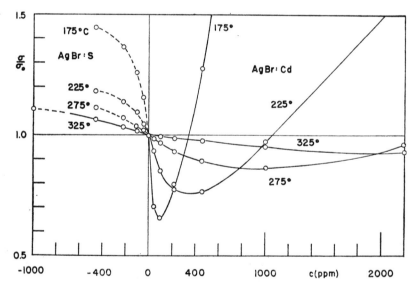

FIG. 10. Conductivity isotherms for AgBr doped with Cd^{2+} (Teltow, 1950a) and S^{2-} (Teltow, 1950b). The dashed lines for AgBr:S are outside the equilibrium solubility limit.

In alkali halides with the NaCl structure, the cation vacancies are usually more mobile, and the mobility ratio $\phi = \mu_-/\mu_+$ is therefore less than one. Addition of a divalent cation impurity, then, which introduces the more mobile cation vacancies, always causes an increase in conductivity, as for

Sr^{2+} in Fig. 9a. Addition of a divalent anion impurity, on the other hand, which introduces the less mobile anion vacancies, causes an initial decrease in conductivity, as seen at high temperatures for CO_3^{2-} in Fig. 9b.

When association becomes important the defect concentrations must be obtained from eqn (9B), which gives an implicit relationship between ξ and c. The relative conductivity is

$$\frac{\sigma(c)}{\sigma_0} = \frac{\xi + \phi\xi^{-1}}{1 + \phi}, \tag{23A}$$

and the initial slope of the conductivity isotherm is

$$\left[\frac{\partial(\sigma/\sigma_0)}{\partial c}\right]_{c=0} = -\frac{1}{2x_{OF}}\frac{\phi-1}{\phi+1}\frac{1}{1+P_a}. \tag{23B}$$

When the more mobile species is suppressed the minimum occurs at $\xi_1 = \phi^{1/2}$, which gives

$$\frac{c_1}{x_{OF}} = \frac{\phi-1}{\phi^{1/2}}(1 + P_a\phi^{1/2}), \quad \frac{\sigma_1}{\sigma_0} = \frac{2\phi^{1/2}}{\phi+1}. \tag{23C}$$

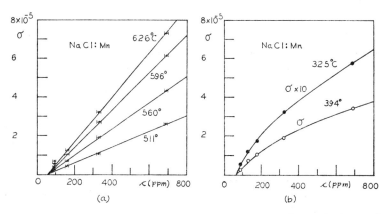

FIG. 11. Conductivity isotherms for NaCl:Mn (a) without association in Stage II and (b) with association in Stage III (Kirk and Pratt, 1967). The conductivity is expressed in $ohm^{-1}\ cm^{-1}$.

Notice that the relative conductivity at the minimum gives the same value of ϕ as eqn (22C) without association! In order to determine x_{OF} and P_a we find ξ for each c from eqn (23A) and then plot eqn (9B) in the form

$$\frac{c}{\xi - \xi^{-1}} = x_{OF} + x_{OF}P_a\xi, \tag{23D}$$

which gives x_{OF} from the intercept and P_a from the slope. When $c/x_{OF} \gg 1$ we may simplify eqns (9B) and (23A) by neglecting ξ^{-1} and obtain

$$\frac{c}{x_{OF}} = (\phi + 1)\frac{\sigma}{\sigma_0} + P_a(\phi + 1)^2 \left(\frac{\sigma}{\sigma_0}\right)^2 ; \qquad (23E)$$

this explicit expression for the conductivity isotherm predicts the parabolic shape shown in Fig. 11b.

IV. Long Range Interactions

A. Coulomb Forces

Many of the defects in ionic crystals carry extra charges with respect to the perfect crystal, and these charges play an important role in both short and long range interactions. The short range interactions have already been taken into account, in some fashion, by recognizing bound vacancy pairs and impurity–vacancy complexes. But the long range nature of the Coulomb force also leads to appreciable interactions at much longer distances than nearest neighbour (n.n.) or next nearest neighbour (n.n.n.) separations. These effects have been incorporated into the theory of defects in ionic crystals by Lidiard (1954, 1957, pp. 307–310), who adapted the Debye–Hückel theory of electrolytic solutions (Fowler and Guggenheim, 1949, Chapter 9; Falkenhagen, 1934) in which the defects are regarded as charged particles moving in a dielectric medium. Each positively charged defect, then, such as an anion vacancy, tends to attract oppositely charged defects, such as cation vacancies, and to repel defects with the same charge. The electrostatic forces are opposed by the natural tendency of defects to spread out uniformly, but a statistical equilibrium is attained in which each defect is surrounded by a diffuse cloud of opposite charges, thereby lowering the average energy per defect in the crystal.

As a specific case let us consider a situation like KCl:Sr where the charged species are cation vacancies, anion vacancies, and divalent cation impurities. A screening constant is defined by

$$\kappa^2 = \frac{4\pi e^2 N[x_+ + x_- + (c - x_a)]}{\varepsilon kT}, \qquad (24A)$$

where ε is the dielectric constant of the crystal. The term $N[x_+ + x_- + (c - x_a)]$ represents in general the sum of the volume concentration of each charged species multiplied by the *square* of its valence[†]; in our example the

[†] This quantity therefore is just twice the *ionic strength* defined by Lewis and Randall (1923), p. 373.

electric neutrality condition of eqn (8) allows us to replace this term simply by $2Nx_+$.

$$\kappa^2 = 8\pi \left(\frac{Ne^2}{kT}\right)\left(\frac{x_+}{\varepsilon}\right) \tag{24B}$$

With N expressed in units of cm^{-3}, e^2 in erg. cm, and kT in erg, the dimensions of κ are cm^{-1}; the length given by $1/\kappa$ represents a screening distance over which the excess charge of a defect is effectively neutralized. For defect concentrations between 1 and 1000 ppm typical values of the screening length range from 300 down to 10 Å, which are indeed rather large distances compared to 3 Å for the n.n. separation.

The change in energy per pair of defects because of the presence of the Debye–Hückel charge cloud is found to be

$$H_{DH} = -\frac{e^2\kappa}{\varepsilon(1 + \kappa R)}, \tag{25A}$$

where R is the distance of closest approach. In electrolytic solutions R can simply be set equal to the sum of the ionic radii; in crystals the choice of R is determined by the extent to which close neighbours are treated as separate species. Since we have explicitly recognized vacancy pairs with a n.n. separation of a_0 and impurity–vacancy complexes with a separation of $\sqrt{2}a_0$, we should choose R either as $\sqrt{3}a_0$ for the n.n.n. position of a cation and anion vacancy or as $2a_0$ for an impurity and a cation vacancy; the actual choice lies between $\sqrt{2}a_0$ and $2a_0$ for different authors. Fortunately the slight arbitrariness in the choice of R, which does represent a slight deficiency in the theory, usually does not influence the results appreciably because the term κR is almost always noticeably less than one. An extension of the theory to avoid this difficulty is provided by a cluster formalism (Allnatt and Cohen, 1964; Allnatt, 1967), but because of the intractability of the mathematical expressions, the simpler theory described here is almost always used. A few calculations using the results of Abbink and Martin (1966) for AgCl:Cd will serve to illustrate the magnitude of the effects to be expected. At 203°C the intrinsic defect concentration is increased from 3·96 to 4·35 ppm by including long range interactions, the screening length is $1/\kappa_0 = 125$ Å, and the Debye–Hückel energy is $-H_{DH} = 0·0078$ eV compared to $kT = 0·041$ eV and $H_F = 1·44$ eV. With 806 ppm of cadmium at this temperature the screening length becomes $1/\kappa = 11$ Å, and the Debye–Hückel energy is $-H_{DH} = 0·069$ eV compared to $-H_a = 0·47$ eV.

B. Defect Concentrations

The influence of long range interactions on defect concentrations is expressed through an *activity coefficient* γ defined by

$$ln\, \gamma = \frac{H_{DH}}{2kT} = -\frac{1}{2kT} \frac{e^2\kappa}{(1 + \kappa R)}. \tag{25B}$$

Then the statistical thermodynamics formulation of the mass action laws is written by comparison to eqns (1D) and (7B) as

$$(\gamma x_+)\,(\gamma x_-) = x_{OS}{}^2 = \exp\,(S_S/k)\exp\,(-H_S/kT), \tag{26A}$$

$$\frac{x_a}{(\gamma x_+)\,[\gamma(c - x_a)]} = K_a(T) = z_a \exp\,(S_a/k)\exp\,(-H_a/kT). \tag{26B}$$

Notice that the same activity coefficient is used for all charged species but that none is introduced for the neutral complex. The result for a pure crystal may be expressed as

$$x_0{}^2 = x_+\,x_- = \frac{x_{OS}{}^2}{\gamma_0{}^2} = \exp\frac{S_S}{k}\exp\left[-\frac{1}{kT}\left(H_S - \frac{e^2\kappa_0}{\varepsilon(1 + \kappa_0 R)}\right)\right], \tag{26C}$$

where κ_0 is to be calculated from eqn (24B) with the appropriate value of $x_+ = x_0 = x_{OS}/\gamma_0$ from above. Since x_0 appears on both sides of the transcendental eqn (26C), it is not possible to obtain an explicit expression for the concentration, but in numerical calculations a self-consistent value may readily be found after a few iterations. The influence of the long range interactions is seen clearly in the last form of eqn (26C), which shows that the formation enthalpy H_S is effectively reduced by the Debye–Hückel energy $-H_{DH}$, thus allowing more defects to be formed at a given temperature than if the charge interactions were not present. This effect is shown for AgCl in Fig. 12 (Abbink and Martin, 1966), where x_0 is 30% larger than x_{OF} at 300°C. At the melting point of 455°C the difference extrapolates to a factor of 4, but since the estimated defect concentration is 0·6 mol %, the range of strict applicability of the Debye–Hückel theory is certainly exceeded.

When it is desired to find defect concentrations in doped crystals, taking association and long range interactions into account, the complete set of equations is obtained from the condition of electric neutrality and the mass action laws of eqns (26).

$$x_+ = x_- + c - x_a \tag{27A}$$

$$x_+\,x_- = x_{OS}{}^2/\gamma^2 \tag{27B}$$

$$x_a/x_+(c - x_a) = \gamma^2 K_a \tag{27C}$$

With the definitions $\xi = x_+/x_{OS}$ and $P_a = x_{OS} K_a$ as for eqns (9), we find

$$(c/x_{OS}) = [\xi - (\gamma^2 \xi)^{-1}] [1 + (\gamma^2 \xi) P_a]. \tag{28A}$$

To start the calculation at a given temperature x_{OS}, K_a, and P_a are evaluated from known or assumed values for S_S, H_S and S_a, H_a. Next a preliminary estimate is made of x_+, probably the larger of x_{OS} and c, to obtain a preliminary value for γ from eqns (24B) and (25B). Then eqn (28A) is solved for ξ, a revised value of γ is calculated with the new $x_+ = x_{OS} \xi$, and the process is repeated until a self-consistent result is obtained for ξ. The concentrations are then given by

$$x_+ = x_{OS} \xi, \quad x_- = x_{OS}/(\gamma^2 \xi), \tag{28B}$$

and the degree of association is

$$x_a/c = \gamma^2 \xi P_a/(1 + \gamma^2 \xi P_a). \tag{28C}$$

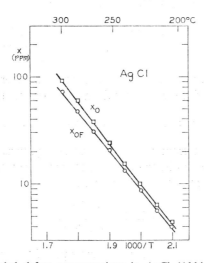

Fig. 12. Intrinsic Frenkel defect concentrations in AgCl (Abbink and Martin, 1966). x_0 is the actual concentration with Debye–Hückel interactions taken into account. x_{0F} is the hypothetical concentration that would exist for the specified values of $H_F = 1\cdot44$ eV and $S_F/k = 9\cdot4$ e.u. if the Debye–Hückel interactions were absent.

Calculations of this type are shown in Fig. 6 for KCl:Sr (Fuller, 1971). The influence of Debye–Hückel interactions becomes noticeable when defect concentrations, either intrinsic or introduced by impurities, exceed 10–100 ppm. The effect of the long range interactions is always to increase the concentration of free defects: we have already seen that the formation enthalpy H_S is reduced by the Coulomb energy, and the association enthalpy

— H_a is similarly decreased, making association less likely because the charge of the impurity is partially screened out. The degree of association at 400°C in Fig. 6, for instance, is reduced from more than 60% to less than 30% by inclusion of the long range Coulomb interactions.

C. Mobility and Conductivity

The presence of a charge cloud around a defect also influences its mobility, for an electric field tries to move the cloud in the opposite direction to the defect, thereby producing a drag. The Onsager (1927) theory of liquid electrolytes has been adapted by Pitts (1953) for ions with a closest distance of approach R, and the result can be expressed with certain approximations as follows (see the discussion by Lidiard, 1957, p. 309). The mobility of a defect in a crystal containing other defects is obtained by multiplying the limiting mobility in the absence of interactions by a mobility drag factor,

$$g = 1 - e^2 \kappa [3\varepsilon kT(\sqrt{2} + 1)(\sqrt{2} + \kappa R)(1 + \kappa R)]^{-1} \qquad (29)$$

This factor is always less than one, but usually by only 1–20% and it changes very slowly and smoothly with temperature. Thus the effect of including g in an analysis of conductivity results is appreciably less noticeable than the changes in concentrations caused by the long range interactions.

The conductivity of the pure crystal, then, is written as

$$\sigma_0 = eNx_0\, g_0(\mu_+ + \mu_-) = eNx_{0S}\, \xi_0\, g_0\, \mu_+(1 + \phi), \qquad (30A)$$

where g_0 is calculated from eqn (29) with the appropriate value of κ_0 and where $\xi_0 = x_0/x_{0S} = 1/\gamma_0$ in analogy to ξ for the doped crystal. The relative conductivity of a doped to a pure crystal is

$$\frac{\sigma}{\sigma_0} = \frac{g\xi[1 + \phi(\gamma^2\,\xi^2)^{-1}]}{g_0\,\xi_0[1 + \phi]}, \qquad (30B)$$

where ξ and γ must be obtained by solving eqn (28A) for the doped crystal. The nature of the conductivity isotherms is shown for AgCl:Cd in Fig. 13 (Abbink and Martin, 1966). For impurity concentrations up to 1000 ppm the difference from including Debye–Hückel effects is scarcely noticeable on the graph, but the least-squares-fit including all concentrations up to 854 ppm is decidedly better when these interactions are included. The right hand portion of the figure shows that the extrapolation of the fit with Debye–Hückel interactions is also much better for larger impurity concentrations. The reason is that the association theory without interactions predicts too large a degree of association; when interactions are included the degree of association is smaller because of partial screening, as we have seen, and therefore the concentration of free vacancies and hence also the conductivity are larger. The isotherms from eqn (21A) for the simple theory without association give a moderately good fit up to several hundred parts per million but rise too rapidly for larger impurity concentrations because of the neglect of association.

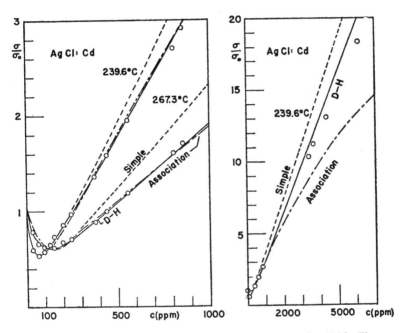

FIG. 13. Conductivity isotherms for AgCl:Cd (Abbink and Martin, 1966). The experimental points and the calculated curves with association and with Debye–Hückel interactions (including association) are taken directly from the reference. The results of the simple theory without association have been calculated for comparison with $x_{0F} = 21.7$ ppm and $\phi = 11.13$ at 239.6°C and $x_{0F} = 45.9$ ppm and $\phi = 8.63$ at 267.3°C.

V. Diffusion

A. Tracer Diffusion

An atomic defect goes through an unending sequence of random, thermally induced jumps that cause a wandering of the defect through the crystal lattice. This phenomenon can be described by a *microscopic* diffusion coefficient, as for cation vacancies in eqn (14D), but it cannot be observed directly in the laboratory. Diffusion experiments therefore are usually carried out with isotopic tracers, which are identical to normal atoms in chemical properties but are distinguishable either by radioactive decay or by differences in mass (e.g. ^{18}O or ^{6}Li). By following the jumps of a cation tracer in a crystal containing cation vacancies, for instance, we obtain a *macroscopic* diffusion coefficient by considerations similar to those of eqns (14),

$$D_+ = \tfrac{1}{6} v_{T+} a_+^2,$$ (31A)

where now the tracer jump frequency v_{T+} must be used. The tracer jumps only when it is on a site next to a vacancy (probability $= z_+ x_+$), only when the vacancy jumps (probability/sec $= v_+$), and only when the vacancy jumps toward the tracer (probability $= 1/z_+$), giving the probability/sec for a tracer jump as

$$v_{T+} = (z_+ x_+)(v_+)(1/z_+) = x_+ v_+.$$ (31B)

Thus we find that the macroscopic diffusion coefficient,

$$D_+ = \tfrac{1}{6} v_+ a_+^2 x_+ = x_+ d_+,$$ (31C)

involves a "dilution factor" x_+ that expresses the probability that a tracer atom is in a situation where it can participate in a vacancy jump.

Notice that this result depends on the product $v_+ x_+$ just as the conductivity does on $\mu_+ x_+$: *any macroscopic transport property always involves the product of a jump frequency times a concentration for the defect causing the transport.* On these physical grounds it is clear that the diffusion caused by cation vacancies should be closely related to the corresponding conductivity in eqn (16A), and the actual relationship is readily established with the microscopic Einstein relation of eqn (15A),

$$D_{\sigma+} = (kT/Ne^2)\sigma_+.$$ (32A)

The *macroscopic Einstein relation* is used here to define $D_{\sigma+} = D_+ = x_+ d_+$, which represents, then, the amount of diffusion to be expected from the conductivity by considering jump frequencies only. The result must be modified slightly for tracer diffusion coefficients by introduction of a correlation factor f_+ as described in Section V.D,

$$D_+^* = f_+ D_{\sigma+} = f_+ x_+ d_+.$$ (32B)

For any given type of defect motion f_+ is of the order of magnitude of unity (see Table I) and is independent of temperature.

B. Temperature Dependence

The temperature dependence of the diffusion coefficient for a particular tracer is governed by the product $x_+ d_+$ in eqn (32B). In the region of intrinsic concentrations, for instance, we find

$$D_+^* = 4f_+ v_0 a_0^2 \exp[(S_{m+} + \tfrac{1}{2} S_S)/k] \exp[-(H_{m+} + \tfrac{1}{2} H_S)/kT], \quad (33A)$$

which should be compared to eqn (18A) for the conductivity. Experimentally measured diffusion coefficients are usually presented as

$$D_+{}^* = D_{0+} \exp\left(-W_+/kT\right). \tag{33B}$$

By comparison

$$W_+ = H_{m+} + \tfrac{1}{2}H_S, \tag{33C}$$

$$D_{0+} = 4f_+\, v_0\, a_0{}^2 \exp\left[(S_{m+} + \tfrac{1}{2}S_S)/k\right], \tag{33D}$$

for intrinsic behaviour.

Measurements of $D_+{}^*$ and $D_-{}^*$ for CsBr are shown in Fig. 14 (Lynch, 1960), which illustrates the expected Arrhenius type of temperature dependence. In this example of intrinsic behaviour the difference between $D_+{}^*$ and $D_-{}^*$ must come from the frequency factors in d_+ and d_-; it is noteworthy that cation diffusion is smaller for this material, as is typical for crystals with the CsCl structure.

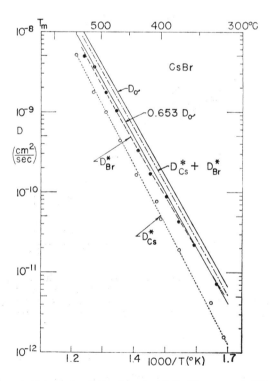

FIG. 14. Diffusion coefficients for CsBr (Lynch, 1960). The sum of diffusion coefficients is compared to D_σ from the total conductivity by using the correlation factor $f_+ = 0.653$ appropriate for vacancies on a s.c. lattice (Table I).

An estimate of the magnitude of the pre-exponential factor for diffusion is often useful. For the intrinsic behaviour in eqn (33D) we have $v_0 \sim 2 \times 10^{12}$ Hz, $a_0 \sim 3 \times 10^{-8}$ cm, and $S_{m+} + \frac{1}{2}S_S \sim 0$ to 10 e.u. and estimate $D_{0+} \sim 10^{-2}$ to 10^{+2} cm²/sec. For CsBr in Fig. 12, for instance, we find $D_{0+} = 15$ and $D_{0-} = 3 \cdot 9$ cm²/sec. If a value of D_0 greatly outside this range is found, it strongly suggests that something other than intrinsic diffusion is being observed. There may be contributions from other types of defects, such as vacancy pairs, or from an entirely different process such as diffusion along grain boundaries or dislocation lines; these two possibilities are shown for the diffusion of Br in KBr in Fig. 15 (Barr and Dawson, 1971). Or there may be a different regime of impurity effects. For extrinsic behaviour in Stage II, for instance, where x_+ is held constant at $c \sim 10^{-6}$ to 10^{-3} instead of contributing $\exp(S_S/2k) \sim 1$ to 10^2, the value of D_{0+} may be reduced to something in the vicinity of 10^{-5} cm²/sec.

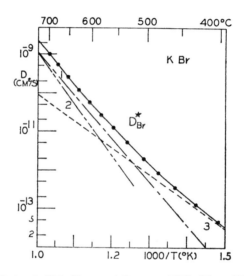

FIG. 15. Anion diffusion in KBr (Barr and Dawson, 1971). The solid points are experimental results. Three separate contributions to D_- have been identified by a family of related experiments: curve 1, anion vacancies, $W = 2 \cdot 10$ eV; curve 2, vacancy pairs, $W = 2 \cdot 60$ eV; curve 3, extrinsic diffusion along dislocations, $W = 1 \cdot 4$ eV for this sample.

C. Comparison of Conductivity and Diffusion

It is often convenient to compare diffusion and conductivity by defining a *diffusion ratio*

$$R_+ = D_+{}^*/D_{\sigma+}, \tag{34A}$$

where $D_{\sigma+}$ is calculated from σ_+ by the macroscopic Einstein relation of eqn (32A). Since both $D_+{}^*$ and σ_+ can be measured directly, the diffusion ratio R_+ is an experimentally determined quantity, and its value should give a good indication of the type of defect motion involved. If all of the cation diffusion is due to the motion of single cation vacancies, for instance, and if σ_+ can be separated unambiguously from σ, perhaps by measurements on doped crystals, the theoretical prediction for R_+ from eqn (32B) is

$$R_+ = f_+. \tag{34B}$$

An experimental check is shown for AgCl:Cd in Fig. 16 (Gracey and Friauf, 1969); the addition of Cd^{2+} suppresses nearly all of the interstitial ions at sufficiently low temperatures, leaving only cation vacancies. A correction must also be made for concentration gradients because the conductivity measures the average concentration over the length of the sample whereas the diffusion coefficient depends only on the concentration in a narrow region at one end. The agreement of theory and experiment is within 1·5% at all but one point, and in particular the average of diffusion from both ends at 130°C coincides almost exactly with the theoretical value.

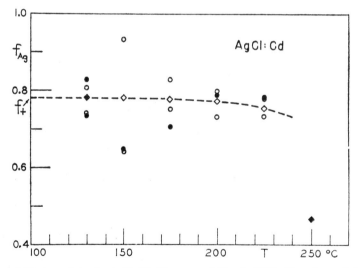

FIG. 16. Diffusion of Ag in AgCl:Cd (Gracey and Frauf, 1969). Experimental diffusion ratios: ● diffusion coefficient measured at one end of the sample, ■ average of diffusion coefficients for both ends. ◆ diffusion coefficient for pure sample. Theoretical correlation factors: $f_v = 0.781$ for vacancies, ◇ f_{Ag} including small contributions of interstitial ions, ○ f_{Ag} corrected for estimated concentration gradient along the sample. The dashed curve does not represent any particular function of temperature since different samples have different concentrations between 130 and 230 ppm, but it helps to show the general appearence of a few interstitial ions at the higher temperatures.

In other cases, such as CsBr in Fig. 14, it may happen that only the total conductivity

$$\sigma = \sigma_+ + \sigma_- = t_+ \sigma + t_- \sigma \qquad (35A)$$

is known experimentally. Here we have introduced the *transport numbers*,

$$t_+ = \sigma_+/\sigma, \quad t_- = \sigma_-/\sigma, \qquad (35B)$$

with $t_+ + t_- = 1$ by definition. If we then express the diffusion ratios, of necessity, in terms of D_σ obtained from the total σ, we find

$$R_+ = D_+^*/D_\sigma = t_+ f_+, \qquad (36A)$$

with a similar result for R_-. This still does not serve for positive identification of the type of defect motion when the transport numbers are not known experimentally, but an overall comparison can be made by adding R_+ and R_-. For this case we expect

$$R_+ + R_- = t_+ f_+ + t_- f_+ = f_+, \qquad (36B)$$

since for an MX compound the cation and anion sublattices have the same geometrical structure and hence identical correlation factors. This sort of comparison is shown in Fig. 14 by plotting $f_+ D_\sigma$ for comparison to $D_{Cs}^* + D_{Br}^*$; the discrepancy indicates that some other diffusion mechanism is present in addition to single vacancies, the most likely possibility being vacancy pairs (see Section V.E).

D. Correlation Factors

The quantity measured in a diffusion experiment is the displacement of tracer atoms, and it therefore becomes necessary to look at the actual motion of a tracer atom through the crystal, which turns out to be somewhat more complicated than that of a vacancy. The situation is illustrated schematically in Fig. 17(a) (Friauf, 1962), which shows a sequence of vacancy and tracer jumps. It is assumed that the vacancy always has equal jump probabilities for each of the four possible n.n. jumps and that therefore the random walk treatment of eqns (14) is indeed correct for the vacancy. The first jump of the tracer caused by a particular vacancy is in a random direction, of course, because the vacancy is equally likely to approach from any side. (But after the first jump of the tracer the surroundings of the tracer in the lattice are no longer isotropic. There is now a preferred direction for the second jump of the tracer, most probably directly opposite to the first jump, as happens in the sequence shown in the figure.) There are other possible sequences of vacancy jumps in which the vacancy can move around the tracer and cause its second jump to occur from the side or even from the front, but these are less probable than those causing a second jump from the back. Hence there exists some correlation between the directions of successive jumps of the tracer. The non-random-walk nature of the motion appears in the analysis by giving a non-zero result for the average of $\mathbf{a}_i \cdot \mathbf{a}_{i+j} = a^2 \cos \theta_{i,i+j}$ in eqn (14B),

$$\langle r_T^{*2} \rangle_{av} = N_T a_+^2 + 2N_T a_+^2 \, \Sigma_i \, \langle \cos \theta_{1,1+i} \rangle_{av}, \qquad (37A)$$

where the star indicates that correlation effects have now been included. One of the sums in the second term has been replaced by the factor N_T since the number assigned to the initial jump of the vacancy has no physical significance. With $N_T = v_{T+} \, t = x_+ \, v_+ \, t$ we find, by the procedure of eqn (14C),

$$D_+^* = f_+ \, x_+ \, d_+, \qquad (37B)$$

with a *correlation factor* given by

$$f_+ = 1 + 2\Sigma_i \, \langle \cos \theta_{1,1+i} \rangle_{av}. \qquad (37C)$$

For jump processes with sufficient symmetry, such as a 2- or 3-fold rotation, axis along the jump direction, it can be shown that (Compaan and Haven) 1956)

$$\langle \cos \theta_{1,1+i} \rangle_{av} = (\langle \cos \theta_{1,2} \rangle_{av})^i. \qquad (37D)$$

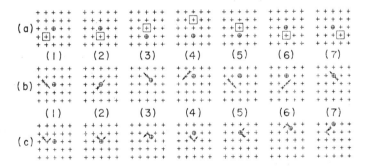

FIG. 17. "Film strips" of tracer diffusion in a two-dimensional lattice (Friauf, 1962). The tracer ⊕ and defect positions are shown in time sequence from (1) to (7). (a) Vacancy. (b) Collinear interstitialcy. (c) Non-collinear interstitialcy.

The remaining sum in eqn (37C) can then be summed as a geometric series, giving

$$f_+ = \frac{1 + \langle \cos \theta_{1,2} \rangle_{av}}{1 - \langle \cos \theta_{1,2} \rangle_{av}}. \qquad (37E)$$

For diffusion caused by any vacancy mechanism the enhanced probability of the backward directed jumps for the tracer makes $\langle \cos \theta_{1,2} \rangle_{av}$ negative, and the correlation factor is therefore less than one.

Somewhat different considerations apply for interstitial ions. For the direct interstitial motion denoted by v_{i0} in Fig. 3, the probability for a tracer atom to be in an interstitial position is simply x_i, giving $v_{Ti} = x_i v_i$, and we have

$$d_{i0} = \tfrac{1}{6} v_{i0} a_0^2 \tag{38A}$$

Furthermore there is no correlation for the motion of the tracer, making $f_{i0} = 1$ and

$$D_{i0} = x_i d_{i0}. \tag{38B}$$

For the collinear interstitialcy process with a jump frequency v_{i1} the charge is displaced by the diagonal of a small cube $b = \sqrt{3} a_0$ in the NaCl structure. In order to maintain the microscopic Einstein relation of eqn (15A) to the mobility, which is defined in terms of motion of charge, the same length must also be used for the microscopic diffusion coefficient

$$d_{i1} = \tfrac{1}{6} v_{i1} b^2 = \tfrac{1}{2} v_{i1} a_0^2. \tag{39A}$$

The displacement of the tracer atom, on the other hand, which is the quantity measured in a diffusion experiment, is only $b/2$, but there are also two atoms involved in each jump, giving $v_T = 2x_i v_{i1}$ and

$$D_{i1} = \tfrac{1}{6} v_T a_T^2 = \tfrac{1}{2} x_i d_{i1} = f_{i1}' x_i d_{i1} \tag{39B}$$

Figure 17b shows that there is also some correlation, but only half the time, after the tracer lands in a lattice position; when the tracer lands in an interstitial site, the surroundings show no preferred direction and the chain of correlations is broken, giving simply

$$f_{i1}'' = 1 + \langle \cos \theta_{1,2} \rangle_{av}. \tag{39C}$$

The tracer diffusion coefficient is then

$$D_{i1}{}^* = f_{i1}' f_{i1}'' x_i d_{i1} = f_{i1} x_i d_{i1}, \tag{39D}$$

with the overall correlation factor $f_{i1} = f_{i1}' f_{i1}''$ including both displacement and genuine correlation effects. In the NaCl structure a non-collinear interstitialcy jump can also occur at an angle $\theta = \cos^{-1}(1/3)$ with a charge displacement of $\sqrt{2} a_0$, giving

$$d_{i2} = \tfrac{1}{3} v_{i2} a_0^2 \tag{40A}$$

and $f_{i2}' = 3/4$. Again there is correlation for half of the jumps, as seen in Fig. 17(c), and we have

$$D_{i2}^* = f_{i2}\, x_i\, d_{i2} \tag{40B}$$

with $f_{i2} = f_{i2}' f_{i2}''$ as for f_{i1}.

The preceding discussion shows how correlation factors are introduced and defined. The theoretical evaluation reduces to the calculation of $\langle \cos\theta_{1,2} \rangle_{av}$ by following the appropriate problem for diffusion of probability. Several methods have been used: analogy to current flow on a corresponding network of resistors (Compaan and Haven, 1956, 1958), inversion of a jump matrix (Franklin, 1965; Howard, 1966), and direct numerical calculation (Friauf, 1957); a recent review has been given by LeClaire (1970). Values for a number of vacancy and interstitial processes in cubic lattices are given in Table I. The importance for the experimentalist is that the correlation factor

TABLE I.   Correlation Factors for Diffusion in Cubic Lattices

(a) Single vacancies

Lattice	Example	Correlation factor
Face centred cubic	NaCl	0·78146
Simple cubic	CsCl	0·65311
Body centred cubic	Na	0·72722
Diamond	C	0·50000

(b) Interstitial and interstitialcy jumps

Lattice	Example	Atom	Interstitial position	Type of jump	$\cos\theta$	f'	f''	f
f.c.c.	AgCl	Ag or Cl	Centre of small cube	Direct		1	1	1
				Collinear	1	1/2	2/3	0·3333
				Non-collinear	1/3	3/4	32/33	0·7273
				Non-collinear	$-1/3$	3/2	0·9643	1·4464
s.c.	CsCl	Cs or Cl	Centre of cube edge	Collinear	1	1/2	2/3	0·3333
				Non-collinear	1/2	2/3	0·9323	0·6216
				Non-collinear	0	1	1	1
				Non-collinear	$-1/2$	2	0·9120	1·8240
s.c.	CsCl	Cs or Cl	Centre of cube face	Collinear	1	1/2	0	0
				Non-collinear	0	1	1	1

The results are taken from Compaan and Haven (1956, 1958). These references also contain results for a number of other lattices.

depends in some detail on the geometry of the lattice and the jump process, thereby providing a fingerprint or signature for each particular type of jump mechanism.

E. Interpretation of Experiments

Diffusion can occur in solids by any of the vacancy, interstitial, or exchange mechanisms in Fig. 3, or even along dislocations as shown in Fig. 15. In all these cases an Arrhenius type of temperature dependence is expected, so that observation of the variation of diffusion with temperature gives no immediate indication by itself of the type of atomic jump process involved. In other types of solids, e.g. metals or semiconductors, indirect evidence—such as thermal expansion, scattering or trapping of electrons, Kirkendall effect, or theoretical calculations of formation energies—must also be relied upon. Such evidence may often be useful in ionic crystals, but an additional direct approach is provided by the comparison of ionic conductivity and diffusion. The comparison is based on the experimental diffusion ratio R of eqn (34A), which in turn involves the macroscopic Einstein relation of eqn (32A). It is the departure of R from unity that provides useful information, and we have already seen that the presence of correlation for tracer diffusion is one cause for such a departure. Before pursuing several examples of the interpretation of diffusion experiments, let us collect here a number of possible causes for deviations of R from the ideal value of unity. The microscopic Einstein relation of eqn (15A) must be strictly satisfied, of course, for each and every type of charged defect since it is firmly based on general statistical mechanics, but in real crystals a number of other effects and processes may also be present. (1) For diffusion by a vacancy mechanism correlations between successive jumps of the tracer introduce a correlation factor. (2) For diffusion by interstitialcy processes differences in displacement of the charge and the tracer occur in addition to some correlation, giving rise to an overall correlation factor that incorporates both displacement and correlation effects. (3) When more than one type of ion contributes to the total conductivity, the transport number of each ion appears in the diffusion ratio unless independent evidence is available, such as conductivity in doped crystals. (4) There may be other contributions to the conductivity, in particular from electrons or holes. It is this feature that destroys the utility of diffusion ratios for semiconductors or transition metal oxides, such as PbS and NiO, to say nothing of metals. (5) There may be neutral processes that contribute to diffusion but not conductivity, such as vacancy pairs or grain boundary diffusion; in such cases there will appear to be an excess amount of diffusion.

The first example is the detection of interstitialcy mechanisms in the silver halides. The presence of cation Frenkel defects is demonstrated conclusively by conductivity measurements in doped crystals (Fig. 10) and is confirmed by the very small magnitude and large temperature dependence of the anion diffusion coefficients (Fig. 2). But the detailed nature of the motion of interstitial ions can be revealed only by observation of the diffusion ratio for silver ions. The experimental results for R_{Ag} in AgCl in Fig. 18 (Weber and Friauf, 1969) lie well below the theoretical value $f_+ = 0.781$ for vacancy diffusion on a f.c.c. lattice, pointing immediately to the presence of some kind of interstitialcy process. The situation is complicated because there is some contribution from cation vacancies to both conductivity and diffusion of silver, and furthermore it turns out that a mixture of both collinear and non-collinear interstitialcy jumps is needed to explain the results in detail. The total conductivity is then

$$\sigma = \sigma_+ + \sigma_{i1} + \sigma_{i2} = eN[x_+ \mu_+ + x_i(\mu_{i1} + \mu_{i2})], \qquad (41A)$$

where the mobilities can be obtained from the corresponding microscopic diffusion coefficients with the microscopic Einstein relation. The diffusion coefficient is

$$D_{Ag}^* = f_+ x_+ d_+ + f_i(v_{i1}/v_{i2}) x_i(d_{i1} + d_{i2}), \qquad (41B)$$

where d_{i1} and d_{i2} are given in eqns (39A) and (40A). The correlation factor f_i depends on the ratio of jump frequencies for the two interstitialcy processes because in a given sequence a tracer atom may be displaced sometimes by a

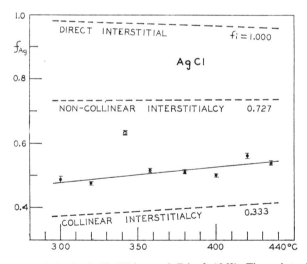

Fig. 18. Diffusion of Ag in AgCl (Weber and Friauf, 1969). The points show experimental values of the diffusion ratio $R_{Ag} = D_{Ag}^*/D_\sigma$. The curves are calculated for the indicated values of f_i with the vacancy contribution determined by the mobility ratio of Abbink and Martin (1966). The solid curve is calculated similarly for a smoothly varying mixture of collinear and non-collinear interstitialcy jumps.

collinear and sometimes by a non-collinear interstitialcy jump. In the analysis the vacancy contribution is first removed by using the mobility ratio $\phi = (\mu_{i1} + \mu_{i2})/\mu_+$ from doped conductivity experiments along with the known value of f_+, and then the relative contribution of the two interstitialcy processes is obtained from the behaviour of f_i. It is found that v_{i1}/v_{i2} lies between 1·0 and 2·5 for the temperature range of 300–440°C, giving values of $f_i = 0·45$ to 0·49, intermediate between the limits of $f_{i1} = 0·333$ and $f_{i2} = 0·727$ in Table I. The solid curve in Fig. 17 is calculated with the resulting mixture of interstitialcy jumps and agrees well with the experimental points. An analysis for AgBr shows similar behaviour (Friauf, 1957; Weber and Friauf, 1969).

The second example concerns contributions from neutral vacancy pairs in the alkali halides. The results for CsBr in Fig. 14 show an amount of diffusion somewhat in excess of that predicted for single vacancies from the conductivity, and similar observations have been made for CsI (Lynch, 1960), NaCl (Downing and Friauf, 1970), KBr (Barr and Dawson, 1971), CsCl (Harvey and Hoodless, 1967), and even TlCl (Friauf, 1971). The excess diffusion strongly suggests the presence of vacancy pairs, but unless transport numbers are known independently, it is not possible to sort out the vacancy pair contributions for each ion. Additional evidence can be provided by two additional kinds of experiments. In the first, anion diffusion is observed in crystals doped with divalent cation impurities. The behaviour for KCl:Sr is shown in Fig. 19 (Fuller et al., 1968), and similar experiments have been performed for NaCl (Laurance, 1960 and Barr et al., 1965), and KBr (Barr

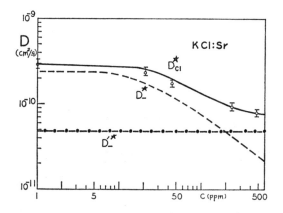

FIG. 19. Anion diffusion in KCl and KCl:Sr at 670°C (Fuller et al., 1968). The vacancy pair diffusion $D_-'^*$ is independent of impurity content, but the single vacancy diffusion D_-^* decreases as the anion vacancy concentration is suppressed by the addition of Sr^{2+}. The solid curve is the sum of the two contributions.

and Dawson, 1971). The diffusion of Cl is now given by the sum of two contributions

$$D_{Cl}{}^* = D_-{}^* + D_-'{}^* = f_- x_- d_- + f_-' x' d_-',$$ (42A)

where d_- is given by eqn (14E) and d_-' is defined similarly as

$$d_-' = \tfrac{1}{6} v_-' a_-'^2 = \tfrac{1}{3} v_-' a_0{}^2.$$ (42B)

The correlation factor f_- for single vacancies has a well-defined value $0\cdot781$ for the f.c.c. lattice, but f_-' for vacancy pairs is a function of the frequency ratio v_-'/v_+' (see Nelson and Friauf, 1970). The effect of adding Sr^{2+} is to increase x_+, thereby decreasing x_- by the mass action law and diminishing the single vacancy contribution to $D_{Cl}{}^*$ in eqn (42A). Unfortunately this method does not appear to be applicable for determining $D_+'{}^*$ because of the very limited solubility of divalent anion impurities.

The other experimental technique is to apply a constant electric field during the diffusion anneal. This should superimpose a drift on the diffusive motion of single vacancies but not of the neutral vacancy pairs. Typical diffusion profiles are shown for Na in NaCl in Fig. 20 (Nelson and Friauf, 1970). The effect of the field on the tracer can be expressed by a *tracer drift mobility*, which is related to the microscopic mobility of a vacancy by

$$M_+ = x_+ \mu_+.$$ (43A)

Notice that this is similar to the relationship of eqn (32B) between $D_+{}^*$ and d_+, except that *no* correlation factor appears for the tracer *mobility*, which

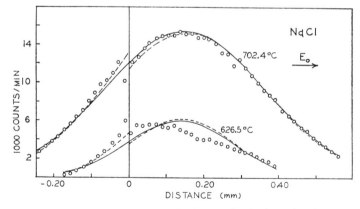

FIG. 20. Diffusion profiles for Na in NaCl (Nelson and Friauf, 1970). The solid lines are computed fits of a Gaussian profile to the experimental points. The dotted lines are computer fits of the solutions to the diffusion equation modified by introducing a partial barrier to crossing the initial interface at zero.

measures strictly the displacement of charge in the field. If a constant field E_0 is applied for a time t, the displacement of the diffusion profile is simply

$$d = M_+ E_0 t. \tag{43B}$$

The entire profile is displaced uniformly by this amount, while at the same time the spreading out from diffusion also occurs. Hence, analysis of profiles like those in Fig. 20 allows the determination of M_+ from the displacement of the peak and of D_{Na}^* from the total width. The amount of diffusion from single vacancies can be readily calculated from M_+,

$$D_+^* = f_+ D_{\sigma+} = f_+ (kT/e) M_+, \tag{44A}$$

and then the vacancy pair contribution $D_+'^*$ is obtained by subtraction,

$$D_+'^* = D_{Na}^* - D_+^*, \tag{44B}$$

in analogy to eqn (42A) for anions. The results for NaCl are shown in Fig. 21 (Nelson and Friauf, 1970), where it is seen that $D_+'^*$ amounts to 40% of D_{Na}^* at the melting point.

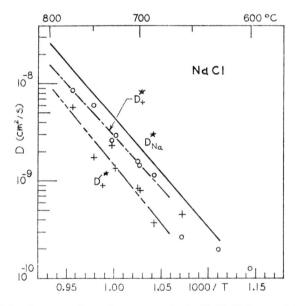

FIG. 21. Diffusion by vacancies and vacancy pairs in NaCl (Nelson and Friauf, 1970). The single vacancy contribution D_+^* is obtained from the tracer drift mobility, and then the vacancy pair contribution is obtained by subtraction from the total diffusion D_{Na}^*.

VI. Conclusion

A. Experimental Techniques

We have seen that the motion of point defects, many of them charged, in ionic crystals gives rise to the macroscopic transport properties of diffusion and ionic conductivity. The purpose of fundamental research in this area is to determine the atomic structure of the defect and the nature of the jump process. Numerical values of defect parameters—formation entropy, jump enthalpy—are also obtained to serve as a guide for theoretical calculations and to provide information for predicting other defect controlled properties. But even to make sense of the activation energies requires some understanding of the basic processes. Hence in Table II we give a summary of the various techniques that can be used for direct study of transport processes in ionic crystals. Some of them are more than forty years old, others are fairly recent, and some are as yet untried.

TABLE II. Experimental Techniques for Studying the Properties of Intrinsic Defects.[a]

Type of measurement	Crystal condition	Property obtained
(1) Conductivity	Pure	$\sigma = \sigma_+ + \sigma_-$
(2) Conductivity	Cation impurity	$\sigma_+ = eNx_+ \, \mu_+$
(3) Conductivity	Anion impurity	$\sigma_- = eNx_- \, \mu_-$
(4) Diffusion, cation tracer	Pure	$D_M{}^* = D_+{}^* + D_+{}'^*$
(5) Diffusion, anion tracer	Pure	$D_X{}^* = D_-{}^* + D_-{}'^*$
(6) Diffusion, anion tracer	Cation impurity	$D_-{}'^* = f_-{}' x' d_-{}'$
(7) Diffusion, cation tracer	Pure, electric field	$D_+{}^* = f_+ \, x_+ \, d_+$
(8) Diffusion, anion tracer	Pure, electric field	$D_-{}^* = f_- \, x_- \, d_-$
(9) Diffusion, cation tracer	Anion impurity	$D_+{}'^* = f_+{}' x' d_+{}'$
(10) Diffusion, cation tracer	Cation impurity	$D_+{}^* = f_+ \, x_+ \, d_+$
(11) Isotope effect, cation tracer	Pure	Average of f_+ and $f_+{}'$

[a] This table is taken with only small changes from Fuller (1971).

A few remarks will amplify the table. (1) Conductivity is relatively easy to measure and is usually one of the first results obtained. But with measurements on a pure crystal only, it is not even possible to distinguish the cation and anion contributions (Fig. 8). And even if one species is dominant, it is not possible to separate the product $x_+ \, \mu_+$ appearing in the conductivity. (2) and (3) The addition of appropriate divalent impurities provides an independent way to control and to measure the defect concentrations. In this way separate values can be found for x_+ and μ_+ (Figs 7 and 9) and for x_- and μ_- (Fig. 9). (4) and (5) Diffusion provides a way of distinguishing between cations and anions by using different radioactive tracers. If only single vacancies were involved, these two measurements would provide an independent determination of the transport numbers, but in recent years it has been discovered that vacancy pair contributions are often important in addition (Figs 14, 15, 19, 21). When Frenkel defects are present, there will still be at least two different processes involving the same ion (Figs 10, 13, 18). (6) and (7) These newer and more elaborate techniques provide an additional variable, either impurity concentration or electric field, that allows the vacancy pair contribution for each tracer to be sorted out. The experiments may be complicated for anions by extrinsic diffusion (Fig. 15), and there are still considerable experimental difficulties for diffusion in a field (Fig. 20). (8) This has not yet been tried extensively, partly because the vacancy pair contribution to anion diffusion can be obtained by (6), but in combination with (7) it would provide a useful overall check. (9) This has not been tried either and appears to have limited possibilities because of the low solubility of polyvalent anions. (10) In favourable cases this kind of experiment ensures a way of measuring the diffusion ratio for one defect at a time (Fig. 16). It is possible that the presence of complexes may cause complications by providing still another mechanism for cation diffusion, but the jump frequency of the divalent impurity is often several orders of magnitude smaller than for the cation. (11) The isotope effect involves observation of the small difference in diffusion coefficient between two isotopes of the same element (LcClaire, 1970). It arises because of the difference in frequencies for different masses but also involves correlation factors. Hence in principle this method could be used to measure the variable correlation factor for vacancy pair diffusion; such experiments are in progress for Na in NaCl and appear to confirm a substantial contribution from vacancy pairs (Rothman et al., 1971).

All of the first seven techniques above the line in Table II have been applied to some crystal, but there is no substance for which all seven have been applied in the same laboratory. The last four techniques have been used only sparsely, if at all, and still remain to be developed in large part. It has also become increasingly evident in the last five years that any refined treatment must take the long range interactions of Section IV into account. Hence, despite the considerable amount of work already carried out in this field, the last word has certainly not been written at this time.

B. Types of Defects

Figures 1 and 2 show the wide range of values, temperatures, and materials involved in ionic transport processes, and Fig. 3 depicts the basic types of defects that can account for these phenomena. We have considered various examples to illustrate applications of the theory and also to give some idea of typical behaviour. In Table III we now present some generalizations, which along with the selection of examples in Figs 1 and 2 provide a survey of defect transport processes in ionic crystals.

TABLE III.   Summary of Defects in Ionic Crystals

Type of substance and examples	Structure	Defect structure and transport mechanisms	Comments
Alkali halides LiF, NaCl, KI	NaCl (f.c.c.)	Schottky defects. Cation vacancies more mobile.	Anion vacancies also mobile at high temperatures. Some diffusion by vacancy pairs.
Cesium halides, etc. CsI, TlCl	CsCl (s.c.)	Schottky defects. Anion vacancies more mobile.	Cation vacancies also mobile. Some diffusion by vacancy pairs or next nearest neighbour jumps.
Silver halides AgCl, AgBr	NaCl (f.c.c.)	Cation Frenkel defects. Cation motion by both vacancy and interstitialcy.	Copper halides show appreciable electronic conductivity. Gold halides are unstable.
Alkaline earth halides CaF_2, $SrCl_2$	fluorite and others	Anion Frenkel defects. Anion vacancy and interstitial both mobile.	Cation diffusion by vacancies.
Other halides $PbBr_2$, $LaCl_3$	various	Schottky defects.	Both cations and anions have some mobility.
Simple salts with complex anions $NaNO_3$, Ag_2SO_4	low symmetry	Cation Frenkel defects.	Presumably electronic conduction is negligible.

TABLE III   Summary of Defects in Ionic Crystals—*continued*

Type of substance and examples	Structure	Defect structure and transport mechanisms	Comments
Small cations and large anions AgI, $RbAg_4I_5$, Li_2SO_4	mostly cubic	Cation disorder.	Large conductivity with small temperature dependence.
Alkaline earth oxides BeO, CaO	wurtzite and NaCl	Schottky defects. Cation concentration controlled by impurities.	Oxygen diffusion along dislocations. Increasing electronic conductivity with atomic number.
Fluorite structure UO_2, ZrO_2:CaO	fluorite	Anion Frenkel defects.	Almost completely ionic conduction.
Transition metal oxides FeO, Cr_2O_3	various	Cation diffusion by vacancies. Oxygen diffusion by dislocations.	Appreciable electronic conduction. Large deviations from stoichiometry.
Divalent chalcogenides ZnS, $PbTe$	NaCl and others	Neutral Frenkel defects, both cation and anion.	Behave as semi-conductors electrically.

The largest conductivities and diffusion coefficients are displayed by the materials with disordered cation sublattices—Li_2SO_4, $AgI(\alpha)$, $Ag_2S(\alpha)$, Ag_2HgI_4, and also $RbAg_4I_5$, which is potentially important because of its large conductivity even at room temperature. Next come materials with Frenkel defects, first of all the familiar silver halides, but also a number of materials with the fluorite structure, which seems to have a remarkable ability to stabilize ionic defects. The anion diffusion in CaF_2 and ZrO_2:CaO is comparable to the cation diffusion in the silver halides and even in Na_2S, with an antifluorite structure. Several salts with complex anions, $CsNO_3$ and Ag_2SO_4, also appear to have cation Frenkel defects. The simple salts with the CsCl structure have moderately large diffusion coefficients because of the fairly open lattice; Schottky defects allow often comparable diffusion of anions and cations, as in CsI, but the anion is usually more mobile, sometimes dramatically so, as in TlCl. The lead halides also seem to belong in this family with fairly mobile Schottky defects. The alkali halides with the closer packed NaCl structure likewise have Schottky defects, but appreciably higher temperatures are needed to make them mobile, and now the cation has the larger mobility. In oxides with the NaCl structure the enthalpies are even larger because of the double charge, and still higher temperatures are required, as for BeO and Cr_2O_3. Even in these oxides electronic conductivity is often noticeable, and in transition metal oxides like NiO and most of the other chalcogenides like PbS the situation is much worse. There is a large amount of interaction between ionic and electronic defects making many different charge states possible for the atomic defects, and the electrical properties are dominated by electrons or holes, greatly limiting the possibility of comparing diffusion and ionic conductivity in any detail. There are also large deviations from stoichiometry (like 10% in FeO), and both the stoichiometry and defect concentrations are often affected greatly by the surrounding atmosphere. For all of these reasons the certainty of the defect assignments decreases gradually from top to bottom in the table, with the basic defects well characterized for the monovalent halides at the top but with many open fundamental questions for the sulphides at the bottom.

Finally there remain only a few acknowledgements and general references. The author has profited greatly from the excellent reviews by Lidiard (1957), which presents the fundamental background for both experimental and theoretical aspects, by Barr and Lidiard (1970), which compiles many experimental results and also contains an extensive treatment of the theoretical calculation of formation and motion enthalpies, and by Fuller (1971), which provides derivations of many of the fundamental equations used here and also considers a number of the alkali halides in some detail. Additional information is provided by Adda and Philibert (1966), especially on diffusion in oxides, and by Süptitz and Teltow (1967) on the silver halides. A more extensive treatment of correlation effects is given by LeClaire (1970).

References

Abbink, H. C. and Martin, D. S., Jr. (1966). *J. Phys. Chem. Solids* **27**, 205.

Adda, Y. and Philibert, J. (1966). "La Diffusion dans les Solides". Presses Univ. de France, Paris.

Allnatt, A. R. (1967). *Adv. Chem. Phys.* **11**, 1.

Allnatt, A. R. and Cohen, M. H. (1964). *J. chem. Phys.* **40**, 1871.

Allnatt, A. R. and Pantelis, P. (1968). *Solid State Comm.* **6**, 309.

Barr, L. W. and Dawson, D. K. (1971) to be published.

Barr, L. W. and Lidiard, A. B. (1970). *In* "Physical Chemistry" (W. Jost, Ed.) Vol. X, p. 151. Academic Press, New York and London.

Barr, L. W., Morrison, J. A., and Schroeder, P. A. (1965). *J. appl. Phys.* **36**, 624 (1965).

Beaumont, J. H. and Jacobs, P. W. M. (1966). *J. chem. Phys.* **45**, 1496.

Brown, N. and Hoodless, I. M. (1967). *J. Phys. Chem. Solids* **28**, 2297.

Chandra, S. and Rolfe, J. (1970). *Can. J. Phys.* **48**, 397.

Compaan, K. and Haven, Y. (1956). *Trans. Faraday Soc.* **52**, 786.

Compaan, K. and Haven, Y. (1958). *Trans. Faraday Soc.* **54**, 1498.

Dawson, D. K. and Barr, L. W. (1967). *Phys. Rev. Letters* **19**, 844.

Dekker, A. J. (1957). "Solid State Physics". Prentice-Hall, Englewood Cliffs, New Jersey.

Downing, H. L., Jr. and Friauf, R. J. (1970). *J. Phys. Chem. Solids* **31**, 845.

Dreyfus, R. W. and Nowick, A. S. (1962a). *J. appl. Phys.* **33**, 473.

Dreyfus, R. W. and Nowick, A. S. (1962b). *Phys. Rev.* **126**, 1367.

Falkenhagen, H. (1934). "Electrolytes". Oxford University Press.

Fowler, R. H. and Guggenheim, E. A. (1949). "Statistical Thermodynamics". Oxford University Press.

Franklin, A. D. (1965). *J. Res. Natl. Bur. Std.* **A69**, 301.

Friauf, R. J. (1957). *Phys. Rev.* **105**, 843.

Friauf, R. J. (1962). *J. appl. Phys.* **33**, 494.

Friauf, R. J. (1971). *Z. Naturf.*, **26a**, 1210.

Fuller, R. G. (1971). *In* "Point Defects in Solids" (J. H. Crawford, Jr. and L. Slijkin, Eds.). Vol. 1. Plenum Press, New York.

Fuller, R. G. and Reilly, M. H. (1967). *Phys. Rev. Letters* **19**, 113.

Fuller, R. G., Marquardt, C. L., Reilly, M. H., and Wells, J. C., Jr. (1968). *Phys. Rev.* **176**, 1036.

Gracey, J. P. and Friauf, R. J. (1969). *J. Phys. Chem. Solids* **30**, 421.

Harvey, P. J. and Hoodless, I. M. (1967). *Phil. Mag.* **16**, 543.

Howard, R. E. (1966). *Phys. Rev.* **144**, 650.

Jost, W. (1952). "Diffusion in Solids, Liquids, Gases". Academic Press, New York and London.

Kirk, D. L. and Pratt, P. L. (1967). *Proc. Br. Ceram. Soc.* **9**, 215.

Kröger, F. A. (1964). "The Chemistry of Imperfect Crystals". North Holland Publ. Co., Amsterdam.

Laurance, N. (1960). *Phys. Rev.* **120**. 57.

LeClaire, A. D. (1970). *In* "Physical Chemistry" (W. Jost, Ed.) Vol. X, p. 261. Academic Press, New York.

Lewis, G. N. and Randall, M. (1923). "Thermodynamics". McGraw–Hill, New York.

Lidiard, A. B. (1954). *Phys. Rev.* **94**, 29.

Lidiard, A. B. (1955). *Phil. Mag.* **46**, 815, 1218.

Lidiard, A. B. (1957). *In* "Encyclopedia of Physics' (S. Flügge, Ed.) Vol. XX, p. 246. Springer-Verlag, Berlin.

Lynch, D. W. (1960). *Phys. Rev.* **118**, 468.

Mott, N. F. and Gurney, R. W. (1948). "Electronic Processes in Ionic Crystals". Oxford University Press.

Nelson, V. C. and Friauf, R. J. (1970). *J. Phys. Chem. Solids* **31**, 825.

Onsager, L. (1927). *Phys. Z.* **28**, 286.

Pitts, E. (1953). *Proc. R. Soc. Lond. Ser.* **A217**, 43.

Rothman, S. J., Peterson, N. L., and Laskar, A. (1971). *Bull. Am. phys. Soc.* **16**, 362.

Süptitz, P. and Teltow, J. (1967). *Phys. Status Solidi* **23**, 9.

Teltow, J. (1950a) *Ann. Physik* **5**, 63.

Teltow, J. (1950b). *Z. phys. Chem.* **195**, 213.

Tharmalingam, K. and Lidiard, A. B. (1961). *Phil. Mag.* **6**, 1157.

Weber, M. D. and Friauf, R. J. (1969). *J. Phys. Chem. Solids* **30**, 407.

6. DIFFUSION IN IONIC CRYSTALS

F. Bénière

Laboratoire d'Electrochimie, Faculté des Sciences de Paris, France.

I. Introduction

Whenever solid materials, and especially crystalline solids, are used in Electrochemistry one is concerned with diffusion. Sometimes only the magnitudes of unknown diffusion coefficients of substances in solids are required and we aim to describe how these may be obtained. Moreover, since diffusion involves the mobilities of ions through solids, and it is the properties of the defects of the lattice that are responsible for this migration of ions, the study of diffusion phenomena appears as the most powerful tool for the understanding of all the transport processes in solids and for the description of the involved defects. Our main purpose is to throw some light on the ways of interpreting the experimental diffusion coefficients in terms of ionic mobilities and defect concentrations.

It is not our aim to describe all the diffusion phenomena that occur under the action of external forces, e.g. diffusion in the presence of an applied electric field (Chemla, 1954; Nelson and Friauf, 1970), thermal diffusion in a temperature gradient (Allnatt and Chadwick, 1967; Crolet, 1970), diffusion in centrifugal fields (Barr, 1970) . . . but we wish to focus on the basic phenomena of diffusion without an external force and at constant pressure and temperature. Furthermore, we shall restrict ourselves to the treatment of systems that seem to be well understood, namely the alkali halides and the silver halides, in order to give in more detail some examples of recent analyses which could be extrapolated to other substances for which less extensive studies have been carried out.

It is well known that in order to measure the self-diffusion coefficients one must use isotopes of the host ions. The radioactive isotopes, when available, are the most convenient; Owing to the sensitivity of radioactive counting techniques, very small amounts of diffusing particles, which then do not alter the composition of the crystals, are sufficient for measuring the diffusion coefficients. We shall denote *tracer-diffusion coefficients* as the diffusion coefficients of the *isotopes* of the host ions. These are generally not equal to the *self-diffusion coefficients*, i.e. the diffusion coefficients of the *indistinguishable* host ions themselves, which can be obtained with some restrictive conditions by measuring the ionic conductivity. The difference is mostly due to correlation effects and to a lesser extent to isotope effects. The advantage of the diffusion method is that it allows the individual mobilities of each species of ion to be measured by following the corresponding isotope through each sub-lattice.

We shall also consider the case of the diffusion of foreign ions (or "impurities") denoting the corresponding diffusion coefficients as *impurity diffusion coefficients*. Such studies will fall into two quite distinct categories according to the valency of the impurity, which will be either the same as that of the host ion, or a different one (we shall speak of the latter case as *aliovalent impurity diffusion coefficients*).

One knows that crystalline solids differ from the fluid states by the fact that their macroscopic shapes are not deformable. On the other hand, it has been known since the first diffusion experiments in lead compounds using natural radioactive thorium (performed by von Hevesy, 1929) that the atoms in solids do not stay in the same positions. Since the atoms or ions that constitute the crystal are indistinguishable, in order to study the diffusion processes one must establish a gradient of concentration of particles which can be distinguished from the host ions. Whenever a concentration gradient is established, the system tends to level the concentrations. This is the definition of the diffusion process, the rate of which is expressed by the magnitude of the diffusion coefficient. In mathematical terms this phenomenon is represented by Fick's law, which connects the diffusion flow— or current of diffusing particles passing through a surface of unit area during unit time—to the concentration gradient; Le Claire's demonstration of this law will be described in Section II.

In order to measure the rate of diffusion, the initial concentration $C(t = 0)$ is given a well-defined shape. After the time t, the concentration at point M becomes $C(M, t)$, which is solution of Fick's law. For some suitable sets of initial and boundary conditions, the experimental determination of the function $C(M, t)$ readily leads to the evaluation of the diffusion coefficient. The main solutions of Fick's law which are of practical interest are summarized in Section III.

The diffusion coefficients are thus determined from the measurement of the macroscopic flows. However, the main interest in diffusion is because one can obtain from the knowledge of the temperature dependence of the diffusion coefficients detailed information on the microscopic properties of the ions and lattice defects: nature, density and mobility of the operative defects. In a general way the diffusion coefficients may be expressed as the product of the density of defects and the mobility of the ions. We describe in Section IV the major models of defects that have been proposed, the physical reasons why lattice defects originate and what determines their concentrations: thermal disorder and electrical neutrality. The expressions for the different diffusion coefficients as functions of the density and mobility of defects are summarized in Section V, and developed in terms of the entropy and enthalpy of formation and migration of defects.

Another term entering into the diffusion coefficient expression is the correlation factor, which arises when the directions of the successive jumps of a given particle are not independent of one another. This is due in the measured tracer-diffusion coefficients to the use of isotopes, i.e. distinguishable particles; here the correlation factor is a mere geometrical factor expressed numerically. In contrast, diffusion of impurities involves more than one kind of jump; in this case, the correlation factor is a function of all the frequencies of the jumps which operate in the migration of the diffusing particles. These effects are denoted in both cases by the same term —"correlation effects"—which are described in Section VI.

The major experimental methods that are used for the measurement of the diffusion coefficients are surveyed in Section VII. A review of the measured diffusion constants in ionic crystals is given at the end of this paper, which may be helpful when only an estimate of the magnitude of a diffusion coefficient is required. In order to give some concrete examples of the ways the theoretical principles developed in the early sections can be applied, attention is focused on a few characteristic problems in Section VIII. These are examples of the detailed investigations which have been carried out in the last few years. The purpose of this section is not only to review the results obtained but also to throw light on the difficulties that arise in analysing the experimental data and on the wealth of the information that can be obtained from diffusion studies. Finally, the experimental results are compared with the theoretical calculations which have been carried out using the classical ionic model.

II. Fick's First Law

Whenever a concentration gradient of a substance is established in a given system, this gradient tends, in the absence of external forces, to decrease with time. In other words, a mean flow of particles—the diffusion flow—occurs from the higher to the lower concentrations. This is the definition of the diffusion phenomenon. The diffusion flow, J, is proportional to the concentration gradient, grad C, according to Fick's well known first law

$$\mathbf{J} = -D \, \mathbf{grad} \, \mathbf{C} \qquad (2.1)$$

where D is the diffusion coefficient; this is analogous to the flow of heat being proportional to the temperature gradient. However, for the case of self-diffusion we will use the approach of Le Claire (1958), which establishes that this law is an approximation and shows the physical significance of the diffusion coefficient.[†]

Let us consider a lattice in which some atoms have been substituted by isotopes and exchange their sites with normal atoms (tracer-diffusion); furthermore, let us consider a distribution where the concentration depends

† For a complete and comprehensive atomic treatment of diffusion in solids, see the book by Adda and Philibert, "La Diffusion dans les Solides" (Bibliothèque des Sciences et techniques nucléaires—Presses Universitaires de France, 1966).

on only one coordinate—let it be the x coordinate—(one-dimensional diffusion). The concentration of the marked atoms is then a function of x and of time; let it be $C(x, t)$. In order to calculate the diffusion flow, we need to count the number of particles which pass through a surface of unit area, perpendicular to the x-axis, in the plane x_0 during the time t. The particles migrate through the lattice by making a sequence of jumps owing to the presence of defects. We have chosen the case of tracer-diffusion, with no external force applied, so that the probability of displacement is the same along both positive x and negative x directions. A given particle makes a large number of jumps but a short mean displacement, the projection of which along the x-axis will be called X. Let us define the distribution function $f(X, t)\, dX$ as the probability that, at a time t, a particle has made a displacement with a projection between X and $X + dX$. It follows from this definition that

$$\int_{-\infty}^{+\infty} f(X, t)\, dX = 1. \tag{2.2}$$

Moreover, since the jumps along both $+x$ and $-x$ directions occur with the same probability, one has

$$f(X, t) = f(-X, t). \tag{2.3}$$

Considering a large number of particles, the projection of the mean displacement, $\langle X \rangle$, may then be written as

$$\langle X \rangle = \int_{-\infty}^{+\infty} X f(X, t)\, dX \tag{2.4}$$

It follows from (2.3) that $\langle X \rangle$ and every $\langle X^{2n+1} \rangle$ is zero.

The most important parameter in diffusion is the mean square displacement, $\langle L^2 \rangle$, the projection of which is then

$$\langle X^2 \rangle = \int_{-\infty}^{+\infty} X^2 f(X, t)\, dX. \tag{2.5}$$

We now calculate the number of particles, initially situated to the left of the plane x_0, which cross the plane from left to right during the time t and the number of particles which were initially to the right of the plane x_0 which, in the same interval of time, cross in the opposite direction (Fig. 1). The net diffusion flow will then be the difference between these two numbers per unit time.

A given particle situated in any plane of abscissa $x < x_0$ at time $t = 0$ has the probability at time t

$$\int_{x_0 - x}^{\infty} f(X, t)\,dX$$

of having made a displacement $X \geqslant x_0 - x$, and thus of falling into the first category. Let $C(x)$ be the number of marked particles per unit volume in the plane of abscissa equal to x. The number of particles situated between two surfaces of unit area of the planes x and $x + dx$ is thus equal to $C(x)\,dx$ At time t, the number of these particles that will have crossed the plane is

$$C(x)\,dx \int_{x_0 - x}^{\infty} f(X, t)\,dX$$

In order to evaluate the flow J_+ of particles that cross from left to right one must add the contributions of all particles initially situated at the left hand side of the plane x_0, which gives

$$J_+ = \frac{1}{t} \int_{-\infty}^{x_0} C(x) \left[\int_{x_0 - x}^{\infty} f(X, t)\,dX \right] dx.$$

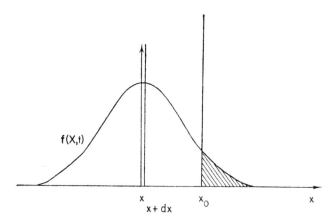

FIG. 1. Probality function $f(X, t)$ for displacement of a particle a time t after it was at x. The dashed part illustrates the probability for every particle initially situated at x of having crossed the plane x_0.

In the same way, one may calculate the flow J_- in the opposite direction

$$J_- = \frac{1}{t} \int_{x_0}^{\infty} C(x) \left[\int_{-\infty}^{x_0 - x} f(X, t)\,dX \right] dx.$$

The net diffusion flow is

$$J = J_+ - J_-.$$

We then expand $C(x)$ around the plane x_0

$$C(x) = C(x_0) + \sum_{n=1}^{\infty} \frac{1}{n!} \left(\frac{\partial^n C}{\partial x^n} \right)_{x=x_0} (x - x_0)^n.$$

Carrying out the integration, one finally obtains

$$J = \frac{1}{t} \left[C(x_0)\langle X \rangle - \left(\frac{\partial C}{\partial x} \right)_{x=x_0} \frac{\langle X^2 \rangle}{2} + \left(\frac{\partial^2 C}{\partial x^2} \right)_{x=x_0} \frac{\langle X^3 \rangle}{3!} \right.$$
$$\left. - \left(\frac{\partial^3 C}{\partial x^3} \right)_{x=x_0} \frac{\langle X^4 \rangle}{4!} + \dots \right].$$

We have seen that $\langle X \rangle = \langle X^3 \rangle = \dots \langle X^{2n+1} \rangle = 0$.
Neglecting the terms in $\langle X^4 \rangle$ and higher, one obtains

$$J = - \frac{\langle X^2 \rangle}{2t} \frac{\partial C}{\partial x}. \tag{2.6}$$

This is Fick's first law which is usually written as

$$J_x = - D_x \frac{\partial C}{\partial x}$$

for one-dimensional diffusion. Le Claire's calculation shows the degree of approximation of this relation, and the definition of the diffusion coefficient, which is

$$D_x = \frac{\langle X^2 \rangle}{2t}.$$

In isotropic structures (cubic crystals) one may decompose every movement along the three axes of Euclidian space. All projections of the mean square displacement are equal

$$\langle X^2 \rangle = \langle Y^2 \rangle = \langle Z^2 \rangle$$

or, in other words, the diffusion coefficient has the same value for every direction

$$D_x = D_y = D_z \equiv D.$$

We may express D as a function of the mean square displacement, $\langle L^2 \rangle$, which is equal to

$$\langle L^2 \rangle = \langle X^2 \rangle + \langle Y^2 \rangle + \langle Z^2 \rangle = 3 \langle X^2 \rangle.$$

Equation (2.6) then becomes

$$J = -D \frac{\partial C}{\partial x} \tag{2.7}$$

where

$$D = \frac{\langle L^2 \rangle}{6t}. \tag{2.8}$$

This relation may be regarded as the most general definition of any diffusion coefficient (Rayleigh, 1894; Einstein, 1905). Diffusion in crystalline solids is special in that the displacement of a particle results from a sequence of individual jumps which are all of the same length, determined by the lattice parameters. Let δ denote the absolute value of the jump length; the vector displacement of a particle that makes n jumps during the time t is

$$\mathbf{L} = \boldsymbol{\delta}_1 + \boldsymbol{\delta}_2 + ... \boldsymbol{\delta}_n = \sum_{i=1}^{n} \boldsymbol{\delta}_i.$$

In the case of tracer-diffusion, i.e. for non-interacting diffusing particles and without external forces being applied, the mean displacement $\langle \mathbf{L} \rangle$ of a large number of particles is zero.

The mean value of the square of the vector displacement may be written as

$$\langle L^2 \rangle = \left\langle \left(\sum_{i=1}^{n} \delta_i{}^2 \right) \right\rangle = \sum_{i=1}^{n} \langle \delta_i{}^2 \rangle + \sum_{i \neq j} \sum \langle \boldsymbol{\delta}_i \boldsymbol{\delta}_j \rangle. \tag{2.9}$$

When the jumps of a given particle are completely random and independent of one another, the second term on the right-hand side of (2.9) is zero, since in calculating this average value it is possible to associate with any term $\boldsymbol{\delta}_i \cdot \boldsymbol{\delta}_j$ a term $\boldsymbol{\delta}_i \cdot (-\boldsymbol{\delta}_j)$ which cancels the former. However, this condition is not always rigidly fulfilled. On the contrary, in many mechanisms each individual jump occurs in a direction that depends on the direction of the preceding one. Thus the jumps are correlated, and the average value of $\langle \boldsymbol{\delta}_i \cdot \boldsymbol{\delta}_j \rangle$ is no longer equal to zero. We shall deal with this important effect in Section VI and we shall consider first ideal systems without any correlation effects, where

$$\langle L^2 \rangle = \sum_{i=1}^{n} \delta_i{}^2 = n \delta^2 \tag{2.10}$$

n being the average number of jumps made during the time t. It is useful to define the average number of jumps made in unit time or jump probability during unit time as

$$\Gamma = \frac{n}{t}$$

so that (2.8), when (2.10) holds, becomes

$$D = \frac{\Gamma \delta^2}{6}. \tag{2.11}$$

When the jumps are correlated the correlation effects may be expressed in the diffusion coefficient by multiplying (2.11) by a factor which will be developed in Section VI and which is called the correlation factor, denoted by f. The general expression of the diffusion coefficient is thus

$$D = f\frac{\Gamma \delta^2}{6}. \tag{2.12}$$

The ions move through the crystal owing to the presence of defects. A given particle may jump into a defect when two conditions are simultaneously fulfilled, namely:

the particle has a defect available on a nearest neighbour site;

the particle has sufficient energy to cross the potential barrier that opposes its migration.

The first condition involves the probability of the presence of a defect, or in other words the molar fraction of defects, while the second one involves the probability of jumps, which for unit time can be related to the jump frequency. Thus Γ is the product of two microscopic quantities of fundamental interest in the understanding of the ionic crystals, namely the density of defects and the frequency of jumps. Equation (2.11) where δ is a mere geometrical parameter, gives a way of determining Γ from the experimental determination of D. We shall decompose Γ into terms of defect concentrations (Section IV) and jump frequencies (Section V). First, in the following section, we shall deal with the relations that lead to the determination of D from the knowledge of the distribution of the diffusing particle concentration.

III. The Main Laws of Diffusion of Practical Interest

We have seen that the diffusion flow is, to a first approximation, proportional to the concentration gradient

$$\mathbf{J} = - D \,\mathbf{grad}\,\mathbf{C}.$$

This fundamental equation is called Fick's first law, D being called the diffusion coefficient, which in some cases is a function of C. In anisotropic structures, D depends on the crystallographic orientation, diffusion occurring along different directions at different rates. In practice however, it is easier to study diffusion in one crystallographic direction in order to obtain a definite diffusion coefficient, and because of the nature of single crystals which tend to cleave along privileged planes. The boundary surface of the sample is made smooth and this defines the initial plane of the diffusion. So, in the experimental case we need consider only diffusion in one direction, perpendicular to the reference surface. Let x be the coordinate in this direction Fick's first law then simplifies to

$$J = -D\frac{\partial C}{\partial x}. \tag{3.1}$$

J is the diffusion flow, i.e. the quantity of the considered substance passing perpendicularly through a surface of unit area during unit time. J is usually expressed as a quantity of substance per cm^2 per second. The unit for the quantity of substance must be the same as in the unit of concentration, which may be a unit of mass (gram) or a number of particles. The diffusion coefficient D is then expressed in cm^2 per second.

By writing the law of mass conservation in an elementary volume one readily finds the relation

$$\frac{\partial C}{\partial t} = \frac{\partial}{\partial x}\left(D\frac{\partial C}{\partial x}\right) \tag{3.2}$$

which is Fick's second law in the case of one-dimensional diffusion.

We shall not be concerned with steady state diffusion for which $\partial C/\partial t = 0$. Generally diffusion is studied in a non-steady state condition with the concentration gradients decreasing with time.

Let $C(x, t = 0)$ denote the concentration function of the considered particles before diffusion is allowed to start. Generally diffusion does not occur at room temperature at an appreciable rate and rather high temperatures are needed to obtain measurable diffusion coefficients. The time at which the system is raised to the considered temperature is taken as the initial time. At time t after the beginning of the diffusion the diffusing particles are distributed according to a new function, $C(x, t)$, which is determined experimentally, This function is a solution of eqn (3.2) for the initial and boundary conditions that have been applied. The measured value of $C(x, t)$ is fitted to this mathematical solution, which leads to the determination of D. A considerable number of diffusion problems have been considered mathematically for planar, cylindrical and spherical diffusion and for many sets of initial and boundary conditions (Jost, 1952; Crank, 1956; Adda and Philibert 1966). However, planar diffusion is the most frequent experimental case and we shall restrict ourselves to one-dimensional diffusion problems. Furthermore, experimentalists attempt to adopt initial conditions that lead to a simple solution of eqn (3.2) in order to determine diffusion coefficients as accurately as possible in a simple way. We shall therefore only consider the main practical cases of diffusion in ionic crystals—planar diffusion in an infinite medium, i.e. diffusion along the x axis, C depending only on x. This is realized in crystals with plane surfaces with large dimensions relative to the diffusion depth. The external sides of the crystal are removed after the experiment, in order to measure C as a function of x for a given t in the central part of the sample.

Two principle sets of initial conditions are encountered: diffusion from an infinitely thin layer and diffusion from a constant concentration. Another subdivision to be considered is whether D is constant or not.

A. Solutions for Constant D

When the diffusion coefficient does not depend on the concentration and so is independent of x, as occurs for instance in the tracer–diffusion experiments, Fick's second law can be expressed as

$$\frac{\partial C}{\partial t} = D \frac{\partial^2 C}{\partial x^2} . \tag{3.3}$$

We shall now look at the solutions of this differential equation for the following initial and boundary conditions.

1. Diffusion from an Infinitely Thin Layer

The simplest way of studying diffusion is to use a radioisotope if it is available. A small amount of the tracer is deposited onto a smoothed surface of the crystal, or, for experimental convenience between two crystals joined face to face. For this last case the initial conditions are

$$t = 0 \begin{cases} C(0,0) = Q\delta(x) \\ C(x,0) = 0 \end{cases}$$

where Q is the total amount of the deposited substance per unit area and $\delta(x)$ is the Dirac's function; and the boundary conditions are

$$t \geqslant 0 \begin{cases} C(\pm \infty, t) = 0 \\ \left(\dfrac{\partial C}{\delta x} \right)_{x = \pm \infty} = 0 \end{cases} .$$

Equation (3.3) is now soluble using Fourier's transform of the C function, denoted by $\bar{C}(w, t)$ which has the form

$$\bar{C}(w, t) = \frac{1}{\sqrt{2\pi}} \int_{-\infty}^{+\infty} \exp\,(iwx)\, C(x, t)\, \mathrm{d}x.$$

Equation (3.3) can now be written as

$$\frac{\partial \bar{C}(w, t)}{\partial t} = - Dw^2 \bar{C}(w, t)$$

which after integration yields

$$\bar{C}(w, t) = K \exp\,(- Dw^2 t).$$

The constant of integration, K, is determined from the initial conditions, which give for $t = 0$

$$\bar{C}(w, 0) = K = \frac{Q}{\sqrt{2\pi}} \int_{-\infty}^{+\infty} \exp\,(iwx)\, \delta(x)\, \mathrm{d}x$$

$$= \frac{Q}{\sqrt{2\pi}}.$$

So we can now write

$$K = \frac{Q}{\sqrt{2\pi}} \text{ and } \bar{C}(w, t) = \frac{Q}{\sqrt{2\pi}} \exp\,(- Dw^2 t).$$

Now we return to $C(x, t)$, which from the Fourier's transform, is equal to

$$C(x, t) = \frac{1}{\sqrt{2\pi}} \int_{-\infty}^{+\infty} \exp\,(- iwx) \bar{C}(w, t)\, \mathrm{d}w$$

$$= \frac{Q}{2\pi} \int_{-\infty}^{+\infty} \exp\,(- iwx) \exp\,(- Dw^2 t)\, \mathrm{d}w$$

$C(x, t)$, being real, can be written as

$$C(x, t) = \frac{Q}{2\pi} \int_{-\infty}^{+\infty} \cos\,(wx) \exp\,(- Dw^2 t)\, \mathrm{d}w$$

and by integrating one then obtains as the final answer

$$C(x, t) = \frac{Q}{2\sqrt{\pi D t}} \exp\left(- \frac{x^2}{4Dt}\right). \tag{3.4}$$

This function is the Gauss error curve. Figure 2 shows an experimental plot of C versus x.

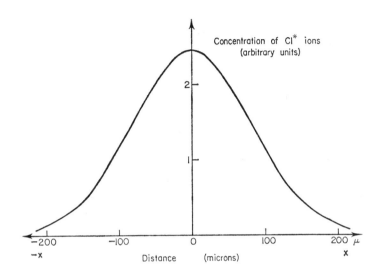

FIG. 2. Diffusion profile for the solution

$$C(x, t) = \frac{Q}{2\sqrt{\pi Dt}} \exp\left(-\frac{x^2}{4Dt}\right).$$

(Diffusion of $^{36}Cl^-$ into KCl, $t = 146\,700$ s, temperature $= 680 \cdot 3°C$; After M. Bénière 1970).

If the diffusion occurs from an infinitely thin layer into only one crystal' the solution differs from (3.4) only by a factor of 2, which expresses the fact that the diffusing species is no longer divided between two crystals. Hence the expression in this case is

$$C(x, t) = \frac{Q}{\sqrt{\pi Dt}} \exp\left(-\frac{x^2}{4Dt}\right). \qquad (3.5)$$

2. Diffusion from a Constant Concentration

In the preceding analysis the whole substance diffuses into the crystal and the concentration in the initial surface layer decreases with time as $1/\sqrt{t}$. Another frequent problem is the diffusion of a substance from a source which is maintained at a fixed concentration outside the crystal. This is the case for instance with the vapour of a volatile compound which is in thermodynamic equilibrium with its solid phase, the concentration being fixed by the vapour pressure. The initial conditions are then

$$t = 0 \begin{cases} C = C_0 & x \leqslant 0 \\ C = 0 & x > 0 \end{cases}$$

while the boundary conditions are

$$x = 0 \{ C = C_0 \quad t \geqslant 0$$

$$x = \infty \begin{cases} C(\infty, t) & = 0 \\ \left(\dfrac{\partial C}{\partial x} \right)_{x = \infty} & = 0 \end{cases}.$$

We can consider the substance diffusing into the crystal by imagining the $x \leqslant 0$ region as an infinite series of infinitely thin layers. Each layer diffuses, introducing a contribution to the concentration inside the crystal of the form given by (3.5). Let us consider one of these layers of unit area (shaded on Fig. 3) situated at a distance 1 from the initial plane ($x = 0$).

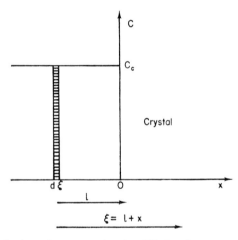

FIG. 3. Initial distribution of concentration for diffusion from a constant concentration.

Let ξ be a new variable defined by $\xi = x + 1$. The amount of substance in this layer of width $d\xi$ is $C_0 d\xi$. This layer gives a contribution to the concentration at x which can be expressed by eqn (3.5), since the layer is infinitely thin. Hence we can write

$$dC(x, t) = \frac{C_0 d\xi}{\sqrt{\pi D t}} \exp \left(- \frac{\xi^2}{4Dt} \right).$$

The total concentration in the plane at x is the sum of the contributions from all layers situated between $x = 0$ and $x = -\infty$, and when $d\xi \to 0$ it is given by the integral

$$C(x, t) = \frac{C_0}{\sqrt{\pi Dt}} \int_x^{+\infty} \exp\left(-\frac{\xi^2}{4Dt}\right) d\xi.$$

Introducing

$$\eta = \frac{\xi}{\sqrt{4Dt}},$$

one gets

$$C(x, t) = \frac{2C_0}{\sqrt{\pi}} \int_{(x/2\sqrt{Dt})}^{+\infty} \exp\left(-\eta^2\right) d\eta.$$

The function $(2/\sqrt{\pi})\int_0^x \exp\left(-\eta^2\right) d\eta$ is the Gauss error function and is denoted by erf (x). So $C(x, t)$ can be written as

$$C(x, t) = C_0[\text{erf}(\infty) - \text{erf}(x/2\sqrt{Dt})].$$

Since erf (∞) is equal to 1, one obtains the final result

$$C(x, t) = C_0[1 - \text{erf}(x/2\sqrt{Dt})]. \tag{3.6}$$

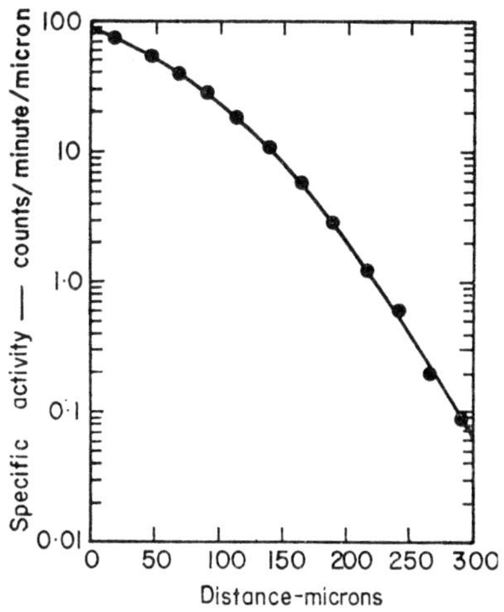

FIG. 4. Diffusion profile for the solution

$$C = C_0\left(1 - \text{erf}\frac{x}{2\sqrt{Dt}}\right).$$

(Diffusion of Pb^{++} from $PbCl_2$ vapour into KCl doped with 2×10^{-5} $PbCl_2$, $t = 1\cdot054$ 10^6 s; temperature $= 373°C$; After Keneshea and Fredericks, 1963).

Numerical tables of the error function have been computed and are used to determine the diffusion coefficient in this case. A typical curve of the distribution of the diffusing particle is shown in Fig. 4 for the diffusion of Pb^{++} from $PbCl_2$ vapour into $PbCl_{2-}$ doped KCl crystals. We shall see later that for these conditions D does not depend on x, if C_0 is sufficiently low.

A similar result is obtained when one considers two samples of different composition joined at the plane $x = 0$. In this case one follows the same treatment using equation (3.4) instead of (3.5) which gives, for the concentration of a substance which has diffused into one of the samples from the other,

$$C(x, t) = \frac{C_0}{2} [1 - \text{erf} (x/2\sqrt{Dt})]. \tag{3.7}$$

B. Treatment for D Dependent on Concentration

We have seen in the preceding section that the concentration of the diffusing substance is a decreasing function of x. When the substance does not alter the nature and concentration of defects the diffusion flow depends on x but the diffusion coefficient remains constant as for example in the tracer-self-diffusion experiments. On the contrary, diffusion of aliovalent impurity ions changes the composition of the crystal and D is no longer a constant. A practical case is the study of divalent cations in crystals composed of monovalent ions; each foreign ion introduces a new defect as will be seen later. In this case diffusion is usually studied with the conditions described above, i.e. with the initial distribution

$$t = 0 \begin{cases} C = 0 & x > 0 \\ C = C_0 & x \leqslant 0 \end{cases}$$

and the boundary conditions

$$\begin{cases} x = 0 & C = C_0 & t \geqslant 0 \\ x = \infty & C = 0 & t \geqslant 0 \end{cases}$$

In order to solve eqn (3.2)

$$\frac{\partial C}{\partial t} = \frac{\partial}{\partial x} \left(D \frac{\partial C}{\partial x} \right).$$

Boltzmann's substitution is used, $y = x/\sqrt{t}$, which gives

$$\frac{d}{dy}\left(D\frac{dC}{dy}\right) = -\frac{y}{2}\frac{dC}{dy}.$$

After the first integration one obtains

$$\int_{C_0}^{C} d\left[D\frac{dC}{dy}\right] = \tfrac{1}{2}\int_{C}^{C_0} y\, dC.$$

This equation cannot be integrated exactly and one must carry out the integration by means of numerical or graphical methods. After the time t of diffusion, C is experimentally measured for different values of x, so that $C(x)$ is obtained for a given t. Since t is then a constant, the last equation may be rewritten as

$$\int_{C_0}^{C} d\left[D\frac{dC}{dx}\right] = \frac{1}{2t}\int_{C}^{C_0} x\, dC$$

and upon integration of the left-hand side

$$D(C)\left(\frac{dC}{dx}\right)_C - D(C_0)\left(\frac{dC}{dx}\right)_{C_0} = \frac{1}{2t}\int_{C}^{C_0} x\, dC. \qquad (3.8)$$

This equation cannot be integrated, but nevertheless D can be evaluated as follows

On the graph of $C = f(x)$, the slope at the origin $(x = 0)$ is equal to $(dC/dx)_{C_0}$, while the slope at the point (x, C) is equal to $(dC/dx)_C$. The right-hand side of eqn (3.8) is obtained by graphical integration of the curve between C and C_0. The unknowns are then $D(C_0)$ which is a constant, and $D(C)$, which decreases with x. The procedure proposed by Keneshea and Fredericks is usually followed, i.e. the total area under the curve C versus x is graphically measured, i.e. $\int_{C \to 0}^{C_0} x\, dC$. For $C \to 0$, $dC/dx \to 0$ and $D(C_0)$ may be deduced from the relation (3.8) which becomes

$$-D(C_0)\left(\frac{dC}{dx}\right)_{C_0} = \frac{1}{2t}\int_{C \to 0}^{C_0} x\, dC$$

$D(C)$ is then obtained at every value of C, that is to say at every x, by carrying out the corresponding integration $\int_C^{C_0} x \, dC$ and using eqn (3.8). Some examples of this kind of diffusion profile are shown in Fig. 5.

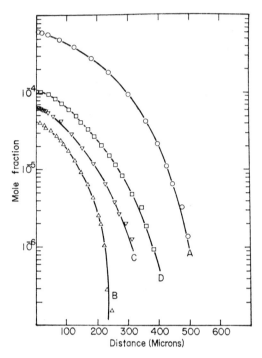

FIG. 5. Diffusion profiles for D depending on the concentration (Diffusion of Cd^{++} from $CdCl_2$ vapour into pure NaCl. A: 422°C at $6·94 \times 10^4$ s, B: 376°C at $8·7 \times 10^4$ s; C: 328°C at $4·10 \times 10^5$ s; D: 301°C at $6·03 \times 10^5$ s; After Allen, Ireland and Fredericks, 1967).

IV. Defects in Ionic Crystals

X-ray diffraction experiments have shown the structure of the crystalline lattices and the general order of the atoms situated on lattice sites. However, when von Hevesy presented evidence for diffusion in solids, the presence of some disorder was necessary to explain the motion of the atoms. A great number of defect models have been proposed. We are at present concerned with lattice defects whose size is of the order of the atomic volume, the so-called point defects, which cannot be observed directly. However, we shall see that diffusion is the phenomenon that gives indirect but the most useful information about the nature of the point defects.

The first models of disorder were proposed by Frenkel and by Schottky and those still remain the most widely used models. To his credit. Frenkel not only gave a simple picture of defect but established the thermodynamics of defects in solids and showed that the existence of point defects is *required* by thermodynamics.

Frenkel's model is based on the assumption that some atoms might jump from normal lattice sites to interstices. Migration of atoms may then be explained either by jumps of interstitials from interstice to interstice (interstitial mechanism, Fig. 6a) or by jumps of interstitials pushing a normal atom to another interstice (interstitialcy mechanism, Fig. 6b). Such mechanisms occur, for instance, in the diffusion of the silver ion in silver halides.

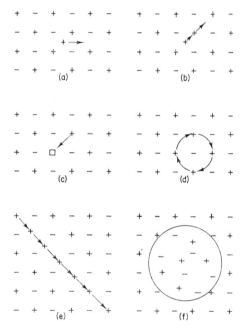

FIG. 6. Diffusion mechanisms in the case of an ionic crystal of NaCl-lattice. 6a: interstitial; 6b: direct interstitialcy; 6c: vacancy; 6d: ring mechanism; 6e: crowdion; 6f: relaxion.

Another suggestion, due to Schottky, is that some atoms can jump from their normal lattice sites on to the surface of the crystal, resulting in unoccupied sites or "vacancies". One can imagine then another diffusion mechanism in which the atoms merely jump into the vacancies (vacancy mechanism, Fig. 6c).

In the case of ionic crystals, the situation is more complex than in metals because one needs to consider all sub-lattices and the kind of disorder present on each sub-lattice may be different. In alkali halide crystals, it is assumed that no interstitials are present but vacancies are, and that these occur in equal numbers on both the anion and cation sub-lattices (to maintain electrical neutrality). The cation vacancy with its corresponding anion vacancy is called a Schottky pair.

Other mechanisms occuring by other defects have been proposed. First, direct exchange between two or more atoms have been considered (ring mechanism, Fig. 6d) but this is not probable in ionic crystals. Defects involving several disordered atoms, have also been suggested—either in a row (Crowdion, Fig. 6e) or in a small volume (relaxion, Fig. 6f).

We shall now describe the calculation of the concentration of Frenkel and Schottky defects using Frenkel's principle, i.e. the defects are in thermal equilibrium. The most stable state of the ions corresponds to the occupation of normal sites; all of these are occupied at $0°K$. Formation of defects requires energy, namely the Gibbs free energy of formation of the defect. At the same time, the existence of defects leads to an increase in the configurational entropy. The concentration of defects is determined when these two terms compensate, i.e. when thermal equilibrium is reached.

A. Concentration of Frenkel Defects

In the case of Frenkel defects, each sub-lattice can be treated independently. Let us consider a lattice in a pure crystal containing N normal sites and n_f Frenkel defects, i.e. n_f interstitials and n_f vacancies. Let G_f be the Gibbs free energy of formation of a Frenkel defect and ΔG the difference in energy between a crystal with and one without defects. ΔG is given by

$$\Delta G = n_f G_f - T S_{\text{conf}}.$$

The configurational entropy, S_{conf}, is obtained by summing the ways of arranging the n_f vacancies on the N normal lattice sites and the n_f interstitials on the N' interstitial sites, namely:

$$S_{\text{conf}} = k \log_e \left[\frac{N!}{(N - n_f)! \, n_f!} \frac{N'!}{(N' - n_f)! \, n_f!} \right].$$

So ΔG can be rewritten as a function of n_f:

$$\Delta G = n_f G_f - kT \log_e \left[\frac{N!}{(N - n_f)! \, n_f!} \frac{N'!}{(N' - n_f)! \, n_f!} \right].$$

Thermodynamic equilibrium is reached when ΔG is minimized:

$$\frac{\partial \Delta G}{\partial n_f} = 0.$$

Using Stirling's approximation, $\log_e (N!) \simeq N(\log_e N - 1)$, and differentiating with respect to n_f, one obtains

$$0 = G_f + kT \log_e \left[\frac{n_f}{N - n_f} \cdot \frac{n_f}{N' - n_f} \right]$$

n_f is always much smaller than N and N' so the ratios $(n_f/N - n_f)$ and $(n_f/N' - n_f)$ are nearly equal to the fractions of vacancies, (n_f/N), and of occupied interstitial sites (n_f/N'). This leads to

$$\frac{n_f}{N} \cdot \frac{n_f}{N'} = \exp\left(-\frac{G_f}{kT} \right). \tag{4.1}$$

Equation (4.1) derived for a pure crystal, still holds in doped crystals where the number of interstitials and vacancies are no longer equal and is essentially, as was pointed out by Lidiard (1957), a "solubility-product" relationship between the fractions of normal sites vacant and interstitial sites occupied. This is emphasized in the next section which deals with Schottky defects in ionic crystals.

B. Concentration of Schottky Defects

Let us consider a crystal composed of two sub-lattices of monovalent anions and cations (e.g. KCl) and let us initially suppose it to be pure. When an ion is removed from the body of the crystal on to the surface, the electrical field that appears inside the lattice must be compensated by an equivalent opposite field, which originates from the formation of a vacancy of an ion of opposite sign. Therefore, anion and cation vacancies are created simultaneously and in equal concentrations in both sub-lattices of a pure crystal.

Now if, for instance, some host cations are replaced by divalent cations doped crystals), each one carries an extra positive charge and its corresponding electrical field must be balanced by an opposite field, resulting in the formation of a cation vacancy (Koch and Wagner, 1937). Therefore, if n_a, n_c and n_b are the numbers of anion vacancies, cation vacancies and bivalent cations respectively, one has the relationship:

$$n_c = n_b + n_a.$$

This relationship expresses the condition of electrical neutrality and may be illustrated in another way. If N, N_+ and N_- are respectively the total number of the sites in each sub-lattice, the number of sites occupied by K^+ ions and the number of anion sites occupied, one has the equality:

$$N = N_+ + n_b + n_c = N_- + n_a.$$

Since the numbers of positive and negative charges are equal, one has

$$2n_b + N_+ = N_-.$$

From these two relationships, one finds that

$$n_b = n_c - n_a.$$

Dividing by N, one obtains the relationship between the fractions of anion vacancies (x_-), cation vacancies (x_+) and bivalent cations:

$$x_+ = c + x_-. \tag{4.2}$$

We shall now attempt to find the concentrations of vacancies at thermal equilibrium. Let g_{s+} and g_{s-} be the Gibbs free energies of formation of a cation and an anion vacancy respectively and let ΔG be the difference between the energy of the crystal under consideration and the energy of the fundamental state, where the two salts would be separated and no vacancies would be present in the crystal. Let g_m be the Gibbs free energy of substitution of a monovalent cation by a bivalent one. The configurational entropy is:

$$S_{\text{conf}} = k \log_e \left[\frac{N!}{(N - n_b)!\, n_b!} \frac{(N - n_b)!}{(N - n_b - n_c)!\, n_c!} \frac{N!}{(N - n_a)!\, n_a!} \right]$$

Using Stirling's approximation one obtains

$$S_{\text{conf}} = -k \left[N \log_e \left(\frac{N - n_a}{N} \right) + N \log_e \left(\frac{N - n_b - n_c}{N} \right) \right.$$

$$+ n_b \log_e \left(\frac{n_b}{N - n_b - n_c} \right) + n_c \log_e \left(\frac{n_c}{N - n_b - n_c} \right)$$

$$\left. + n_a \log_e \left(\frac{n_a}{N - n_a} \right) \right].$$

This can now be substituted into

$$\Delta G = n_c g_{s+} + n_a g_{s-} + n_b g_m - T S_{\text{conf}}$$

which yields

$$\Delta G = n_c g_{s+} + n_a g_{s-} + n_b g_m + kT \left[N \log_e \left(\frac{N - n_a}{N} \right) \right.$$

$$+ N \log_e \left(\frac{N - n_b - n_c}{N} \right) + n_b \log_e \left(\frac{n_b}{N - n_b - n_c} \right)$$

$$\left. + n_c \log_e \left(\frac{n_c}{N - n_b - n_c} \right) + n_a \log_e \left(\frac{n_a}{N - n_a} \right) \right].$$

In a given doped crystal, n_b is a constant (obviously less than the saturation value) and the numbers of vacancies n_a and n_c at thermodynamic equilibrium are obtained by minimizing the function ΔG, i.e. when $d(\Delta G) = 0$. The derivative is to be taken with respect to both variables n_a and n_c and not to n_b since the concentration of bivalent cations is fixed in the present case of a crystal with a given impurity content.† Hence, equilibrium is attained when

$$\frac{\partial \Delta G}{\partial n_c} dn_c + \frac{\partial \Delta G}{\partial n_a} dn_a = 0$$

where

$$\frac{\partial \Delta G}{\partial n_c} = g_{s+} + kT \log_e \left(\frac{n_c}{N - n_b - n_c} \right)$$

$$\frac{\partial \Delta G}{\partial n_a} = g_{s-} + kT \log_e \left(\frac{n_a}{N - n_a} \right)$$

and one obtains the relation

$$\left[g_{s+} + kT \log_e \left(\frac{n_c}{N - n_b - n_c} \right) \right] dn_c$$

$$+ \left[g_{s-} + kT \log_e \left(\frac{n_a}{N - n_a} \right) \right] dn_a = 0$$

n_a and n_c must also obey the condition of electrical neutrality

$$n_c = n_b + n_a$$

the derivative of which is

$$dn_c - dn_a = 0.$$

Multiplying this equation by Lagrange's undetermined multiplier, λ, and adding this to the previous differential equation, one obtains

$$g_{s+} + kT \log_e \left(\frac{n_c}{N - n_b - n_c} \right) + \lambda = 0$$

$$g_{s-} + kT \log_e \left(\frac{n_a}{N - n_a} \right) - \lambda = 0.$$

† The derivative with respect to n_b leads to the result $n_b/N = \exp(-gm/kT)$, which is the impurity content at saturation.

This leads to the relation

$$G_s \equiv g_{s+} + g_{s-}$$

$$= kT \log_e \left[\left(\frac{n_c}{N - n_b - n_c} \right) \left(\frac{n_a}{N - n_a} \right) \right].$$

The quantities in brackets are very nearly equal to the molar fractions of cation and anion vacancies, denoted by x_+ and x_-, so one obtains the relation

$$x_+ x_- = \exp \left(- \frac{G_s}{kT} \right) \tag{4.3}$$

Again we find a solubility–product relation between the anion and cation vacancy concentrations, equally valid in pure crystals as well as in the presence of aliovalent impurities (Lidiard, 1957). This product is a function of the quantity G_s which is the Gibbs formation energy of a Schottky *pair*. It is this energy that is determined experimentally and never g_{s+} and g_{s-} independently, as usually occurs in Electrochemistry.

Strictly speaking eqn (4.3) is only valid when the defects dispersed in the matrix do not interact, and this is only true for infinitely dilute solutions. Lidiard (1954) has suggested that the defects in the crystal behave in a similar way to ions in electrolytic solutions since they carry effective charges, opposite in sign to the ion which has been removed in vacancy formation. Applying the Debye–Hückel theory to allow for the long-range Coulombic interactions, eqn (4.3) becomes, according to Lidiard

$$x_+ x_- = \exp \left(- \frac{G_s}{kT} \right) \exp \left(\frac{e^2 \kappa}{\varepsilon kT (1 + \kappa R)} \right) \tag{4.4}$$

where κ, the Debye–Hückel screening constant, is given by

$$\kappa^2 = \frac{8 \pi e^2 x_+}{V \varepsilon kT} .$$

R being the distance of closest approach, usually taken as the next-nearest neighbour spacing, V the molecular volume and ε the dielectric constant.

Qualitatively, this effect should increase the defect concentration at high temperature relative to its value extrapolated from lower temperatures, since x_+ increases with temperature. Quantitatively, however, this corrective factor $\exp \left[(e^2 \kappa)/[\varepsilon kT (1 + \kappa R)] \right\}$ is small and the accuracy of the diffusion and conductivity experiments needs to be increased by at least an order of magnitude before this phenomenon can clearly be distinguished from other effects in the analysis of the temperature dependence of the experimental data.

The molar fractions of vacancies x_+ and x_- may be independently determined as a function of temperature by combining eqns (4.2) and (4.3) to give

$$x_+ = \tfrac{1}{2}c \left\{ 1 + \sqrt{\left[1 + \frac{4}{c^2} \exp\left(-\frac{G_s}{kT} \right) \right]} \right\} \tag{4.5}$$

$$x_- = \tfrac{1}{2}c \left\{ -1 + \sqrt{\left[1 + \frac{4}{c^2} \exp\left(-\frac{G_s}{kT} \right) \right]} \right\}. \tag{4.6}$$

The fractions x_+ and x_- increase with temperature, whereas the molar fraction of bivalent cations, c, already present as background impurities or added by doping the crystal, is a constant. So at high temperatures where

$$c \ll \exp\left(\frac{G_s}{2kT} \right)$$

eqns (4.5) and (4.6) become

$$x_+ \simeq x_- \simeq \exp\left(-\frac{G_s}{2kT} \right) \tag{4.7}$$

which obviously holds for pure crystals. The temperature range for which this condition is fulfilled is called the "intrinsic range".

On the other hand at lower temperatures where

$$c \gg \exp\left(-\frac{G_s}{2kT} \right)$$

the fractions of vacancies are approximately

$$x_+ \simeq c \tag{4.8}$$

$$x_- \simeq \frac{1}{c} \exp\left(-\frac{G_s}{kT} \right) \tag{4.9}$$

defining the "extrinsic range".

So far we have considered the following defects: cation vacancies, anion vacancies and aliovalent ions as free defects dispersed in the matrix. However, when two oppositely charged defects arrive at nearest neighbour sites they acquire distinct properties and must be considered as defects distinct from free vacancies.

C. Concentration of Associated Defects

1. Vacancy Pairs

The association of an anion vacancy with a cation vacancy at nearest neighbour spacing is usually called a vacancy pair. In an electric field the vacancy pair behave as a dipole and do not participate in the transport of current. Hence the vacancy pairs could be studied by relaxation methods but not by low frequency conductivity measurements. On the other hand, they make a non-negligible contribution to the diffusion of the ions, as will be seen later.

If again one assumes that vacancy pairs are in thermal equilibrium, application of the law of mass action to the reaction

anion vacancy + cation vacancy $\rightleftharpoons$ vacancy pair

leads to the relation

$$\frac{x'}{x_+ x_-} = z \exp\left(-\frac{G_{pr}}{kT}\right)$$

where x' is the molar fraction of vacancy pairs, G_{pr} the Gibbs free energy of the reaction (this reaction written from left to right corresponds to an exoenergetic process and is thus characterized by a *negative* free energy change) and z the number of distinct orientations of the pair. In the sodium chloride lattice, where the length of the pair is equal to the anion–cation separation distance (let it be a), z is equal to 6.

Substituting for the product $x_+ x_-$ from eqn (4.3) one obtains

$$x' = z \exp\left(-\frac{G_s + G_{pr}}{kT}\right). \tag{4.10}$$

This equation shows another important consequence of the solubility–product relation (4.3), namely that the concentration of vacancy pairs does not depend on the concentration c and on the nature of aliovalent impurity present.

2. Impurity–Cation Vacancy Pair

In the same way, because of the Coulombic attraction, a bivalent cation (net charge $+e$) and a cation vacancy (net charge $-e$) can form a stable entity at nearest neighbour spacing; this is called a "complex" or "cation vacancy–impurity pair". These defects behave like vacancy pairs, i.e. as neutral dipoles and they do not contribute to the low frequency electrical conductivity.

We can again apply the law of mass action to the reaction (Lidiard, 1957)

cation vacancy + impurity $\rightleftharpoons$ impurity–vacancy complex.

Denoting p as the degree of association, the molar fractions of associated impurities and non-associated impurities are respectively pc and $(1 - p)c$, so that one obtains

$$\frac{p}{1 - p} = z'x_+ \exp\left(-\frac{G_a}{kT}\right) \tag{4.11}$$

where G_a is the Gibbs free energy of the equilibrium reaction written from left to right (thus G_a, like G_{pr}, has a *negative* value) and z' is the number of distinct orientations of the complex ($z' = 12$ in the NaCl lattice).

Existence of such complexes has been shown by relaxation methods (Breckenridge, 1950) since they act as dipoles. It must also be pointed out that higher complexes have been found at low temperatures, especially by ionic thermo-current measurements (Laj, 1969).

The effect of impurity–vacancy complexes is to make the concentration of free vacancies smaller than c in the extrinsic range and so leads to a decrease in the conductivity at lower temperatures to a value lower than would be expected from the behaviour at high temperatures where eqn (4.8) holds. This temperature range is called the association region (Dreyfus and Nowick, 1962). On the other hand in diffusion when both associated and free vacancies are in appreciable concentrations, diffusion coefficients must be analysed as the sum of the two mechanisms which involve each defect. In general, when several types of defect are operative in diffusion, the total diffusion coefficient must be interpreted as the sum of the individual contributions due to each mechanism. We shall now give the expressions for the diffusion coefficients for the main mechanisms.

V. Expressions for the Diffusion Coefficients

Let us return to the basic definition of the diffusion coefficient (eqn (2.11))

$$D = \frac{\Gamma\delta^2}{6}.$$

The jump probability Γ is the product of two terms:

(1) the probability that a given ion has a defect on a nearest neighbour site, which is the molar fraction of defects multiplied by the number of nearest neighbour sites;

(2) the probability for the ion to jump into the defect in a given direction in unit time, which is the jump frequency v.

The first term has been evaluated in the preceding section. We shall now give a simplified calculation of the second term, assuming that the classical

Einstein model is valid in ionic crystals and that a saddle-point position can be defined for the jumping ion where the potential energy is at a maximum. We assume that under the influence of thermal agitation the ions vibrate harmonically around their equilibrium positions, with a vibrational frequency, v_0, in the direction of the defects. Let G_m be the difference between the free energy of the ion at the saddle-point position and that at the lattice site position (Fig. 7). In other words, G_m is the free energy barrier that opposes the migration of the ion. Now, assuming that the energy is distributed among the ions according to a Maxwell–Boltzmann distribution, the probability that a given ion possesses equal or higher energy than that necessary to cross the barrier is $\exp(-G_m/kT)$. The jump frequency in a given direction, v, is thus equal to the product of this probability and the vibrational frequency

$$v = v_0 \exp\left(-\frac{G_m}{kT}\right).$$

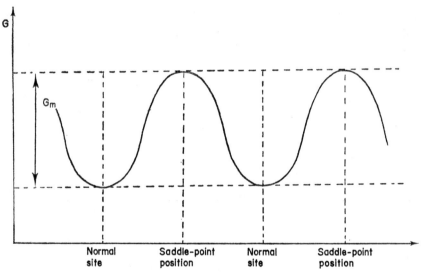

FIG. 7. Schematic representation of the energy function along the jump direction. The difference of the energies of the saddle-point configuration and the ground configuration is taken to be equal to the migration energy.

G_m will be called the free energy of migration and may be dissociated into an entropy and enthalpy term according to the formula

$$G_m = H_m - TS_m,$$

thus v becomes

$$v = v_0 \exp\left(\frac{S_m}{k}\right) \exp\left(-\frac{H_m}{kT}\right). \qquad (5.1)$$

We shall denote v_+ as the jump frequency of a cation into a cation vacancy and v_- as the jump frequency of an anion into an anion vacancy. More detailed treatments (Wert, 1950; Lidiard, 1957; Adda and Philibert, 1966) lead to the same result i.e. an exponential dependence of v on temperature. The pre-exponential factor, $v_0 \exp (S_m/k)$, is experimentally found to be of the same order of magnitude as the Debye frequency. Sometimes v_0 is conventionally identified with the Debye frequency, for both the ions, anion and cation, in order to obtain an estimate of S_m. However, as yet, no adequate theory is available to account for the physical significance of the pre-exponential factor and we shall not discuss this term any further. The important point is that the predicted temperature dependence of v is found to hold experimentally, and this leads to the determination of the migration enthalpy, H_m. This term has a crucial importance as it can be compared to theoretical values. This comparison offers a way of testing the jump models upon which the theoretical calculations are based.

We can now write explicit expressions for D as a function of temperature and the thermodynamic parameters involved in the different diffusion mechanisms; self-diffusion by free vacancies, vacancy pairs and impurity-vacancy pairs and diffusion of impurities.

A. Self Diffusion Coefficients

1. Diffusion by Free Vacancies

To be more concrete let us consider the case of the cation self-diffusion coefficient in the NaCl lattice. Here, the length of a jump is $a\sqrt{2}$ where a is the anion–cation separation distance. Thus eqn (2.12) becomes

$$D = f\frac{\Gamma a^2}{3}.$$

The probability of finding a vacancy next to a given cation is $12x_+$. Substituting for Γ according to the preceding treatment yields

$$D_+ = 4a^2 f v_0 \exp\left(-\frac{G_{m+}}{kT}\right) x_+ \qquad (5.2)$$

where x_+ is the cation free vacancy molar fraction and G_{m+} the free energy of migration of a cation. The analogous expression for self-diffusion by anion free vacancies is

$$D_- = 4a^2 f v_0 \exp\left(-\frac{G_{m-}}{kT}\right) x_-. \tag{5.3}$$

It is of interest to distinguish between the temperature dependence of D in the intrinsic and extrinsic regions by substituting for x_+ and x_- using eqns (4.7, 4.8 and 4.9). The diffusion coefficients of the cation and anion in the intrinsic range are thus

$$D_+ = 4a^2 f v_0 \exp\left(\frac{S_{m+} + S_s/2}{k}\right) \exp\left(-\frac{H_{m+} + H_s/2}{kT}\right) \tag{5.4}$$

$$D_- = 4a^2 f v_0 \exp\left(\frac{S_{m-} + S_s/2}{k}\right) \exp\left(-\frac{H_{m-} + H_s/2}{kT}\right) \tag{5.5}$$

whilst in the extrinsic range

$$D_+ = 4a^2 f v_0 c \exp\left(\frac{S_{m+}}{k}\right) \exp\left(-\frac{H_{m+}}{kT}\right) \tag{5.6}$$

$$D_- = \frac{4a^2 f v_0}{c} \exp\left(\frac{S_{m-} + S_s}{k}\right) \exp\left(-\frac{H_{m-} + H_s}{kT}\right). \tag{5.7}$$

2. Diffusion by Vacancy Pairs

The cation vacancy site of a given vacancy pair is surrounded by 12 cations at nearest neighbour sites. However, only 4 of these cations can jump into the pair without dissociating it (Fig. 8). Thus the probability that a given cation is next to a vacancy pair into which it may jump is equal to $4x'$, x' being the molar fraction of vacancy pairs, given by eqn (4.10). The jump length is again $a\sqrt{2}$ and the vacancy pair contribution to the cation self-diffusion coefficient, denoted by D_+', is given by

$$D_+' = \frac{4a^2 f_+' v_0}{3} \exp\left(-\frac{G_{m+}'}{kT}\right) x'$$

where G_{m+}' is the free energy of migration of a cation into a vacancy pair. Substituting for x' from eqn (4.10) with $z = 6$, one finds

$$D_+' = 8a^2 f_+' v_0 \exp\left(\frac{S_s + S_{pr} + S_{m+}'}{k}\right) \exp\left(-\frac{H_s + H_{pr} + H_{m+}'}{kT}\right). \tag{5.8}$$

The term independent of temperature (assuming as above that the enthalpies of defect formation, H_s, vacancy pair association, H_{pr}, and migration, H_{m+}', are independent of temperature) is particularly complex in this case. Hence D_+' will be used in the condensed form,

$$D_+' = f_+' D_{0+}' \exp\left(-\frac{H_+'}{kT}\right) \tag{5.9}$$

and the diffusion coefficient of the anion via vacancy pairs will be represented in the same way as

$$D'_- = f_-' D_{0-}' \exp\left(-\frac{H'_-}{kT}\right) \tag{5.10}$$

f_+' and f_-' being the correlation factors for these mechanisms, which are functions of v_+'/v_-', the ratio of the individual jump frequencies of each type of ion into the pair.

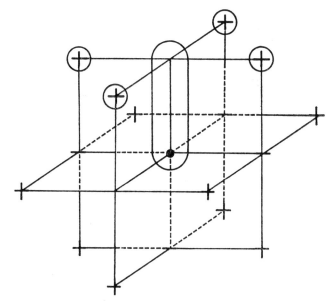

FIG. 8. Vacancy pair with the 12 cations $(+)$ which are nearest neighbours of the cation vacant site $(\bullet)$. At a given time, the only four upper cations $(\oplus)$ may jump into the pair without making it dissociate.

3. Diffusion by Impurity–Vacancy Pairs

The bivalent-impurity + cation-vacancy pair migrate through the crystal by a series of two different kinds of jump, according to the Johnson mechanism (Johnson, 1939);—the impurity and vacancy exchanging their sites with a frequency ω_2†—the vacancy jumping around the impurity into one of the four occupied sites which are nearest neighbours of both the impurity and the vacancy (Fig. 9) with a frequency ω_1. Thus migration of impurity–vacancy pairs implies jumps of host cations and hence a contribution to the cation self-diffusion coefficient.

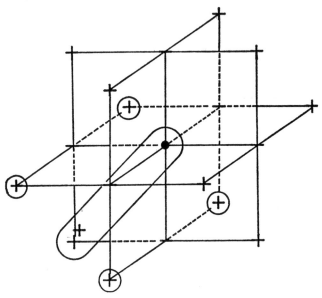

FIG. 9. Bivalent-cation $(++)$-cation-vacancy ($\bullet$)-pair. The impurity jumps into the vacancy with the frequency ω_2. The cations which are nearest neighbours of both impurity and vacancy ($\oplus$) jump into the vacancy with the frequency ω_1.

In the extrinsic range, where the number of thermally produced vacancies is negligible relative to the number of vacancies due to the bivalent impurities, the total concentration of cation vacancies is nearly equal to c. Therefore, we must distinguish between the two following categories of vacancies:

(1) the free vacancies, with concentration equal to $(1-p)c$, p being the degree of association, which give a contribution to the total diffusion coefficient

$$D = 4a^2 f(1-p)cv_+ \tag{5.11a}$$

† The different jump frequencies which have been considered above have been denoted by the symbol v. However, the jump frequencies of the different kinds of jump a vacancy can make in the vicinity of a divalent cation are usually denoted by the letter ω, thus, we follow the usual convention (though ω is obviously not an angular velocity).

with

$$v_+ = v_0 \exp\left(\frac{S_{m+}}{k}\right) \exp\left(-\frac{H_{m+}}{kT}\right).$$

(2) the associated vacancies, with concentration equal to pc, which give the contribution (Lidiard, 1957)

$$D = \frac{4a^2}{3} fpc\omega_1. \tag{5.11b}$$

B. Impurity Diffusion Coefficients

In the case of self-diffusion by free vacancies the expression for D was easy to obtain since there was only one jump frequency to consider, namely the jump frequency v of the host ions, neglecting the small mass dependence of v due to the use of isotopes, and since, as will be seen later, the correlation factor is a mere geometrical factor. We will now deal with the diffusion coefficients of impurities, which involve the jump frequency of the impurity. The valency of the impurity must be borne in mind in this case, which can either be the same as the host ion (homovalent impurity) or a different one (aliovalent impurity).

1. Diffusion of Homovalent Ions

In the case of ions entering the crystal substitutionally and migrating by a vacancy mechanism, it is clear that we may proceed as for tracer diffusion. We have simply to consider the jump frequency of the impurity instead of the host ion jump frequency, which leads to a formula like eqn (5.2). We shall return to the effect of size, mass and polarizability of the impurity ion in the sections dealing with numerical values. The expression of the correlation factor for the diffusion of impurities, which does not depend on the valency of the impurity, will be discussed in the next chapter.

2. Diffusion of Aliovalent Ions

To be more explicit we will consider the frequently encountered case of diffusion of bivalent cations in alkali halides and silver halides. Two further effects must now be taken into account:

(1) the impurity can only make a jump when there is a vacancy available at a nearest neighbour site, defined then as an impurity–vacancy pair. Thus the migration of the pair involves at least the two jump frequencies ω_1 and ω_2.

(2) each bivalent cation introduces a cation vacancy and if impurities in non-negligible molar fraction diffuse into the crystal the molar fraction of vacancies will be increased, increasing the diffusion coefficient at the same time.

The impurities migrate only when they are associated with a vacancy and a complete treatment would imply a statistical calculation of the length of every "walk" made by the impurity during the time it is next to an available vacancy, taking into account the association–dissociation kinetics. However, when the pairs have a long lifetime, one may consider that only the fraction of impurities that are associated diffuse, giving rise to the flow (Lidiard, 1955a)

$$J = - D_0 \frac{d}{dx} (pNc).$$ (5.12)

Here c is the molar fraction of impurities, N the number of cation sites per unit volume and p the degree of association (pNc is thus the number of associated impurities per unit volume), and D_0 the diffusion coefficient of the impurity–vacancy complex.

Let us discuss first the expression for D_0. Proceeding as above with $a\sqrt{2}$ as the jump length and ω_2 the frequency of exchange of the impurity and vacancy, one obtains

$$D_0 = \frac{fa^2\omega_2}{3}.$$ (5.13)

The significance of the correlation factor is very clear in this case. The Johnson mechanism involves a series of jumps which exchange the vacancy sometimes with the impurity (ω_2) and sometimes with the neighbouring host ions (ω_1). There are obviously two limiting cases:

(1) $\omega_2 \gg \omega_1$: The impurity makes a large number of forward and backward jumps without moving further through the crystal. Thus successive jumps are completely correlated and f tends to zero.

(2) $\omega_1 \gg \omega_2$: The vacancy makes a large number of jumps around the impurity, and when the next jump of the impurity occurs the vacancy has "forgotten" the position it occupied in the preceding jump of the impurity. Hence, the jump of the impurity has an equal probability in every direction. In this case there is no appreciable correlation effect and f tends to unity.

We shall return to more general expressions of f which were first given by Lidiard (1955). For the present, we will look at how the basic eqn (5.12) is applied in the important experimental cases.

(a) Diffusion of tracers in the intrinsic range

When the concentration of impurities is negligible relative to the concentration of thermally produced vacancies, the concentration of free cation vacancies, x_+, is unaffected by the diffusing impurities and is given by eqn (4.7). Furthermore, it is clear that p decreases with increasing temperature and decreasing impurity content, so that p is small in these conditions, thus one can make the approximation

$$\frac{p}{1-p} \simeq p.$$

Substituting for x_+ from eqn (4.7) in the expression for p (eqn 4.11) one obtains

$$p = 12 \exp\left(-\frac{G_s/2 + G_a}{kT}\right). \tag{5.14}$$

The degree of association is thus independent of c and therefore independent of the x coordinate, so that eqn (5.12) becomes

$$J = -D_0 p \frac{\mathrm{d}}{\mathrm{d}x}(Nc).$$

The number of bivalent cations is the sum of the background bivalent impurities (Nc_0) and of the diffusing isotopes (Nc^*) so that

$$\frac{\mathrm{d}}{\mathrm{d}x}(Nc) = \frac{\mathrm{d}}{\mathrm{d}x}(Nc_0 + Nc^*) = \frac{\mathrm{d}}{\mathrm{d}x}(Nc^*)$$

since one may assume that background impurities are uniformly distributed. The last quantity is the concentration gradient of the diffusing particles, the diffusion coefficient of which being

$$D = 4a^2 f \omega_2 \exp\left(-\frac{G_s/2 + G_a}{kT}\right). \tag{5.15}$$

Developing ω_2 as above yields

$$\omega_2 = \nu_0 \exp\left(-\frac{G_{m++}}{kT}\right)$$

where G_{m++} is the migration enthalpy of the bivalent cation into the vacancy. Now eqn (5.15) can be rewritten, when $\omega_1 \gg \omega_2$ ($f = 1$), as

$$D = 4a^2 \nu_0 \exp\left(\frac{S_s/2 + S_a + S_{m++}}{k}\right) \exp\left(-\frac{H_s/2 + H_a + H_{m++}}{kT}\right) \tag{5.16}$$

leading in this case to a simple Arrhenius law relationship with the activation enthalpy: $H_s/2 + H_a + H_{m++}$.

(b) Diffusion of tracers in highly doped crystals

The opposite limiting case to that described above is that where p is equal to 1, which can occur at low temperatures in highly doped crystals. Hence in this case $d(pNc)/dx$ is directly equal to $d(Nc^*)/dx$, the concentration gradient of the particles under study, the diffusion coefficient of which may be obtained from eqns (5.12) and (5.13) as

$$D = \frac{fa^2\omega_2}{3}. \tag{5.17}$$

Here again D is independent of x. When the inequality $\omega_1 \gg \omega_2$ holds, the temperature dependence of D again obeys an Arrhenius law, the activation enthalpy of which being equal to H_{m++}.

(c) Diffusion with variable D and negligible thermal disorder

We now consider the case of doped crystals at temperatures where the thermal vacancies are in negligible concentration relative to the impurity concentration. The molar fraction of *free* cation vacancies is

$$x_+ = (1 - p)c$$

and eqn (4.11) becomes

$$\frac{p}{(1 - p)^2} = 12c \exp\left(-\frac{G_a}{kT}\right) \tag{5.18}$$

so that p is here a function of c. The derivative in eqn (5.12) may be rewritten as

$$\frac{d(pc)}{dx} = \left(p + c\frac{dp}{dc}\right)\frac{dc}{dx}. \tag{5.19}$$

Differentiating eqn (5.18) with respect to c one obtains

$$\frac{dp}{dc} = \frac{p}{c}\frac{1 + p}{1 - p}$$

so that the term in brackets in eqn (5.19) may be rewritten as

$$p + c\frac{dp}{dc} = \frac{2p}{1 - p}.$$

Substituting for p in this relation by the expression obtained by solving eqn (5.18) one obtains

$$\frac{2p}{1 - p} = 1 - \left[1 + 48c \exp\left(-\frac{G_a}{kT}\right)\right]^{-\frac{1}{2}}.$$

Using the basic eqns (5.12 and 5.13) one can write the final result (Lidiard, 1957)

$$D = \frac{fa^2\omega_2}{3}\left[1 - \left\{1 + 48c\exp\left(-\frac{G_a}{kT}\right)\right\}^{-\frac{1}{2}}\right]. \qquad (5.20)$$

The diffusion coefficient is clearly a function of c, except in the case where the association is almost total and in this case eqn (5.20) reduces to (5.17).

(d) General Case

One must bear in mind that the preceding expression (eqn (5.20)) is valid only when the thermal disorder is negligible, i.e. only for low temperatures. The temperature dependence of D predicted by eqn (5.20) has been experimentally confirmed (Fredericks *et al.*, 1963), assuming moreover that f is nearly equal to 1, at low temperature.

However, it is possible in the frame of the Stasiw–Teltow association model to obtain a more complete expression valid over the whole temperature range. To do this we have to solve the system of the three following basic equations

$$\begin{cases} x_+ x_- = \exp\left(-\frac{G_s}{kT}\right) = \beta \\[2mm] x_+ = x_- + c(1 - p) \\[2mm] \frac{p}{(1 - p)x_+} = 12\exp\left(-\frac{G_a}{kT}\right) = \alpha \end{cases}$$

which gives

$$p^3 c - (2c - \alpha\beta + 1/\alpha)p^2 + (c - 2\alpha\beta)p + \alpha\beta = 0 \qquad (5.21)$$

This equation is difficult to handle and the experiments have been mainly performed in the preceding limiting cases. However, the analysis of the impurity coefficient

$$D = \frac{fa^2\omega_2}{3}\left(p + c\frac{dp}{dc}\right)$$

over the whole temperature range where D is measurable would be possible with the help of computers.†

---

† Note added in proof—See for instance: J. L. Krause and W. J. Fredericks "The Simultaneous Diffusion of Pb^{++} and Ca^{++} in purified NaCl Single Crystals", *Physics Chem. Solids* **32** (1971) and F. Bénière, M. Bénière and M. Chemla "Diffusion of Impurity Ions in Ionic Crystals. Treatment of the Diffusion Equations for Concentration Dependent Diffusion Coefficients", *J. Chem. Phys.* **56**, p. 549 (1972).

In this section we have dealt with several mechanisms denoting all that concerns correlation effects simply with a letter f. The correlation factor has obviously not the same form for every case, and it is the aim of the next section to attempt to give explicit forms for f in order to complete the expressions for the different diffusion coefficients.

VI. Correlation Factors

A. Intrinsic Interest of the Correlation Effects

The experimental results obtained from the diffusion coefficient and electrical conductivity measurements give direct evidence for the presence of defects in the lattice of the ionic crystals. The advantage of the diffusion methods is that it is possible to study separately each sub-lattice when radio-isotopes are available. The analysis of the temperature dependence of the self-diffusion coefficients, interpreted according to the preceding eqns (5.2–5.11), leads in favourable cases to a determination of the defect concentrations and jump frequencies, or in other words to a determination of the thermo-dynamic parameters involved in defect formation and migration. Concerning the microscopic structure of the defects we have briefly described some models and especially those of Frenkel and Schottky. The important point to be kept in mind is that all calculations of defect concentrations are based on Frenkel's theory, i.e. defects formed under the influence of thermal agitation and in thermodynamic equilibrium, so that the concentration of any kind of defect would be given by an equation like (4.3). Secondly, all theories dealing with the rate of diffusion imply an activated process and thus a jump frequency with an exponential dependence on temperature. Thus for any kind of defect one expects the self-diffusion coefficient to obey an Arrhenius law, which is experimentally well supported.

One way of investigating the defect structure is to compare the thermo-dynamic parameters, especially the defect formation energy (or enthalpy) obtained from the diffusion coefficient measurements, with the theoretical values that have been calculated assuming a given model, usually by Mott and Littleton's method. An agreement between the theoretical and experi-mental values is a good indication in favour of the model. However, the theoretical calculations have only been based on the Frenkel and Schottky models. For example Mott and Littleton (1938) calculated values of 1·86 and 2·50 eV, respectively, for the Schottky and Frenkel defect formation energies in NaCl. These values have been only slightly modified in more elaborate calculations (Boswarva and Lidiard, 1967). As we have mentioned, the molar fraction of every defect has the form $\exp(-G_d/kT)$, so that it has been concluded that the predominant defects in NaCl are of the Schottky type. The main feature of these models is that the vacancy and interstitial are supposed to be localized on a given lattice or interstitial site, respectively, in which cases the calculations can be carried through. The above criterion would be more significant if the experimental values could be compared with theoretical values obtained for a wider range of defect models. For instance, it could be interesting to have the values for more complex defect structures, involving a higher degree of relaxation of the lattice and giving rise to defects extending over several lattice sites (as, for example, in the Nachtrieb and Handler model (1954)), which could be compared to the values of the classical models and those from experiments.

Another way of investigating the defect structures indirectly is from an analysis of correlation effects. The correlation factors in self-diffusion can be measured by the use of suitable radioisotopes. Since the correlation factor depends on the diffusion mechanism it can be used to characterize the nature of the defects involved in the mechanism.

B. Main Results of the Correlation Theory

In the preceding section we saw that in Johnson's mechanism of bivalent cation diffusion the directions of consecutive jumps may be highly correlated. This is a far more general effect, occurring in many mechanisms and even in tracer-diffusion. This was only pointed out in 1951 by Bardeen and Herring, perhaps because it was not until then that extensive measurements of diffusion coefficients were started following the production of artificial radioisotopes.

We shall begin with a qualitative description of the correlation effect in the tracer diffusion of, say, the cation, occurring by the localized vacancy mechanism in the NaCl lattice. Let (0) denote the initial site of the tracer (Fig. 10) and (1) the site of the supposed vacancy at one of the twelve nearest

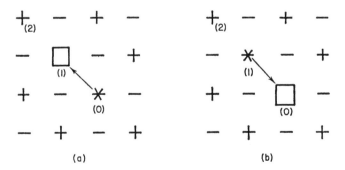

FIG. 10. Correlation effect for diffusion via free vacancies (NaCl lattice). (a) Initial jump of the tracer; (b) Next jump of the tracer whose probability is the highest relative to the eleven other possible directions.

neighbour cation sites. Let $(0) \to (1)$ be the first jump of the tracer, resulting in the vacancy moving to (0). We may deal with the jumps of the same tracer because of the smallness of the tracer molar fraction. Furthermore, the molar fraction of vacancies is also generally very small and there is a high probability, therefore, for the next jump of the tracer to occur by exchanging its site with the same vacancy. Every jump of the vacancy can occur in the twelve possible directions with equal probability and thus the jumps of the vacancy are not correlated. Let us now consider the next jump of the tracer. The jump of highest probability is $(1) \to (0)$ since (0) is now vacant. On the other hand, a jump in the opposite direction $(1) \to (0)$ implies that the vacancy has made a complex walk about site (1) before arriving at (2). resulting in a jump of lower probability. So, each two consecutive jumps occur with maximum probability in opposite directions (net displacement equal to zero) and with minimum probability if they take place in the same direction (net displacement equal to twice the jump length—2δ); the consequence of this effect is thus to decrease the tracer diffusion coefficient to a lower value than would be obtained in a pure random walk process.

In order to give a numerical evaluation of this effect, one must consider the definition of the diffusion coefficient given by eqn (2.8), in which the mean square length is expressed in the form of eqn (2.9). When the jumps are correlated, the sum of the $\delta_i \cdot \delta_j$ terms no longer cancels out. The average value (over a large number of particles) of the sum of $\delta_i \cdot \delta_j$ for different i and j gives the magnitude of the correlation effect. It is known that

$$\sum_i \sum_{i \neq j} \langle \delta_i \cdot \delta_j \rangle = 2 \sum_{k=1}^{n-1} \sum_{i=1}^{n-k} \langle \delta_i \cdot \delta_{i+k} \rangle.$$

When all jump vectors δ_i are of equal magnitude δ, one has

$$\delta_i \cdot \delta_{i+k} = \delta^2 \cos \theta_{i,i+k}$$

so that

$$\sum_i \sum_{i \neq j} \langle \delta_i \cdot \delta_j \rangle = 2 \delta^2 \sum_{k=1}^{n-1} \sum_{i=1}^{n-k} \langle \cos \theta_{i,i+k} \rangle.$$

For a given k and a given particle, the term $\sum_{i=1}^{n-k} \cos \theta_{i,i+k}$ expresses the sum of the cosines of the angles between all pairs of jumps (among the n jumps made by the particle during the time t) that are separated by $(k-1)$ intermediate jumps. In order to take the average value for a large number of particles, one may consider the same particle for a very long time; then passing to the limit:

$$\sum_{i=1}^{n-k} \langle \cos \theta_{i,i+k} \rangle = (n-k) \lim_{N \to \infty} \frac{1}{N} \sum_{i=1}^{N} \cos \theta_{i,i+k} \equiv (n-k) \langle \cos \theta_k \rangle.$$

It may be shown (Le Claire and Lidiard, 1956) that in the vacancy mechanism there is a *direct* correlation only between consecutive jumps, the correlation between non-consecutive jumps being indirect and given by the addition of the effects of correlation between the pairs of consecutive jumps. This is mathematically expressed by the relation

$$\langle \cos \theta_k \rangle = \langle \cos \theta_{k-1} \rangle \langle \cos \theta_1 \rangle = \ldots = \langle \cos \theta_1 \rangle^k$$

under the condition that each jump vector is an axis of at least two-fold symmetry. Now summing with respect to k, one obtains

$$\sum_i \sum_{i \neq j} \langle \delta_i \cdot \delta_j \rangle = 2 \, n \delta^2 \, \frac{\langle \cos \theta_1 \rangle}{1 - \langle \cos \theta_1 \rangle}.$$

We may now write the expression for the diffusion coefficient as follows

$$D = \frac{L^2}{6t} = \frac{n}{t} \frac{\delta^2}{6} \left[1 + \frac{2 \langle \cos \theta_1 \rangle}{1 - \langle \cos \theta_1 \rangle} \right]. \tag{6.1}$$

The jump frequency is given by $\Gamma = n/t$, so

$$D = f \frac{\Gamma \delta^2}{6} \tag{6.2}$$

with

$$f = \frac{1 + \langle \cos \theta_1 \rangle}{1 - \langle \cos \theta_1 \rangle}. \tag{6.3}$$

In the case of the interstitialcy mechanisms, the tracer occupies alter, nately interstitial sites (i) and lattice sites (1). When at an interstitial site the tracer has equal probabilities of jumping and pushing any one of the ions on neighbouring sites so that every (i) → (1) jump is uncorrelated with the preceding (1) → (i) jump. Now, the interstitial non-tracer ion will push one of its normal neighbours; this neighbour can, of course, be the tracer so that this jump (1) → (i) is correlated with the preceding (i) → (1) jump. Following the preceding calculation of f, valid for the vacancy mechanism, one sees that all terms $\langle \cos \theta_{i,i+k} \rangle$ with $k > 1$ are zero, and for $k = 1$ only the alternate pairs of jumps (i) → (1) → (i) are correlated. This simplifies the expression for $\langle L^2 \rangle$ and finally one obtains for the interstitialcy mechanism that

$$f = 1 + \langle \cos \theta_1 \rangle \tag{6.4}$$

We notice that the correlation factor depends only on the average value of the cosine between the pairs of consecutive jumps. In order to calculate the form in which to express it (it is either a geometrical factor for the simplest mechanisms or a function of frequencies for the mechanisms involving more than one jump frequency) one considers, after an initial jump by the particle, all the possible walks of the defect that make the particle move for the second time, calculating the cosine of the angle involved and the probability of occurence of such a walk. Then summing all probabilities for each value of the cosine, one obtains the average value $\langle \cos \theta_1 \rangle$. However, this would involve lengthy calculations if one did not use the elegant methods introduced by Le Claire and Lidiard (1956) and Compaan and Haven (1956), to whose original papers the reader is referred.[†]

Correlation factors have been calculated for nearly all structures and for the main mechanisms. We shall restrict ourselves to reviewing the main results for the most common cases. We begin with the simple case of the correlation factor for tracer diffusion. The value of the correlation factor depends on the lattice structure, and, in a given structure, on the diffusion mechanism. Thus it is of crucial interest in identifying mechanisms and defects.

1. Correlation Factors for Tracer Diffusion

(a) Correlation factors for tracer diffusion via free defects (interstitial and vacancies)

(i) *Diffusion by direct movement of interstitials.* It is obvious that when the interstitials jump directly from one interstitial site to another, there is no correlation between the directions of the successive jumps ($f_i = 1$). However, in a pure crystal containing Frenkel disorder there are equal numbers of vacancies and interstitials, and diffusion may occur by both defect species. Let v_i and v_v denote the jump frequencies for the mechanisms by interstitials and by vacancies, respectively. In f.c.c. lattices with anion–cation separation distance equal to a, the jump length is $a\sqrt{2}$ for a vacancy jump and a for an interstitial jump. The contribution of the vacancies to the diffusion coefficient is given by eqn (5.2) with the correlation factor f_v (see below). The contribution of the interstitials may easily be calculated in the same way. The probability of a tracer occupying an interstitial site is obviously the molar fraction of defects, say x_v. Let v_i denote the jump frequency of the interstitial. Since an interstitial may jump into six interstitial sites in the NaCl lattice, the diffusion coefficient for diffusion via interstitials is, according to eqn (6.2)

$$D_i = a^2 v_i x_v$$

[†] For detailed accounts of the more recent results concerning correlation effects, see the books of Adda and Philibert, "La diffusion dans les solides" (1966), Manning, "Diffusion Kinetics for Atoms in Crystals" (1968), and Le Claire in "Physical Chemistry" (1970).

since f is obviously unity for this mechanism. The total diffusion coefficient is therefore

$$D = a^2(v_i + 4f_v v_v)x_v \qquad (6.5)$$

in a pure crystal.

(ii) *Diffusion by interstitialcy jumps.* The correlation factors for interstitialcy mechanisms have been determined by Compaan and Haven (1958) in the main structures (AgCl, CsCl, CaF$_2$, ZnS, BaTiO$_3$, CdCl$_2$, diamond). Several distinct interstititialcy mechanisms have generally to be considered in each structure, namely the direct and indirect interstitialcy mechanisms characterized by distinct angles between the consecutive jumps (i) → (1) → (i) and distinct jump frequencies. Compaan and Haven have performed the calculations for many mechanisms and we shall restrict ourselves to the important case of AgCl which has been extensively studied. The eight interstitial sites surrounding an Ag$^+$ ion on site (0) are represented in Fig. 11. Suppose site (1) is initially occupied by a tracer Ag* which jumps on to (0). The Ag$^+$ ion may be pushed into the seven neighbouring sites, which may be catalogued as follows:

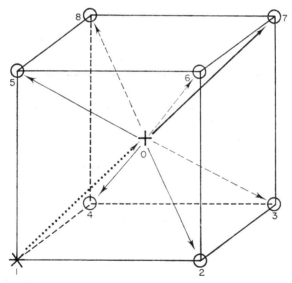

FIG. 11. Interstitialcy jumps in AgCl. The interstitial Ag$^+$ ion (*) jumps and pushes the Ag$^+$ ion (+) initially at normal site into one of the surrounding interstitial sites (○) with a jump frequency depending on the orientation of the second jump relative to the first one: ➝ frequency v_1

--→ frequency v_2

→ frequency v_3

(7): direct interstitialcy, frequency v_1; $f = 2/3$

(3) or (6) or (8): indirect interstitialcy, frequency v_2; $f = 32/33$

(2) or (4) or (5): indirect interstitialcy, frequency v_3; $f = 0.9643$

If one of these frequencies is much greater than any of the others, the correlation factor entering into the diffusion coefficient takes one of the above values and is thus a numerical factor. On the other hand, if all frequencies are of the same order of magnitude, the correlation factor will be a function of the ratios of the corresponding jump frequencies (Compaan and Haven, 1958).

(iii) *Diffusion by free vacancies.* The correlation factor for tracer diffusion via localized vacancies is given by eqn (6.3) from the calculation of $\langle \cos \theta_1 \rangle$. This has been done by Compaan and Haven (1956, 1958) for the simple but most common structures (Table I). With the exception of the very slight difference between the correlation factors for the directions within and out of hexagonal planes in the h.c.p. lattice when the corresponding jump frequencies are assumed to be equal, the migration via free vacancies involves a single jump frequency in all the structures listed in Table I, so that the correlation factor here is merely a geometrical factor, expressed by a numerical value given in the table.

TABLE I. Correlation factors for tracer diffusion via localized vacancies (After Compaan and Haven)

Lattice	f
diamond lattice	$1/2$
cubic lattice	0.65311
body-centred cubic lattice	0.72722
face-centred cubic lattice	0.78146
hexagonal close-packing lattice	$f_x = f_y = 0.78121$
	$f_z = 0.78146$

This is no longer valid for anisotropic diffusion. For instance, Compaan and Haven have calculated the correlation factors for the x- and z-directions in the corundum lattice for various values of the ratio v_z/v_x, v_z and v_x denoting the jump frequencies along the z direction and in the xy plane respectively. These values are given in Table II in order to illustrate a general fact: when there are two jump frequencies to be considered, say v_i and v_j, the higher the ratio v_i/v_j, the lower the correlation factor, f_i, involved in the process by jumps of frequency v_i.

TABLE II.   Correlation factors for diffusion via free vacancies in the Al sub-lattice of corundum (After Compaan and Haven)

v_z/v_x	f_x	f_z
0	0·33333	1
0·1	0·37408	0·9115
0·5	0·45160	0·7428
1	0·50000	0·6495
2	0·55112	0·5621
10	0·63538	0·4372
∞	0·65549	0·3646

Lastly, Mullen (1961b) has calculated the correlation factors for other anisotropic lattices (primitive tetragonal, body-centred tetragonal and close-packed hexagonal). Here again, one must consider two frequencies, namely the frequencies within and out of the basal planes respectively, the correlation factor for each x-, y- and z-axis being a function of the frequency ratio.

(b) Correlation factor for tracer diffusion via vacancy pairs.

Consider the case of the NaCl lattice. The migration of the pair occurs by successive jumps of cations *and* anions into the pair. Suppose the pair to be tightly bound, so that at any time only the four ions situated in the plane perpendicular to the pair direction (Fig. 12) are available to jump into the pair (and similarly for ions of opposite sign). We have already denoted by a "prime" the parameters concerning the vacancy pair, and by the respective subscripts $_+$ and $_-$ those relative to the cation and anion. So, let v_+' and v_-' respectively denote the jump frequencies of the cation and anion into the pair (we shall see later that v_+' and v_-' may be quite different from v_+ and v_-, the jump frequencies of the ions into the free vacancies). The correlation factor for each ion is a function of the ratio v_+'/v_-' and has been calculated for some values of this ratio by Compaan and Haven (1956) (Table III) and by Howard (1966). Table III shows that the higher the ratio v_+'/v_-', the lower the correlation factor of the cation f_+' and at the limit, f_+' is zero when v_+'/v_-' is infinite. This can be visualized as follows; assuming v_+' is much larger than v_-', let us look at the cation jumps after the first jump of the anion and before the next one: the neighbouring cations (at sites 1, 2, 3, 4 and 5 in Fig. 12) make many jumps into the cation vacancy of the pair, which only rotates around the anion vacancy (site 0) without progressing further into the crystal. So, the neighbouring cations make many, but highly correlated, jumps and the cation diffusion coefficient, although involving a large jump frequency, is greatly depressed by a small correlation factor. At the other limit one sees that $f_+' = 0.7815$ for $v_-'/v_+' = \infty$. This expresses the fact that after a first jump of a tracer (cation), the pair has exchanged its anion vacancy with surrounding anions so many times that it is oriented in the six directions with equal probability before the next cation jump. The tracer has then a probability of 1/12 of jumping back into the pair and we find the same correlation factor as for free vacancies, as it must be.

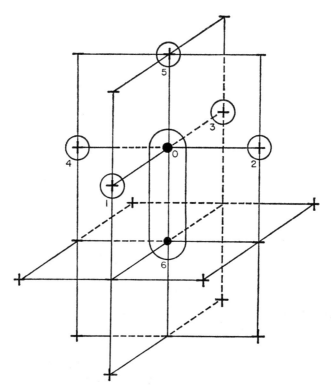

FIG. 12. Correlation effect for diffusion via vacancy pairs (NaCl lattice). In the case of the jump frequency of the cation is very larger than that of the anion, the vacancy pair rotates many times times around the anion vacant lattice site (0), the cation vacant site of the pair occupying successively the sites 6, 1, 2, 3, 4, 5 without moving further into the crystal before a next jump of the anion occurs.

The anion diffusion coefficient by vacancy pairs (D_-') can often be measured and it is important to determine the cation diffusion coefficient via vacancy pairs (D_+'), which is far more difficult to reach experimentally. The relation between D_+' and D_-' follows from eqn (5.8),

$$\frac{D_+'}{D_-'} = \frac{f_+'}{f_-'} \frac{v_+'}{v_-'}. \qquad (6.6)$$

As a consequence of the preceding remarks, the ratio D_+'/D_-' has a value closer to one than the value of the ratio v_+'/v_-'. This is numerically emphasized in Table III.

TABLE III.   Correlation factor for the cation diffusion via vacancy pairs in the NaCl lattice (after Compaan and Haven) and values of the cation to anion diffusion coefficients

v_-'/v_+'	f_+'	D_+'/D_-'
0	0	
0·1	0·2682	3·441
0·24	0·4136	2·315
0·5	0·5283	1·533
1	0·6189	1·000
2	0·6894	0·6525
4·17	0·7451	0·4324
10	0·7793	0·2906
∞	0·7815	

(c) *Correlation factor for tracer diffusion via impurity–vacancy pairs.*

The contribution of the associated vacancies to the tracer diffusion coefficient was expressed by equation (5.11b). If we consider the case of tightly bound pairs (non-dissociative) the correlation factor is a function of the ratio ω_2/ω_1 and has been calculated by Compaan and Haven for various values of this ratio (Table IV).

TABLE IV   Correlation factor for tracer (self)diffusion via impurity–vacancy pairs in the NaCl lattice (After Compaan and Haven)

ω_2/ω_1	0	0·1	0·5	1	10	∞
f	0	0·2047	0·3540	0·3977	0·4711	0·4862

2. Correlation Factor for Impurity Diffusion via Vacancies

Let us consider the case of diffusion of bivalent cations in a NaCl structure. In a preliminary treatment one can assume that the association of the vacancies with the bivalent cations is almost total and that the association obeys the Stasiw and Teltow configuration (impurity and vacancy at nearest neighbour positions). The diffusion of the impurity by the Johnson mechanism involves then only the two frequencies ω_1 and ω_2 and the correlation factor has the simple form

$$f = \frac{\omega_1}{\omega_1 + \omega_2}. \tag{6.7}$$

This was first derived by Lidiard (1955b) using a kinetic theory. More refined expressions have been derived, in the hope of eliminating the following two assumptions which are inherent in eqn (6.7):

(1) an impurity and a vacancy are regarded as paired only if they are on nearest neighbour sites (i.e. at a distance of $a\sqrt{2}$)

(2) it has been assumed that the pair is tightly bound so that any possibility for the vacancy to escape out of the first shell is excluded.

Lidiard (1955b) and Le Claire and Lidiard (1956) have partly removed the latter restriction by taking into account the probability of dissociative jumps. Let ω_3 denote the jump frequency of the vacancy to a particular site among the seven cation sites which are not nearest neighbour to the impurity. The expression for the correlation factor obtained is then

$$f = \frac{\omega_1 + 7\omega_3/2}{\omega_1 + \omega_2 + 7\omega_3/2}. \tag{6.8}$$

In this calculation the return probability of the escaped vacancy is neglected. This has, however, been included by Manning (1959) who introduces the fraction F of dissociating vacancies that do not return to associate again with the impurity, resulting in the expression

$$f = \frac{\omega_1 + 7F\omega_3/2}{\omega_1 + \omega_2 + 7F\omega_3/2}. \tag{6.9}$$

Note: One particular case of impurity diffusion is that of self-diffusion, if one considers the host ion tracer as an impurity. Here, all the jump frequencies are equal so that $\omega_1 = \omega_2 = \omega_3 = \nu_+$. Identifying the latter expression with the correlation factor for tracer diffusion calculated by Compaan and Haven ($f = 0.78146$), one obtains F equal to 0.7359.

In the case of diffusion of aliovalent ions, one must consider the frequencies ω_1, ω_2 and ω_3, which differ from ν_+, the frequency for jumps of the vacancy far removed from the impurity. This is due to the influence of the impurity on the proximate ions, in the same way that the frequency of associative jumps, let it be ω_4, can differ from v_+. The fraction F of lost vacancies is thus a function of the ratio ω_4/v_+ and has been calculated by Manning (1962). Manning's plot of $7F$ against ω_4/v_+ is shown in Fig. 13 for the f.c.c. lattice.

Now, let us return to the first restriction, which was that only pairs of first-neighbours were treated as associations. It has been shown, mainly from ionic thermo-current measurements (Laj, 1969), that in some cases the vacancy and impurity at next-nearest-neighbour (n.n.n. or second-neighbour) behave as an electric dipole and are to be treated as an association distinct from the nearest-neighbour association (n.n. or first-neighbour). Since the ratio of the densities of the vacancies at first- and second-neighbours is equal to the ratio of the vacancy jump frequency from a second- to a first-neighbour to the frequency of the reverse jump, the frequency of dissociative jumps to second-neighbours may be distinct from the frequencies of dissociative jumps to further neighbours. Manning (1964) has calculated f assuming that the first jumps occur with the frequency ω_3' and the latter jumps with the frequency ω_3'', all other jumps from third- and fourth-neighbours occuring with the frequency v_+ (Fig. 14), leading to the result

$$f = \frac{\omega_1 + 7F\omega_3'/2}{\omega_1 + \omega_2 + 7F\omega_3'/2} \tag{6.10}$$

with

$$7F = \frac{6\cdot33 + 6\cdot40\,(\omega_3'/\omega_3'') + (\omega_3'/\omega_3'')^2}{1\cdot67 + (\omega_3'/\omega_3'')}.$$

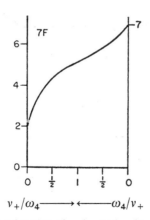

FIG. 13. Values of $7F$ as a function of ω_4/v_+ and v_+/ω_4 (After Manning, 1962).

Some attempts have been made to determine each of the frequencies involved from dielectric and elastic relaxation and I.T.C. techniques, more or less successfully. However, no use of eqn (6.10) has been made in the analysis of impurity diffusion coefficient measurements. On the contrary, one generally assumes that the frequency ω_2 is much smaller than all the other frequencies, so that f reduces to 1 and therefore the diffusion coefficient of bivalent cations diffusing as tracers in the intrinsic range (eqn 5.16) is supposed to obey a simple Arrhenius law. When the experiments are carried out in a limited temperature range, the adjustment of experimental measurements to this law is approximately obtained. However, refined measurements in temperature ranges as extended as possible show that this treatment is not completely sufficient (F. Bénière, 1970).

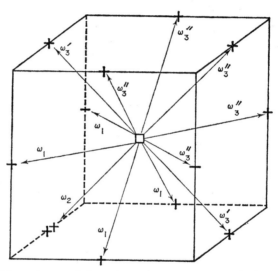

FIG. 14. The different jumps of the cation vacancy at nearest neighbour position of an impurity. ω_2: jump frequency of the impurity into the vacancy; ω_1: frequency of the jumps (non dissociative) of the neighbouring cations of both impurity and vacancy; ω_3': frequency of the dissociative jumps bringing the vacancy at next-nearest-neighbour of the impurity; ω_3'': frequency of the other dissociative jumps which appear in relation (6.10) of the correlation factor for impurity diffusion.

C. Experimental Methods of Correlation Factor Determination

We have seen that the correlation factor is either a numerical constant, when only one frequency is involved as in self-diffusion, or a function of two or more frequencies. In the latter case, if the activation energies of the distinct operative jumps are different, the correlation factor is temperature dependent. This could be seen on the plots of $\ln(D)$ versus $1/T$ as departures from pure straight lines, increasing the complexity of the analysis of experimental data. We shall deal mostly with the first case because the correlation factor for tracer diffusion should be easier to measure and because its determination should be of considerable interest in identifying the diffusion mechanism and the structure of the operative defects. Two main methods of experimental determination of f have been proposed.

1. Isotope Effects Measurement

The first measurements of isotope effects were performed by Chemla in 1954 for the pair of isotopes ^{22}Na and ^{24}Na diffusing in NaCl. The isotope effect is a *small* effect and difficult to measure. At that time, however, Chemla carried out an elegant method of amplifying the experimental shift between the two isotopes by adding the action of an electrical field. In his pioneer work, Chemla showed that the isotope effect approximately obeys the theoretical law in $1/\sqrt{M}$:

$$\frac{D' - D''}{D'} \equiv \frac{\Delta D}{D} \simeq \tfrac{1}{2}\frac{\Delta M}{M} \tag{6.11}$$

where M and D are the mass and diffusion coefficients of the two isotopes denoted by a prime and a double prime respectively.

However, the recent and extensive measurements of isotope effects seem to show that in many systems the observed effects are significantly lower than those predicted by the preceding law. If we define the isotope effect E as the ratio

$$E = \left(\frac{D'}{D''} - 1\right)\Big/\left(\sqrt{\frac{M''}{M'}} - 1\right)$$

we find in the literature (Gerl, 1968) values spreading from 0 to 1, depending on the system. The isotope effects in self-diffusion has a value of 0·7 or 0·8 for some metals such as Pd (Peterson, 1964), Ag (Peterson and Barr, 1965), Zn (Peterson and Rothman, 1967) Fe (Graham, 1966), but only 0·36 for Na (Mundy et al., 1966), while in NaCl there is a reported value of 0·73 (Barr and Le Claire, 1964). Two refinements of the theory of the mass effect on the diffusion coefficients have been proposed, which both lead to a decrease in the isotope shift, to a lower value than $\Delta M/2M$, i.e. decrease of E to a value lower than unity.

First, the correlation factor does not cancel out of the ratio D'/D'' but, on the contrary, gives for the isotope effect the following value (Tharmalingam and Lidiard, 1959):

$$\frac{\Delta D}{D''} = f'\frac{\Delta \omega}{\omega''}$$

where f' is the correlation factor of the isotope denoted by a prime, and ω'' and $\omega' = \omega'' + \Delta\omega$ are the jump frequencies of the two isotopes. If the jumps involve only the diffusing atom, the jump frequency has the form

$$\omega = \frac{1}{2\pi}\sqrt{\frac{K}{M}}\exp\left(-Q/kT\right).$$

For both isotopes the free energy barrier Q is the same, and this gives

$$\frac{\omega'}{\omega''} = \sqrt{\frac{M''}{M'}}.$$

However, when jumping, the ion displaces its neighbours and imparts to them some of its kinetic energy and the ratio ω'/ω'' must then be related to the ratio of the effective masses (Vineyard, 1957; Mullen, 1961a; Le Claire, 1966). The isotope effect is then reduced to

$$\frac{\Delta D}{D''} = f\,\Delta K\left(\sqrt{\frac{M''}{M'}} - 1\right). \tag{6.12}$$

Strictly speaking, the correlation factor in this relation is f', the slight mass effect on f being given by (Adda and Philibert, 1966):

$$\frac{\Delta f}{f} = (1 - f')\left(1 - \sqrt{\frac{M'}{M''}}\right).$$

ΔK is the fraction of the kinetic energy that resides on the migrating ion and is obviously a dimensionless factor (and not an increment as might be suspected from the notation).

The value of ΔK may give some information about the diffusion mechanism. In a simple mechanism where no outer ion is displaced, ΔK should be equal to unity. On the other hand, if a large number of ions are involved in the diffusive jump step, ΔK should have a very small value. For example, Chadwick et al. (1970) have measured the isotope effects in benzene and cyclohexane. In the former case, ΔK is nearly equal to unity which the authors interpret by a vacancy mechanism, involving single molecule jumps. In the latter case they interpret the very small value of ΔK by a much more complicated process, involving the cooperative motion of many molecules in the diffusive step.

Considering the determination of the correlation factor itself from isotope effect measurements, it is clear that such measurements give only the product $f\,\Delta K$, where ΔK is poorly known. For this reason, the second method we shall describe seems to be more informative.

2. Comparison of the Tracer Diffusion Coefficients with the Ionic Conductivity

The ionic conductivity may be easily interpreted in terms of the net drift of the lattice defects in an electric field, the charge carried by the defect being equal to the charge of the ion for migrating interstitials and equal to the opposite charge of the ion vacated for conduction via vacancies. The successive jump directions of defects are uncorrelated with one another, so that no correlation effect appears in the measurement of ionic conductivity.

The very general Nernst–Einstein relation connects the self-diffusion coefficient, which corresponds to the movement of the ions without an external force, with the ionic mobility due to the application of any force field. In the case of an electric field this relation is

$$\frac{\sigma}{D} = \frac{Nq^2}{kT}.$$

σ: ionic conductivity

N: number of molecules per unit volume

q: charge on the particles (equal to e for monovalent ions)

k: Boltzmann's constant

T: absolute temperature

D: *true* self-diffusion coefficient, i.e. the self-diffusion coefficient of all the indistinguishable ions. We must remember that we have defined as tracer diffusion coefficient that which was measured with radioisotopes. In future we shall use the following notation:

D^* for the tracer diffusion coefficient

D_{calc} for the self-diffusion coefficient deduced from the conductivity measurements by application of the Nernst–Einstein relation, i.e.

$$D_{calc} = \frac{\sigma kT}{Nq^2}.$$

When both diffusion and conductivity are due to the same species of defect, e.g. cation single vacancies, the correlation factor is given directly by the ratio

$$f = \frac{D^*}{D_{calc}}$$

as was pointed out by Haven in 1955, who suggested this method for measuring f. However, this is directly applicable in only a few particular cases. In most cases, some species give contributions to only one phenomenon, e.g. a supplementary electronic conductivity to σ in crystals that are not purely ionic or diffusion by neutral species which contribute to the diffusion but not to the conductivity. This means that the ratio D^*/D_{calc}, denoted by some authors as the "experimental correlation factor" may be distinct from the theoretical correlation factor defined above. To avoid any confusion, we shall follow Le Claire (1970) who denotes as the "Haven ratio" the quantity

$$D^*/D_{calc} \equiv H_r$$

When both σ and D^* can be measured, a value of H_r distinct from unity may be due to a competition between the following effects:

(1) existence of correlation effects ($\rightarrow H_r < 1$)

(2) participation of electronic conductivity ($\rightarrow H_r < 1$)

(3) participation in the diffusion of defects such as vacancy pairs and impurity–vacancy pairs, which are not "seen" in conductivity ($\rightarrow H_r > 1$).

This will be illustrated by some examples of measurement and analysis in Section VIII, which is devoted to numerical results, but before this, it would be useful to describe how the experimental results are obtained.

VII. The Measurement of the Diffusion Coefficients

Generally, a certain amount of the material whose diffusion coefficient is to be determined is allowed to diffuse into a single crystal. The diffusion coefficients of solids have values of the order of magnitude 10^{-10} cm^2/s at high temperatures and extremely low values at ordinary temperatures. The diffusion experiments must therefore be carried out at high temperatures and over long periods of time. After the time t of diffusion, the distribution of the concentration C is determined as accurately as possible. The initial and boundary conditions are chosen in order to deal with a function $C(x, t)$ in one of the simple forms described in Section III. The total amount of diffusing substance must be as low as possible in order to keep the initial structure and to avoid the introduction of impurities altering the chemical composition of the crystal. Then, when radioactive isotopes are available, counting methods are the best. To these generalities, it must be added that the accuracy of the measurements depends heavily on the following factors:

(1) The diffusion coefficients depend exponentially on temperature and to give an idea of the importance of this parameter, one can say that, at $T = 1000°K$ for an activation energy of 2 eV, and error of 1°C in T would imply an error of 2·3 % in D. This emphasizes the necessity of having a constant and well-defined temperature during the whole of the diffusion time.

(2) In most cases, the diffusion is considerably enhanced by the presence of very small amounts of impurities and every source of possible contamination must be avoided by working with vessels of high quality materials and under slight pressures of purified inert gases.

Let us follow how a typical measurement is carried out in a system where D is a constant and there is a suitable radioactive isotope available. We shall attempt to follow as faithfully as possible the conditions of diffusion from an infinitely thin layer in order to obtain for the concentration $C(x, t)$ the function given by (3.4) or (3.5):

(1) A surface of a single crystal is smoothed and will be the initial plane of a one-dimensional diffusion process.

(2) A small amount of the tracer is deposited on this plane, or between two adjacent samples, by subliming the substance if it is sufficiently volatile; one then has an initial layer which is practically infinitely thin and of homogeneous concentration on the surface.

(3) The penetration depth is generally far smaller than the sample thickness, so that the boundary condition of infinite medium $(C(\infty, t) = 0)$ is fulfilled.

(4) Diffusion is allowed to occur at a given temperature for the time t.

(5) After diffusion, the sides of the sample are removed to avoid edge effects.

(6) The concentration $C(x, t)$ of the tracer inside the crystal should then obey eqn (3.4). The sample is then divided into a given number of slices, parallel to the front plane, by sectioning with a microtome. This is the most delicate operation because of the smallness of the diffusion coefficients in solids. To give an example, the self-diffusion coefficient of Na^+ in $NaCl$ is $D = 18.5 \times 10^{-10}$ cm^2/s at $698.2°C$, so that for $t = 24h$, the distance $x_{1/2}$ for which $C(x_{1/2}, t = 24h) = \frac{1}{2}C(x = 0, t = 24h)$ is about 0.21 mm; this shows the necessity of having a high accuracy in the mechanical sectioning. This method is limited to the measurement of diffusion coefficients higher than 10^{-12} cm^2/s; for this value, $C(x_{1/2})$ equals $\frac{1}{2}C(x = 0)$ at only 27 µm penetration after 30 days.

(7) The radioactive intensity of each slice is then counted and by plotting the logarithm of the specific activity against x^2, one should obtain a good straight line, the slope of which is equal to $-1/4Dt$.

This method, first applied by Mapother et al. (1950) is the most frequently used and, when applicable, the most convenient for accurate measurements. The measurement of the diffusion coefficients of volatile compounds is carried out using the same method; diffusion occurs from a concentration maintained at the value given by the vapour pressure of the compound and the diffusion coefficient is calculated from the diffusion profile of the tracer, either given by eqn (3.6) if D is a constant or by eqn (3.8) if D is not.

Among some other radioactive isotope techniques (Barr, 1970), one must cite the isotope exchange method elaborated by Morrison and his co-workers (Patterson et al., 1956); this is applicable in compounds where one of the constituents can become gaseous, such as in the measurement of the self-diffusion coefficients of halide ions in alkali halide crystals (Barr et al., 1960). The diffusion coefficient here is deduced from the measurement of the rate of appearance in the gas phase of an isotope of the gas originally incorporated in the solid. This method has the advantage of enabling one to measure very low diffusion coefficients, say down to 10^{-17} cm^2/s, but has the disadvantage that the diffusion profile is not observed, so that the sectioning technique is to be preferred for the measurement of higher diffusion coefficients (Barr, 1970).

As well as the radioactive isotope techniques, some other methods have been applied for determining the distribution $C(x, t)$: mass spectrometry analysis for stable isotopes (Ptashnik and Naumov, 1968), characteristic light absorbance measurement for impurity diffusion coefficients (Ikeda, 1964), spectrophotometric method (Reisfeld and Honigbaum, 1968), electron spin resonance absorption intensity (Stewart and Reed, 1965). Finally, we should mention that magnetic resonance techniques are studied, which could give, by non-destructive methods, diffusion coefficients from relaxation time measurements.

VIII. Numerical Results

Diffusion processes are so much involved in so many fields, such as metallurgy, semi-conductor engineering, catalytic chemistry, photography, that both applied and fundamental research has been extensively performed. We have already restricted ourselves to the study of ionic crystals, on which numerous studies have been carried out for the last twenty years and with which the electro-chemist is most concerned. A full account of all the existing experimental data has been given in the review article by Süptitz and Teltow (1967) and we shall merely give a table of diffusion constants at the end of the paper. Instead we wish to focus on a few typical and recent sets of experiments concerning alkali and silver halides, for which rather extensive and precise data exist, in order to give concrete examples of data collecting and analysing which may be easily extrapolated to other systems. We shall begin with some self-diffusion studies which lead to numerical values for the thermodynamic parameters involved in the formation of defects and migration of ions, then we shall deal with the experimental measurement of correlation factors and end with a few examples of impurity diffusion.

A. Self Diffusion

1. Alkali Halides

We shall describe three recent sets of experiments performed respectively in NaCl, KCl and KBr. Though dealing with the same equations, the analyses are based on different types of experiments. Nevertheless, they lead to similar results and, moreover, we shall find a strong analogy between the three compounds.

(a) NaCl (F. *Bénière et al.*, 1970)

(i) *Cation self-diffusion in* NaCl. The first measurements of diffusion in ionic crystals were performed twenty years ago by Mapother *et al.* (1950) who measured the diffusion coefficients of the isotope ^{24}Na in "pure" sodium chloride single crystals. These measurements have been repeated by many workers and one can appreciate the scatter of the pioneer results from Fig. 15 where the reported values of $D_{(Na^+)}$ obtained in undoped crystals of more or less high purity at 650°C are shown. It is interesting to note that the two most recent results agree within a few percent, in the same way as many other diffusion data tend to converge as the techniques are improved, giving more confidence to the basic data for further analyses.

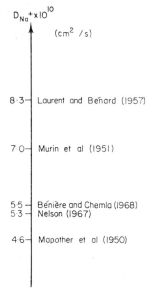

FIG. 15. Comparison of some measurements of the tracer-diffusion coefficient of Na$^+$ for the temperature of 650°C in NaCl single crystals.

Some diffusion coefficients of the isotope ^{22}Na measured in two kinds of "pure" crystals and in NaCl crystals doped with a molar fraction of 27 × 10^{-6} Sr^{++} are shown in Fig. 16, plotted as $\log_{10}(D)$ versus $1/T$. We recognize on these curves the two temperature ranges that have already been defined.

(1) At high temperatures, the diffusion coefficients are the same for all crystals. This is typical of the intrinsic range where one is mainly concerned with the thermodynamically produced vacancies, namely cation vacancies and vacancy pairs for the present case.

(2) At a lower temperature, one sees a "knee" on the curves and the diffusion below the knee is characterized by a lower activation energy and by diffusion coefficients that are no longer independent of the crystal impurity content, but increase with the molar fraction of aliovalent cations.

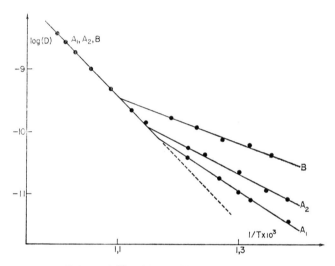

FIG. 16. Diffusion coefficients of ^{22}Na$^+$ in NaCl single crystals. A_1 and A_2: pure crystals of different origins, B: crystals doped by 27 × 10^{-6} SrCl$_2$, straight lines have schematically been drawn. (After F. Bénière, 1970).

As a preliminary explanation, one could say that in the intrinsic range the thermal cation vacancies are responsible for the diffusion, while in the extrinsic range diffusion is mainly due to the cation vacancies introduced by the aliovalent impurities. Then the expression for D would be given by eqn (5.4) at high temperature and by eqn (5.6) at low temperature. This would explain the general appearance of the temperature and impurity concentration dependence on D, according to Koch and Wagner (1937) who observed similar behaviour in the ionic conductivity. However, application of eqn (5.6) would assign the same activation energy for doped and undoped crystals and comparison with experiment shows that, in the extrinsic range, the free cation vacancies are not the only defects responsible for diffusion. It is thought that amongst the background impurities of the "pure" crystals, there are very associative ions and therefore associated vacancies that give a contribution to the cation diffusion. This point can be seen more directly by comparing the measured diffusion coefficients with those calculated from the conductivity measurements. This is shown in Figs. 17 and 18 for undoped crystal, the difference $D_{exp} - D_{calc}$ giving an order of magnitude for the diffusion by the vacancies associated with the background impurities. On the contrary, in crystals doped with Sr^{++} ions for concentrations significantly higher than that of background impurities and sufficiently small to be almost totally dissociated in a given temperature range (which is elsewhere observed on the conductivity plots) D_{exp} and D_{calc} have nearly the same values (Fig. 19) and one observes the same activation energy for both diffusion and conductivity (0·72 eV). If there were appreciable association, the Npc associated vacancies would give a contribution to D_{exp} given by eqn (5.11b) or perhaps even higher (Trnovcova, 1969) besides the contribution of the $N(1-p)c$ free vacancies given by eqn (5.11a) which would assign to the apparent activation energy of D_{exp} a value different from that observed in the conductivity measurements, since conductivity involves

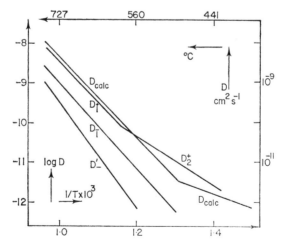

FIG. 17. Diffusion coefficients in "pure" NaCl single crystals (denoted A_1 on Fig. 16) $D_1{}^+$: cation tracer-diffusion coefficient in the intrinsic range; $D_2{}^+$: cation tracer-diffusion coefficient in the extrinsic range; $D_1{}^-$: anion tracer-diffusion coefficient; D_-' anion diffusion coefficient via vacancy pairs; D_{calc}: diffusion coefficient calculated from the conductivity measurements by application of the Nernst–Einstein relation (After F. Bénière et al., 1970).

only the $N(1 - p)c$ free vacancies. Therefore, in crystals doped by convenient concentrations of suitable bivalent cations, the temperature dependence of the experimental cation self-diffusion coefficients may be fitted to eqn (5.6).

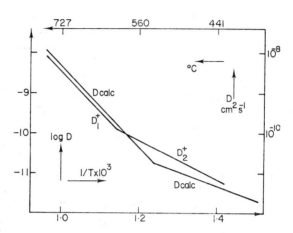

FIG. 18. Diffusion coefficients in "pure" NaCl single crystals (denoted A_2 on Fig. 16). D^+: cation tracer-diffusion coefficient; D_{calc}: diffusion coefficient calculated from measurements of the conductivity (σ):

$$D_{calc} = \frac{kT}{Ne^2}\,\sigma.$$

(After Bénière et al., 1970).

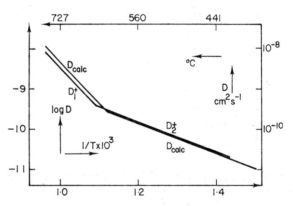

FIG. 19. Diffusion coefficients in NaCl single crystals doped by 27×10^{-6} SrCl$_2$ (denoted B on Fig. 16). D^+: cation tracer-diffusion coefficient; D_{calc}: diffusion coefficient calculated from measurements of the conductivity (σ). (After F. Bénière et al., 1970).

If c, the molar fraction of impurities, is determined from a distinct measurement, as for instance by a radioactivity counting technique (Bénière and Chemla, 1968) one then obtains the value of the enthalpy of migration of the cation (H_{m+}) and the constant pre-exponential term $v_0 \exp(S_{m+}/k)$ and thus the jump frequency as a function of temperature.

By considering the cation diffusion coefficients of the intrinsic range, one may assume to a first approximation that the thermal free vacancies only are responsible for diffusion of the cation; then, using eqn (5.4) and substituting $v_0 \exp(S_{m+}/k)$ and H_{m+} by the preceding values, one obtains approximate values for the entropy and enthalpy of formation of defects $(S_s$ and $H_s)$. A more refined analysis requires the subtracting of the contribution of the vacancy pairs; this one can be deduced from the anion diffusion coefficients measured in doped crystals.

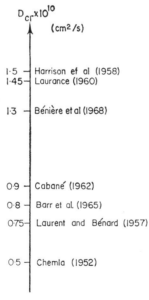

FIG. 20. Comparison of some measurements of the tracer-diffusion coefficient of Cl^- for the temperature of 650°C in NaCl single crystals. The lowest values of the diffusion coefficient could be supposed to be refered to crystals doped by divalent cation impurities.

(ii) *Anion self-diffusion in* NaCl. Many workers have measured the self-diffusion coefficient of the chloride ion with the isotope ^{36}Cl, either by sectioning or isotope exchange techniques, since the first experiments carried out by Chemla (1952). Some results calculated by interpolation on the experimental curves at the same temperature (650°C) are collected in

Fig. 20. The corresponding activation energies deduced from the mean slopes of the curves in $Ln(D)$ versus $(1/T)$ are shown in Table V. Here again one sees the convergence of the recent results for the activation energies, some of the older results being clearly explained by the presence of noticeable amounts of impurities in the crystals used at that time.

TABLE V. Measurements of the activation energy for anion self-diffusion in NaCl (fitting the experimental diffusion coefficients to a single exponential)

W(eV)	Authors
2.70	Chemla (1952)
2·23	Laurent and Bénard (1957)
2·29	Harrison et al. (1958)
2·12	Laurance (1960)
2·16	Barr et al. (1965)
2·14	Bénière et al. (1968)

Some anion self-diffusion coefficients for pure and Sr^{++}-doped NaCl crystals are plotted as $\log_{10} D$ against $1/T$ in Fig. 21. Considering the experimental points in undoped crystals (curve A), one can see that they fall approximately on a straight line down to 500°C. This may be defined as the "intrinsic" range of the anion diffusion. This range thus extends down to the temperature at which the knee in the conductivity curve occurs in pure crystals (Kirk and Pratt, 1967; F. Bénière, 1970). On the other hand, we remember that the cation diffusion intrinsic range was observed down to only about 580°C, which gives further evidence of associated vacancies due to cation-aliovalent background impurities in the *cation* sub-lattice. We may also conclude from the behaviour of curve A that appreciable diffusion by dislocations is absent, at least for the temperatures considered.

For the lightly doped crystals (curves B and C) one finds that, at high temperature, the experimental points fall on the curve of the pure crystal, which is typical of the intrinsic range of these doped crystals. For lower temperatures, one observes that the diffusion coefficients have lower values than that of the pure crystal. This gives direct evidence for the validity of the solubility product relation written by Lidiard (1957) as

$$x_+ \, x_- = \exp\left(- \, G_s/kT\right)$$

since the predicted influence of doping is to increase x_+ (enhancing the cation diffusion) and to decrease x_- simultaneously (depressing the anion diffusion) relative to their values in undoped crystals. As predicted by the solubility product and electroneutrality relations (eqns 4.2 and 4.3 leading to 4.6), the break between the intrinsic and extrinsic anion diffusion ranges occurs at higher temperature for larger $SrCl_2$ content. Comparing the anion and cation diffusion data in the same crystals, good agreement with the preceding solubility product relationship is quantitatively obtained. This gives definite evidence for the existence of Schottky defects rather than Frenkel defects in NaCl, since in the latter case, the concentrations of defects in each sub-lattice would be independent of each other. In other words, one may conclude that the defects are caused by the departure of ions from their normal lattice sites on to the surface of the crystal (giving rise to a relation between the molar fractions of the anion and cation vacancies because of the electro-neutrality requirement which is included in eqn (4.3) connecting x_+ and x_-).

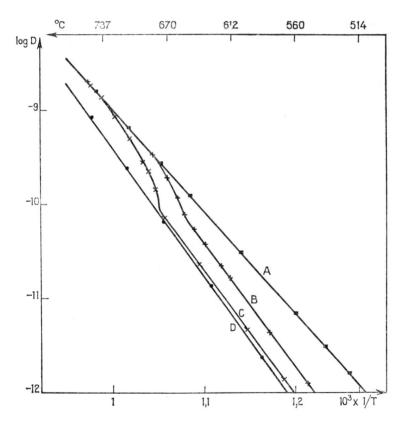

FIG. 21. Diffusion coefficients of $^{36}Cl^-$ in NaCl single crystals. A: "pure" crystals; B: crystals doped by 27×10^{-6} $SrCl_2$; C: crystals doped by 65×10^{-6} $SrCl_2$; D: crystals doped by 363×10^{-6} $SrCl_2$ (in molar fraction). (After Bénière et al., 1968).

Considering the lower temperature sections of the diffusion plots, one sees that the diffusion coefficients tend to a constant value independent of the impurity content. If the free anion vacancies were the only defects responsible for diffusion, the functional form of D would be given by eqn (5.7) at low temperature, i.e. inversely proportional to c and with the temperature dependence given by the large activation energy $H_s + H_{m-}$. Remembering that the molar fraction of vacancy pairs (eqn 4.10) is independent of the impurity content, this suggests that, besides the free vacancy contribution, the vacancy pairs participate in the measured diffusion coefficients. In the intrinsic range, the main contribution is due to the free vacancies whilst at low temperatures in doped crystals—the free anion vacancies being almost totally salted out—the contribution from the vacancy pairs becomes the main term. At the limit for heavily doped crystals, one obtains a diffusion due mainly to vacancy pairs in the whole temperature range considered (curve D). Let us mention that Laurance (1960) and Barr et al. (1965) have carried out anion diffusion coefficient measurements in NaCl crystals containing large amounts of Ca^{++} ions (10^{-4}–10^{-3} in molar fraction) and obtained results similar to those depicted in curve D (Table VI).

TABLE VI.   Measurements of the activation energy for anion self-diffusion in heavily doped NaCl (fitting the experimental diffusion coefficients to a single exponential)

W(eV)	Authors
2·5	Laurance (1960)
2·4	Barr et al. (1965)
2·7	Bénière et al. (1968)

A more refined quantitative analysis can be performed by fitting all the data: diffusion coefficients of the cation and of the anion and electrical conductivity measured as a function of temperature and divalent cation content, to the theoretical laws involving both contributions of free vacancies and vacancy pairs by the least-squares method with the help of computers. The final results are (F. Bénière, 1970):

$$(x_+ x_-)^{\frac{1}{2}} = 258 \exp\left(-2·50/2kT\right)$$
$$v_+ = 3·6 \times 10^{13} \exp\left(-0·72/kT\right) s^{-1}$$
$$v_- = 4·4 \times 10^{13} \exp\left(-0·86/kT\right) s^{-1}$$
$$D_-' = 5200 \exp\left(-2·63/kT\right) cm^2/s$$

(*b*) KCl (*Fuller et al.*, 1968a)

The preceding scheme of analysis of cation + anion self-diffusion coefficient measurements has also been applied to pure and $SrCl_2$ doped KCl crystals (M. Bénière *et al.*, 1970). We shall also describe another method of determining the parameters from an analysis of ionic conductivity and anion self-diffusion coefficient measurements in pure and $SrCl_2$ doped KCl crystals. This method was applied by Fuller and his co-workers in the case of KCl. The two sets of results will be compared.

Before going any further the care needed in the computer fitting must be emphasized. To give an example, Fuller *et al.* (1968b) found that by best fitting the electrical conductivity in the intrinsic range to the sum of two exponentials led to a value of $H_{m-} - H_{m+}$ equal to 0·7 eV. On the other hand, in the treatment which will be described below Fuller *et al.* (1968a) give a value of about 0·1 eV for the same quantity. Hence it is preferable to carry out the determination of the set of parameters involved in the formation, association and migration of defects in a body of *distinct* measurements rather than to place too much confidence in values obtained by fitting a single type of measurement.

The general outline of Fuller's analysis is to fit both conductivity data and anion diffusion data (Fuller, 1966) to the theoretical functional forms according to a model involving free anion vacancies, free cation vacancies, vacancy pairs and impurity–vacancy pairs. Two kinds of fitting have been performed, the first one taking no account of the long-range Coulomb interactions (which these authors denote as "simple theory including association" or STIA). In the second kind the long-range interactions are included by use of the Debye–Hückel approximation according to the Lidiard theory (1954); this modifies the functional form of the concentration of every charge defect (e.g. eqn (4.4) is used instead of eqn (4.3)). In both cases the aim is to determine the values of the following parameters which give the best fit to the experimental data:

(1) S_s and H_s, entropy and enthalpy of Schottky defect formation,

(2) S_{m+} and H_{m+}, entropy and enthalpy of cation migration,

(3) S_{m-} and H_{m-}, entropy and enthalpy of anion migration,

(4) S_a and H_a, entropy and enthalpy of divalent impurity–cation vacancies (at nearest neighbour sites) association,

(5) $D_0{_-}'$ and H_-', pre-exponential factor and activation energy of the vacancy pair contribution to the chloride ion tracer diffusion coefficient.

(6) v_0, the effective vibrational frequency of the ions on their equilibrium sites (assumed identical for the anion and cation vacancies).

The adopted procedure of the cycle for computer fitting is outlined in Fig. 22. It is obvious that each phenomenon does not involve all the eleven parameters at the same time, e.g. the vacancy pairs are inoperative in the electrical conductivity, impurity–vacancy pairs are not involved in the anion tracer diffusion, etc. The figure indicates the parameters that are adjusted in each process involving a given kind of measurement, and whose values are used as the starting values of the subsequent minimization.

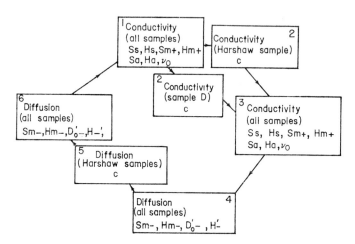

FIG. 22. Procedure cycle for the computer analysis of anion tracer-diffusion coefficient and conductivity data in KCl single crystals of different contents: "pure" (Harshaw) and doped by $SrCl_2$ (A: 237 ppm; B: 469 ppm; C: 44 ppm; D: 21 ppm) Each box represents a different analysis. The parameters listed in each box are the ones varied during that analysis. (After Fuller et al., 1968).

According to this model, Fuller obtained for the average fractional deviation in the least-squares analyses of the conductivity a value equal to 2·4% using the Lidiard theory and 3% using the STIA.† The final values of the enthalpies are reported in Table VII together with the values obtained from the anion and cation tracer diffusion coefficient measurements according to the preceding analysis (M. Bénière et al., 1970).

(c) KBr (Barr and Dawson, 1969)

In this analysis the basic data are sets of bromide diffusion coefficients measured in pure and $CaBr_2$- and $SrBr_2$-doped KBr crystals. The self-

† Note added in proof. From new measurements of the ionic conductivity of KCl crystals' P. W. M. Jacobs and P. Pantelis, Phys. Rev. (1971) vol. 4, p. 3757, have computed the same parameters, with and without including Debye–Hückel interactions. No significant changes either in the parameters or in the average fractional deviation are found.

TABLE VII.   Experimental values of the enthalpy parameters for ionic transport in KCl (in eV)

Quantity	Fuller et al. analysis using Lidiard theory	Fuller et al. analysis using STIA	Bénière et al. analysis
Schottky defect formation energy, H_s	2·49	2·59	2·64
Cation migration enthalpy, H_{m+}	0·76	0·79	0·79
Anion migration enthalpy, H_{m-}	0·89	0·82	0·85
Sr^{++}-cation vacancy association enthalpy, H_a	0·57	0·36	
Vacancy pair contribution to anion diffusion activation energy, H_-'	2·62	2·59	2·49

diffusion of the isotope ^{82}Br has been studied using both the sectioning technique $(1·5 \times 10^{-10} < D < 10^{-9}\,cm^2/s)$ and the radioactive isotopic exchange technique $(10^{-14} < D < 10^{-9}\,cm^2/s)$. In the common temperature range where both methods were applied, the same values of D were obtained, showing that the two techniques measure the same diffusion process. By using the exchange technique (see Section VII) diffusion coefficients have been measured down to 338°C (which is the lowest reported temperature for an experiment carried out in 25 ppm Ca^{++}-doped crystals where $D = 1·32 \times 10^{-14}\,cm^2/s$. Diffusion along dislocations has been shown (Laurent and Bénard, 1958; Barr et al., 1960; Dawson and Barr, 1967) to be of importance in anion diffusion in alkali halides at temperatures below about $0·75\,T_m$, where T_m is the melting temperature in °K. For KBr $T_m = 1003°K$ and the lowest temperature is thus equal to $0·6\,T_m$. In order to take account of the diffusion down dislocations, Barr and Dawson assumed that the contribution of this process to the total diffusion coefficient obeys an Arrhenius law, i.e. characterized by an activation enthalpy H_d and a pre-exponential constant D_{0d}.

The analysis of the anion diffusion coefficients of pure and doped crystals has thus been carried out with a model involving anion diffusion by the three distinct processes due to free anion vacancies, vacancy pairs and dislocations in order to evaluate the nine parameters S_{m-}, H_{m-}, S_s, H_s, D_{0-}', H_-', H_d, D_{0d}, and c including Debye–Hückel corrections.

Separation of the experimental data has been made in order to simplify the process of calculation. Doping crystals with bivalent cations is supposed to depress the single anion vacancy diffusion to negligible proportions. The diffusion coefficient obtained on each doped crystal is then fitted to the sum of the two exponential functions involving the vacancy pair and dislocation diffusion, which yields values for the corresponding parameters. The others are then determined by fitting the complete equation to the diffusion coefficients measured on pure crystals. The values for the enthalpies are reported in Table VIII.

TABLE VIII.   Experimental values of the enthalpy parameters for anion diffusion in KBr (in eV) (After Barr and Dawson, 1969)

Schottky defect formation enthalpy, H_s	2·54
Anion migration enthalpy, H_{m-}	0·83
Vacancy pair contribution to anion diffusion activation enthalpy, H_-'	2·60
Dislocation contribution to anion diffusion activation energy, H_d	1·3

In order to compare the three crystalline compounds we have dealt with the all main results are shown in Table IX. The similarity of the general behaviour of the three compounds could have been seen by comparing the diffusion coefficients themselves, which are of the same order of magnitude. It can be seen in this comparative table that enthalpies of

TABLE IX.   Comparison of the experimental values of the enthalpy parameters for ionic transport in alkali halides (in eV)

Quantity	NaCl	KCl		KBr
Schottky defect formation enthalpy, H_s	2·50[a]	2·49[b]	2·64[c]	2·54[d]
Cation migration enthalpy, H_{m+}	0·72[a]	0·76[b]	0·79[c]	
Anion migration enthalpy, H_{m-}	0·86[a]	0·89[b]	0·85[c]	0·83[d]
Vacancy pair contribution to anion diffusion activation energy, H_-'	2·63[a]	2·62[b]	2·49[c]	2·60[d]

[a] F. Bénière et al. (1970)
[b] Fuller et al. (1968a)
[c] M. Bénière et al. (1970)
[d] Barr and Dawson (1969)

defect formation and migration are nearly the same for all three compounds. Also, it may be noticed in parenthesis that the differences between the values for these three different compounds are much smaller than the scatter between the earlier results for one given compound. The similarity of the activation energies (and also the entropy terms, which can be found in the original papers) clearly shows that the same processes occur in this category of ionic crystals (alkali halides); this could give useful information for the theoretical work.

2. Silver Halides (Weber and Friauf, 1969)

The anion mobility in alkali halide crystals is lower than the cation mobility, but non-negligible (see the section on transference numbers), and both ion contributions must be taken into account in the analysis of the conductivity data. In contrast, the tracer diffusion coefficients of $^{36}Cl^-$ in AgCl are three to four orders of magnitude smaller than the diffusion coefficients of the tracer cation $^{110}Ag^+$ (Compton and Maurer, 1956), so that the anion mobility can be neglected in the comparison of D_{Ag^+} and σ. As will be seen the thermal disorder in the cation sub-lattice of the silver halide crystals is (Koch and Wagner, 1937) of the Frenkel type, namely silver ion vacancies and interstitial silver ions. Let n_v and n_i be the numbers of vacancies and interstitials, respectively, in a crystal containing N cation lattice sites and let $x_v = n_v/N$ and $x_i = n_i/N$ denote the molar fractions of both defects. Equation (4.1) may be rewritten as

$$x_v x_i = 2 \exp \left(- \frac{G_f}{kT} \right) = x_0{}^2. \tag{8.1}$$

In pure crystals the molar fractions are equal, $x_v = x_i = x_0$. One must first determine the respective mobilities of the vacancies and interstitials since both defects are able to contribute to the electrical conductivity. This question can be quickly answered by the elegant method used by Teltow (1949) and Ebert and Teltow (1955) who measured respectively the conductivity of AgBr doped with $CdBr_2$ and $PbBr_2$, and AgCl doped with $CdCl_2$ and $PbCl_2$.

We have already mentioned that doping alkali halides with bivalent cations enhances the cation diffusion and ionic conductivity in the extrinsic range. The conductivity, σ, is approximately directly proportional to c, as long as the impurity–vacancy association can be neglected (Kelting and Witt, 1949; Haven, 1955). From this single observation two distinct hypotheses about the defect structure could have been proposed: either Schottky defects with a negligible mobility of the anion or Frenkel disorder with a negligible mobility of the interstitials. On the other hand, in the silver halides Teltow has shown that the isotherms $\sigma = f(c)$ are not linear; as c increases from zero σ decreases to reach a minimum value and then increases at higher impurity contents. Doping crystals containing Frenkel defects increases the molar fraction of vacancies, x_v, and simultaneously depresses the molar fraction of interstitials, x_i, because of the solubility product relation (eqn (8.1)). So that Tetlow's results prove that the silver halides contain Frenkel defects where both interstitials and vacancies are mobile, and, moreover, the cation vacancy is less mobile than the interstitial. The quantitative analysis shows that in AgBr the ratio of the interstitial mobility to the vacancy mobility varies from more than 7 at 175°C down to 2 at 350°C.

Weber and Friauf (1969) have measured the diffusion coefficient of the tracer $^{110}Ag^+$ (D^*) in AgCl and compared D^* to the diffusion coefficient deduced from ionic conductivity data (D_{calc}). Several distinct values of the corresponding Haven ratio, H_r, may be expected *a priori*:

(i) vacancy mechanism $\rightarrow H_r = f = 0.7815$

(ii) interstitial mechanism $\rightarrow H_r = f = 1$

(iii) interstitialcy mechanisms
  (a) colinear interstitialcy $\rightarrow H_r = \frac{1}{2}f = 0.3333$
  (b) non-colinear interstitialcy $\rightarrow H_r = \frac{3}{4}f = 0.7273$

We notice that the Haven ratio is not identical to the theoretical correlation factor of eqn (6.4) calculated by Compaan and Haven (1958) (see Section VI). This arises from the fact that in an interstitialcy jump, the jump length of the tracer ion alone is involved in D^*, while at the same time two Ag^+ ions have jumped and the total charge displacement involved in D_{calc} is then generally longer than the tracer jump length. In the colinear interstitialcy jump the interstitial (let us assume it is a tracer ion) jumps toward a silver ion on an adjacent lattice site (Fig. 11), pushes the lattice ion into the opposite interstitial position and occupies the vacated site. If we denote the cation–anion separation distance by a, the displacement of the tracer is $a\sqrt{3}/2$ and the displacement of the lattice ion is $a\sqrt{3}/2$ in the same direction, so that the electric charge jumps twice the distance moved by the silver ion alone. Hence, in the colinear interstitialcy mechanism, $H_r = \frac{1}{2} \times 0.6666 = 0.3333$.

Weber and Friauf's results are shown in Fig. 23. The fact that H_r is considerably smaller than 1 and 0.7815 shows that the interstitialcy processes must be prominent for the motion of interstitial ions, and the intermediate values for H_r also make it clear that at least two kinds of interstitialcy jumps must be present. These authors have separated out the vacancy contribution by using the conductivity data in order to determine the respective participations of the two types of mechanism—colinear and non-colinear. Some of the results obtained by Weber and Friauf are shown in Table X.

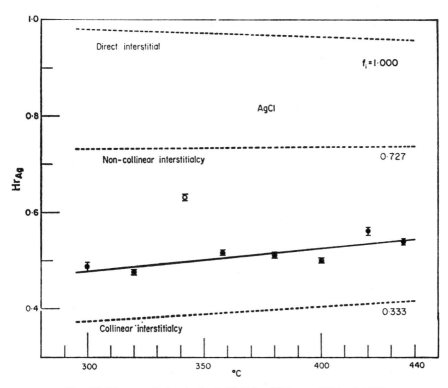

FIG. 23. Haven ratio for Ag in AgCl (After Weber and Friauf, 1969).

B. Correlation Factors in Tracer-Diffusion

In the preceding section we have already given an example of correlation factor determination and application in identifying the diffusion mechanisms operative in pure silver halide crystals. Historically, the correlation factor for the vacancy mechanism in alkali halides was the first to be considered and we shall devote the first part of this section to the expression of the Haven ratio in the intrinsic range of alkali halide crystals, and especially in NaCl. The second part will deal with the Haven ratio in the extrinsic range of alkali and silver halides.

TABLE X.   Experimental values of the enthalpy parameters for ionic transport in AgCl and AgBr (in eV)(After Weber and Friauf, 1969, and the references cited by these authors)

Quantity	AgCl[a]	AgBr[b]
Frenkel defect formation energy H_f		
Simple theory	1·6	1·27
Debye–Hückel interactions	1·55	1·13
Vacancy migration enthalpy	0·26	0·30
Colinear interstitialcy mechanism activation energy	0·008	0·058
Non-colinear interstitialcy mechanism activation energy	0·132	0·274

[a] With Abbink's mobilities (Abbink and Martin, 1966) with Debye–Hückel interactions.
[b] With Friauf's cation tracer diffusion coefficients (Friauf, 1957) and Teltow's mobilities (Teltow, 1949) with Debye–Hückel interactions.

1. Haven Ratio in NaCl (intrinsic range)

In their famous pioneer work, Maurer and his co-workers (1950) measured the tracer diffusion coefficients of sodium ions and electrical conductivity in NaCl and NaBr with the purpose of examining the validity of the Nernst–Einstein relation. On the basis of Tubandt's transference number measurements (see the section on transference numbers) they assumed that the electrical conductivity of sodium chloride is due entirely to migration of the sodium ion. Hence, they directly compared the ratio σ/D_+ to the ratio Ne^2/kT. The conclusion was that the Nernst–Einstein relation was verified in the intrinsic range for the two compounds $(D_+/D_{\text{calc}} \simeq 1)$.

However, a short time after the above-mentioned experiments, Bardeen and Herring (1952) pointed out that tracer diffusion occurring by the vacancy mechanism should be affected by correlation effects and Haven (1955) suggested that the ratio D_+/D_{calc} should differ from unity. Furthermore, Haven realised that this ratio should be equal to the product of the correlation factor and the cation transport number in order to take into account the fact that a non-negligible part of the charge transport could be due to the anion mobility. The ratio D_+/D_{calc} should then be equal to ft_+; taking the recent values for NaCl, $f = 0·7815$ (Compaan and Haven, 1956) and $t_+ = 0·83$ (F. Bénière et al., 1970) one would get $ft_+ \simeq 0·65$. This value is not in agreement with Maurer's result of 1·04 nor with more recent measurements (e.g. 0·91 at 650°C (Bénière, 1970)). A part of the discrepancy is certainly due to the influence of vacancy-pairs, since we have seen that the pairs contribute a non-negligible part to the tracer diffusion and none to the ionic conductivity. The correlation factor should then be related to the ratio

$$H_r' = \frac{(D_+ - D_+') + (D_- - D_-')}{D_{\text{calc}}}. \tag{8.2}$$

If diffusion occurs in NaCl by a vacancy mechanism, which has been previously demonstrated, and if, furthermore, the vacancy is localized on a lattice site in such a way that it could exchange its site with twelve neighbouring ions, this ratio should have the well-known value $f = 0.7815$.

In the present case of Schottky defects where both ionic species are mobile, the definition of H_r would be

$$H_r = \frac{D_+ + D_-}{D_{\text{calc}}}. \tag{8.3}$$

As usual, H_r is an experimental factor readily obtained since D_+ and D_- are the tracer-diffusion coefficients of the two ions and D_{calc} is obtained from the σ measurement. H_r expresses the ratio of the tracer-diffusion coefficients to the self-diffusion coefficients. Strictly speaking, since it is obviously not possible to measure the tracer diffusion of the host ions themselves, this ratio is affected by the slight mass effect due to the use of, say ^{22}Na in measuring D_+, whilst D_{calc} is related to the isotope ^{23}Na. Correction for this effect in the case of NaCl with the isotopes ^{22}Na and ^{36}Cl depresses H_r by about 2%. To give a numerical example, H_r, including this correction, is equal to 1·10 at 650°C and is slightly dependent on temperature (F. Bénière, 1970). This gives further evidence for the participation of vacancy pairs in the tracer-diffusion coefficients (which are not involved in the process of charge transport since they carry no effective charge). It is thus necessary to determine D_+' and D_-', the respective contributions of the vacancy pairs to the cation and anion diffusion coefficients. We have seen how D_-' can be calculated and there remains the problem of determining D_+'; we shall describe two distinct ways of performing this calculation.

In the first method we make use of eqn (6.6), which relates D_+' and D_-',

$$D_+' = D_-' \frac{f_+' \, v_+'}{f_-' \, v_-'}. \tag{8.4}$$

Taking the experimental value of D_-' and theoretical values for f_+', f_-', v_+' and v_-' calculated on the basis of the classical rigid lattice model, D_+' can be evaluated. The jump frequencies of the two species of ions into the pair have been calculated by Tharmalingam and Lidiard (1961) by defining a saddle-point position in the rigid lattice model. The correlation factors involved in this mechanism have already been discussed and their values for the corresponding ratio v_+'/v_-' may be taken from the calculations of Compaan and Haven (1956, Table III) and Howard (1966). Substituting v_+' and v_-' and the corresponding f_+' and f_-' from these theoretical values into eqn (8.4) leads to the evaluation of D_+'. Substitution of D_+' into eqn (8.2) then leads to a value for H_r' of 1.00 ± 0.2, instead of the predicted value $f = 0.7815$. However, if the classical ionic model is to be refected, this way of calculating D_+' should also be rejected and one must attempt to determine D_+' experimentally, and independently of D_-'.

Such a determination of the contribution of the vacancy pairs to the cation diffusion may be obtained from the transference number measurements. Since the cation transference number t_+ may be expressed, by combining its definition with the Nernst–Einstein relation, as

$$t_+ = \frac{D_+ - D_-'}{(D_+ - D_+') + (D_- - D_-')} \qquad (8.5)$$

where t_+, D_+, D_- and D_-' are known from experiment, one may then deduce the value of D_+'. Taking into account the experimental errors of transference number ($\sim 3\%$) and that of the tracer diffusion coefficient (1%), this method yields a value of H_r' between 0.98 and 1.06, therefore again nearly unity instead of 0.7815.

Why H_r' is not identical to 0.7815 in NaCl remains an open question. First, another species of defect (e.g. dislocations) which would give a higher contribution to the diffusion coefficients than to the ionic conductivity would depress H_r' to, say, H_r''. Second, D_+' might have been under evaluated because of uncertainties in the theoretical jump frequencies and in the transference numbers. This would also depress H_r'. Lastly, if H_r' is nearly equal to 1, one should have to reconsider the model of the vacancies itself. As a matter of fact the value of $f = 0.7815$ originates from the localized vacancy model where it is supposed that only the twelve ions in the first shell around a definite site (vacant) may jump into the localized vacancy.

2. Haven Ratio in AgCl (extrinsic range)

Doping alkali halides with bivalent cations increases concentration of cation vacancies and decreases that of the anion vacancies. In a similar way, doping silver halides increases the concentration of Ag^+ vacancies and decreases that of Ag^+ interstitials. Thus, in either crystal the molar fraction of the vacancies can be made dominant relative to that of anion vacancies (alkali halides) and interstitial cations (silver halides). Therefore, the ratio of the cation tracer-diffusion coefficient to the self-diffusion coefficient (related to the ionic conductivity) could be directly identified with the theoretical correlation factor for the vacancy mechanism, provided that no other defect is operative in either process such as free electrons, vacancy pairs, residual concentration of either anion vacancies or interstitials and above all, associations of aliovalent ions (either added by doping or contained among the background impurities) with the cation vacancies.

Gracey and Friauf (1969) have measured the tracer-diffusion coefficients of the Ag^+ ion and the ionic mobility in AgCl containing 100 to 250 mol ppm Cd^{2+}. In order to get a valid comparison of the two quantities, these authors have simultaneously performed the measurements of D^* and σ. However, the doped crystals obtained by crystallizing melts of AgCl + $CdCl_2$ contain appreciable concentration gradients and the tracer-diffusion coefficient is measured in a region where the concentration of Cd^{2+} may differ from the mean concentration of the whole sample to which σ is related. A method of correcting for this effect is indicated by these authors assuming a linear concentration gradient. Moreover, calculated corrections for the contributions of the associations of Cd^{2+}-cation vacancy (Friauf, 1969) and of the interstitial Ag^+ ions have been included in the Haven ratio. With these corrections Gracey and Friauf obtained a mean value of $f = 0.780 \pm 0.012$, in agreement with the theoretical value of 0.7815 in the case of the extrinsic range of AgCl.

We will now go on to illustrate with concrete examples the use of the fundamental equations described in the preceding sections and deal with some experimental results concerning impurity diffusion.

C. Diffusion of Impurities

1. Diffusion of Homovalent Impurities

Comparison of the diffusion coefficients of ions of the same valency as the host ions is of particular interest since the effect of ion size can thus be separated and studied independently of the other effects. The simplest case, which should give the most reliable results, is that of monovalent impurity ions entering the lattice substitutionally and diffusing by the vacancy mechanism. For this reason, we shall focus on such systems and especially on the diffusion of impurity halide ions in silver halides and on the diffusion of impurity alkali ions in alkali halides, for which rather extensive and recent data exist. The difference between the diffusion coefficients of these foreign ions and those of the host ions may arise from the change in the jump frequency, and to a lesser extent, to the change in the probability of finding a vacancy next to the foreign ion and to the change in the correlation factor. Thus, Mullen's calculations (1966) for the alkali halides indicate that the contribution from the frequency change is dominant for a homovalent ion larger than the host ion. Comparison of the diffusion coefficients of the ions from the same group (halides and alkali ions) should therefore indicate the influence of ion size on the frequency factor and the migration enthalpy. On the other hand, theoretical calculations have been carried out in order to evaluate the influence of the ion size on the migration enthalpy, especially for alkali halides, based on the classical models: localized vacancy and migration via the classical saddle-point position (Mott and Littleton, 1938; Tosi and Doyama, 1966). The theoretical calculations predict an increase of the energy barrier with increasing ionic size because the barrier ions should be displaced to a greater extent for larger ions in order to effect interchange with a vacancy. So, comparison of the experimental values for the enthalpy of motion of ions of different size gives another way to test the models.

Such a set of measurements was first obtained by Chemla (1953, 1954), who found that the activation energies of the ions K^+, Rb^+, Cs^+ and even Ag^+ were all very similar to that of Na^+ (Mapother et al., 1950). In the same way, Beaumont and Cabané (1961) have found that the halide impurity tracers diffuse in alkali halides with approximately the same activation energy as for halide self-diffusion, but with a different frequency factor. Other studies of monovalent impurity diffusion have been carried out (Arnikar and Chemla, 1956; Tannhauser, 1958; Arai and Mullen, 1966; Peterson and Rothman, 1969) and we shall describe two distinct sets of results in more detail.

(a) Impurity halide diffusion in silver chloride (Batra and Slifkin, 1969)

The diffusion coefficients of the halides Br^- and I^- (Batra and Slifkin, 1969) and Cl^- (Compton and Maurer, 1956; Lakatos and Lieser, 1966) in AgCl (Fig. 24) obey well an Arrhenius law $D = D_0 \exp(-Q/RT)$. The values of D_0, the frequency factor and Q, the activation energy obtained by these authors are listed in Table XI. It is seen that the frequency factors show no systematic progression as a function of size or mass of the tracer and, above all, that the activation energies for all three halides are the same within the limits of experimental error, in spite of widely differing ionic radii (Cl^- 1·81 Å; Br^- 1·95 Å; I^- 2·16 Å). Batra and Slifkin report a model suggested by Condit which could explain this constancy of activation energy in which the jumping chloride ion displaces the silver barrier ions (forming a "gate") beyond the displacement corresponding to the maximum of the energy, owing to the relative ease of producing interstitial silver ions (where the energy would pass by a metastable minimum). Then larger ions could jump through the gate with no greater migration energy than that required for the chloride ion.

TABLE XI. Experimental parameters for diffusion of halide ions in silver chloride
(After Batra and Slifkin, 1969)

Diffusing ion	Frequency factor (cm^2/s)	Diffusion activation energy $(kcal/mole)$	Authors
Chloride	133	37·0	Compton and Maurer
Chloride	85	36·3	Lakatos and Leiser
Bromide	90	36·6	Batra and Slifkin
Iodide	167	36·2	Batra and Slifkin

(b) *Impurity cation diffusion in sodium chloride* (*F. Bénière et al., 1969a*)

The impurity diffusion coefficients of ions Rb^+ and Cs^+ have been found to follow the same temperature dependence as shown by the host ion tracer diffusion (Na^+) in NaCl (Fig. 25) with, in each case, both intrinsic and extrinsic temperature ranges separating at the same temperature to within a few degrees. Though the diffusion coefficients have different values,

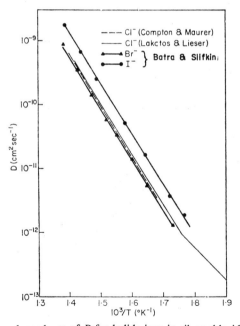

FIG. 24. Temperature dependence of D for halide ions in silver chloride (After Batra and Slifkin, 1969).

especially that of the Cs^+ ion which is the most mobile, the activation energies in each range are approximately the same. This is consistent with monovalent cations entering the lattice substitutionally and involving no appreciable change in the vacancy molar fraction since the knees between the intrinsic and extrinsic ranges occur at the same temperature. In the intrinsic range, the concentration of the thermal defects is known with a fair degree of accuracy so that it is possible to determine the jump frequency and migration enthalpy of these impurity cations. Fitting the experimental points to an Arrhenius law gives the values of D_0, the frequency factor and W, the activation energy of diffusion which are listed in Table XII

TABLE XII.   Experimental parameters for diffusion in the intrinsic range of alkali ions in sodium chloride (After F. Bénière et al., 1969)

Diffusing ion	Frequency factor, D_0 (cm^2/s)	Diffusion activation energy (eV)	$D_0\sqrt{M}$
Sodium	33	$1·97_5$	55
Rubidium	28	$1·97_7$	264
Cesium	162	$1·99_9$	1900

for the intrinsic range. One notices the strong similarity of these results with those previously reported for halide diffusion in AgCl: first, no monotonous progression of the frequency factor as a function of size or mass of

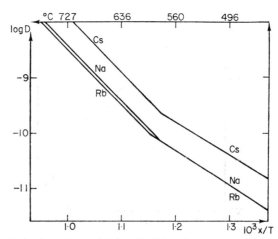

FIG. 25. Temperature dependence of D for alkali ions in sodium chloride (After F. Bénière et al., 1969).

the tracer, and, second, nearly equal activation energies for all three alkali ions in spite of even more widely differing ionic radii than those of the halides studied by Batra and Slifkin ($Na^+ = 0.97$ Å; $Rb^+ = 1.48$ Å; $Cs^+ = 1.69$ Å). To separate the respective effects of mass and size on the frequency factor one may assume in the very crude approximation of the Einstein model that the variation of the frequency factor is essentially due to the change in the vibrational frequency

$$\frac{1}{2\Pi}\sqrt{\frac{K}{M}},$$

where M is the mass of the tracer and K the constant of the restoring force acting on a particle moving in the potential energy field

$$V(x) = V(x_0) + \tfrac{1}{2}K(x - x_0)^2.$$

One can thus evaluate the effect of ion size on K by comparing the quantity $D_0\sqrt{M}$ for the three ions, as is shown in Table XII. A rapid increase in this quantity can be seen with increasing ionic radius. The reason for this variation can qualitatively be explained by the fact that a larger ion would be affected by a higher repulsive force. However, the constancy of the activation energy, which is the outstanding feature of the results, is not understandable in a model of hard spheres and localized vacancies, where the mass, size and polarizability of the ion are involved in the theoretical calculations of the migration energy, since it cannot be reasonably thought that all these effects compensate in all the systems that have been considered. These results, observed elsewhere for impurity diffusion in metals (Ott and Lodding, 1968), strongly suggest a relaxation in the region of the lattice where there is a vacated ion higher than is usually supposed in the classical ionic model.

2. Diffusion of Aliovalent Impurities

The diffusion mechanism of aliovalent impurities is quite different from that of monovalent ions and it would be very difficult to relate the diffusion coefficients in the general case to the numerous parameters involved. These parameters fall into two categories:

(1) the jump frequencies $\omega_1, \omega_2, \ldots$ of the successive jumps of the bound vacancy that operate in the migration of the impurity and that are included in the expression of the correlation factor (eqns (6.7), (6.8), (6.9), (6.10), which is then a rather complicated function of temperature.

(2) the terms involved in the formation of the impurity–vacancy pairs, since the density of vacancies around an impurity is not the same

as in the bulk of the crystal. At the present time both nearest-neighbour and next-nearest-neighbour associations should be considered since the real situation could be a mixture of the two.

As a matter of fact, the accuracy of the diffusion experiments would have to be improved by several orders of magnitude in order to analyse the experimental data as a function of all the parameters involved in the general case.

The first assumption which is usually made is that ω_2, the frequency of the jump of the impurity into the vacancy, has a far lower value than all other jump frequencies. This is well supported by the activation energies obtained in relaxation methods (see, for example, Barr and Lidiard, 1970) in the range of low temperatures where such methods are applied. The assumption that $\omega_2 \ll \omega_1$ is also supposed to be valid in the range of high temperatures where the diffusion experiments are carried out, so that f is assumed to be unity.

The second assumption is that one generally interprets the results on the model of the simple theory of association, considering only one kind of association, namely impurity–vacancy pairs at nearest neighbour sites.

Furthermore, experimental workers generally attempt to study impurity diffusion in distinct cases for which only a few parameters are involved, in order to obtain individual and accurate determinations of these parameters.

Slifkin and Brebec (1968) have thus measured the diffusion coefficients of the calcium ion as a tracer in pure and highly doped NaCl crystals (600 ppm $CaCl_2$). Assuming that in both systems the correlation factor is unity, and that p, the degree of association in doped crystals is unity, the diffusion coefficients are supposed to obey eqn (5.16) in the pure crystals, and eqn (5.17) in the doped crystals. Fitting the diffusion coefficients to Arrhenius equation, Slifkin and Brebec obtain the respective activation energies:

$$H_s/2 + H_{m++} + H_a = 1\cdot55 \text{ eV for pure crystals}$$

$$H_{m++} = 0\cdot87 \text{ eV} \qquad \text{for doped crystals}$$

where H_{m++} denotes the activation enthalpy for the jump of the Ca^{++} ion into the vacancy (jump frequency ω_2). The association enthalpy, H_a, is then calculated; taking the value of $H_s = 2\cdot38$ eV (Rothman et al., 1966) gives $H_a = -0\cdot51$ eV, while the value of $H_s = 2\cdot50$ eV (F. Bénière et al., 1970) gives $H_a = -0\cdot57$ eV.

Rothman et al. (1966) have carried out an identical study of the diffusion of an impurity of smaller ionic radius than that of Na^+ in NaCl, namely the diffusion of the Zn^{++} ion in pure and $ZnCl_2$-doped NaCl. They obtained the following activation energies: $0\cdot52$ eV in the doped crystals ($= H_{m++}$) and $1\cdot05$ eV in the pure crystals leading to $H_a = -0\cdot48$ eV.

The preceding results were obtained by the usual technique of the diffusion of an infinitely thin layer of tracers in crystals of given impurity content. Under these conditions D is a constant, provided that the specific activity of the isotope is very high (Hanlon, 1960; F. Bénière et al., 1969b). On the other hand, one can study diffusion of rather large amounts of bivalent cations of volatile alkaline earth halides, the concentration of which is maintained at a constant value outside the crystal by the vapour pressure. Since the degree of association varies with the molar fraction of the impurity, the impurity diffusion coefficient is a function of the impurity content which is then a function of x and t inside the crystal. In this case the diffusion profile must be analysed according to the diffusion equation for D dependent on concentration (eqn 3.8). The advantage of this method, first applied by Keneshea and Fredericks (1963), is that it yields from a single experiment the impurity concentration dependence of the diffusion coefficient. It is noteworthy that in all the systems experimentally studied: Pb^{++}–KCl (Keneshea and Fredericks, 1963, 1964 and 1965b; Reisfeld et al., 1965); Cd^{++}–KCl (Keneshea and Fredericks, 1965a); Pb^{++}–NaCl (Allen et al., 1967a); Cd^{++}–NaCl (Allen et al., 1967b); Pb^{++}–purified NaCl (Mannion et al., 1968); Bi^{++}–KCl (Reisfeld and Honigbaum, 1968); Ca^{++}–NaCl (Murin et al., 1961); Cd^{++}–AgCl (Reade and Martin, 1960), the functional form $D(c)$ is well represented by Lidiard's equation (eqn (5.20)),

$$D(c) = D_s \left[1 - \left\{ 1 + 48c \exp\left(- \frac{G_a}{kT} \right) \right\}^{-\frac{1}{2}} \right]$$

where the assumption that the associations have a long lifetime is included. Assuming also that the correlation factor is unity ($\omega_1 \gg \omega_2$), the fitting of the experimental data to this equation leads to the values of D_s and G_a at the temperature of the diffusion experiment. This is done for different temperatures, giving the temperature dependence of D_s and G_a. Plotting $\ln(D_s)$ versus $(1/T)$ gives a reasonably straight line, the slope of which is related to H_{m++} since $D_s = (a^2\omega_2)/3$ if $f = 1$. In the model of the simple Stasiw and Teltow association plotting G_a versus $(1/T)$ should also give a straight line and the parameters H_a and S_a. However, such plots are not accurately linear and there is some uncertainty in the decomposition of G_a into the two terms H_a and S_a.

Extensive studies of aliovalent impurity have been carried out, especially diffusion of bivalent cations in alkali halides and silver halides (for references, see the table of the diffusion constants at the end of this chapter and Süptitz and Teltow, 1967) and the data have been generally analysed according to the previous assumptions, i.e. as functions of the parameters G_s, G_a and G_{m++} (the Gibbs free energy for the jump of the bivalent cation into the vacancy). For instance, we have seen that diffusion of an impurity ion as a tracer in the intrinsic range should obey an Arrhenius law with the activation energy $H_s/2 + H_{m++} + H_a$. When D is measured in a rather narrow temperature range, linear plots of $\ln(D)$ versus $(1/T)$ are readily obtained. However, it has been shown (F. Bénière, 1970) that the measurements of the diffusion coefficient of the carrier-free tracer ^{90}Sr carried out in a wide temperature range (520–800°C) in pure sodium chloride do not perfectly fit a simple Arrhenius law. Figure 26 shows the diffusivity curve which is approximately linear owing to the rather slow variation of the logarithm function. Identifying this curve with a single straight line would give a mean activation energy of 1·31 eV. However, if one compares for a series of considered temperatures D_{exp}, the experimental diffusion coefficient, with D_{calc}, the value computed from the fitted linear equation and plots the quantity $(D_{exp} - D_{calc})/D_{calc}$ against $1/T$ as is shown on the same figure, one realizes the significant curvature of the plot $\log D = f(1/T)$, which shows the departure from the expected Arrhenius law. Allnatt and Pantelis (1968)

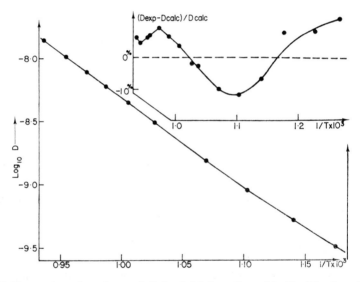

FIG. 26. Temperature dependence of D for Sr^{++} in sodium chloride. The departure of the experimental points (D_{exp}) to the values (D_{calc}) obtained by the least-squares fit of all the D_{exp} to the Arrhenius law

$$D_{calc} = D_0 \exp\left(-\frac{w}{kT}\right)$$

is shown on the plot of

$$\frac{D_{exp} - D_{calc}}{D_{calc}} - vs - 1/T.$$

have performed similar measurements of diffusion of Sr^{++} in pure NaCl in the shorter temperature range 600–750°C, obtaining an activation energy of 1·36 eV. It is noteworthy that fitting the preceding values measured in the *same* temperature range also gives an activation energy of 1·35 eV, which shows agreement of the basic data. However, the measurements for the whole temperature range indicate that eqn (5.16) is not perfectly suitable for the representation of the impurity diffusion process. This seems to be due to some other effect entailing a different temperature dependence, either due to correlation effects or to competition of nearest-neighbour and next-nearest-neighbour associations.

In a general way, this observation suggests that the diffusion measurements must be measured as accurately as possible over as wide a temperature range as possible in order to improve the theoretical interpretations.

IX. Comparison with Theory

We have described in the preceding sections the main parameters that are involved in diffusion and some methods of determining their values from diffusion experiments. On the other hand, these parameters have been calculated theoretically using the classical ionic model by many workers. If both experimental and theoretical values were determined with a high degree of accuracy, comparison of the two would give a crucial test for the validity of the theoretical models upon which the calculations are based. Of course, one must be more realistic and keep in mind that both values are known only within a range of errors, often difficult to estimate However, it is interesting to note the characteristic energies obtained from calculations and comparison with the experimental measurements may give an order of magnitude of the suitability of the values expected from the predicted models.

Of the possible solids, ionic crystals are at first sight the most favourable for theoretical calculations which have followed the successful evaluation of the lattice energy of sodium chloride, where only the Coulomb forces and short-range overlap repulsions are involved. Calculation of the lattice defect parameters are more complex because the defects bearing an effective electrical charge (e.g. vacancies) polarize the lattice and entail displacements of the surrounding ions from their normal sites. For instance, the polarization energy, divided into the electronic polarization which would appear on a rigid lattice and the polarization due to the displacements of the ions, appears as an important part of the total energy which is calculated by taking into account the contribution of all these terms. Most calculations have been based on the treatment of Mott and Littleton (1938). The main feature of these calculations is to search for the static states of the lattice for which the energy function is a minimum around the defect after its formation and for the saddle-point position of the jumping ions. The energies of the equilibrium configurations are then taken to be equal to the corresponding enthalpies, giving respectively the enthalpies of formation and migration of the defects.† Fewer calculations have been performed for defect entropies and it is not obvious that these may be expressed simply as functions of harmonic vibration frequencies.

We shall focus on some examples of numerical results relative to the characteristic defect energies that have been obtained *both* theoretically and from recent diffusion experiments.‡ This restricts us to dealing mainly with, the alkali halides—the most extensively studied systems.

A. Formation Enthalpies of Schottky Defects (H_s)

The defect formation enthalpies for NaCl, KCl and KBr are shown in Table XIII. The rather wide range for the theoretical value in NaCl shows the effect of varying the input data as has been demonstrated by Boswarva and Lidiard (1967). However, theorists currently working in the field suggest that a value of about 2 eV is the most consistent with the classical model.

TABLE XIII. Experimental and Calculated formation enthalpies of Schottky defects (eV)

Substance	NaCl	KCl	KBr
Experimental	$2\cdot38^a$, $2\cdot50^b$ *	$2\cdot49 - 2\cdot64^{c,d}$	$2\cdot54^e$
Theoretical	$1\cdot30 - 2\cdot20^{f-m}$	$1\cdot75 - 2\cdot26^{f-l,n}$	$1\cdot68 - 2\cdot14^{f,h,j,k,n}$

[a] Rothman *et al.* (1966)
[b] F. Bénière *et al.* (1970)
[c] Fuller *et al.* (1968a)
[d] M. Bénière *et al.* (1970)
[e] Barr and Dawson (1969)
[f] Mott and Littleton (1938)
[g] Fumi and Tosi (1957)
[h] Kurosawa (1958)
[i] Tosi and Doyama (1966)
[j] Boswarva and Lidiard (1967)
[k] Scholz (1968)
[l] Brauer (1952)
[m] Pantaloni *et al.* (1969)
[n] Rao and Rao (1968)

* Note added in proof: Allnatt, Pantelis and Sime, *J. Phys. C. Solid St. Physics* **4**, 1778, 1971, report the value 2.4–2.5 eV obtained from recent conductivity measurements.

† An excellent and comprehensive account of this subject, together with a large number of experimental and theoretical defect energies, has recently been given by Professors Barr and Lidiard in "Physical Chemistry", Vol. X, Academic Press, New York (1970). In order to appreciate the crucial influence of the input data in computing the activation energies, see the article by Boswarva and Lidiard (1967) who give numerical results for a large number of alkali halide crystals and for different choices of parameters and repulsive potentials.

‡ Many experimental results have been obtained from conductivity measurements and are in reasonable agreement with the following sets of diffusion results.

The table shows a systematic disagreement between theory and experiment,† the theoretical values being significantly lower than the experimentally determined values. It is improbable that the discrepancies are due to either experimental or calculation errors, since these values come from many sources.‡

B. Migration Enthalpies of the Host Ions (H_{m+} and H_{m-})

Table XIV shows the activation energies for the jump of the cation in NaCl and KCl. The experimental values obtained from tracer diffusion experiments are in good agreement with those obtained from conductivity data (Barr and Lidiard, 1970, Table II; Fuller *et al.*, 1968). The theoretical values have been calculated for the NaCl-structure assuming that the jumping ions follow the direct path, along 110 axes. One defines as the saddle-point position the configuration where the ion, being at the middle of its jump, is at the mid-point between the two neighbouring ions of opposite sign. The migration enthalpy is then taken to be equal to the height of the enthalpy barrier between the saddle-point configuration and the ground configuration. No calculations have been carried out for other configurations, although Laurent and Bénard (1957) have suggested an indirect path for the jumping ion.

TABLE XIV.   Experimental and calculated migration enthalpies of the host cation (eV)

Substance	NaCl	KCl
Experimental	$0{\cdot}72^a$	$0{\cdot}79^{b,c}$
Theoretical	$0{\cdot}70 - 0{\cdot}92^{d,e,g}$	$0{\cdot}77 - 1{\cdot}13^{d-g}$

[a] F. Bénière *et al.* (1970)
[b] M. Bénière *et al.* (1970)
[c] Fuller *et al.* (1968a)
[d] Guccione *et al.* (1959) using Born–Mayer–Verwey repulsion.
[e] Tosi and Doyama (1966)
[f] Rao and Rao (1968)
[g] Tosi (1967)

These calculations are very sensitive to the choice of the repulsion potential. Guccione *et al.*, (1959) have shown that adoption of the Born–

† Earlier experimental results indicated lower values of H_s and NaCl. The often reported values of 2·02 eV (Mapother *et al.*, 1950) and 2·12 eV (Dreyfus and Nowick, 1962) seem to be due to both an overestimate of the activation energy of the cation diffusion and conductivity in the extrinsic range and an underestimate of the activation energy in the intrinsic range.

‡ Note added in proof: Faux and Lidiard, *Z. Naturforsch.* A26, 62, 1971, obtain from new calculations $H_s = 2{\cdot}23$ eV for NaCl.

Mayer potential (with Goldschmidt radii) for the repulsion interaction energy leads to values of 0·08 and 0·48 eV for the cation migration enthalpy for NaCl and KCl respectively. Using the harder potential of Tosi and Fumi for the short range interionic interactions, Tosi and Doyama have obtained more consistent values (0·85 eV in both substances).

Similar values for the anion are reported in Table XV. One notices that the migration enthalpies of the anion, measured in NaCl, KCl and KBr have nearly the same value and that they are larger than those of the cation. On the other hand, theoretical calculations give for the three alkali chlorides larger values as the ionic radius of the cation increases. This observation will be related to the next results.

TABLE XV.   Experimental and calculated migration enthalpies of the host anion (eV)

Substance	NaCl	KCl	RbCl	KBr
Experimental	$0·86^a, 0·90^b(1·11^c)$	$0·82^d, 0·85^e$		$0·83^f$
Theoretical	$0·75 - 1·11^{g-i}$	$0·83 - 1·21^{g-j}$	$0·99 - 1·12^{h-j}$	

[a] F. Bénière et al. (1970)
[b] Barr et al. (1965)
[c] Laurance (1960) where the activation energy for anion diffusion is taken equal to $H_s/2 + H_m$. The value $H_s = 2·50$ eV (ref. b, Table XIII) would give $H_{m-} = 0·87$ eV, in good agreement with references a and b.
[d] M. Bénière et al. (1970)
[e] Fuller et al. (1968a)
[f] Barr and Dawson (1969)
[g] Guccione et al. (1959) using B.M.V. repulsion potential.
[h] Tosi and Doyama (1966)
[i] Tosi (1967)
[j] Rao and Rao (1968)

C. Migration Enthalpies of Substitutional Monovalent Impurity Ions

Many terms are involved in the calculations of the formation enthalpy of the vacancy and migration enthalpy of the host ions. However, it is possible to study the influence of the ionic radius independently of the other effects by comparing the values of the migration enthalpy of different ions relative to that of the host ion. Tosi and Doyama (1966) have computed the activation enthalpies of host ions and alkali impurities in alkali halides. No extensive studies have been made of impurities of smaller ionic radius than that of the host cation, apart from the diffusion coefficient measurements of Na^+ in RbCl performed by Peterson and Rothman (1969). These authors obtained a value of 0·55 eV for the migration enthalpy; this is not in good agreement with the calculations of Tosi and Doyama who predict a value of 0·22 eV. For impurities of larger ionic radius than that of the host cation, it has already been mentioned that a change in the ion size does not lead to any significant change in the migration enthalpy. Table XVI gives the values of the migration enthalpy for the jump of the ions Na^+, K^+, Rb^+ and Cs^+ in NaCl. The theoretical values show a behaviour quite different from that of the experimental values, the theoretical enthalpy increases very rapidly with the increase in the radius of the migrating ion. Possible hypotheses to explain this discrepancy have been suggested: for instance, larger displacements of the gate ions, this suggestion being most applicable to crystals containing Frenkel disorder (Batra and Slifkin, 1969); or a migration path different from the usually chosen direct path (Laurent and Bénard, 1957); or a delocalized region of the lattice around the vacancy (Nachtrieb and Handler, 1954; F. Bénière, 1970).

TABLE XVI.   Experimental and calculated migration enthalpies of substitutional alkali impurities and host cation in sodium chloride (eV)

Ion	Na^+	K^+	Rb^+	Cs^+
Experimental	0.72^a	0.72^b	0.73^a	0.74^a
Theoretical	0.85^c	1.14^c	1.35^c	

[a] F. Bénière et al. (1969)   [c] Tosi and Doyama (1966)
[b] Arnikar and Chemla (1956)

D. Activation Enthalpy for Anion Diffusion via Vacancy Pairs

Several attempts have been made to determine the activation enthalpy for anion diffusion via vacancy pairs. Values obtained for the alkali halides NaCl, KCl and KBr are summarized in Table XVII. These values have been obtained by computer fitting of the experimental diffusion coefficients of the halide ion in crystals doped with divalent cations, assuming that the temperature dependence of the correlation factor for tracer diffusion via vacancy pairs is negligible or, at least, that it entails no significant departure of the anion diffusion via vacancy pairs from an Arrhenius law. The table also contains "theoretical" values. It must be borne in mind that H_-' is a composite parameter made up of the three terms H_s, the Schottky defect formation enthalpy, H_{pr} the enthalpy of association of two isolated vacancies of opposite signs and H_{m-}', the migration enthalpy of the anion into the vacancy pair. Some of these values (reference g) result from the theoretical calculations of Tharmalingam and Lidiard (1961) who calculated the energies of formation of a vacancy pair $(H_s - |H_{pr}|)$, finding 1.27 eV and 1.28 eV for NaCl and KCl respectively, and the activation enthalpy for the jump of the anion into the pair (H_{m-}'). The other values are obtained by adding the values of the three contributing terms obtained from different sources. In order to examine mainly the influence of H_{m-}', we have reported for H_s the experimental values of Table XIII instead of the more scattered theoretical estimates of the same table. The value of H_{pr} is a calculated one, as is indicated, and the H_{m-}' values are again those of Tharmalingam and Lidiard. We have also given the same analysis using Rao and Rao's results for H_{m-}' in KCl. The very large value obtained by these authors (1·54 eV) thus leads to a much larger value for H_-' than the observed one.

TABLE XVII. Experimental and calculated activation enthalpies for anion diffusion via vacancy pairs (eV)

Substance	NaCl	KCl	KBr
Experimental	$2·49^a, 2·37^b, 2·63^c$	$2·59 - 2·65^d, 2·49^e$	$2·60^f$
Theoretical	$2·73^g, 3·05 - 3·27^h$	$2·43^g, 2·88 - 3·07^i, 3·27 - 3·46^j$	

[a] Laurance (1960)
[b] Barr et al. (1965)
[c] F. Bénière et al. (1970)
[d] Fuller et al. (1968a) from Fuller (1966)
[e] M. Bénière et al. (1970)
[f] Barr and Dawson (1969)
[g] Tharmalingam and Lidiard (1961), using the B.M.V. potential.
[h] Writing $H_-' = H_s + H_{pr} + H_{m-}'$, with experimental values of H_s from Table XIII and the theoretical value $H_{pr} = -0·60$ eV calculated by Tosi and Fumi (1958) and H_{m-}' of ref. g.
[i] As in ref. h in the range of the values of H_{pr} calculated by Tosi and Fumi (1958), Tosi and Airoldi (1958) and Rao and Rao (1968).
[j] As for i with $H_{m-}' = 1·54$ eV obtained by Rao and Rao (1968).

We see that the experimental values for H_-' for the three crystals are all about 2·5 eV. We may notice, as a general conclusion of the results for the three alkali halides with which we have been most concerned, the close similarity of the diffusion processes in these three ionic crystals.

X. Conclusion

In the past, the temperature dependence of the diffusion coefficients and the ionic conductivity was systematically fitted to an Arrhenius law, assuming that only one species of defect was operative, the mobility of the others being neglected. In the early sections of this chapter, we have reviewed the main methods of determination of the diffusion coefficients and emphasized that it is now possible to obtain the experimental diffusion coefficients with an accuracy of about 1 % when sufficient care is taken and it is encouraging to notice the actual convergence of the basic data measured in different laboratories. Nowadays, this higher accuracy, connected with the availability of powerful computers, allows one to carry out more refined analyses of the basic data. In this way, quite accurate data about the individual defects (free cation vacancies, free anion vacancies, interstitials, vacancy pairs, ...) have been obtained in some ionic crystals.

However, there remains for every parameter a large variation in both experimental and theoretical values, the former being due to variation in the interpretation of the data and the latter being due to variation in the method of calculation used, though nearly all are based on the same models. Much more remains to be done, firstly to reduce the scatter in the experimental values, secondly, to improve agreement between the various calculated values and thirdly, to find the perfect (?) description of the ionic model which would then lead to full agreement between theory and experiment.

Acknowledgement

It is a pleasure to acknowledge the considerable help given by Professor Alan Chadwick who advised on the translation.

General References

In order to avoid an excessive number of references, we have focussed on the works dealing with diffusion in ionic crystals, though there are other means of studying the defects especially through the measurement of ionic conductivity. (For references about the latter subject matter see the chapters of Dr. Friauf and Dr. Kvist in this book.) For a systematic review of the results obtained by different methods on the transport of matter in ionic crystals see:

1. Süptitz, P. and Teltow, J. (1967). *Phys. Status Solidü,* **23,** 9.
   In our own references mainly the papers of the last three years have been referred to explicitly. A rather more complete review of the works dealing with diffusion in ionic crystals is given in the next table where the diffusion parameters obtained by empirical fits to Arrhenius laws are reported.
   For general accounts of the transport phenomena in solids the reader is referred to
2. Lidiard, A. B. (1957), Ionic Conductivity. *In* "Handbuch der Physik" (S. Flügge, ed.), Vol. XX. Springer, Berlin.
   The pioneer paper which is still the basic text
3. Shewmon, P. G. (1963). "Diffusion in Solids". McGraw–Hill, New York.
4. Adda, Y. and Philibert, J. (1966). "La Diffusion dans les Solides". Presses Universitaires de France, Paris.
   An excellent and comprehensive account covering all the fundamental questions in diffusion.
5. Manning, J. R. (1968). "Diffusion Kinetics for Atoms in Crystals". Van Nostrand, Princeton, New Jersey.

6. Le Claire, A. D. (1970). Correlation Effects in Diffusion in Solids, *In* "Physical Chemistry" (W. Jost, ed.), Vol. X, Academic Press, New York and London. A thorough and comprehensive examination of the correlation effects, and last but not least

7. Barr, L. W. and Lidiard, A. B. (1970). Defects in Ionic Crystals, *In* "Physical Chemistry" (W. Jost, ed.), Vol. X, Academic Press, New York and London. For an excellent account of both the experimental and theoretical methods for the study of the chacteristic energies of the point defects in ionic crystals.

References

Abbink, H. C. and Martin, D. S., Jr. (1966). *J. Phys. Chem. Solids* **27**, 205.

Adda, Y. and Philibert, J. (1966). "La Diffusion dans les Solides". Presses Univ. de France, Paris

Allen, C. A., Ireland, D. T. and Fredericks, W. J. (1967a). *J. chem. Phys.* **46**, 2000.

Allen, C. A., Ireland, D. T. and Fredericks, W. J. (1967b), *J. chem. Phys.* **47**, 3068.

Allnatt, A. R. and Chadwick, A. V. (1967). *Trans. Faraday Soc.* **63**, 1929.

Allnatt, A. R. and Pantelis, P. (1968). *Trans. Faraday Soc.* **64**, 2100.

Arai, G. and Mullen, J. G. (1966). *Phys. Rev.* **143**, 663.

Arnikar, H. J. and Chemla, M. (1956). *C. R. Acad. Sci. Paris* **242**, 2132.

Bardeen, J. and Herring, C. (1951). *In* "Atom Movements". Am. Soc. for Metals, Cleveland.

Bardeen, J. and Herring, C. (1952). *In* "Imperfections in Nearly Perfect Crystals", (W. Shockley, ed.). Wiley, New York.

Barr, L. W. (1970a). Report AERE–R 6236.

Barr, L. W. (1970b). *In* Meeting of the Society for Electro-chemistry held at the Atomic Energy Research Establishment, Harwell, p.5.

Barr, L. W. and Dawson, D. K. (1969). Report AERE–R 6324.

Barr, L. W. and Le Claire, A. D. (1964). *Proc. Br. Ceram. Soc.* **1**, 109.

Barr, L. W. and Lidiard, A. B. (1970). *In* "Physical Chemistry", vol. X (W. Jost, ed.). Academic Press, New York and London.

Barr, L. W., Hoodless, I. M., Morrison, J. A. and Rudham, R. (1960). *Trans. Faraday Soc.* **56**, 697.

Barr, L. W., Morrison, J. A. and Schroeder, P. A. (1965). *J. appl. Phys.* **36**, 624.

Batra, A. P. and Slifkin, L. (1969). *Physics Chem. Solids* **30**, 1315.

Beaumont, J. C. and Cabane, J. (1961). *C. R. Acad. Sci. Paris,* **252**, 113.

Bénière, F. (1970). Thesis, University of Paris, Orsay.

Bénière, F. and Chemla, M. (1968). *C. R. Acad. Sci. Paris* **266**, 660.

Bénière, F., Bénière, M. and Chemla, M. (1968). *C. R. Acad. Sci. Paris* **267**, 633.

Bénière, F., Bénière, M. and Chemla, M. (1969a). *J. Chim. Phys.* **66**, 898.

Bénière, F., Bénière, M. and Chemla, M. (1969b), *C. R. Acad. Sci. Paris* **268**, 1461.

Bénière, F., Bénière, M. and Chemla, M. (1970), *Physics Chem. Solids* **31**, 1205.

Bénière, M. (1970). Thesis, University of Paris, Paris.

Bénière, M., Bénière, F. and Chemla, M. (1970). *J. Chim. phys.* **67**, 1312.

Boswarva, I. M. and Lidiard, A. B. (1967). *Phil. Mag.* **16**, 805.

Brauer, P. (1952). *Z. Naturforsch.* **7a**, 372.

Breckenridge, R. G. (1950), *J. chem. Phys.* **18**, 913.

Cabane, J. (1962). *J. Chim. Phys.* **59**, 1135.

Chadwick, A. V., Fox, R. and Sherwood, J. N. (1970). *In* Proc. Europhysics Conference "Atomic Transport in Solids and Liquids", Marstrand, 1970 (to be published).

Chemla, M. (1952). *C. R. Acad. Sci. Paris* **234**, 2601.
Chemla, M. (1953). *C. R. Acad. Sci. Paris* **236**, 484.
Chemla, M. (1954). Thesis, University of Paris, Paris.
Compaan, K. and Haven, Y. (1956). *Trans. Faraday Soc.* **52**, 786.
Compaan, K. and Haven, Y. (1958). *Trans. Faraday Soc.* **54**, 1498.
Compton, W. D. and Maurer, R. J. (1956). *Physics Chem. Solids* **1**, 191.
Condit, R. Private communication to Batra and Slifkin (1969). *Physics Chem. Solids* **30**, 1315.
Crank, J. (1956). *In* "Mathematics of Diffusion". Clarendon Press, Oxford.
Crolet, J. L. (1970). *In* Proc. Europhysics Conference "Atomic Transport in Solids and Liquids", Marstrand, 1970 (to be published).
Dawson, D. K. and Barr, L. W. (1967). *Proc. Br. Ceram. Soc.* **9**, 171.
Dreyfus, R. W. and Nowick, A. S. (1962). *J. appl. Phys.* **33**, 473.
Ebert, I. and Teltow, J. (1955). *Ann. Phys.* **15**, 1955.
Einstein, A. (1905). *Ann. Phys.* **17**, 549.
Friauf, R. J. (1957). *Phys. Rev.* **105**, 843.
Friauf, R. J. (1969). *Physics Chem. Solids* **30**, 429.
Fuller, R. G. (1966). *Phys. Rev.* **142**, 524.
Fuller, R. G., Marquardt, C. L., Reilly, M. H. and Wells, J. C., Jr. (1968a). *Phys. Rev.* **176**, 1036.
Fuller, R. G., Reilly, M. H., Marquardt, C. L. and Wells, J. C., Jr. (1968b). *Phys. Rev. Letters* **20**, 662.
Fumi, F. G. and Tosi, M. P. (1957). *Disc. Faraday Soc.* **23**, 92.
Gerl, M. (1968). CEA–BIB–120.
Gracey, J. P. and Friauf, J. (1969). *Physics Chem. Solids* **30**, 421.
Graham, D. (1966). *Bull. Am. phys. Soc.* **11**, 331.
Guccione, R., Tosi, M. P. and Asdente, M. (1959). *Physics Chem. Solids* **10**, 162.
Hanlon, J. E. (1960). *J. chem. phys.* **32**, 1492.
Harrison, L. G., Morrison, J. A. and Rudham, R. (1958). *Trans. Faraday Soc.* **54**, 106.
Haven, Y. (1955), Rept. Conf. Defects in Crystalline Solids. Bristol.
Hevesy, von, G. and Seith, W. (1929). *Z. Physik.* **51**, 790.
Howard, R. E. (1966). *Phys. Rev.* **144**, 650.
Ikeda, T. (1964). *J. phys. Soc. Japan* **19**, 858.
Johnson, R. P. (1939). *Phys. Rev.* **56**, 14.
Jost, W. (1952). *In* "Diffusion in Solids, Liquids, Gases". Academic Press, New York.
Jost, W. (1969). *Z. phys. Chemie* **64**, 154.
Kelting, M. and Witt, H. (1949). *Z. Physik.* **126**, 697.
Keneshea, F. J. and Fredericks, W. J. (1963). *J. chem. Phys.* **38**, 1952.
Keneshea, F. J. and Fredericks, W. J. (1964). *J. chem. Phys.* **41**, 3271.
Keneshea, F. J. and Fredericks, W. J. (1965a). *J. chem. Phys.* **26**, 501.
Keneshea, F. J. and Fredericks, W. J. (1965b). *J. chem. Phys.* **43**, 2925.
Kirk, D. L. and Pratt, P. L. (1967). *Proc. Br. Ceram. Soc.* **9**, 215.
Koch, E. and Wagner, C. (1937). *Z. phys. Chem.* **B38**, 295.
Kurosawa, T. (1958). *J. phys. Soc. Japan* **13**, 153.
Laj, J. (1969). Thesis, University of Paris, Orsay.
Lakatos, E. and Lieser, K. (1966). *J. phys. Chem.* **48**, 213.
Laurance, N. (1960). *Phys. Rev.* **120**, 57.
Laurent, J. L. and Bénard, J. (1957), *Physics Chem. Solids* **3**, 7.

Laurent, J. L. and Bénard, J. (1958). *Physics Chem. Solids* **7**, 218.
Le Claire, A. D. (1958). *Phil. Mag.* **3**, 921.
Le Claire, A. D. (1966). *Phil Mag.* **14**, 1271.
Le Claire, A. D. (1970). *In* "Physical Chemistry", Vol. X, (W. Jost, ed.), Academic Press, New York and London.
Le Claire, A. D. and Lidiard, A. B. (1956). *Phil. Mag.* **1**, 518.
Lidiard, A. B. (1954). *Phys. Rev.* **94**, 29.
Lidiard, A. B. (1955a). *Phil. Mag.* **46**, 815.
Lidiard, A. B. (1955b). *Phil. Mag.* **46**, 1218.
Lidiard, A. B. (1957). *In* "Handbuch der Physik" (S. Flügge, ed.), Vol. XX.
Manning, J. R. (1959). *Phys. Rev.* **116**, 819.
Manning, J. R. (1962). *Phys. Rev.* **128**, 2169.
Manning, J. R. (1964). *Phys. Rev.* **136A**, 1758.
Manning, J. R. (1968). "Diffusion Kinetics for Atoms in Crystals". Van Nostrand, Princeton, New Jersey.
Mannion, W. A., Allen, C. A. and Fredericks, W. J. (1968). *J. chem. Phys.* **48**, 1537.
Mapother, D., Crooks, N. H. and Maurer, R. (1950). *J. chem. Phys.* **18**, 1231.
Mott, N. F. and Littleton, M. J. (1938). *Trans. Faraday Soc.* **34**, 485.
Mullen, J. G. (1961a). *Phys. Rev.* **121**, 1649.
Mullen, J. G. (1961b). *Phys. Rev.* **124**, 1723.
Mullen, J. G. (1966). *Phys. Rev.* **143**, 568.
Mundy, J. N., Barr, L. W. and Smith, F. A. (1966). *Phil. Mag.* **14**, 785.
Murin, A. N., Banasevich, S. N. and Grushko, Yu.S. (1961). *Fiz. Tverd. Tela,* **3**, 2427.
Murin, A. N. and Lure, B. (1950). *Dokl. Akad. Nauk. S.S.S.R.* **73**, 933.
Nachtrieb, N. H. and Handler, G. S. (1954). *Acta Met.* **2**, 797,
Nelson, V. C. (1967). Thesis, University of Kansas, Laurence.
Nelson, V. C. and Friauf, R. J. (1970). *Physics. Chem. Solids* **31**, 825.
Ott, A. and Lodding, A. (1968). Int. Conf. Vacancies Interstitial Metals.
Patterson, D., Rose, G. S. and Morrison, J. A. (1956). *Phil. Mag.* **1**, 393.
Pantaloni, J., Bizouard, M. and Gaune, P. (1969). *C. R. Acad. Sci. Paris* **268**, 1028.
Peterson, N. L. (1964). *Phys. Rev.* **136A**, 568.
Peterson, N. L. and Barr, L. W., cited by Le Claire (1966).
Peterson, N. L. and Rothman, S. J. (1967). *Phys. Rev.* **163**, 645.
Peterson, N. L. and Rothman, S. J. (1969). *Phys. Rev.* **177**, 1329.
Ptashnik, V. B. and Naumov, A. N. (1968). *Fiz. Tverd. Tela* **10**, 880.
Rao, K. J. and Rao, C. N. R. (1968). *Phys. Status Solidi* **28**, 157.
Rayleigh, Lord (1894). "Theory of Sound", Vol. I. Macmillan, London.
Reade, R. F. and Martin, D. S. (1960). *J. appl. Phys.* **31**. 1965.
Reisfeld, R. and Honigbaum, A. (1968). *J. chem. Phys.* **48**, 5565.
Reisfeld, R., Glassner, A. and Honigbaum, A. (1965). *J. chem. Phys.* **42**, 1892.
Rothman, S. J., Barr, L. W., Rowe, A. H. and Selwood, P. G. (1966). *Phil. Mag.* **14**, 501.
Scholz, A. (1968). *Phys. Status Solidi* **25**, 285.
Shewmon, P. G. (1963). "Diffusion in Solids". McGraw–Hill, New York.
Slifkin, L. and Brébec, G. (1968). Rapport CEA–DM/1750.
Stasiw, O. and Teltow, J. (1947). *Ann. Phys. leipzig.* **1**, 261.
Stewart, W. H. and Reed, C. A. (1965). *J. chem. Phys.* **43**, 2890.
Süptitz, P. and Teltow, J. (1967). *Phys. Status Solidi* **23**, 9.

Tannhauser, D. (1958). *Physics Chem. Solids* **5**, 224.
Teltow, J. (1949). *Ann. Phys. leipzig*. **5**, 63, 71.
Tharmalingam, K. and Lidiard, A. B. (1959). *Phil. Mag.* **4**, 899.
Tharmalingam, K. and Lidiard, A. B. (1961). *Phil. Mag.* **6**, 1157.
Tosi, M. P. (1967). *U. S. Natl. But. Std. Misc. Publ.* **287**, 1.
Tosi, M. P. and Airoldi, G. (1958). *Nuovo Cim.* **8**, 584.
Tosi, M. P. and Doyama, M. (1966). *Phys. Rev.* **151**, 642.
Tosi, M. P. and Fumi, F. G. (1958). *Nuovo Cim.* **7**, 95.
Trnovcova, V. (1969). *Czech. J. Phys.* **B19**, 663.
Vineyard, G. H. (1957). *Physics Chem. Solids* **3**, 121.
Weber, M. D. and Friauf, R. J. (1969). *Physics Chem. Solids* **30**, 407.
Wert, C. (1950). *J. appl. Phys.* **21**, 1196.

Table of the Diffusion Constants in Alkali Halide and Silver Halide Single Crystals

The parameters D_0 (cm²/s) and W (eV) are the values obtained by fitting the experimental data to the equation $D = D_0 \exp(-W/kT)$ in the indicated temperature range (°C). It must be kept in mind that diffusion is generally the result of several simultaneous processes, which needs a more refined treatment than a fit to a simple Arrhenius law. However, these values allow a ready estimate of the order of magnitude of D. When several investigations of the same system have been carried out, the more recent values have only been reported. We have selected the values that should not depend on the presence of impurities not well defined in their nature and content. Hence, results relative to the extrinsic range of "pure" crystals are not reported here. The values obtained in the intrinsic temperature range are shown without any mention in the column "method". On the other hand, results concerning crystals doped with accurately defined impurity contents are reported with a special mention in this column. Ds is the saturation value (See eqns 5.17 and 5.20).

Compound	Diffusing ion	Temperature range	D_0	W	Method	Ref.
NaCl	Na⁺	550–720	3·1	1·80		1
		570–790	0·5	1·61		2
		640–790	1300	2·27		3
		600–726	33·1	1·975		4
		466–570	$3·5 \times 10^{-6}$	0·72	27 ppm SrCl₂	4
	Cl⁻	520–740	56	2·12		5
		300–700		2·16		6
		500–750	60·7	2·14		7
	Rb⁺	599–787	205	2·11		8
		600–746	28·5	1·98		9
	Cs⁺	596–698	162	2·00		9
	Br⁻	612–748	$2·8 \times 10^{-4}$	2·66		10
		500–650	20	1·94		67
	I⁻	592–736	80	2·29		10
		530–700	500	2·24		11
	Ca⁺⁺	430–750	$6·0 \times 10^{-4}$	0·90		12
		680–795	0.13	1·55		13
		360–500	$2·35 \times 10^{-4}$	0·87	600 ppm Ca	13
		619–737	$0·94 \times 10^{-3}$	1·14		14
	Sr⁺⁺	600–750	$4·13 \times 10^{-2}$	1·36		15
		517–795	$1·7 \times 10^{-2}$	1·31		16

Table of the Diffusion Constants—*continued*

Compound	Diffusing ion	Temperature range	D_0	W	Method	Ref.
	Cd^{++}	350–500	$1·2 \times c$	0·64	c: molar fraction of $CdCl_2$	17
		275–500	$2·06 \times 10^{-2}$	0·92	D_s	18
	Mn^{++}	350–700	$3·48 \times 10^{-3}$	0·95	diffusion from a large source	19
		450–750	2×10^{-5}	0·66		20
	Zn^{++}	590–800	2×10^{-2}	1·03		21
		550–780	$1·5 \times 10^{-4}$	0·51	heavily doped $(ZnCl_2)$	21
	Pb^{++}	348–553	$1·75 \times 10^{-2}$	0·99	D_s	22
	Cu^+	350–650	33·8	1·43		23
	Ag^+	575–726	380	2·0		10
	Co^{++}	610–760	8×10^{-3}	1·1		24
		600–750	3×10^{-3}	1·06		15
	Ni^{++}	620–750	2×10^{-2}	1·3		24
NaBr	Na^+	500–680	0·67	1·53		1
	Br^-	650–750	1·0	1·70		67
NaI	Tl^+	443–620	100	1·8		25
		400–635	$5·3 \times 10^{-3}$	1·17		26
LiF	Li^+	650–800	9	1·90		27
KF	K^+	600–820	2	1·78		2
KCl	K^+	590–738	137	2·15		28
		526–675	$1·84 \times 10^{-5}$	0·79	61 ppm $SrCl_2$	28
	Cl^-	530–730	10	2·0		2
		560–750	61	2·12		29
		500–740	178	2·25		28
	Li^+	500–730	20	1·53		68
	Na^+	570–750	2·2	1·75		30
	Rb^+	607–763	26·8	2·04		8
	Cs^+	570–750	0·7	1·75		30
	I^-	500–650	50	2·0		11
	Tl^+	550–730	2	1·70		31
	Cd^{++}	350–500	$4·68 \times 10^{-5}$	0·54	D_s	32
	Pb^{++}	200–475	$1·02 \times 10^{-3}$	1·01		33
		275–465	$1·82 \times 10^{-2}$	1·11	D_s	34
	Cu^+	350–650	10·6	1·23		23
	Co^{++}	200–650		0·20		35
	Bi^{+++}	275–400	$1·7 \times 10^{-3}$	0·63		36
	Bi^{++}	400–674	$5·6 \times 10^{-3}$	0·97		36
	Ce^{z+}	500–700	$1·1 \times 10^{-3}$	1·03	D_s	37
	Eu^{z+}	418–550	$6·45 \times 10^{-2}$	1·28	Ds	38
	H_2O	180–750	62	0·80		39
KBr	K^+	460–720	10^{-2}	1·26		2
	Br^-	–700	3×10^{-4}	2·61		40
		400–	3×10^{-3}	1·49		40
		570–700	6×10^{-3}	1·30		67
	Tl^+	350–500	50	2·01		41
		550–700	4×10^{-5}	1·03		41
	Pb^{++}	275–400	$1·5 \times 10^{-3}$	0·91		42
	H_2O	180–750	7·7	0·69		39
	Ar	20–300	10^5	1·5		43
	Xe	20–300	10	1·4		43
KI	K^+	460–680	10^{-5}	0·64		2
	I^-	460–680	$1·2 \times 10^{-3}$	1·12		2
	Tl^+	440–650	8×10^{-3}	1·17		25
	Cl^-	500–650	$1·5 \times 10^{-3}$	1·13		11
	H_2O	180–750	0·48	0·56		39
RbCl	Rb^+	568–697	33·3	1·99		8
	Cl^-	600–700	$3·37 \times 10^{-5}$	1·35		44
	Na^+	500–707	$1·03 \times 10^3$	2·06		45
CsCl	Cs^+	490–610	0·1	1·39		2

Table of the Diffusion Constants—*continued*

Compound	Diffusing ion	Temperature range	D_0	W	Method	Ref.
		280–460	24	1·53		69
	Cl⁻	490–610	0·7	1·56		2
		280–460	1·51	1·27		69
	Xe	490–600	0·1	0·90		46
CsI	Cs⁺	294–500	80	1·64		57
	Cs⁺	250–500	225	1·74		48
	I⁻	405–560	0.39	1·27		47
	Na⁺	368–593	78·5	1·52		70
	Tl⁺	440–570	9×10^{-2}	1·09		31
	Xe	150–500	0.57	1·01		49
TlCl	Tl⁺	290–400	0.58	1·10		50
	Cl⁻	270–420	$3·3 \times 10^{-2}$	0·77		50
AgCl	Ag⁺	150–350	1.46	0·89		51
		200–400	936	1·00		58
	Cl⁻	300–400	133	1·61		52
		300–400	85	1·58		53
	Li⁺	250–400	10·8	1·04		54
	Na⁺	180–300	8·81	1·19		55
	Ca⁺⁺	260–440	0·27	1·07		56
	Sr⁺⁺	255–398	0.33	0·98		57
	Cd⁺⁺	350–400	32·8	1·36		58
	Au	260–440	$5·0 \times 10^{-3}$	0·47	1 torr Cl₂	71
	Mn⁺⁺	300–430	7·71	1·27		59
	Cu⁺	170–445	$9·79 \times 10^{-3}$	0·40		60
	Co⁺⁺	300–425	$2·5 \times 10^{-5}$	0·76		61
	Br⁻	304–427	90	1·59		62
	I⁻	307–448	167	1·57		62
AgBr	Ag⁺	268–400	100	1·00		51
	Br⁻	150–350	0.05	1·06		65
	Cd⁺⁺	300–405	10^4	1·45		63
		185–360	$2·6 \times 10^{-3}$	0·55	heavily doped (CdCl₂)	63
	Mn⁺⁺	350–415	$2·02 \times 10^7$	1·93		59
	Cu⁺	70–405	$5·04 \times 10^{-2}$	0·46		60
AgI	Ag⁺	380–555		0·16		64
	Na⁺	380–555		0·31		64
	Ag⁺	157–222	$1·63 \times 10^{-4}$	0·97		66
	Cl⁻	157–297	$4·8 \times 10^{-5}$	0·63		66

1. Mapother, D., Crooks, H. N. and Maurer, R. (1950). *J. Chem. Phys.* **18**, 1231.
2. Laurent, J. F. and Bénard, J. (1957). *J. Phys. Chem. Solids* **3**, 7.
3. Friauf, R. J. and Nelson, V. C. (1968). *US At. Energy Comm. Report* 290–621.
4. Bénière, F., Bénière, M. and Chemla, M. (1970). *J. Phys. Chem. Solids* **31**, 1205.
5. Laurance, N. (1960). *Phys. Rev.* **1**, 57.
6. Barr, L. W., Morrison, J. A. and Schroeder, P. A. (1965). *J. Appl. Phys.* **36**, 624.
7. Bénière, F., Bénière, M. and Chemla, M. (1968). *C.R. Acad. Sci. Paris* **267**, 633.
8. Arai, G. and Mullen, J. G. (1966). *Phys. Rev.* **143**, 663.
9. Bénière, F., Bénière, M. and Chemla, M. (1969). *J. Chem. Phys.* **66**, 898.
10. Chemla, M. (1954). Thesis, University of Paris, Paris.
11. Beaumont, J. C. and Cabane, J. (1961). *C.R. Acad. Sci. Paris* **252**, 113; *ibid*, **252**, 266.
12. Banasevich, S. N., Lure, B. G. and Murin, A. N. (1960). *Soviet Physics Solid State* **2**, 72.
13. Slifkin, L. and Brébec, G. (1968). Rept. CEA DM/1750.
14. Bénière, F., Bénière, M. and Chemla, M. (1969). *C.R. Acad. Sci. Paris* **268**, 1461.
15. Allnatt, A. R. and Pantelis, A. (1968). *Trans. Faraday Soc.* **64**, 2100.
16. Bénière, F. (1970) Thesis, University of Paris, Orsay.
17. Ikeda, T. (1964). *J. Phys. Soc. Japan* **19**, 858.
18. Allen, C. A., Ireland, D. T. and Fredericks, W. J. (1967). *J. Chem. Phys.* **47**, 3068.

19. Stewart, W. H. and Reed, C. A. (1965). *J. Chem. Phys.* 1965, **43**, 2890.
20. Lure, B. G., Murin, A. N. and Brigevich, R. F. (1963). *Soviet Physics Solid State* **4**, 1432.
21. Rothman, S. J., Barr, L. W., Rowe, A. and Selwood, P. G. (1966). *Phil. Mag.* **14**, 501.
22. Mannion, W. A., Allen, C. A. and Fredericks, W. J. (1968). *J. Chem. Phys.* **48**, 1537.
23. Haneda, K., Ikeda, T. and Yoshida, S. (1968). *J. Phys. Soc. Japan* **25**, 643.
24. Iida, Y. and Tomono, Y. (1964). *J. Phys. Soc. Japan* **19**, 1264.
25. Geguzin, Y., Dobrovinskaya, E. R. and Podorshanskaya, N. M. (1965). *Zh. prikl. Spektr.* **2**, 552.
26. Schmidt, K. and Staube, H. (1968). *Z; Physik. Chem. N.F.* **60**, 90.
27. Naumov, A. N. and Ptashnik, V. B. (1968). *Fiz. Tverd. tela*, **10**, 3710.
28. Bénière, M., Bénière, F. and Chemla, M. (1970). *J. Chem. Phys.* **67**, 1312.
29. Fuller, R. G. (1966). *Phys. Rev.* **142**, 524.
30. Arnikar, H. J. and Chemla, M. (1956). *C.R. Acad. Sci. Paris* **242**, 2132.
31. Dobrovinskaya, E. R. and Podorshanskaya, N. M. (1966). *Ukr. fiz. ZR.* **11**, 227.
32. Keneshea, F. J. and Fredericks, W. J. (1965). *J. Phys. Chem. Solids* **26**, 201.
33. Keneshea, F. J. and Fredericks, W. J. (1963). *J. Chem. Phys.* **38**, 1952.
34. Reisfeld, R., Glassner, A. and Honigbaum, A. (1965). *J. Chem. Phys.* **43**, 2923.
35. Geguzin, Y. E., Dobrovinskaya, E. R., Lev, I. E. and Mozharov, M. V. (1966). *Fiz. tverd. Tela* **8**, 3248.
36. Reisfeld, R. and Honigbaum, A. (1968). *J. Chem. Phys.* **48**, 5565.
37. Keneshea, F. J. and Fredericks, W. J. (1965). *J. Phys. Chem. Solids* **26**, 1787.
38. Reisfeld, R. and Honigbaum, A. (1968). *Israel J. Chem.* **6**, 53.
39. Ruehenbeck, C. (1967). *Z. Phys.* **207**, 446.
40. Dawson, D. K. and Barr, L. W. (1967). *Proc. Brit. Ceram. Soc.* **9**, 171.
41. Illingworth, R. (1963). *J. Phys. Chem. Solids* **24**, 129.
42. Reisfeld, R. and Glasner, A. (1965). *J. Chem. Phys.* **42**, 2983.
43. Matzke, H. (1967). *Z. Naturforshg.* **22a**, 507.
44. Kakaishi, T. and Sensui, Y. (1969). *Trans. Faraday Soc.* **65**, 131.
45. Peterson, N. L. and Rothman, S. J. (1969). *Phys. Rev.* **177**, 1329.
46. Felix, F. W. and Meier, K. (1969). *Phys. Stat. Solidi* **32**, 139.
47. Klotsman, S. M., Polikarpova, I. P., Timofeev, A. N. and Trakhtenberg, I. S. (1967). *Fiz. tverd. Tela* **9**, 2487.
48. Hoodless, I. M. and Nicol, Mc, B.D. (1968). *Phil. Mag.* **17**, 1223.
49. Elleman, T. S., Fox, C. H. and Mears, L. D. (1969). *J. Nucl. Mat.* **30**, 89.
50. Friauf, R. J. (1970). Europhysics Conference "Atomic Transport in Solids and Liquids" Marstrand.
51. Friauf, R. J. (1957). *Phys. Rev.* **105**, 843.
52. Compton, W. D. and Maurer, R. J. (1956). *J. Phys. Chem. Solids* **1**, 191.
53. Lakatos, E. and Lieser, K. (1966). *Z. phys. Chem., Neue Folge* **48**, 213.
54. Naumov, A. N. and Ptashnik, V. B. (1970). Europhysics Conference "Atomic Transport in Solids and Liquids". Marstrand.
55. Suptitz, P. (1965). *Phys. Stat. Solidi* **12**, 555.
56. Slifkin, L. and Brebec, G. (1968). Rept. CEA.DM/1751.
57. Laskar, A. L., Batra, A. P. and Slifkin, L. (1969). *J. Phys. Chem. Solids* **30**, 1173.
58. Reade, R. F. and Martin, D. S. (1960). *J. Appl. Phys.* **31**, 1965.
59. Suptitz, P. and Wiedmann, J. (1968). *Phys. Stat. Solidi* **27**, 631.
60. Suptitz, P. (1966). *Phys. Stat. Solidi* **13**, 135.
61. Murin, A. N., Lure, B. G., Seregin, P. P. and Cherezov, N. K. (1967). *Soviet Physics—Solid State* **8**, 2632.
62. Batra, A. P. and Slifkin, L. (1969). *J. Phys. Chem. Solids* **30**, 1315.
63. Hanlon, J. E. (1960). *J. Chem. Phys.* **32**, 1492.
64. Kvist, A., Tarneberg, R. and Josefson, A. M. (1970). Europhysics Conference "Atomic Transport in Solids and Liquids". Marstrand.
65. Mrin, A. (1957). Conf. on Use Radioisotopes, Unesco, Paris.
66. Jordan, P. and Pochon, M. (1957). *Helv. Phys. Acta* **30**, 33.
67. Dobrovinskaya, O. R., Solunskii, V. I. and Shakhova, A. G. (1967). *Ukr. Fiz. Zh.*, **12**, 868.
68. Hanson, R. C. (1968). *Bull. Am. Phys. Soc.,* ser. II, Vol. 13, 902.
69. Harvey, P. J. and Hoodless, I. M. (1967). *Phil. Mag.* **16**, 3408.
70. Klotzman, S. M., Polikarpova, I. P. and Timofeev, A. N. (1967). *Fiz. Tverd. Tela* **11**, 2710.
71. Batra, A. P., Laskar, A. L. and Slifkin, L. (1969). *J. Phys. Chem. Solids* **30**, 2053.

7. TRANSFERENCE NUMBERS IN IONIC CRYSTALS

F. Bénière

Laboratorie d'Electrochimie, Faculté des Sciences de Paris, France.

I. Introduction

Historically, the investigation of the mean mobilities of constituents in ionic crystals began about half-a-century ago with the measurement of electrical conductivity by Phipps and his co-workers (1926) in the United States, and, to a greater extent, in Germany by Tubandt and Lorenz (1914), Seith (1929), von Seelen (1924), von Rautenfeldt (1923), von Hevesy (1921), Jost (1926, Smekal (1925), Wagenr (1930) and other pioneer scientists.

It is noteworthy that the experimental techniques for the measurement of conductivity were already quite satisfactory and have not undergone much change since that time. The accuracy of the measurements has obviously been improved; however, the main features of the temperature dependence on the conductivity had already been observed by these authors. The almost linear variation of $\log \sigma$ (specific conductivity) as a function of $1/T$ (absolute temperature) in solids had been shown even earlier (Rasch and Hinrichsen, 1908; Königsberger, 1907). One may notice that at that time the activation energy, as one would call it today, was interpreted as the "heat of liberation of a gram ion in a crystal lattice, or heat of activation which the ions of a lattice must acquire in order to be free to take part in electrolytic conduction" (Phipps et al., 1926). The second point observed was that the plots of log σ vs. $1/T$ was divided in sodium chloride into two straight lines with a gradual change of the slope (von Seelen, 1924; Phipps et al., 1926). Such curves, obtained in a great number of ionic crystals (see, e.g. Lehfeldt, 1933), are now quite well interpreted in terms of Schottky defects by the existence of two temperature ranges where the vacancies are due to thermal disorder (intrinsic range) and to the influence of bivalent impurities (extrinsic range), respectively. However, this is a recent explanation (Koch and Wagner, 1937). It was suggested that the lower temperature part of the curve, i.e. the part of lowest slope, was connected to the heat of liberation of the sodium ion, according to the first results of Tubandt (1920) who had shown that in most cases the positive ion is the electrolytic carrier. Concerning the upper range where the slope appeared to be nearly double the lower slope, Phipps thought that in the high temperature range both ions conduct simultaneously. Corroboration of this speculation obviously needed the knowledge of the respective transference numbers of the anions and cations. It is therefore not surprising that among the first investigations of ionic crystals a good many of them dealt with measurements of transference numbers, being pioneered by Tubandt (1920).

If several types of ions are mobile, each one is characterised by its mobility v_i, i.e. the velocity acquired under the influence of unit force. The partial ionic conductivity of every ion is σ_i, given by

$$\sigma_i = n_i z_i^2 e^2 v_i \qquad (1.1)$$

where n_i is the number of the ions considered per unit volume, z_i the valency of the ion and e the electronic charge.

Furthermore, if more than one mechanism of migration is responsible for the conduction of one species of ion (for instance, migration of vacancies and interstitial ions) the mobility v_i is then the sum of the contributions due to every operative mechanism.

Denoting σ as the total conductivity of the ionic crystal, t_i, the transference number of each particle is defined by the relation

$$t_i = \frac{\sigma_i}{\sigma}. \qquad (1.2)$$

Moreover, if the electronic component of conductivity is not negligible a term σ_{el} is involved in the total conductivity and a transference number of electrons, t_{el}, must be considered, defined by

$$t_{el} = \frac{\sigma_{el}}{\sigma}. \qquad (1.3)$$

The means of separating the electronic component of σ will be described in Section II, while those of separating the individual ionic components are reviewed in Section III for the classical methods and in Section IV for the method based on self-diffusion coefficient measurements. A particular application of use of transference numbers will be briefly discussed in Section V.

II. Faraday's Law

Electrolysis of a solid salt occurs, as for electrolytic solutions, when U, the tension applied between the electrodes exceeds E, the value of the electromotive force of the cell constituted by the salt and the products of decomposition. Thus if one plots I, the electric current passing through the circuit of Fig. 1 against U, the applied tension, the electronic component of the current, I^{el} should appear as a straight line passing through the origin, i.e. given by the function

$$I_{el} = k\sigma_{el}U$$

where k is a geometrical factor (cell constant).
On the other hand, I_{ion}, the ionic component should be given by a straight line appearing only for $U \geqslant E$ of functional form

$$I_{ion} = k\sigma_{ion}(U - E).$$

In this way, Chemla (1954) has shown (Fig. 2) that the conductivity in NaCl is essentially of ionic nature.

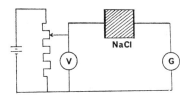

Fig. 1. Schematic set-up for testing Ohm's law.

The nature of the conductivity in ionic crystals, either ionic or electronic, may also be determined by measuring the amount of the products of decomposition at the electrodes compared with the quantity of electricity passing through the crystal.

This principle was applied first by Tubandt (1920) who verified Faraday's law in many ionic compounds. A particularly simple case was obtained for α-AgI, which Tubandt found stable above 144·6°C. Tubandt proceeded as follows. A cylinder of AgI obtained by compressing precipitated AgI is brought between a platinum cathode and a silver anode and electrolyzed. The quantity of electricity is measured with a coulometer $Ag–AgNO_3–Ag$. After the experiment the cylinder is separated from the anode, which is weighed, while the cylinder, the cathode and the silver deposited, are not separable and are weighed together. This part was found to have increased in weight by an amount—due to the silver deposited—which was equal to the loss of weight of the silver anode within very narrow limits of error. Furthermore this difference of weight was found to be almost completely equal to the weight of silver deposited in the coulometer. Hence, this experiment proved that the electrolytic current in AgI obeys Faraday's law perfectly, or, in other words, that the conduction of electricity in this compound is purely ionic, i.e. due to migration of the ions Ag^+ and/or I^-. Applying the same method with a slightly different arrangement, Tubandt showed that it was possible to determine the respective contributions of the Ag^+ and I^- ions to the ionic conductivity, i.e. the transference numbers, as described below.

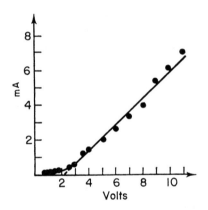

Fig. 2. Chemla's experimental verification of the occurrence of electrolytic conduction in NaCl single crystal

III. The Measurement of Transference Numbers

A. Tubandt's Methods

1. Procedure with Dissolving Anode without Protective Electrolytes

Let us consider again the case of α-AgI. Three cylindrical pressed pellets of AgI are brought between a platinum cathode and a silver anode (Fig. 3).

After passage of a current of a few milliamperes for several hours, the platinum cathode is weighed together with pellet 3, while the anode, pellet 1 and pellet 2 are separable and weighed individually. Let us suppose that

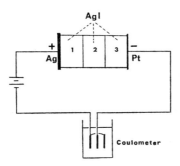

FIG. 3. Tubandt's set-up for measuring transference numbers in α-AgI (pressed pellets).

both types of ions migrate, their respective transference numbers being $t+$ and $t-$ and that a quantity of electricity equal to one Faraday has passed through the system, which has deposited one gram-equivalent of silver in the coulometer. One expects to observe the following:

Cylinder 1 loses $t+$ of an equivalent of Ag^+ and gains $t-$ of an equivalent of I^- which can be regarded as coming from cylinder 3. There is therefore one gram-equivalent of I^- ions which reacts with the anode to grow one equivalent of AgI on cylinder 1. Hence, the anode should decrease in weight by an amount equal to one gram-equivalent of silver, while the weight of pellet 1 should finally be increased by an amount of $t-$ equivalent of I^- and $(1 - t+)$ equivalent of Ag^+, i.e. of $t-$ equivalent of AgI;

The weight of cylinder 2 should have remained unchanged since for each species of ions there are equal numbers of migrating ions arriving from the preceding pellet and leaving it to the next one in the same direction;

Cylinder 3 loses $t-$ gram-equivalent of I^- ions and gains $t+$ equivalent of Ag^+. So there is one gram-equivalent of Ag^+ ions which is reduced at the platinum cathode. The total weight of the cathode and cylinder 3 should be simultaneously increased by an amount of $t+$ equivalent of silver and decreased by an amount of $t-$ equivalent of I^- ions.

Tubandt's observations were: (1) the weight of cylinder 2 remains unchanged, (2) the weight of the silver anode is decreased by an amount equal to the weight of silver deposited in the coulometer, showing that no appreciable electronic conductivity occurs ($t_{el} = 0$) as it has been seen above, (3) cylinder 1 does not change in weight, proving that no anionic conductivity occurs ($t- = 0$), (4) the weight of cylinder 3 + platinum cathode is increased in weight by an amount equal to the weight of silver deposited in the coulometer, which demonstrates that the conduction in α-AgI is entirely cationic ($t+ = 1$).

In the same way, Tubandt and Reinhold (1923) found that it was possible to measure the transference numbers in $PbCl_2$ simply by putting in series a silver anode, three cylindrical pellets of pressed $PbCl_2$ and a platinum cathode. Here again the anode is separable and its weight is decreased by an amount equal to the silver deposited in the coulometer, and cylinder 2 does not change in weight. However, this time, the weight of cylinder 1 is increased by an amount of AgCl equivalent to the amount of electricity having passed through the system, while pellet 3 has decreased its weight by an amount of Cl^- ions equal to the same equivalent of electricity. It is easy to see that the passage of, say, 2 Faradays of electricity should have made (1) the anode decrease its weight by an amount equal to two equivalents of Ag, as is observed showing that $t_{el} = 0$, (2) the cylinder 1 decrease of $t+$ gram-equivalent of Pb^{++} ions and increase simultaneously of $2t-$ gram-equivalent of Cl^- ions and 2 gram-equivalent of Ag^+ ions and, (3) pellet 3 + cathode decrease of $2t-$ gram-equivalent of Cl^- and increase of $t+$ gram-equivalent of Pb^{++} ions. Tubandt's results show therefore that in $PbCl_2 : t_{el} = 0$, $t+ = 0$ and $t- = 1$, within the limits of error. Entirely anionic conduction was also found to occur in PbF_2, $PbBr_2$, BaF_2, $BaCl_2$ and $BaBr_2$ (Tubandt, 1932).

It must be noticed that the compounds obtained by compressing powdered salts, such as AgI or $PbCl_2$, are particularly favourable. Firstly, owing to the dissolution of the anode, the silver anode and the adjacent pellet may be separated and weighed independently of each other. Secondly, in these compounds the metal is deposited onto the cathode, without penetrating into the adjacent pellet. With many other solid electrolytes obtained as pressed pellets, similar experiments fail because the metal deposited at the cathode grows through the pellet, forming thin filaments along the grain boundaries and causing a metallic short circuit of the system. In this case, more complicated arrangements have to be used.

2. Procedure with Dissolving Anode and Protective Electrolytes Adjacent to the Cathode

In most cases where cylinders of compressed powdered salts were used, Tubandt found it necessary to interpose between the cylinders of the substance and the electrodes, sets of pellets of another substance in which the metal deposited at the cathode forms no threads, and hence no metallic short circuit. Such pellets were called by Tubandt "protective electrolytes". Typically the pellets are used in sets of three cylinders because they sometimes stick together at the interfaces between unlike materials, so that the couples of adjacent pellets of different nature are weighed together before and after electrolysis.

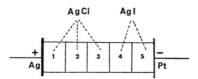

FIG. 4. Tubandt's set-up for measuring transference numbers in AgCl with α-AgI as protective electrolytes (pressed pellets).

In the case of AgCl and AgBr, Tubandt put in series the silver anode, three pellets of AgCl and two protective electrolytes of AgI (Fig. 4). Since AgI has been found to be a purely cationic conductor the silver ions coming from the decomposition of AgCl pass through the protective electrolytes to be finally deposited at the cathode as Ag metal which does not grow through AgI, while it could have grown through AgCl.

Supposing that the conduction in AgCl is due to migration of Ag^+ ions $(t+)$ and Cl^- ions $(t-)$ there would be for every Faraday of electricity passing through the system $t+$ gram-equivalent of Ag^+ ions arriving from AgCl at the interface of pellets 3 and 4, which would at the same time lose one equivalent of Ag^+ crossing through AgI to the cathode and $t-$ equivalent of Cl^- ions going out from the interface and passing through the AgCl pellets to react with the anode. Hence, the total weight of cylinders 3 and 4 should finally be decreased by an amount equal to $t-$ of a gram-equivalent of AgCl. In this case the weight of the anode should be decreased by an amount of one gram-equivalent of silver and that of cylinder 1 increased by an amount equal to $t-$ of an equivalent of AgCl.

In fact, Tubandt found that the weights of cylinders 1, 2 and 3 + 4 all remained unchanged. As in AgI the electrical conductivity is thus exclusively cationic $(t_{el} = 0, t- = 0, t+ = 1)$ in AgCl and AgBr.

3. Procedure for Mixed Conductors

For substances allowing both anionic and cationic conduction, the preceding arrangement fails for measuring the transference numbers in pressed powdered salts and protective electrolytes adjacent to both platinum electrodes have to be inserted. Furthermore, since the pellets of different nature stick together by the passage of current, series of three sets of three pellets are to be used. Figure 5 shows a typical arrangement used for the measurement of the transference numbers in NaCl, with $BaCl_2$ as protective electrolytes. The weight of the cylinders 2, 5 and 7 must obviously remain unchanged if no evaporation occurs. Theoretically, since $BaCl_2$ is an anionic conductor, for every Faraday of electricity there is one gram-equivalent of Cl^- ions which passes through the protective electrolytes and which may be regarded as having left cylinder 9 to arrive at the cathode; here, after oxidation, they leave the system as chlorine gas. The cylinders 3 and 4,

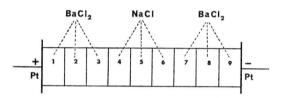

FIG. 5. Tubandt's set-up for measuring transference numbers in NaCl with $BaCl_2$ as protective electrolytes (pressed pellets).

considered together, lose $t+$ of a gram-equivalent of Na^+, gain $t-$ of a gram-equivalent of Cl^- arriving from the right, and lose one gram-equivalent of Cl^- leaving to the left so that finally the weight of these two pellets is decreased by an amount $t+$ of an equivalent of NaCl. At the interface 6–7 there is one gram-equivalent of Cl^- arriving from the $BaCl_2$ pellets of the cathode part and $t-$ of an equivalent of Cl^- which leaves the interface in the direction of the anode, so that the net result is the arrival of $t+$ of an equivalent of Cl^- ions at this interface. In the same way $t+$ of an equivalent of Na^+ arrive from the left coming from cylinder 4. The net increase in weight of the pellets $6+7$ is thus $t+$ equivalent of NaCl per Faraday of electricity. Tubandt did find that the increase in weight of the pair of cylinders 6 and 7 was equal to the loss in weight of the pair of cylinders 3 and 4. Applying Faraday's law, the quantity of electricity being measured with the coulometer, the cation transport number is then readily obtained. Tubandt observed that in the alkali halides both species of ions contribute to the transport of current and that the mobility of the cation is generally far higher than that of the anion. However Tubandt's measurements led generally to large underestimates of the anion transference number, as will be seen later.

To these methods used by Tubandt and his co-workers we might add the method of determination of transference numbers by measuring the displacement of the interface between the pellet, next to the anode and the adjacent one, by measuring microscopically the displacement of a quartz fibre situated at the interface relative to a platinum wire connected with the anode (Jost and Schweitzer, 1933).

Until now, we have dealt with the earlier measurements of transference numbers, based on measurements of weights or displacement of interfaces in pressed pellets of powdered salts. Let us denote this body of results as the first generation of transference numbers.

B. Typical Results of the First Generation of Transference Numbers

Many ionic compounds have been investigated as pressed pellets according to the previous methods. The conduction was found to be exclusively of an ionic nature in almost all halides, namely alkali halides, silver halides, thallous halides, lead halides and alkaline earth halides, though an electronic conduction was also found in the cuprous halides together with an ionic conduction, the latter becoming predominant at high temperature. In the case of the semi-conductors, oxides, sulphides and selenides, a predominance of electronic conduction was found and sometimes underestimated relative to the ionic conduction (e.g. in α-Ag_2S—Tubandt $et\ al.$, 1931). Some of these results are shown in Table I.

TABLE I. Typical results of the first generation of transference numbers. The reliability of these results is discussed in the text.

Substance	Temperature °C	t_+	t_-	t_{el}	Main outlines
NaCl[a]	400	1·00	0·00	0	Exclusively ionic conduction
	500	0·98	0·02	0	in the alkali halides.
	550	0·94	0·06	0	Mixed anionic and cationic
	580	0·92	0·08	0	conduction is found to occur
	600	0·90	0·10	0	with a cationic conduction
	620	0·88	0·12	0	generally predominant (and
		(0·77)[b]	(0·23)[b]		often overestimated)
KCl[a]	435	0·96	0·04	0	
	500	0·94	0·06	0	
	550	0·92	0·08	0	
	600	0·88	0·12	0	
NaF[a]	550	1·00	0·00	0	
	570	0·97	0·03	0	
	600	0·92	0·08	0	
	625	0·86	0·14	0	

TABLE I. *Continued.*

Substance	Temperature °C	t_+	t_-	t_{el}	Main outlines
KBr[c]	605	0·5	0·5	0	
	660	0·4	0·6	0	
KI[c]	610	0·9	0·1	0	
AgCl[d]	20–350	1·00	0·00	0	Entirely cationic conduction
AgBr[d]	20–300	1·00	0·00	0	found in silver halides
β-AgI[d]	20–140	1·00	0·00	0	(as had been corroborated
α-AgI[d]	150–400	1·00	0·00	0	later).
PbF_2[d]	200	0·00	1·00	0	Exclusively anionic conduction
$PbCl_2$[d]	200–450	0·00	1·00	0	in these compounds
$PbBr_2$[d]	250–365	0·00	1·00	0	(PbI_2 excepted), which are
PbI_2[d]	255	0·39	0·61	0	frequently used as protective
	290	0·67	0·33	0	electrolytes.
BaF_2[e]	500	0·00	1·00	0	
$BaCl_2$[e]	400–700	0·00	1·00	0	
$BaBr_2$[e]	350–450	0·00	1·00	0	
CuCl[f]	18	0·00	0·00	1·00	Mixed electronic and ionic
	110	0·03	0·00	0·97	conduction was found to
	232	0·50	0·00	0·50	occur in the cuprous halides.
	300	0·98	0·00	0·02	
	366	1·00	0·00	0·00	
CuBr[f,g]	27	0·00	0·00	1·00	
	223	0·14	0·00	0·86	
	299	0·87	0·00	0·13	
	390	1·00	0·00	0·00	
CuI[h]	200	0·00	0·00	1·00	
	306	0·32	0·00	0·68	
	358	0·84	0·00	0·16	
	400	1·00	0·00	0·00	

[a] Tubandt (1933)　　　　　　　　　　　　[e] Tubandt, Reinhold and Liebold (1931)
[b] Phipps and Leslie (1928)　　　　　　　　[f] Tubandt (1931)
[c] Jost and Schweitzer (1933)　　　　　　　[g] Geiler (1928)
[d] Tubandt (1932)　　　　　　　　　　　　[h] Tubandt et al. (1927).

C. Reliability of the First Generation of Transference Numbers

1. Chemical Composition of the Samples

It is now well established from conductivity and self-diffusion coefficient measurements that the ratio of the anion and cation mobilities depends on the purity of the samples, especially at low temperature. The influence of heterovalent ions present as impurities determines extrinsic ranges and, for instance, some transference numbers of the cations in alkali halides equal to 1 may certainly be interpreted as measurements carried out in samples doped by divalent cationic impurities. This has been clearly demonstrated by Kerkhoff (1951) who found for the transference number of K^+ in KCl crystals containing 2×10^{-4} mole fraction of $CaCl_2$, values nearly equal to unity, even at high temperatures (up to 600°C). In the same way the electronic part of the conductivity in semi-conductors depends on the chemical composition of the substance and on departures from stoichiometry. Thus, the results obtained in the older works are generally not intrinsic values of pure salts, except perhaps in some cases at the highest temperatures, but are specific of samples whose history and impurity contents should have been determined simultaneously.

2. Physical State of the Samples

At the time when Tubandt carried out these experiments, no large artificial single crystals were available. The authors used samples obtained by pressing the powdered salt into disks under high pressure. For example Phipps *et al.* (1926) have reported that disks of NaCl obtained under a pressure of 9000 atm were quite transparent, and showed a conductivity nearly equal to or slightly higher than that of natural rock salt crystals in the whole temperature range 280–770°C. This may give a rough estimate of the purity of the samples used in the older works.

Secondly, the mobilities of the ions in the pressed pellets may be quite different from those in single crystals and dependent on the particle size. This has been shown for the electrical conductance of granular conglomerates (von Hevesy, 1922), and for diffusion (Laurent and Bénard, 1955), by measuring the self-diffusion coefficients of NaCl with the isotopes ^{22}Na and ^{36}Cl in single crystals and in compressed powdered salts. While the cation diffusion coefficient has approximately the same value in either sample, they found that the diffusion coefficient of the chloride ion increases in magnitude as the particle size becomes smaller, giving evidence for appreciable migration through the grain boundaries in the polycrystals.

Thirdly, we have seen that in order to prevent metal threads from growing through the system, Tubandt had to place sets of so-called protective electrolytes between the samples considered and the electrodes. For instance in NaCl the transference numbers were measured by interposing disks of $BaCl_2$. Though the conductivity in $BaCl_2$ was found to be purely anionic within the limits of error, a very low mobility of the Ba^{++} ions would be enough to give rise to an appreciable diffusion of these ions into the NaCl disks, leading to measurements in NaCl disks doped by divalent cations and therefore to an overestimate of the cation transference number. This has been also clearly proved by Kerkhoff (1951) by measuring the electrical conductivity before and after electrolysis.

In the same way, Ronge and Wagner (1950) have measured the transference numbers of solid potassium chloride with strontium chloride, potassium oxide and soldium sulphide as additives. Addition of strontium chloride causes an increase of the transference number of the cation approaching unity as had been observed by Kerkhoff in $CaCl_2$-doped KCl. Addition of potassium oxide and sodium sulphide, i.e. of divalent anions, should on the contrary increase the magnitude of the mole fraction of anion vacancies to a value higher than that of pure crystals. Though solubility of the latter additives is very low, Ronge and Wagner did observe that these ions lower the transference number of K^+ and accordingly increase that of Cl^-.

D. The Measurement of Transference Numbers in Single Crystals

As soon as it was found possible to grow large single crystals, some attempts were made to avoid some of the complications involved by the use of pressed pellets which have been reviewed above.

The dependence of the transference numbers on purity in crystals has been shown by Kerkhoff according to the arrangement indicated in Table II. This author has measured the ionic conductivity and the transference

TABLE II. Scheme of the arrangements which have been used for measuring transference numbers in alkali halides. Numbering of the different parts is the same as in Fig. 5. In all cases, protective electrolytes are pressed pellets.

Sample	a, b	c
1	$BaCl_2$	$BaBr_2$
2	$BaCl_2$	$BaBr_2$
3	$BaCl_2$	$BaBr_2$
4	KCl	CsBr
5	KCl	CsBr
6	KCl	CsBr
7	$BaCl_2$	$BaBr_2$
8	$BaCl_2$	$BaBr_2$
9	$BaCl_2$	$BaBr_2$

[a] Ronge and Wagner (1950) (KCl pressed pellets and single crystals)
[b] Kerkhoff (1951) (KCl single crystals)
[c] Laurance (1960a) (CsBr single crystals)

numbers in three kinds of KCl crystals: (1) doped by 2×10^{-4} CaCl$_2$, (2) analytically pure, and (3) recrystallised KCl. Conductivity in doped crystals was found to be almost entirely extrinsic while the knee of the conductivity curve occurred approximately at 580°C in the analytically pure and 510°C in the recrystallised samples. The corresponding transport numbers are shown in Table III. One may notice for the temperature of 600°C falling in the intrinsic range, the lower value of $t+$ obtained in the recrystallised samples. Comparison of these values with those obtained by Tubandt (Table I) show that Tubandt's results are relative to doped samples.

TABLE III. Transference number of K^+ in different KCl crystals (After Kerkhoff, 1951).

Temperature °C	KCl + 2×10^{-4} CaCl$_2$	Analytically pure	Recrystallised
430	0·994		
450		0·96	
500		0·93	
510	0·993		
525			0·88
550	0·998		
560		0·91	
565			0·85
570			0·81, 0·82
580			0·79, 0·79
590	0·986	0·87	
600	0·993	0·84	0·69, 0·71, 0·72

In general the problem of obtaining a good contact at the interface of the samples is more difficult than with pressed disks. Laurance (1960a) has reported in the case of single crystals of cesium bromide (see arrangement in Table II) that it was difficult to make the separation between tablets 4 and 5 or between 5 and 6 after electrolysis. Separation between unlike materials is also difficult but this does not interfere with the measurement since tablets 3 and 4 and tablets 6 and 7 are weighed together. It was observed, furthermore, that small areas of new CsBr were raised above the surface of crystal 6 next to 5, while corresponding depressions were visible on the surfaces facing the cathode. Laurance interpreted these as areas of more intimate contact during electrolysis and, hence, of highest current density which could make the crystals fuse and stick at these points.

Laruance also suggested as a possible explanation that a part of the bromide ions would remain behind the interface 5, 6—instead of crossing it—to nucleate new crystals.

These observations, also reported by Kerkhoff (1951) who found that in pure KCl the crystals were sometimes stuck together, emphasize the requirement of using crystals with surfaces as perfectly smoothed as possible in order to ensure a constant density of current on the whole interface. Furthermore, the pile of crystals must be maintained together between platinum foil cathodes by some mechanical pressure. Too light a pressure would not ensure good electrical contact, while too strong a one would make the crystals stick to one another. Though purely technical this question is crucial for reliable measurements.

Nevertheless, the use of single crystals, when available, is to be preferred to pressed pellets. However, in the body of investigations which have been reviewed in Table II, protective electrolytes were used as in Tubandt's method. Here again it is to be feared that some of the Ba^{++} ions diffuse even in the single crystals, which would dope them, leading to erroneously high cation transference numbers.

In the purpose of avoiding occurence of this possible effect, F. Bénière et al. (1970) have measured the transference numbers in single crystals of pure sodium chloride without any protective electrolytes according to the simple arrangement shown on Fig. 6. The problem of the electrical contact has been already raised and remains the most delicate point of these experiments which require perfectly smoothed surfaces by accurate microtoming.

The Cl^- ions which are oxidised at the platinum anode are transformed to chlorine gas which is evacuated in order to prevent nucleation of NaCl at the cathode part by reaction with the sodium produced. If the electrolysis is carried out under an atmosphere of argon, a proportion of the sodium atoms diffuse back into the crystals, causing a coloration of the crystal owing to formation of F-centres (Bénière, 1970; Brébec, 1970) and leading to electronic conductivity. This effect is avoided by performing the experiments in the presence of oxygen, which causes the sodium atoms to be deposited as sodium oxide at the interface of the cathode and adjacent crystal. The current must not be higher than 0·2 mA and the time of

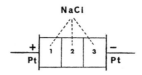

FIG. 6. Set-up for measuring transference numbers in NaCl (single crystals).

electrolysis, depending on the magnitude of the mobilities, i.e. on temperature, must be as short as possible in order to prevent noticeable damage of the single crystals. Typically, the experiments are carried out during the time which corresponds to electrolysis of about 10 mg of NaCl, the crystals being weighed before and after electrolysis to an accuracy of 0·01 mg. Many experiments fail, mainly because of the problem of contact between the different parts and one must select those where the following conditions are fulfilled simultaneously: (1) constancy of the current passing through the circuit during the whole experiment, (2) easy separation of the samples after electrolysis, and (3) no change in weight of crystal 2.

For every Faraday of electricity passing through the system, crystal 1 loses $t+$ of an equivalent of Na^+ crossing the crystals to the cathode and simultaneously t^+ of an equivalent of Cl^- escaping as Cl_2, so that finally the weight of crystal 1 is decreased by an amount equal to $t+$ of an equivalent of NaCl. The weight of crystal 2 remains unchanged while the weight of crystal 3 should decrease by an amount equal to $t-$ of an equivalent of NaCl. However, because of the deposit of the sodium oxide which is not perfectly separable from the surface of this crystal, measurement of the change in weight of crystal 3 is less reliable than that of crystal 1. The results obtained in this way in pure NaCl single crystals, with a reproducibility of 4%, are reported in Table IV. The differences between the values of t^+ for the indicated temperatures fall thus into the range of errors and the observed temperature dependence is therefore not significant. In the same way the measurements of transference numbers in CsBr carried out by Laurance over the temperature range 350 to 450°C gave a mean value of $0·49 \pm 0·05$ without allowing determination of the temperature dependence.

More precise information on the transference numbers may be deduced from measurements of the individual mobilities (see Section IV).

TABLE IV. Transference number measurements of Na^+ in pure NaCl single crystal (After Bénière et al., 1970).

Temperature, °C	580	600	650
$t^+ \pm 0·03$	0·81	0·83	0·84

IV. Possible Determination of the Transference Numbers from Self-diffusion Coefficient Measurements

Let us consider the case of an ionic crystal where the conduction is exclusively ionic, e.g. NaCl. Let $\sigma+$ and $\sigma-$ denote the partial conductivities of the ions Na^+ and Cl^- respectively. The respective transference numbers are, by definition

$$t+ = \frac{\sigma+}{\sigma_+ + \sigma_-} \qquad t- = \frac{\sigma-}{\sigma_+ + \sigma_-} \qquad (4.1)$$

Let us suppose that only Schottky defects, i.e. free anion vacancies and free cation vacancies operate for migration of the ions. Application of the Nernst–Einstein relation, which connects the self-diffusion coefficients $D+$ and $D-$ of the cations and anions, respectively, with the conductivities $\sigma+$ and $\sigma-$ leads to the relations

$$\frac{\sigma+}{D+} = \frac{ne^2}{fkT} \qquad \frac{\sigma-}{D-} = \frac{ne^2}{fkT} \qquad (4.2)$$

where f is the correlation factor, n the number of ions per unit volume, e the electronic charge, k Boltzmann's constant and T the absolute temperature. It follows that the transference numbers may be also obtained from the relations

$$t+ = \frac{D+}{D+ + D-} \qquad t- = \frac{D-}{D+ + D-} \qquad (4.3)$$

At the same time as the first measurements of conductivity and transference numbers were carried out, the first coefficients of *inter-diffusion* in ionic crystals were also determined (Jost, 1926; Tubandt *et al.*, 1928) by measuring analytically the change in concentration in pairs of two adjacent mixed crystals or of one pure component and one mixed crystal. However, determination of the transference numbers obviously requires a previous knowledge of the *self-diffusion* coefficients. It was also at that time that the first self-diffusion coefficients were measured, but in the limited case of lead and lead compounds by making use of the *natural radioactivity* of the lead isotope ThB (von Hevesy, 1921).

Von Hevesy and Seith (1929) have deduced from the measurements of the self-diffusion coefficients of Pb^{++} in PbI_2, connected with those of the electrical conductivity, numerical values for the transference numbers of the Pb^{++} and I^- ions in PbI_2 by applying the Nernst–Einstein relation. As had been pointed out by Mott and Gurney (1940) these results are difficult to interpret because the models of point defects do not seem to be applicable in this compound, the partial conductivity of the iodide ions being due to some effect other than migration via lattice ions.

Indirect determination of reliable transference numbers from eqn (4.3) requires the measurement of both $D+$ and $D-$. It is only after Joliot's discovery of *artificial radioactivity* that such measurements of self-diffusion coefficients in ionic crystals were possible, namely in 1948 with the pioneer work of Maurer and Mapother who measured the self-diffusion coefficients of the isotope ^{24}Na in NaCl. Use of radioactive isotopes was at that time expected to lead to considerable progress for the determination of transference numbers (Jost, 1952). Extensive application of artificial radioactive isotopes has indeed been made for the last two decades for measuring self-diffusion coefficients in a considerable number of compounds (see Chapter 6) giving rise to what we could define as the second generation of transference numbers.

Among the first compounds where self-diffusion of both cations and anions have been investigated one may cite NaCl (Mapother *et al.*, 1950 $(D+)$; Chelma, 1952 $(D-)$; Patterson *et al.*, 1956 $(D-)$; Laurent and Bénard, 1955 $(D+$ and $D-)$) and AgCl (Compton and Maurer, 1956). Compton measured the diffusion coefficient of ^{36}Cl in AgCl and found that it was about one thousandth of that of ^{110}Ag, while similar results were observed in AgBr (Friauf, 1957 $(D+)$; Tannhauser, 1958 $(D-)$) corroborating in this case the transference number measurements of Tubandt (Table I) who found that in the silver halides the chloride ion mobility was far too small to be detected.

On the contrary, in the alkali halides the transference numbers obtained from self-diffusion coefficients show that Tubandt's measurements gave erroneously high cation transport numbers, part of the discrepancy being certainly due to the use of $BaCl_2$ "protective electrolytes". Generally, in this group of ionic crystals $t+$ is higher than $t-$, as had been observed in NaCl, KCl, KI, KBr (Laurent and Bénard, 1957), NaBr (Schamp and Katz, 1954),

TABLE V. Transference number measurements of K^+ in KCl.

Temperature, °C	a	b	c
525		0·88	0·75
550	0·92		
570		0·81, 0·82	0·70
600	0·88	0·69–0·72	0·67
650			0·60
700			0·55
750			0·49

a Tubandt (1933)

b Kerkhoff (1951)

c Fuller (1966), calculated values from Fuller's anion self-diffusion coefficient measurements and Aschner's cation self-diffusion coefficient measurements.

though the opposite has been shown to occur in both structures of CsCl (Laurent and Bénard, 1957) and in CsBr (Lynch, 1960).

The transference numbers calculated according to eqn (4.3) may easily be obtained for the compounds where both $D+$ and $D-$ have been determined (See Table of diffusion constants in Chapter 6) and we shall merely give here the transference numbers of KCl computed in this way by Fuller (1966, using Aschner's values of $D+$, 1954) compared with the measurements of Tubandt (1933) and Kerkhoff (1951) in Table V.

The calculated values, which we have defined as the second generation of transference numbers, are certainly more reliable than those obtained by the first generation. The preceding results indicate that it is generally not possible to assume as has commonly been done, that the anion contribution to the high temperature conductivity is negligible in the alkali halides.

V. Possible Determination of the Diffusion Coefficients via Neutral Defects from Transference Number Measurements

Strictly, eqn (4.3) holds only for systems in which both species of ions migrate via free vacancies or interstitial ions. In the case where interstitialcy mechanisms are operative for migration of one kind of ions, e.g. cation migration in silver halides while the anion moves via vacancy mechanism, this relation should be corrected by a geometrical factor since the total displacement of the electric charge in an interstitialcy jump is not equal to the displacement of the tracer ion (See Chapter 6). In the case of alkali halides, which have been found to suffer Schottky disorder, i.e. vacancies in both sublattices, eqn (4.3) is not quite valid because of existence of associated defects bearing no net charge relative to the lattice, namely impurity–vacancy pairs and vacancy pairs, which may contribute to diffusion of the ions and not to transport of current.

Diffusion via vacancy pairs has been shown by Laurance (1960b) to occur in NaCl and the contribution of the vacancy pairs to self-diffusion of the anions has been determined in KCl (Fuller et al., 1968; M. Bénière et al., 1970), KBr (Barr and Dawson, 1969) and NaCl (F. Bérnière et al., 1970).

Thus, the self-diffusion coefficients measured experimentally include a term due to diffusion via vacancy pairs, let this be $D'+$ and $D'-$ for the diffusion of the cations and anions, respectively, besides $Dv+$ and $Dv-$, the diffusion coefficients by the free cation and anion vacancies, respectively, so that the total diffusion coefficients may be written as

$$D+ = Dv+ + D'+ \tag{5.1}$$

$$D- = Dv- + D'-. \tag{5.2}$$

The contribution of vacancy pairs is not involved in the displacement of electrical charges, and hence neither in the relation (4.3) connecting the transference numbers to the self-diffusion coefficients, which must be rewritten as

$$t+ = \frac{Dv+}{Dv+ + Dv-} = \frac{D+ - D'+}{(D+ + D-) - (D'+ + D'-)} \tag{5.3}$$

$$t- = \frac{Dv-}{Dv+ + Dv-} = \frac{D- - D'-}{(D+ + D-) - (D'+ + D'-)}. \tag{5.4}$$

The coefficients $D+$ and $D-$ are the experimental self-diffusion coefficients and $D'-$ may also quite easily be obtained from measurement of the anion diffusion coefficient in crystals doped by small amounts of bivalent cations. Futhermore, if the transference numbers can also be measured, then the contribution of the vacancy pairs to the cation self-diffusion coefficient could be determined from the foliowing equation

$$D_+' = D_+ - (D^- - D'^-)t_+/t_-. \tag{5.5}$$

The analytical form of this equation shows that a high degree of accuracy is needed in the measurement of $t+$ for a reliable determination of $D'+$. If the transference numbers could be measured with improved accuracy, this would give a possible method of determining the influence of vacancy pairs on the cation diffusion in alkali halides. This important question could give rise to a third generation of transference numbers aiming at the investigation of the ion migration via neutral defects.

References

Aschner, J. F. (1954). Thesis, University of Illinois, Urbana.
Barr, L. W. and Dawson, D. K. (1969). At. Energy Res. Estab. Rept. R 6234.
Bénière, F. (1970). Thesis, University of Paris, Orsay.
Bénière, F., Bénière, M. and Chemla, M. (1970). *Physics Chem. Solids* **31**, 1205.
Bénière, M., Bénière, F. and Chemla, M. (1970). *J. chim. Phys.* **67**, 1312.
Brébec, G. (1970). Private communication to the author.
Chemla, M. (1952). *C.R. Acad. Sci. Paris* **234**, 2601.
Chemla, M. (1954). Thesis, University of Paris, Paris.
Compton, W. D. and Maurer, R. J. (1956). *Physics Chem. Solids* **1**, 191.
Friauf, R. J. (1957). *Phys. Rev.* **105**, 843.
Fuller, R. G. (1966). *Phys. Rev.* **142**, 524.
Fuller, R. G., Marquardt, C. L., Reilly, M. H. and Wells, J. C. (1968). *Phys. Rev.* **176**, 1036.
Geiler, J. (1928). Dissertation, Halle.
Hevesy, von, G. (1921). *Annln Phys.* **65**, 216.
Hevesy, von, G. (1922). *Z. Phys.* **10**, 80.

Hevesy, von, G. and Seith, W. (1929). *Z. Phys.* **56**, 790.

Jost, W. (1926). Dissertation, Halle.

Jost, W. and Schweitzer, H. (1933). *Z. phys. Chem.* **B20**, 118.

Jost, W. (1952). *In* "Diffusion in Solids, Liquids, Gases". Academic Press, New York.

Kerkhoff, F. (1951). *Z. Phys.* **130**, 449.

Koch, E. and Wagner, C. (1937). *Z. phys. Chem.* **B38**, 295.

Königsberger (1907). *Z. Phys.* **8**, 833.

Laurance, N. (1960a). *Phys. Rev.* **118**, 988.

Laurance, N. (1960b). *Phys. Rev.* **120**, 57.

Laurent, J. F. and Bénard, J. (1955). *C.R. Acad. Sci. Paris* **241**, 1204.

Laurent, J. F. and Bénard, J. (1957). *Physics Chem. Solids* **3**, 7.

Lehfeldt, W. (1933). *Z. Phys.* **85**, 717.

Lynch, D. W. (1960). *Phys. Rev.* **118**, 468.

Mapother, D., Crooks, H. N. and Maurer, R. J. (1950). *J. chem. Phys.* **18**, 1231.

Maurer, R. J. and Mapother, D. (1948). *Phys. Rev.* **73**, 1260.

Mott, N. F. and Gurney, R. W. (1940). *In* "Electronic Processes in Ionic Crystals". Oxford University Press.

Patterson, D., Rose, G. S. and Morrison, J. A. (1956). *Phil. Mag.* ser. 8, **1**, 393.

Phipps, T. E., Lansing, W. D. and Cooke, T. G. (1926). *J. Am. chem. Soc.* **48**, 112.

Phipps, T. E. and Leslie, R. T. (1928). *J. Am. chem. Soc.* **50**, 2412.

Rasch and Hinrichsen (1908). *Z. Elektrochem.* **14**, 41.

Rautenfeldt, von (1923). *Annln. Phys.* **72**, 617.

Ronge, G. and Wagner, C. (1950). *J. chem. Phys.* **18**, 74.

Schamp, H. W. and Katz, E. (1954). *Phys. Rev.* **94**, 828.

Seelen, von, D. (1924). *Z. Phys.* **29**, 125.

Seith, W. (1929). *Z. Phys.* **56**, 802.

Smekal, A. (1925). *Z. Phys.* **26**, 707.

Tannhauser, D. (1958). *Physics Chem. Solids* **5**, 224.

Tubandt, C. (1914). *Z. phys. Chem.* **87**, 523.

Tubandt, C. (1920). *Z. anorg. allgem. Chem.* **110**, 234 and **115**, 105.

Tubandt, C. (1931). *In* "Landolt–Börnstein", *Phys. Chem. Tabellen*, Supplement II, part 2, p. 1042.

Tubandt, C. (1932). *In* "Handbuch der Experimentalphysik", Vol. XII, 383.

Tubandt, C. (1933). *Z. Elektrochem.* **39**, 500.

Tubandt, C. and Lorenz, E. (1914). *Z. phys. Chem.* **87**, 513, 543.

Tubandt, C. and Reinhold, H. (1923). *Z. Elektrochem.* **29**, 313.

Tubandt, C., Rindtorff, E. and Jost, W. (1927). *Z. anorg. allgem. Chem.* **165**, 195.

Tubandt, C., Reinhold, J. and Jost, W. (1928). *Z. anorg. allgem. Chem.* **177**, 253.

Tubandt, C., Reinhold, H. and Liebold, G. (1931). *Z. anorg. allgem. Chem.* **197**, 225.

Wagner, C. (1930). *Z. phys. Chem.* **B11**, 139.

8. ELECTRICAL CONDUCTIVITY

Arnold Kvist

*Department of Physics, Chalmers University of Technology,
Göteborg, Sweden.*

Summary

Experimental techniques and results for conductivity measurements in different solid electrolytes are discussed. For the oxygen ion conducting oxides results have been compiled from a number of different investigations, while for the other systems examples are given for the different main groups.

I. Introduction

Many different types of solids have been used as solid electrolytes during the last fifty years and a great number of investigations of different transport properties have been performed on such materials. The solid electrolytes are characterized by a relatively high ionic conductivity, negligible or small electronic conduction and the current should in many of the technical applications be transported either by the cation or the anion. Both good anion and cation conductors have been found. We have here divided the electrolytes into two main groups; oxygen conducting oxides with very high melting points and different kinds of ionic salts.

During the last ten years a number of new compounds suitable as solid electrolytes have been detected, and especially different oxide systems, for instance stabilized zirconia, and silver ion conductors like $RbAg_4I_5$ have been thoroughly investigated by several authors. Electrical conductivities have been studied as functions of temperature, composition, partial pressures of different gases and time.

Electrical conductivity measurements have been performed with different types of samples, for instance compressed cylinders, which can be sintered in different ways, grown single crystals or poly-crystallines, or salt that has been molten and is allowed to solidify in a cell of glass or ceramics with a known cell constant. Since the conductivity for different compounds varies from at least about 10^{-4} mho/cm up to 1 mho/cm and the temperatures from below room temperature up to at least 1200°C, a number of different experimental methods have been developed.

In this chapter we will consider experimental technique and results obtained for different groups of solid electrolytes.

II. Experimental

When a conductor is placed in an electric field there are four different charged species which can move. These are cations, anions, electrons (n-conduction) or electron holes (p-conduction).

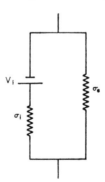

FIG. 1. Equivalent circuit for a mixed ionic and electronic conductor. σ_i is the ionic conductivity, σ_e is the electronic conductivity and V_i is a potential due to electrode reactions.

The total conductivity of a conductor is the sum of the ionic conductivity and the electronic conductivity. Figure 1 shows an equivalent circuit for a mixed ionic and electronic conductor. σ_i and σ_e are the conductivities of the two paths due to ionic and electronic conduction, respectively, and V_i is a potential due to electrode processes. The two paths in the figure are completely independent.

We will only consider electrolytes with neglectable electronic conduction, i.e. $\sigma_e = 0$.

A. Measuring Principles

Either DC or AC methods can be used for measurements of the electrical conductivity of ionic conductors. We shall discuss here three conventional experimental methods.

1. DC Measurements with Four Inert Electrodes

When a sample is mounted between two inert electrodes, DC measurements cannot be performed directly owing to polarization of the electrodes, e.g. the voltage V_i in Fig. 1 cannot be neglected. These polarization phenomena can be avoided by making use of a method with four electrodes (Fig. 2). A voltage is applied between the two outer electrodes and by measuring the current in the circuit and the voltage drop between the two inner electrodes, the electrical conductivity can be calculated. Since no current flows through the upper mV-meter in the figure, no polarization effects nor contact resistances occur at the inner electrodes. This method gives very high accuracy, but in many cases is complicated.

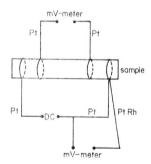

FIG. 2. Four electrode DC method for measurements of the electrical conductivity of solid ionic conductors. The upper mV-meter is used for the measurements of the potential difference between two points on the sample and the lower mV-meter for the temperature measurement.

2. AC Measurements with Two Inert Electrodes

Almost the same accuracy as with the method above can be obtained by an AC measuring technique. The sample is mounted between two inert electrodes and AC with a frequency of between 1000 and 3000 c/s is used. A very small frequency dependence of the electrical conductivity has generally been found in this frequency interval (less than 2%) and the capacity should not exceed 200 pF. A great number of different commercial impedance bridges with accuracies better than 0·5% have been used.

This AC method is simpler than the DC method with four electrodes and the polarization effects at the electrodes are also negligible, but contact resistances might occur, making the method somewhat less exact. Several authors have compared results obtained by the DC and the AC method and have succeeded in obtaining complete agreement.

Instead of AC, DC measurements with very short current pulses can be used.

3. DC Measurements with Two Reversible Electrodes

In some cases it is possible to find electrodes which are reversible to one of the ions in the sample and it is then possible to use these electrodes and DC, e.g. for a cell of the type Ag/AgI/Ag.

For all three methods the current should be in the range $0.01-100\,\mu A$ and the voltage should not exceed 1 V. When the resistance of the sample is high it is important to keep the cell and the wires well shielded and keep the entire circuit very well isolated from earth.

B. The Furnace

The sample can be mounted in a furnace in different ways. Figure 3 shows a

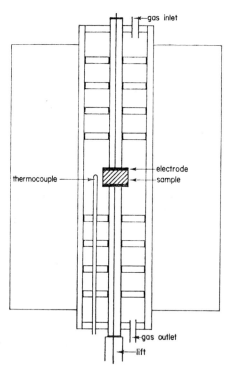

FIG. 3. Experimental set-up for measurements of electrical conductivities.

simple furnace which with small modifications can be used at different temperatures. At temperatures above 500°C, the furnace can be heated up electrically, while at lower temperatures different types of thermostat baths can be used. The baffles in the furnace reduce the thermal convection and in that way the temperature fluctuations can be kept less than 0·2°C. It is possible to use different types of protecting gases. To get as good contact as possible between the sample and the electrodes a lift is placed at the bottom of the furnace.

III. Measurements in Oxide Systems

In certain substitutional solid solutions of oxides, oxygen vacancies appear. Such systems, within specified ranges of temperature, concentration and oxygen partial pressure, exhibit almost pure ionic conduction.

Mainly during the last ten years, the electrical conductivity of mixtures between metal oxides (MgO, CaO, SrO, Sc_2O_3, Y_2O_3 etc. and rare earth oxides) and e.g. Zr_2O, ThO_2 and HfO_2 have been studied in a number of publications. Also a number of other systems have been investigated and new compounds suitable for use as solid electrolytes have been found. Owing to the high defect concentration in the anion lattice, the oxygen ion transport number is nearly unity.

Pure thoria possesses the flourite structure and pure ionic conduction, but in zirconia and hafnia the flourite structure must be stabilized with e.g. 15 mol % CaO or Y_2O_3.

A. Preparation of Samples

The oxide samples can be obtained from different chemical reactions and sintering processes. Very pure materials are commercially available (thorium nitrate 99·999%, yttrium oxide 99·98 etc.) and it is, in some cases, also possible to get commercial samples. The powder can be cold or hot pressed and cylinders obtained are sintered at very high temperatures. The method chosen should give as low porosity as possible and in recent papers porosities from less than 2% up to 20% have been reported.

Systematic investigations of the influence on electrical conductivity by sintering processes, thermal pretreatment and gain sizes have recently been performed by several authors. Carter and Roth (1967), for example, working on calcia stabilized zirconia, have obtained the same results with single crystals and poly-crystallines and the conduction is thus a bulk property for the poly-crystallines with negligible grain boundary migration. Baukal (1969) has reported on ageing processes in zirconia–yttria solid solutions and has also discussed the order–disorder transitions. Similar studies have also been performed in other systems.

B. Electrodes

Platinum or other inert metals have generally been used as electrodes in contact with the oxides. The pellets can be polished with diamond paste to get as smooth a surface as possible and platinum foils are then pressed against the surfaces. Other techniques have also been developed; it is for instance possible to use platinum paint or sputtered platinum electrodes to minimize the contact resistances.

C. Results for Binary Oxide Systems

The results of a number of measurements of the electrical conductivity in a number of oxide solid solutions are given in Table I. We have tabulated the investigated composition and temperature intervals, the sintering temperatures, the results at 800°C or 1000°C, the Arrhenius activation energy Q,

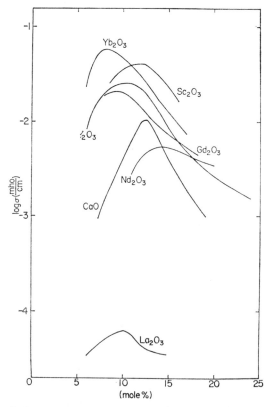

FIG. 4. The electrical conductivity of zirconia stabilized with different oxides at 800°C. Yb_2O_3, Nd_2O_3 and Gd_2O_3: Tannenberger *et al.*, 1966; La_2O_3 and T_2O_3: Stricker and Carlsson, 1965; CaO: Tien and Subbarao 1963; Sc_2O_3: Obshinnikov *et al.*, 1969.

obtained from the relation $\sigma = \sigma_0.\exp(-Q/RT)$, the used atmosphere and also some other information on the measuring technique. For further information we refer to the original papers. Owing to the great differences in measuring techniques and in samples used by different authors we have tried to make the table as complete as possible.

A difference by a factor of ten between results obtained by different authors is not unusual. The differences, however, are caused not only by the porosities, and the contact resistances, but also by the very important differences in the thermal pretreatment of the samples, which probably cause the greatest discrepancies.

Several different oxides can be used to stabilize the flourite phase in zirconia and some selected values of the concentration dependence of the electrical conductivity are given in Fig. 4. The maximal conductivity is obtained at the zirconia rich end of the flourite phase.

Zirconia and hafnia are completely miscible in all proportions (Ruh *et al.*, 1968) and stabilized zirconia and hafnia behave in the same manner, but the conductivity of the zirconia based solid solutions are much higher than those based on hafnia. The electrical conductivity of pure hafnia, however, is at least 100 times lower than for stabilized hafnia.

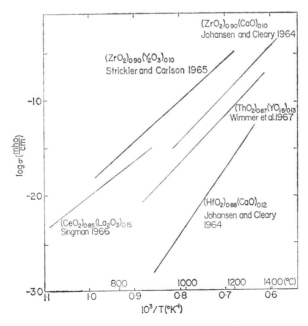

FIG. 5. The temperature dependence of the electrical conductivity of some common oxygen ion conducting solid solutions.

TABLE I. The electrical conductivity of solid ion conducting solids.

Author (only first name)	Ref.	Year	Studied compositions (mol % first component)	Studied temperature interval (°C)	Sintering process	Results at 1000°C				Atmosphere Oxygen partial press in atm.	Remarks
						c (mol %)	$\sigma 10^2$ (mho /cm)	Q (kcal /mol)	Cond. max. (mol %)		
The system ZrO₂–CaO											
Reynolds	60	1902	10	827–1301	—	10	0.96	27	—	air	Cited by Möbius (1966)
Hund	29	1952	15·1	482–1230	5 h 1460°C + 5 h 1500°C	15	0·21	28	—	air	Pt-electrodes, AC
Trombe	86	1953	2–90	1000	—	15	0·4	—	—	air	Whole system
Kingery	33	1959	15	700–1725	7 h 2000°C	15	1·4	29	—	$p_{O_2} > 10^{-10}$	AC 1000 c/s
Carter	10	1960	18	998,1472	H₂ 1900°C/16 h O₂ 1450°C	18	3·3	26	—	$p_{O_2} > 10^{-12}$	—
Volchenkova	89	1961	0–100	300–1000	2 h 1200°C/1 h 1200°C	15	0·28	26	—	air	Cited by Möbius (1966)
Hoffmann	28	1962	14·3–18·0	800–1700	2×4 h 1600°C/3–5 h 1400°C	14·3	14	29	—	O₂, air Ar	—
Cocco	12	1963	12·5–19·5	930–1330	200 h 1330°C/6 h 1730°C	15	2·0	27	—	air	Porosity, electrodes. Cited by Möbius (1966)
Dixon	15	1963	8–24	550–1200	air 1500–1700°C	15	4·0	30	13	air	4 electrodes AC 1–1000 c/s
Tien	84	1963	12–22	500–1400	24 h 1350°C + 2 h 2000°C 1 week 1400°C	15	3·3	27	12	air	Order–disorder transitions
Neuimin	46	1964	15	400–1100	—	15	6·2	30	—	air	Fe₂O₃ and NiO additivities, AC
Johansen	31	1964	8–100	800–2000	1000°C/Ar 1900°C	16	0·63	34	12·5	Ar	comparisons with HfO₂–CaO
Strickler	68	1964	10–18	600–1300	5 h 1350°C + 3 h 1800°C	16	1·6	31	13	air	System CaO–Y₂O₃–ZrO₂

The system ZrO_2–CaO_2

Author	Ref	Year	Comp	Temp range	Heat treatment					Atmosphere	Remarks
Tien	82	1964	16	600–1250	24 h 1350°C + 15 min 1400°C	16	2·9	30	—	air	Sintering processes
					2 h 1600°C	16	2·6	29	—	air	Grain sizes
Subbarao	69	1964	18	600–1200	8 h 2000°C	18	1·4	28	—	air	Order–disorder transitions
					2000°C	18	1·0	30	—	air	—
Tien	83	1964	4–50	500–1400	64 h 1000°C	15	3·4	28	—	air	—
Grap	23	1964	15–21	600–1400	2 h 1350°C + 2 h 1900°C 1 week air 1400°C	15	0·5	26	—	O_2	Sintering process
					1 h air 900°C 1 h 1400°C	15	3·7	29	—	O_2	Cited by Möbius (1966)
Freitag	20	1964	0–30	500–1400	1 h 2000°C	15	2·1	26	—	O_2	Sintering process
					1 h air 1850°C + 40 min H_2 2045°C + 2 h air 1400°C						Cited by Möbius (1966)
Vest	88	1965	15	100–1100	6 h 1900°C	—	—	—	—	—	Polarisation measurements
Kröger	35	1966	—	—	—	—	—	—	—	—	Electronic cond.
Egerskii	17	1966	8–17·5	600–1000	—	15	1·9	—	12·5	—	—
Palguev	55	1966	13–17	500–1300	2 h 1600°C	15	3·6	not linear	—	—	—
Patterson	57	1967	12–21	800–1000	4 h 1100°C + 4 h 1600°C 2 h 1800°C	15	4·3	12	12	O_2	AC 1592 c/s Different oxygen partial pressures Cited by Eysel (1967)
Archer	2	1967	15	660–1300	—	15	1·5	33	—	—	—
Carter	11	1967	9–21	810–1425	2000°C	15	4·0	30	13	O_2, H_2	4 electrodes, DC, AC single cryst, poly-cryst. Cited by Hartung (1969)
Hartung	25	1968	11	300–820	—	11	—	26	—	—	—

TABLE I.—continued

Author (only first name)	Ref.	Year	Studied compositions (mol % first component)	Studied temperature interval (°C)	Sintering process	Results at 1000°C			Cond. max. (mol %)	Atmosphere Oxygen partial press in atm.	Remarks
						c (mol %)	$\sigma 10^2$ (mho /cm)	Q (kcal /mol)			
The system ZrO₂–MgO						*Results at 800°C*					
Palguev	56	1966	13–17	500–1300	2 h 1600°C	15	1·0	not linear	—	air	—
Rohland	61	1967	12–16	650–1400	45 min 1850°C	14	2·1	not linear	—	air	Decomposes, AC 2000 c/s, DC 4 electrodes Cited by Hartung (1969)
Hartung	25	1968	14	300–800	—	14	0·9	31	—	air	Cited by Hartung (1969)
The system ZrO₂–Y₂O₃						*Results at 1000°C*					
Dixon	15	1963	7–30	550–1200	1500–1700°C	10	1·6	20	8	air	AC, 1–1000 c/s 4 electrodes
Archer	2	1963	10	550–1200	—	10	1·3	25	10	—	Cited by Eysel (1967)
Strickler	68	1964	5–35	700–1300	5 h 1350°C + 3 h 1800°C	10	2·1	20	10	—	—
Möbius	42	1964	26–75	600–1400	2050°C	—	—	—	—	O₂ or CO/CO₂	AC 2000 c/s, infl. from atmosphere 2 or 4 electrodes
Strickler	67	1965	6–24	800–1300	2–4 h 1800–2000°C	10	2·8	20	10	air	
Rohland	61	1965	8–11	600–1300	45 min 1850°C	10	2·9	18	8	air	AC 20000 c/s, DC, 4 electrodes
Hartung	25	1968	10	300–800	—	10	1·9	26	—	—	Cited by Hartung (1969)
Baukal	6	1969	9	800	Commercial	—	—	—	—	H₂, air	Aging, AC different frequencies

	ref	year	mol%	temp. range	heat treatment	Results				atmosphere	notes
The system ZrO_2–Sc_2O_3						*Results at 1000°C*					
Dixon	15	1963	10–15	600–1150	Several h 1400°C	15	0·56	not linear	—	air	AC, 1–1000 c/s 4 electrodes
Strickler	67	1965	6–24	800–1300	2–4 h 1800–2000°C	12	21	18	12	air	2 or 4 electrodes
Möbius	43	1965	8–43	600–1400	—	8	1·2	not linear	—	O_2	AC, influence from atmosphere
Obshinnikov	51	1969	8–16	500–1000	5 h 1600°C + 2 h 1500°C	10	16	20	12	—	—
The system ZrO_2–Nd_2O_3						*Results at 800°C*					
Dixon	15	1963	10	600–1150	several h 1700°C	10	0·10	24	—	air	4 electrodes AC 1–1000 c/s
Neuimin	49	1964	28–30	300–1100	—	23	0·028	25	—	—	—
Tannenberger	79	1966	12–20	400–800	6 h 1900°C + 3 h 1000°C	14	0·56	27	14	Ar	—
Guillou	24	1967	2–19	700–1400	8 h 1000°C + 48 h 1550°C	14·6	0·22	25	—	O_2	DC 4 electrodes
						14·6	0·18	26	—	Ar	
The system ZrO_2–Sm_2O_3						*Results at 800°C*					
Strickler	67	1965	6–24	800–1300	2–4 h 1800–2000°C	10	1·1	22	10	air	2 or 4 electrodes
The system ZrO_2–Gd_2O_3						*Results at 800°C*					
Tannenberger	79	1966	8–16	400–850	6 h 1900°C + 3 h 1000°C	8	2·0	23	8	Ar	—
The system ZrO_2–Yb_2O_3						*Results at 800°C*					
Dixon	15	1963	9,15	600–1150	several h 1700°C	9	2·5	not linear	—	air	4 electrodes
Strickler	67	1965	6–24	800–1300	2–4 h 1800–2000°C	8	2·5	17	10+	air	+ at 800°C, increases with the temperature
Siegert	63	1965	10	650–820	1900°C	10	2·9	23	—	O_2	—

TABLE I.—continued

Author (only first name) Ref. Year	Studied compositions (mol %) first component	Studied temperature interval (°C)	Sintering process	Results at 1000°C			Cond. max. (mol %)	Atmosphere Oxygen partial press in atm	Remarks
				c (mol %)	$\sigma 10^2$ (mho /cm)	Q (kcal /mol)			
The system ZrO_2–Yb_2O_3				*Results at 800°C*					
Tannenberger 79 1966	6–20	400–850	6 h 1900°C + 3 h 1000°C	8	6·0	30+	8++	Ar	+below 700°C, ++ between 400 and 850°C
Tannenberger 80 1969	10	650–820	1900°C	10	2·9	23	—	O_2	—
The system ZrO_2–Lu_2O_3				*Results at 800°C*					
Möbius 43 1965	8–38	600–1400	—	8	1·0	not linear	—	O_2	AC
The system HfO_2–CaO				*Results at 1000°C*					
Johansen 31 1964	0–80	800–2000	Ar 1900°C	12	0·38	31	12·5	Ar	Comparisons with ZrO_2–CaO
Volchenkova 90 1964	0–100	500 1000	2 h 1500°C	15	0·19	32	15	—	—
The system HfO_2–MgO				*Results at 800°C*					
Volchenkova 90 1964	0–100	500–1000	2 h 1500°C	15	0·036	34	—	—	—
The system HfO_2–Y_2O_3				*Results at 1000°C*					
Besson 7 1966	2–40	900–1600	4 h 1800°C	8	2·9	26	8	—	AC, 10000 c/s
Pure ThO_2				*Results at 1000°C*					
Hund 30 1952	—	900–1350	5 h 1500°C + several h 1200°C	—	5·5 10^{-5}	30	—	air	—

	Ref.	Year				Results				Atmosphere	Pressure dependence
Rudolph	62	1959	—	850–1500	1500–1600°C	—	—	—	—	inert gas $+O_2$	Pressure dependence
Bauerle	5	1966	—	1000	3 h 2200°C or 2 h 2200–2800°C	—	—	—	—	—	Pressure dependence sintering process
Lasker	39	1966	—	800–1100	2·5 h 2100°C (vac.) + 5 h 1400°C (air)	—	0·056	—	—	different p_{O_2}	AC 1592 c/s, press. dependence
The system ThO_2–CaO											
Alcock	1	1965	15	700–1000	3 h 2000°C (vac) + 8 h 1400°C (air)	15	0·092	26	—	air	AC 1500 c/s
Steele	65	1965	0–15	1000	2000°C (vac.)	15	0·092	—	6	inert gas $+O_2$	AC, p_{O_2} = 1 atm.
The system $YO_{1·5}$–CaO						*Results at 1000°C*					
Steele	66	1968	3	700–1100	vac. 1900–2000°C	3	0·23$^+$	33$^+$	—	inert gas $+O_2$	$^+p_{O_2}$ = 10^{-15} atm, AC
The system CeO_2–BeO						*Results at 800°C*					
Palguev	54	1961	0–100	500–1000	1 h 1550°C	15	0·060	46$^+$	17	—	$^+$below 750°C
The system CeO_2–MgO						*Results at 800°C*					
Palguev	54	1961	0–100	500–1000	1 h 1550°C	15	0·68	30$^+$	18	—	$^+$above 700°C
The system CeO_2–CaO						*Results at 800°C*					
Palguev	54	1961	0–100	500–1000	1 h 1550°C	15	0·60	35$^+$	12·5	—	$^+$above 700°C
The system CeO_2–SrO						*Results at 800°C*					
Palguev	54	1961	0–100	500–1000	1 h 1550°C	15	1·4	28$^+$	18	—	$^+$above 600°C
The system CeO_2–BaO						*Results at 800°C*					
Palguev	54	1961	0–100	500–1000	1 h 1550°C	10	0·15	28$^+$	10	—	$^+$above 600°C

TABLE I. The electrical conductivity of solid ion conducting solids.

Author (only first name)	Ref.	Year	Studied compositions (mol %) first component	Studied temperature interval (°C)	Sintering process	c (mol %)	σ10² (mho /cm)	Q (kcal /mol)	Cond. max. (mol %)	Atmosphere Oxygen partial press. in atm.	Remarks
The system CeO₂–YO₁.₅						*Results at 800°C*					
Neumin	47	1964	0–100	400–1100	—	10	1·3	not linear	10	—	—
The system ThO₂–YO₁.₁						*Results at 1000°C*					
Hund	30	1952	15,36	700–1300	5 h 1500°C + several h 1200°C	15	3·2 / 10^{-3}	28	—	air	AC
Alcock	1	1965	25	700–1000	3 h 1200°C (vac.)+ 8 h 1400°C (air)	25	0·24	25	—	air	AC 1500 c/s
Steele	65	1965	1–25	1000	2000°C	15	0·22⁺	—	12	inert gas + O₂	⁺$p_{O_2}=10^{-13}$, AC
Subbarao	70	1965	0–5	500–1400	O₂ 1400–2200°C	5	3·2	26⁺	—	air	⁺$\sigma T = \sigma T \exp(-Q/RT)$
Bauerle	5	1966	1,5,10	1000	3 h 2200°C	10	1·3⁺	—	—	—	⁺$p_{O_2}=10^{-13}$ atm, different atmospheres
Lasker	39	1966	0–25	800–1100	2·5 h 2100°C (vac.)+ 5 h 1400°C	6	0·36⁺	—	14	—	⁺$p_{O_2}=10^{-10}$ atm, AC
Wimmer	91	1967	13	900–1600	vacuum 2000°C	13	2·5	26	—	CO + CO₂	AC or DC
The system ThO₂–LaO₁.₅						*Results at 1000°C*					
Steele	65	1965	10–15	1000	2000°C	15	0·24⁺	—	—	inert gas + O₂	⁺$p_{O_2}=10^{-13}$ atm, AC
The system La₂O₃–CaO						*Results at 1000°C*					
Palguev	54	1966	0–100	500–1000	3 h 1380°C	15	0·75	18	18	—	—
Etsell	18	1969	1–25	600–1100	3 h 1900°C (air) or 1500°C (vacuum)	15	0·56	20	17·5	—	AC 3000 c/s, pressure dependence

The system $SmO_{1.5}$–CaO

	Ref	Year				Results at 1000°C					
Steele	66	1968	3	700–1100	vac. 1900–2000°C	3	1·3+	20+	—	inert gas + O_2	+po_2 = 10^{-15} atm, AC

The system $ScO_{1.5}$–CaO

	Ref	Year				Results at 1000°C					
Steele	66	1968	3	700–1100	vac. 1900–2000°C	3	0·093+	33+	—	inert gas + O_2	+po_2 = 10^{-15} atm, AC

The system CeO_2–$LaO_{1.5}$

	Ref	Year				Results at 800°C					
Croatto	14	1953	26	500–1300	—	26	1·9	15	—	air	—
Neuimin	45	1961	0–100	400–1000	—	16	2·4	15	16	—	—
Takahashi	77	1965	0–100	400–1200	20 h 1600	20	22	—	20	air	AC
Singman	64	1966	26	550–900	several h 1000°C	26	1·9	21	—	—	—

The system CeO_2–$NdO_{1.5}$

	Ref	Year				Results at 1000°C					
Neuimin	45	1961	0–100	400–1100	—	26	2·2	not linear	26	—	—

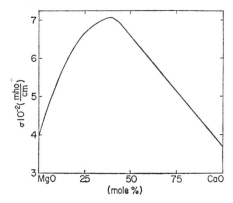

FIG. 6. The electrical conductivity of 85 mol% ZrO_2 + 15 mol% $(Mg_xCa_y)0$ at 1000°C according to Palguev *et al.*, 1966.

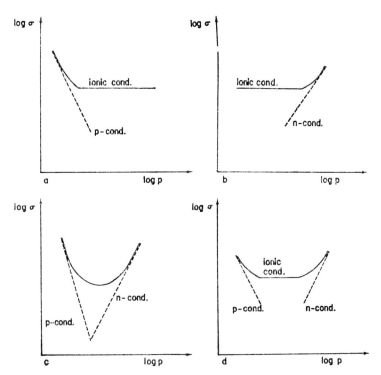

FIG. 7. Different types of oxygen partial pressure dependence of the electrical conductivity for solid oxides.

TABLE II. Different electrodes used for measurements of the oxygen partial pressure dependence of the electrical conductivity of oxygen ion conducting electrolytes (Pattersson et al., 1967).

Electrode	$-\log p_{O_2}$	
	1000°C	800°C
Cu, CuO	0·9	2·9
Cu, Cu_2O	6·3	8·8
Ni, NiO	10·3	13·9
Co, CoO	12·0	15·1
Fe, FeO	14·9	18·9
Cr, Cr_2O_3	21·8	27·5
Nb, NbO	25·1	31·5
V, VO	26·4	32·9
Ti, TiO	34·8	42·8

TABLE III. The electrical conductivity of some pure oxygen ion conductors and mixed conductors. For the pure oxygen ion conductors, Q and σ_0 are independent of the pressure (Steele et al., 1968).

Composition	Q (kcal/mol)			σ_0 (mho/cm)		
	1 atm	10^{-6} atm	10^{-15} atm	1 atm	10^{-6} atm	10^{-15} atm
$Zr_{0.852} Sc_{0.148} O_{1.926}$	15·2	15·2	15·2	210	210	210
$Zr_{0.852} Y_{0.148} O_{1.926}$	17·0	17·0	17·0	86	86	86
$Zr_{0.855} Ti_{0.054} Y_{0.091} O_{1.954}$	17·3	16·8	16·8	9·8	8·0	8·0
$Zr_{0.818} Ti_{0.091} Y_{0.091} O_{1.954}$	20·9	20·5	20·5	14·1	10·5	20·0
$Zr_{0.727} Ti_{0.182} Y_{0.091} O_{1.954}$	22·9	22·1	24·2	7·1	4·3	18·0
$Zr_{0.5} Sm_{0.5} O_{1.75}$	32·5	37·0	32·8	381	1130	190
$Zr_{0.43} Sm_{0.57} O_{1.715}$	25·0	25·3	20·4	34	27·5	40·0
$Sc_{0.97} Ca_{0.03} O_{1.485}$	39·1	35·7	33·5	4110	191	50·2
$Y_{0.97} Ca_{0.03} O_{1.485}$	37·5	33·2	33·5	1350	110	145
$Sm_{0.97} Ca_{0.03} O_{1.485}$	21·4	23·3	20·5	10·3	3·3	0·47
$LaAl_{0.94} Mg_{0.06} O_{2.970}$	16	22	28	1·2	1·9	11·6
$SrZr_{0.94} Mg_{0.06} O_{2.970}$	20	18	16	2·3	0·2	0·07
$Ce_{0.45} Zr_{0.45} Sc_{0.1} O_{1.95}$	22	23	5	26	110	0·1
$Ce_{0.40} Zr_{0.40} Sc_{0.2} O_{1.90}$	27	32	9	44	1130	0·08

Figure 5 shows the temperature dependence of the electrical conductivity of some common oxide electrolytes. The lowest resistivity is obtained with the zirconia based solid solutions.

TABLE IV.   The cell resistances for some battery constructions. From G. R. Argue, I. J. Groce and B. Owens, "Solid State Batteries", presented at the Sixth international Power Sources Symposium, Brighton 1968.

System	Cell voltage (V)	Cell resistance (ohm)
$Ag/AgBr/CuBr_2$	0·7	4×10^7
$Ni–Cr/SnSO_4/PbO_2$	1·5	2×10^6
$Ag/AgI/V_2O_5$	0·4	4×10^5
$Ag/AgBr–Te/CuBr_2$	0·8	—
$Ag/AgCl/KICl_4$	1·0	5×10^4
$Ag/Ag_3SI/I_2$	0·7	4

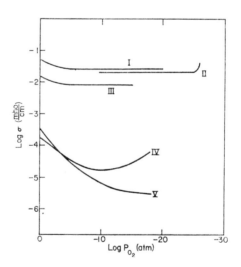

FIG. 8. The pressure dependence of the specific electrical conductivity for some oxides and oxide solid solutions at 1000°C.
  I. $(La_2O_3)_{0.85} (CaO)_{0.15}$ (Etsell and Flengas, 1969).
  II. $(ZrO_2)_{0.85} (CaO)_{0.15}$ (Patterson et al., 1967).
  III. $(ThO_2)_{0.95} (YO_{1.5})_{0.05}$ (Bauerle, 1966).
  IV. ThO_2 (Steele and Alcock, 1965).
  V. HfO_2 (Tallan et al., 1967).

It should be observed that the values given in Table I and Figs 4–5 have mainly been obtained from graphs in the cited papers, which might have caused small additional errors.

MgO, Al_2O_3 and mullite, which are all mixed conductors, have recently been used as solid electrolytes. A summary of conductivity measurements in Al_2O_3 has been given by Davies (1965), and Mitoff (1962) has reported on conductivity measurements in MgO. A number of other pure oxides have been studied by Noddack *et al.* (1959).

Measurements of the electrical conductivity of a number of other oxide mixtures have also been reported in the literature. Neuimin *et al.* (1964c) have for instance found that $(BiO_3)_{0\cdot8}(SrO_2)_{0\cdot2}$ exhibits about 50% ionic conduction. It should also be observed that the systems ZrO_2–La_2O_3 and ZrO_2–CeO_2 are semiconductors.

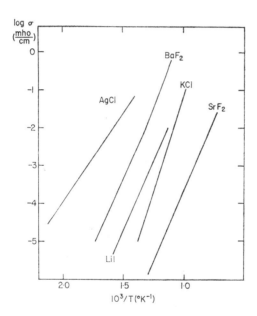

FIG. 9. The electrical conductivity of some pure ionic crystals. Refs: AgCl: Ebert and Teltow, 1955; BaF_2: Barsis and Taylor, 1968; LiI: Haven, 1950; KCl: Fuller *et al.*, 1968; SrF_2: Barsis and Taylor, 1966.

D. Ternary Oxide Systems

To minimize the electrical resistivity and to get as good mechanical properties as possible some ternary oxide systems have also been studied. Strickler and Carlsson (1964) measured the electrical conductivity of the system ZrO_2–

Y_2O_3–CaO, Eysel (1967) of ZrO_2–Yb_2O_3–Y_2O_3, Steele *et al.* (1968) have studied some mixtures with different structures and Rohland and Möbius (1968) have reported on conductivity measurements in ZrO_2–Y_2O_3–MgO.

Figure 6 shows the electrical conductivity of $(ZrO_2)_{0.85}(MgO)_x(CaO)_{1-x}$. It is seen that in this system it is possible to increase the conductivity by a factor of two compared with the pure binary solid solutions.

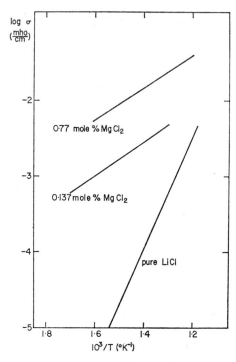

FIG. 10. The electrical conductivity of pure LiCl and LiCl with small quantities of $MgCl_2$.

E. Different Oxygen Partial Pressures

The energy gap between the valence band and the conduction band is very different for different oxide systems. The electrical current might therefore be transported either by positive holes (*p*-type conduction), electrons (*n*-type conduction) or ions.

The total conductivity can be written as the sum of these three partial conductivities.

$$\sigma_{tot} = \sigma_p + \sigma_n + \sigma_i, \tag{1.1}$$

where σ_p = the electrical conductivity due to holes

σ_n = the electrical conductivity due to electrons

σ_i = the electrical conductivity due to ions.

The transport mechanism for an oxide system is a function both of the temperature and the oxygen partial pressure and measurements have been performed from 1 atm down to 10^{-40} atm. To obtain these very low and well specified oxygen partial pressures special electrodes must be used. Table II shows the electrodes used by Patterson et al. (1967). To obtain the correct atmosphere in the furnace, it was filled with He, which first passed a combustion boat filled with the two-phase electrode mixture placed immediately upstream from the cell.

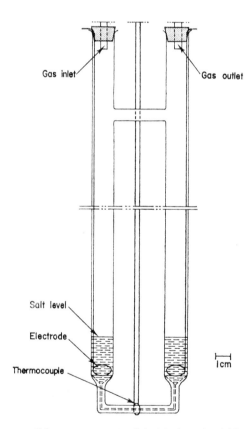

FIG. 11. A pure quartz cell for measurements of electrical conductivities of solid and molten salts.

For a mathematical description of the partial pressure dependence of the electrical conductivity eqn. (1.1) can be rewritten

$$\sigma = \sigma_{ion} = k_1 p_{O_2}^{-1/4} + k_2 p_{O_2}^{+1/4},$$

where k_1 and k_2 are constants.

A pressure dependence of the total conductivity should appear if there is any appreciable contribution due to semiconduction.

Four different pressure dependences are possible (Fig. 7). Type a has been found for thoria based solutions, type b for example stabilized zirconia, type c is general for pure oxygen and type d has been found for pure La_2O_3.

Figure 8 shows the results obtained for some pure oxides and oxide solid solutions. Further information on investigations of partial pressure dependences can be obtained from Table I.

A great number of oxides are probably pure oxygen conductors within limited temperature and concentration intervals, but relatively little has been done until now in this field. Steele et $al.$ (1968) have, however, reported on measurements in a number of solid solutions with the pyrochore and perovskite structures (Table III).

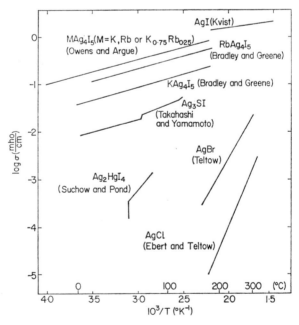

FIG. 12. The electrical conductivity of some ionic salts forming high temperature phases. Ref. Kvist, 1967; Kvist and Josefson, 1968; Josefson and Kvist, 1969.

A complete investigation of the electrical conductivity of a solid oxide system thus includes not only the concentration and temperature dependence, but also the dependence on the oxygen partial pressure.

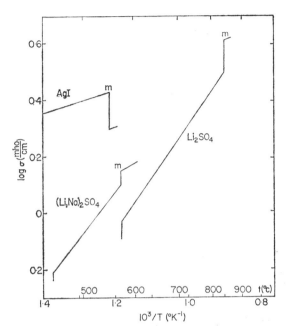

FIG. 13. The electrical conductivity of some salts forming high conducting cubic high temperature phases.

IV. Measurements in Ion Conducting Salts

Many ion conducting salts have been used as solid electrolytes during the last fifty years. Friauf *et al.*, in the American Institute of Physics Handbook 1963, have compiled the electrical conductivities for a great number of ionic crystals and we will therefore only discuss results for a few groups of salts, which have particular interest as solid electrolytes.

Most pure ionic salts have very low conductivities at room temperature and this has to a great extent limited the use of ionic salts as solid electrolytes. Figure 9 shows the electrical conductivity of some pure salts, which show conductivities that are normal for crystals.

It is, however, well known that it is possible to increase the electrical conductivity of a crystal appreciably by adding small quantities of, for instance, divalent ions to a univalent salt. Figure 10 shows the electrical conductivity of pure LiCl and LiCl doped with small quantities of $MgCl_2$.

The conductivity of $LiCl + 0.77 \, mol \% \, MgCl_2$ is almost a factor of 10^3 higher than for the pure salt. Similar effects can be found for other crystals and for instance Toshima *et al.* (1968) have recently reported that it is possible to increase the electrical conductivity of $PbCl_2$ 10-fold by addition of a small amount of KCl.

The experimental methods are mainly the same as for the measurements in the oxides and both DC and AC measurements have been used with reversible or irreversible electrodes. We shall discuss here only some additional experimental problems and possibilities.

Platinum or silver foil electrodes generally give good contact with the samples, but Owens and Argue (1967) have reported for $RbAg_4I_5$ and KAg_4I_5 that flat silver electrodes, evaporated silver contacts and amalgamed silver electrodes gave a very high contact resistance. They succeeded, however, in reducing the resistance by mixing the electrolyte with powdered silver. The conductivity values obtained are much higher than those reported by Bradley and Greene (1967), who used Pt electrodes in direct contact with the samples. It is worth noting that such difficulties have not been reported for other similar salts.

Many salts have low melting temperatures and are also thermally stable upon melting. In such cases very accurate results can be obtained by first melting the salt and then letting it solidify in a glass or ceramic cell. An example of such cell is given in Fig. 11. This cell has been used by the author

TABLE V. The electrical conductivity of some silver conducting salts. Some of the values have been obtained from Takahashi (1968).

Salt	σ (25°C) (mho/cm)	Q (kcal/mol)	Structure	Ref.
$RbAg_4I_5$	2.4×10^{-1}	—	cub.	53
KAg_4I_5	2.4×10^{-1}	—	cub.	53
$(AgI)_{0.55} (Ag_2S)_{0.30} (HgI_2)_{0.15}$	7×10^{-2}	3.2	b.c.c.	72
$(Ag_2 Se)_2 (HgI_2)$	2×10^{-2}	3.5	b.c.c.	76
$Ag_3 SI$	1×10^{-2}	3.3	simp. cub.	58, 59, 73
$(Ag_2 S)_{0.7} (AgI_2)_{0.3}$	3×10^{-3}	—	—	76
$Ag_3 SBr$	2×10^{-3}	5.5	hex.	58, 59
AgI	2×10^{-6}	15.7	orthorhomb.	40
$Ag_2 HgI_4$	1.5×10^{-6}	16	tetra.	75, 52
$Cu_2 HgI_4$	7.6×10^{-8}	9	—	52
$AgCl$	3×10^{-8}	8	f.c.c.	13
$AgBr$	4×10^{-9}	7	f.c.c.	41

and co-workers for measurements of electrical conductivities in different sulphate systems and in silver iodide. If two electrodes are placed in each arm of the cell it is also possible to use the four electrodes DC technique.

Ionic salts have often been used as electrolytes in solid state batteries, but for the construction of batteries it is often important to get low internal cell resistance of the cells. Table IV shows typical resistance values for some battery constructions.

The discovery that $RbAg_4I_5$ (1967) and related compounds can be used as solid electrolytes has in recent years stimulated interest in solid-state batteries and a number of ionic salts have been tried.

Figure 12 shows the electrical conductivity of some silver ion-conducting solid electrolytes. Only a few salts have a conductivity above 10^{-3} mho/cm at room temperature (Table V). The high-conducting salts form cubic lattices, which are built up by the anions, and there are then more cation positions than cations in the lattice. Similar phases can be found in Li_2SO_4, $(Li,Ag)_2$ SO_4 and $(Li,Na)_2SO_4$. Li_2SO_4 forms a f.c.c. high temperature modification, while the other two compounds have b.c.c. phases. These phases are, however, stable only at high temperatures (Fig. 13). A discussion of the transport mechanism and structure of the b.c.c. high temperature phases has recently been performed by Krogh-Moe (1966).

V. Measurements in Other Systems

Some aluminates have also been found useful as solid electrolytes, but very little has been published on the electrical conductivity of these materials. Kummer and Weber (1967) have, however, reported conductivity results for beta-alumina, $Na_2O . 11 Al_2O_3$. This conductivity is shown in Fig. 14.

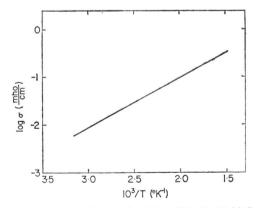

FIG. 14. The electrical conductivity of $Na_2O . 11 Al_2O_3$.

References

REVIEWS AND SUMMARIES

Friauf, R. J., Morgan, S. O. and Merz, W. J. (1963). American Institute of Physics Handbook p. 63. McGraw-Hill, New York.

Jakes, D. (1969). *Chem. Listy* **63,** 1073.

Jost, W. (1960). "Diffusion in Solids, Liquids and Gases". Academic Press, New York.

Kummer, J. and Milberg, M. (1969). *Chem. Eng. News* **47,** 90.

Lidiard, R. J. (1957). "Handbook der Physik". **20,** 246. Springer Verlag, Berlin.

Möbius, H. H. (1966). *Silikattechnik* **17,** 358.

Shewmon, P. G. (1963). "Diffusion in Solids". McGraw-Hill, New York.

Steele, B. (1968). "Electromotive Force Measurements in High Temperature Systems", p. 3. IMM, London.

Takahashi, T. (1968). Denki Kagaku **36,** 402.

GENERAL REFERENCES

1. Alcock, C. B. and Steele, B. C. H. (1965). "Science of Ceramics", **2,** 397. Academic Press Inc., New York and London.
2. Archer, D. A. (1962). Astia reports Nos. 283434 and 292064. Gmeling Institut.
3. Barsis, E. and Taylor, A. (1966). *J. chem. Phys.* **45,** 1154.
4. Barsis, E. and Taylor, A. (1968). *J. chem. Phys.* **48,** 4357.
5. Bauerle, J. E. (1966). *J. chem. Phys.* **45,** 4162.
6. Baukal, W. (1969). *Electrochim. Acta* **14,** 1071.
7. Besson, J., Deportes, C. and Robert, G. (1966). C.R. Acad. Sci. Paris **C262,** 527.
8. Bradley, J. N. and Greene, P. D. (1966). *Trans. Faraday Soc.* **62,** 2069.
9. Bradley, J. N. and Greene, P. D. (1967). *Trans. Faraday Soc.* **63,** 424.
10. Carter, R. E. (1960). *J. Am. Ceram. Soc.* **43,** 448.
11. Carter, R. E. and Roth, W. L. (1967). *Proc. Nuffield Research Group,* p. 125. Imperial College, London.
12. Cocco, A. and Barbiol, I. (1963). *Univ. Trieste, Inst. chim. appl.* Nos. 14, 15, 17.
13. Compton, D. and Maurer, R. (1956). *Physics Chem. Solids* **1,** 191.
14. Croatto, V. and Bruno, M. (1948). *Gazz. chim. ital.* **78,** 95.
14a. Davies, M. O. (1965). NASA Technical Note, NASA TN D-2765.
15. Dixon, J. M., LaGrange, L. D., Merten, U., Miller, C. F. and Porter, J. T. (1963). *J. Electrochem. Soc.* **110,** 276.
16. Ebert, I. and Teltow, J. (1955). *Annln. Phys.* **15,** 268.
17. Egerskij, M. L. *et al.* (1966). *Izv. Akad. Nauk SSSR* **2,** 1811.
18. Etsell, T. H. and Flengas, S. N. (1969). *J. electrochem. Soc.* **116,** 771.
19. Eysel, H. H. (1967). *B.B.C. Nachr.* p. 532.
20. Freitag, U. (1960–63). Unpublished. Cited by Möbius.
21. Friauf, R. J. *et al.* (1963). American Institute of Physics Handbook (D. E. Gray, ed.), New York.
22. Fuller, R., Reilly, M., Marquardt, C. and Wells, J. (1968). *Phys. Rev. Letters* **20,** 662.
23. Grap, S. (1964). Thesis, Griefswald.
24. Guillou, M., Millet, J., Asquedge, M., Busson, N., Jacquin, M., Palous, S., Pithon, M. and Lecante, A. (1967). *Rev. Int. hautes Temp. Réfract.* **4,** 273.

25. Hartung, R. (1968). Thesis, Greifswald.
26. Hartung, R. and Möbius, H. H. (1969). *Z. Chem.* **9**, 197.
27. Haven, Y. (1950). Recueil **69**, 1471.
28. Hoffmann, A. and Fischer, W. (1962). *Z. phys. Chem.* **35**, 95.
29. Hund, F. (1952). *Z. phys. Chem.* **199**, 142.
30. Hund, F. and Mezger, F. (1952). *Z. phys. Chem.* **201**, 268.
31. Johansen, H. A. and Cleary, J. G. (1964). *J. electrochem. Soc.* **111**, 100.
32. Josefson, A. M. and Kvist, A. (1969). *Z. Naturf.* **24a**, 466.
33. Kingery, W. D., Pappis, J., Doty, M. E. and Hill, D. C. (1959). *J. Am. Ceram. Soc.* **42**, 393.
34. Krogh-Moe, J. (1966). "Selected Topics in High Temperature Chemistry". p. 79. Oslo.
35. Kröger, F. A. (1966). *J. Am. Ceram. Soc.* **49**, 215.
35a. Kummer, J. T. and Weber, N. Automotive Eng. Congress 1967.
36. Kvist, A. (1966). *Z. Naturf.* **21a**, 487.
37. Kvist, A. (1967). *Z. Naturf.* **22a**, 208.
38. Kvist, A. and Josefson, A.-M. (1968). *Z. Naturf.* **23a**, 625.
39. Lasker, M. F. and Rapp, R. A. (1966). *Z. phys. Chem.* **49**, 198.
40. Lieser, K. H. (1956). *Z. phys. Chem.* **9**, 302.
41. Miller, A. and Maurer, R. (1958). *Physics Chem. Solids* **4**, 196.
41a. Mitoff, S. P. (1962). *J. chem. Phys.* **36**, 1383.
42. Möbius, H. H. (1966). *Silikattechnik* **17**, 358.
43. Möbius, H. H. and Pröve G. (1965). *Z. Chem.* **5**, 431.
44. Möbius, H. H., Witzmann, H. and Pröve, G. (1964). *Z. Chemie* **4**, 195.
45. Neuimin, A. D. and Palguev, S. F. (1961). *Akad. Nauk SSSR, Uralsk filial* **2**, 185.
46. Neuimin, A. D. and Palguev, S. F. (1964). *Akad. Nauk SSSR, Uralsk filial* **5**, 145.
47. Neuimin, A. D., Palguev, S. F. and Chebotin, V. N. (1964b). *Trans. Electrochem. Soc. Sci., Ural. Filial* (Engl. transl.) **2**, 79.
48. Neuimin, A. D., Palguev, S. F., Strekalovskii, V. N. and Burov, G. V. (1964a). *Trans. Electrochem Soc. Sci., Ural. Filial* (Engl. transl.) **2**, 66.
49. Neuimin, A. D., Yushina, L. D., Obshinnikov, Yu. M. and Palguev, S. F. (1964c). *Trans. Electrochem. Soc. Sci., Ural. Filial* (Engl. transl.) **2**, 92.
50. Noddack, W. and Walch, H. (1959). *Z. Elektrochem.* **63**, 269.
50a. Noddack, W., Walch, H. and Dobner, W. (1959). *Z. phys. Chem.* **211**, 180.
51. Obshinnikov, M., Neuimin, A. D., Palguev, S. F. and Linilin, A. S. (1969). *Elektrochimija* **5**, 1224.
52. Owens, B. B. (1969). The Sixth International Power Sources Symposium, Brighton.
53. Owens, B. B. and Argue, G. R. (1967). *Science* **157**, 308.
54. Palguev, S. F. and Volchenkova, S. (1961). *Akad. Nauk SSSR, Uralsk Filial* **2**, 157.
55. Palguev, S. F. and Volchenkova, S. (1966). *Akad. Nauk SSSR, Uralsk Filial* **9**, 133.
56. Palguev, S. F., Neuimin, A. D. and Strekalovskii, V. N. (1966). *Akad. Nauk SSSR, Uralsk Filial* **9**, 149.
57. Patterson, J. W., Bogren, E. C. and Rapp, R. A. (1967). *J. electrochem. Soc.* **114**, 752.
58. Reuter, B. and Hardel, K. (1961). *Naturwiss.* **48**, 161.
59. Reuter, B. and Hardel, K. (1966). *Z. Electrochem.* **70**, 82.
60. Reynolds, H. (1902). Thesis, Göttingen.

61. Rohland, B. and Möbius, H. H. (1968). *Abh. sachs, Akad. Wiss.* **49**, 355.
62. Rudolph, J. (1959). *Z. Naturf.* **14a**, 727.
62a. Ruh, R., Gerrett, H. J., Domagala, R. F. and Tallan, N. M. (1968). *J. Am. Ceram. Soc.* **51**, 23.
63. Siegert, H. and Tannenberger, H. (1963). 2es Journées Internationales d'Etude des Piles à combustible.
64. Singman, D. (1966). *J. electrochem. Soc.* **113**, 502.
65. Steele, B. and Alcock, C. (1965). *Trans. AIME* **233**, 1359.
66. Steele, B., Powell, B. and Moody, P. (1968). *Proc. Br. Ceram. Soc.* **10**, 87.
67. Strickler, D. W. and Carlsson, W. G. (1965). *J. Am. Ceram. Soc.* **48**, 286.
68. Strickler, D. W. and Carlsson, W. G. (1964). *J. Am. Ceram. Soc.* **47**, 122.
69. Subbarao, E. C. and Sutter, P. H. (1964). *Physics Chem. Solids.* **25**, 148.
70. Subbarao, E. C., Sutter, P. H. and Hrizo, J. (1965). *J. Am. Ceram. Soc.* **48**, 443.
71. Suchow, L. and Pond, G. R. (1953). *J. Am. Chem. Soc.* **75**, 5242.
72. Takahashi, T. and Yamamoto, O. (1966). *J. electrochem. Soc. Japan* **34**, 121.
73. Takahashi, T. and Yamamoto, O. (1964). *Denki Kagaku* **32**, 610.
74. Takahashi, T. and Yamamoto, O. (1965a). *Denki Kagaku* **33**, 346.
75. Takahashi, T. and Yamamoto, O. (1965b). *Denki Kagaku* **33**, 733.
76. Takahashi, T. Yamamoto, O. and Kuwabara, K. (1967). *Denki Kagaku* **35**, 264.
77. Takahashi, T., Kaname, I. and Iwahara, H. (1965). Journées Internationales d'Etude des Piles à Combustible.
78. Tallan, N. M., Tripp, W. C. and Vest, R. W. (1967). *J. Am. Chem. Soc.* **50**, 279.
79. Tannenberger, H. and Siegert, H. (1969). *Avd. Chem.* **90**, 281.
80. Tannenberger, H., Schachner, H. and Kovacs, P. (1966). *EPE* **2**, 1.
81. Teltow, J. (1949). *Annln. Phys.* **5**, 63.
82. Tien, T. Y. (1964). *J. appl. Phys.* **35**, 122.
83. Tien, T. Y. (1964). *J. Am. Ceram. Soc.* **47**, 430.
84. Tien, T. Y. and Subbarao, E. C. (1963). *J. chem. Phys.* **39**, 1041.
85. Toshima, T. *et al.* (1968). *Denki Kagaku* **36**, 69.
86. Trombe, F. and Foex, M. (1953). *C. R. Acad. Sci. Paris* **236**, 1783.
87. Vest, R. W. and Tallan, N. M. (1965). *J. appl. Phys.* **36**, 543.
88. Vest, R. W., Tallan, N. M. and Tripp, W. C. (1964). *J. Am. Ceram. Soc.* **47**, 635.
89. Volchenkova, S. and Palguev, S. F. (1961). *Akad. Nauk SSSR, Uralsk Filial* **2**, 173.
90. Volchenkova, S. and Palguev, S. F. (1964). *Akad. nauk SSSR, Uralsk Filial* **5**, 133.
91. Wimmer, J. M., Bidwell, L. R. and Tallan, N. M. (1967). *J. Am. Ceram. Soc.* **50**, 198.

9. THE IONIC CONDUCTIVITY OF WHISKERS

E. Hartmann

Technical University, Budapest, Hungary

Whiskers are single crystals one dimension of which is much larger than the other two; they are usually a few microns thick. The physical properties of the whiskers are in many respects quite different from those of the bulk single crystals. Their mechanical strength for example is from ten to one hundred times greater than the strength of the large crystals, and in some cases approaches the value calculated theoretically for ideal single crystals (Gyulai, 1954; Coleman, 1964; Bereskhova, 1969).

The electrical properties of metal and semiconductor whiskers are very often also dissimilar to those of bulk single crystals of the same material. This can be explained by the structural perfection of the whiskers as well as by the greater effect of their relatively large surfaces. The results in this field are briefly summarized in the monograph of Bereskhova (1969).

Only a few research workers have investigated the electrical conductivity of ionic whiskers, mainly as a result of experimental difficulties. Dawood and Forty (1962) first measured the ionic conductivity of a sodium chloride whisker which was only a few microns thick. The sample was carefully pressed, by means of two nickel plates, on to a Teflon block, the nickel plates serving as electrodes. The resistance of the insulating Teflon block was by several orders of magnitude larger than that of the whisker. The electrode assembly was connected in series with the input resistance of a vibrating-reed electrometer across a stable d.c. source. The measurements were carried out within the temperature range of 130°C–350°C. It was found that the conductivity values on heating corresponded to the values obtained at cooling. The activation enthalpy as determined from the experiment was 20,240 cal/mol (0·88 eV), which according to the authors is an excellent agreement with the value of 20,500 cal/mol (0·89 eV) obtained with bulk single crystals in 1933.

It should be noted however that various authors obtained rather different activation enthalpies for sodium chloride bulk single crystals in the extrinsic temperature ranges (the values, summarised in tables, are presented in articles by Süptitz and Teltow, 1967; and Hartmann, 1968a). According to more recent investigations (Trnovcova, 1969) the association-free extrinsic region yielded an activation enthalpy of 0·74 eV, whereas the extrinsic associated range had an activation enthalpy value of 0·88 eV for Ca^{++} impurities. Since it is highly probable that the main impurity of the NaCl whisker investigated by Dawood and Forty was calcium, and the temperature range in which the measurements of these authors carried out was the extrinsic associated range it may be correctly stated that their results agreed quite well with results obtained with bulk single crystals.

Dawood and Forty (1962) also investigated the ionic conductivity of 2000 Å thick PbJ_2 plates by the same method, and obtained the activation enthalpy 9600 cal/mol (0·42 eV) within the temperature range of 195°C–275°C, and 30,100 cal/mol (1·31 eV) above 275°C. The results were explained as values belonging to the extrinsic, and intrinsic range respectively. The enthalpies corresponded to values obtained with disks compressed from powder material.

Ballaro et al. (1965) measured the ionic conductivity of potassium chloride whiskers in the temperature range of 300°C–650°C by a d.c. method, which enabled them to measure resistances up to 10^{14} Ohm. The whisker was attached with colloidal graphite or silver paint to horizontal electrodes. Care was taken in compensating the heat expansion of the electrodes to avoid any deformation of the whiskers while measuring the temperature dependence of their conductivity. The measurements were carried out in a purified He atmosphere at decreasing temperature. Before the experiments the whiskers were heat-treated at 700°C for 2h. According to the experimental results the slowly-grown and purposely uncontaminated whiskers contained a smaller amount of divalent cation impurities than the Harshaw crystals. (The solution from which the whiskers were grown was obtained by dissolving a Harshaw crystal.) If the whiskers were grown quickly or contaminated with $SrCl_2$ the extrinsic range was above the extrinsic range of a Harshaw single crystal. Though Ballaro et al. (1965) do not give any activation enthalpy values one may discern from their graphs that the slope of the specific conductivity of their whiskers grown slowly on cellophane was smaller in the extrinsic range than the slope of the Harshaw bulk-material. The slope, however, corresponded to that of the Harshaw crystals if the whiskers were grown fast from a hot solution.

A great number of ionic conductivity measurements with sodium chloride whiskers were carried out by Hartmann (1968a, b). The thickness of the samples varied between 4 and 50µ. The whisker was placed vertically in the measuring device, and was attached to platinum electrodes with colloidal graphite. The voltage on the electrodes, the distance of which was a few millimeters, was 100V. The current flowing through the sample was measured with a vibrating-reed electrometer. The measurements were carried out in a dry N_2 atmosphere in the temperature range of 150°C–600°C, after a 3h heat treatment at an elevated temperature the aim of which was to avoid the influence of any surface contamination.

The temperature dependence of the conductivity of the sodium chloride crystals consists in most cases of three regions (Fig. 1a): (1) the intrinsic region, (2) the extrinsic region free of associations, and (3) the extrinsic associated region. In this third region one fraction of the cation vacancies forms complexes, each of which consists of one cation vacancy and one divalent impurity cation. The average values of the activation enthalpies in the regions were:

$$\varepsilon_1 = 1\cdot80 \pm 0\cdot15\,\text{eV}, \quad \varepsilon_2 = 0\cdot71 \pm 0\cdot06\,\text{eV}, \quad \varepsilon_3 = 0\cdot86 \pm 0\cdot06\,\text{eV}.$$

These values are somewhat smaller than the values obtained recently with bulk single crystals (Trnovcova, 1969). In some cases a larger deviation from the average than the error of measurement was found; this may be accounted for by dislocations along the whisker axes.

Hartmann (1968a, b) determined the concentration of divalent impurity cations substitutionally incorporated in the lattice from the position of the association-free extrinsic region of the sodium chloride whiskers. It was

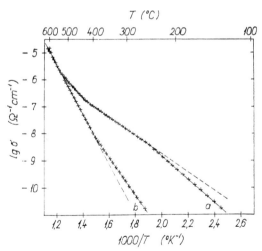

FIG. 1. Ionic conductivity of a NaCl whisker (a) recorded in dry N_2 on cooling, (b) recorded in air on cooling, (Hartmann, 1968a).

found that in the case of "pure" whiskers the impurity concentration values were in the range of 1×10^{-5}–20×10^{-5} mol %. In the case of whiskers grown from a solution contaminated with 1 mol % $CaCl_2$ the maximal impurity concentration was 85×10^{-5} mol %. The pH of the solution from which the whiskers were grown did not seem to influence the position of the association-free extrinsic range of the conductivity. It may be concluded from this that the incorporation of impurities into the lattice during growth from solution is less in the case of whiskers than in that of bulk crystals.

The large specific surface of the whiskers provides a simple opportunity to determine the effect of the surrounding atmosphere on the conductivity of these crystals. A whisker was cut into two equal pieces. The temperature dependence of the conductivity of both halves was measured, one half in a dry N_2 atmosphere, the other in air after heating for 3h up to 600°C. The results obtained at the dry N_2 atmosphere are presented in Fig. 1a, whereas Fig. 1b shows the results of the measurement in atmospheric air. As can be seen from the figure heating in air considerably decreases the conductivity of the whisker. According to Hartmann (1968a, b) this result may be accounted for by anion contaminations containing oxygen which penetrate into the sample from the air at high temperatures. These anions compensate for the effect of the divalent cation impurities already present in the divalent cation impurities already present in the whisker, by decreasing the concentration of the cation vacancies.

According to the temperature dependence of the ionic conductivity of the whiskers, and according to the values of the activation enthalpies no substantial difference can be detected between the ionic conductivity of the bulk crystals and that of the whiskers. The existing differences can be explained partly by the differences between the dislocation content and the dislocation arrangement, and partly by the large surface to volume ratio of the whiskers.

References

Ballaro, S., Chiarotti, G., Cubiotti, G. and Grasso, V. (1965). *Physics Chem. Solids* 26, 729–734.

Bereskhova, G. V. (1969). "Nitevidnie kristalli" ("Whiskers"). Izd. Nauka, Moscow.

Coleman, R. V. (1964). *Metal. Rev.* 9, 261–304.

Dawood, R. J. and Forty, A. J. (1962). *Phil. Mag.* 7, 1633–1651.

Gyulai, Z. (1954). *Z. Phys.* 138, 317–321.

Hartmann, E. (1968a). *Acta phys. Hung.* 24, 225–232.

Hartmann, E. (1968b). *Kristallografiya* (USSR) 13, 1089–1090.

Süptitz, P. and Teltow, J. (1967). *Phys. Stat. sol.* 23, 9–56.

Trnovcova, V. (1969). *Czech. J. Phys.* 19, 663–676.

10. IONIC TRANSPORT IN GLASSES

K. Hughes

Webb Corbett Limited, Stourbridge, Worcestershire, England

and

J. O. Isard

Department of Glass Technology, University of Sheffield, England

I. Introduction

The ionic nature of conduction in glass has been recognized for about a century. The electric current is carried entirely by alkali ions in common soda lime glass as well as in many other commercial glasses containing alkali oxides. The conductivity increases continuously with increasing temperature so that, although such glasses are fair insulators at room temperature, all-electric glass-melting furnaces can be run by means of the Joule heating between immersed electrodes at low potentials. There is a considerable variation of conductivity with composition but, although extensive data exist, only very qualitative explanations are available at present. Cation exchange processes are of great technological importance in connection with surface strengthening treatments, with the glass electrode, and with chemical durability.

A great deal of attention is now being paid to electronically conducting glasses; some of these are based on sulphide, selenide and telluride compositions and some on oxides incorporating a high proportion of transition metal ions. However there remains a wide range of glass compositions for which the current carriers have not been identified although the electrical conductivity can be measured and related experimentally to the composition.

The present chapter reviews the current ideas on ionic migration in glass and summarizes the experimental data on the low field conductivity and on the electrolysis of alkali-containing glasses in the solid state. The relation of diffusion to conduction is discussed and some recent work is described in which mixed alkali and alkali-free glasses were studied. Useful earlier reviews are those of Stevels (1957), Sutton (1960), Owen (1963) and Mazurin (1965) on electrical properties, and of Doremus (1962) on diffusion.

II. Structure of Glass

As a glass is cooled from the melt its properties vary continuously with temperature; no sharp transitions are discernible. The viscosity increases steeply with decreasing temperature, and when it reaches a value of about 10^{15} poise the glass exhibits the mechanical properties of an elastic solid. The narrow temperature range over which the viscosity varies from about 10^{12} to 10^{15} poise (typically 550°–490°C) is called the transformation range, and the properties of the glass at all lower temperatures depend to some extent on the rate of cooling in this range. Various features of the atomic structure become "frozen-in" during cooling through the transformation range. The structure of a solid glass can therefore be regarded as that of the liquid at a temperature in the transformation range.

The structure is characterized by well defined nearest neighbour distances and first co-ordination shells, but beyond a few atomic distances there is no ordering of the atomic positions. Zachariasen (1932) drew attention to the importance of directed bonds in glass-forming liquids and described the structure of a glass as a three-dimensional network, lacking in periodicity, but with an energy content comparable with that of the crystal. He proposed the following rules of glass formation:

1. An oxygen atom is linked to not more than two atoms A;
2. The number of oxygen atoms surrounding A must be small;

3. The oxygen polyhedra share corners with each other, not edges or faces, and form three-dimensional networks;

4. At least two corners† of each polyhedron must be shared.

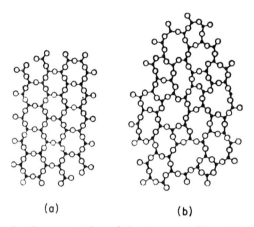

(a)   (b)

Fig. 1. Two-dimensional representation of the structure of hypothetical oxide A_2O_3 in (a) the crystalline, and (b) the vitreous forms (after Zachariasen, 1932).

These requirements can be met by certain oxides of the type A_2O_3, and AO_2 and A_2O_5 but not by those of type A_2O and AO. The oxides which form the structural skeleton, e.g. SiO_2, GeO_2, B_2O_3 and P_2O_5, are termed network formers. Other oxides, e.g. alkali oxides, CaO and BaO, are termed modifiers; the modifier cations are bound ionically and occupy holes in the network, the holes being filled as the framework is formed, so that their dimensions are determined by the occupying cations. Other oxides, e.g. Al_2O_3, have a less clear role and are termed intermediates. In the framework itself, oxygens linked to two silicons are termed doubly bonded or bridging oxygens, while those linked to one silicon are termed singly bonded or non-bridging. Figure 1 shows a schematic two-dimensional representation of the structures of an A_2O_3 type network former in both the crystalline and vitreous states, as proposed by Zachariasen (1932). Figure 2 shows the Warren and Biscoe (1938) model of the structure of soda–silica glass. X-ray diffraction studies of Warren and others have confirmed the random network theory, in general, (see Stanworth, 1950; Morey, 1954) but only the first shell co-ordination numbers and distances can be derived in the radial distribution functions, due to the overlapping of the relatively broad shells.

† Originally stated by Zachariasen as three.

While the Zachariasen–Warren model gives a useful first approximation for correlating the physical properties to composition it is inadequate to explain all effects. In particular, it has been found that his "rules" are contravened by many compositions. Even in the silicate system, glasses with more than 50% modifier oxides may be prepared; at these compositions a continuous network of Si–O–Si linkages joining all the Si atoms together cannot exist, although the SiO_4 tetrahedron will remain the basic structural unit. Notable among these are the "invert" glasses of Trap and Stevels (1959, 1960a, b, 1963a, b) and Trap (1964). Mackenzie (1960), for example, has suggested possible structures at the metasilicate composition as given in Fig. 3. These are: (a) $Si_3O_9^{6-}$ rings, (b) SiO_4 tetrahedra forming infinite chains, and (c) a random network of continuous Si–O–Si linkages. For the binary silicates, Mackenzie suggested that the following types of structure occur as modifier oxide is added:

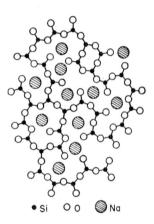

● Si   ○ O   ◎ Na

Fig. 2. Two-dimensional representation of a soda–silica glass (after Warren and Biscoe, 1938).

1. Up to between 10 and 20 mol % of alkali and alkaline earth metal oxides, the structure is essentially a random network.

2. From about 20 to 40%, relatively small units in the form of "islets" of vitreous silica, discrete ions such as $Si_8O_{20}^{8-}$ and rings such as $Si_3O_9^{6-}$ are probably present.

3. Between 40 and 50 mol % the predominant units will be small rings and discrete ions.

4. At 50 and 60 mol % the units will be chains and rings.

By incorporating several modifier oxides together, the proportion of glass-forming oxide can be reduced below the Zachariasen limit for a continuous network. Trap and Stevels (1959, 1960a, b, 1963a, b) prepared "invert" glasses of composition $1{\cdot}0$ ($1 Na_2O + 1 K_2O + 1 CaO + 1 SrO + 1 BaO){\cdot}0{\cdot}4 SiO_2$; at this composition there can only be one bridging oxygen per SiO_4 tetrahedron on average. The role of PbO is particularly interesting since both silicate and borate glasses containing up to more than 90 mol % PbO can be prepared. Stanworth (1950) suggested that some Pb could be incorporated in four-fold co-ordination as a network former, but Fajans and Kreidl (1948) considered that the high polarizability of the Pb^{++} ion is responsible for the stability of the lead glasses. In general it is noted that the failure of a melt to crystallize on cooling below the liquids is a kinetic problem and may depend on a great variety of factors (see Jones, 1956). Most discussions about glass structure refer chiefly to the silicates and borates, but the total range of glass-forming melts is very wide and includes many mixtures of salts in which none of the components form glasses on their own.

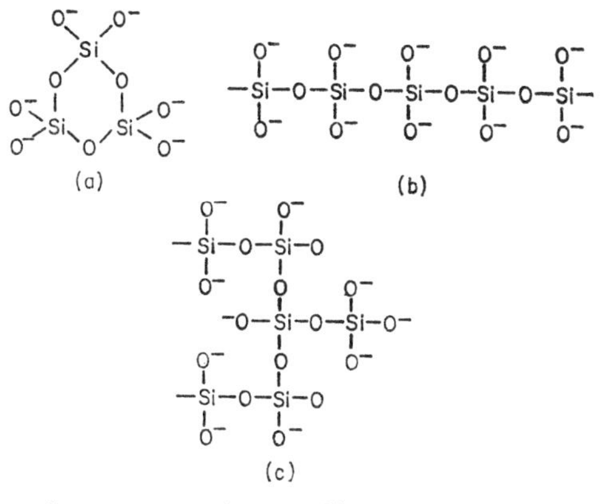

FIG. 3. Possible network structures at the metasilicate composition (after Mackenzie, 1960).

The crystalline theory of Porai-Koshits (see e.g. Valenkov and Porai-Koshits, 1936; Porai-Koshits, 1958) is often used by Russian workers to relate physical properties to composition. Using the results of X-ray investigations they concluded that some groups of atoms will be assembled in a highly ordered state compared with the general network. These regions, termed crystallites, were regarded as small disordered crystals, separated from each other by zones of lesser order. It was assumed that even in one component glasses there are regions with different degrees of ordering. The crystalline and random network theories probably should not be regarded as mutually exclusive alternatives, but as proposing different degrees of ordering: that of the random network theory being limited to 5–6Å, compared to 10–12Å for the crystallite theory.

Many glass compositions are now known to show the phenomenon of liquid–liquid phase separation at temperatures below the liquidus. The scale of the separated regions is often so small that the glass is transparent; it only becomes opalescent when it is heat-treated to allow the separated regions to grow. The bulk properties of phase-separated material will be related to the compositions of the phases. For example the steady-current conduction is governed largely by the composition of the continuous phase so that the measurements on phase-separated glass will not be characteristic of the overall bulk composition (Charles, 1963, 1964, 1965, 1966).

III. Theory of Ionic Transport in Glass

Ionic migration in crystals is usually dependent on the presence of point defects—vacant lattice sites and interstitial ions—in the perfect lattice. These may arise from the aleovalent impurities in solid solution or from the thermo-dynamic equilibrium established at the experimental, or a higher, temperature. A lattice defect arises from the necessity to preserve the long range order of the perfect crystal at large distances. In a liquid structure, small atomic rearrangements can occur, spreading out indefinitely from a given centre, so that missing atoms or aleovalent impurities will not give rise to defect centres; structural rearrangements will occur to satisfy the co-ordination requirements both at the impurity atom and at the atoms of the host network. The concept of a point defect can therefore hardly be applied to a glass formed from a melt. On the other hand, a liquid structure is essentially more open than that of a corresponding crystal and may be considered to provide an excess of vacancies for ionic migration. Certainly most salts show a large increase of ionic mobility on melting. A solid glass may therefore be considered to have a large distribution of vacancies permanently built into its structure. In particular, the network structures of the silicates tend to have relatively large amounts of volume unoccupied by atoms, compared to the structures of simple ionic compounds. Most authors have therefore assumed that there is an excess of interstices over ions so that each ion has several positions all of about equal energy to which it can migrate freely over an energy barrier. Myuller (1960a) and most Soviet authors, however, have assumed that the cation must be dissociated from its original site before it could migrate from interstice to interstice, and the theory of cationic migration is then the same in form as for the case of a pure ionic crystal with Frenkel disorder in equilibrium.

Experimentally the variation of resistivity with temperature may be described by the equation:

$$\log \sigma = A - B/T \tag{1}$$

where σ is the conductivity at temperature $T°K$ and A and B are constants. The equation is found to hold accurately up to the transformation range, but below about 50°C surface conduction will limit the resistance of a specimen unless precautions are taken to avoid it. Morey (1954), Sutton (1960) and Owen (1963), have reviewed exceptions to this law and Kaneko and Isard (1968) studied the effects within the transformation range.

Stevels (1957) derived the conductivity assuming that each alkali ion vibrates at frequency v in a potential well, and has a small probability p of surmounting the potential barriers of height $\Delta H_{DC}/N$, where N is Avagadro's number. Assuming a Boltzmann energy distribution,

$$p = v \exp\left(-\Delta H_{DC}/NkT\right) \tag{2}$$

where k is the Boltzmann constant. It is assumed that each occupied potentia well is surrounded by b vacant wells to which the ion can jump. On the application of an electric field E the energy barrier system will be disturbed, the migration of the ions now being favoured in the direction of the field; a potential barrier in a direction θ to the field will be raised by $Ee(\lambda/2)\cos\theta$ where λ is the distance between potential wells. The current density is obtained from the net flow of ions in the forward and reverse directions, and is proportional to:

$$\exp\left(-\Delta H_{DC}/NkT\right)\left[\exp\left(Ee\lambda\cos\theta/2kT\right) - \exp\left(-Ee\lambda\cos\theta/2kT\right)\right].$$

Averaging over all θ, and assuming the low field condition $Ee\lambda \leqslant kT$, Stevels obtained an expression equivalent to:

$$\ln(\sigma) = \ln\left(v\,be^2\,\lambda^2 n/6kT\right) - \Delta H_{DC}/RT \tag{3}$$

where n is the ionic concentration and R is the gas constant. Although the "pre-exponential factor" in (3) includes the temperature, so that the temperature dependence is not identical with that of (1), the experimental data generally fit either form equally well; however the value of ΔH_{DC} obtained from the slope of a $\ln(\sigma) - 1/T$ plot will be slightly different from that obtained from a $\log(\sigma T) - 1/T$ plot.

The derivation of conductivity may be carried through using Eyring's rate process theory (Owen, 1963) the energy barriers being characterized by a free energy of activation ΔF_{DC}. Then, if ΔS_{DC} is the entropy of activation

$$\Delta F_{DC} = \Delta H_{DC} - T\,\Delta S_{DC}, \tag{4}$$

and Owen (1963) obtained:

$$\ln (\sigma) = \ln (e^2 \lambda^2 n/2h) + \Delta S_{DC}/R - \Delta H_{DC}/RT \qquad (5)$$

where h is Planck's constant; in Eqn 5 the pre-exponential constant is not explicitly dependent upon temperature. The values of the atomic parameters λ and v or ΔS in the pre-exponential terms of (3) and (5) are not accurately known, but approximate values give reasonable agreement with low field conductivity data. With respect to the activation energy the derivations assume that the free energy barriers separating adjacent potential wells are all of the same magnitude. This is unlikely to be the case for the irregular amorphous structure found in glasses. The measured values may reflect either an average of the distribution of potential barriers, or the highest potential barriers which an ion encounters in a long path through the glass. Stevels (1957) and Taylor (1957, 1959) considered that the d.c. conduction was controlled by the highest barriers, while the additional a.c. conduction was due to limited movements over lower barriers; but, experimentally, Taylor found that the value of activation energy for the a.c. processes is the same as that for d.c. conduction.

Under high fields the current is no longer expected to be ohmic; the term with positive exponent in E is expected to dominate, giving an exponential rise of current with field strength, as found by Vermeer (1956). Zager and Papanikolau (1969) found that the current varied as sinh $(Ee\lambda/2kT)$ but that λ took values very much greater than the mean ionic separation. Barton (1970) showed that both ionic and electronic glasses obey the Poole–Frenkel equation $\log i = a - (b - cE^{\frac{1}{2}})/T$ which arises from the coulombic attraction of a charge carrier to an oppositely charged fixed centre. The Poole–Frenkel effect applies to coulombic fields operating over distances much greater than the mean ionic separation and Barton considers that its application to glass arises from the fluctuations in structure and charge distribution which also give rise to dielectric relaxation. Vermeer (1956) found that the exponential increase of current with field and temperature would give rise to a "runaway" condition due to Joule heating alone and would explain the observed breakdown fields of ionically conducting glasses; values of 10^5–10^6 V.cm^{-1} are obtained which depend on starting temperature, voltage rise time and specimen thickness. At liquid air temperatures an electronic breakdown mechanism operates at fields of 10^7 V.cm^{-1} which is independent of conditions; the breakdown of high resistance alkali-free glasses is also electronic at normal temperatures.

Variations in glass composition affect mainly the activation energy, the pre-exponential constant changing relatively little. This means that, generally, the higher the activation energy of a glass the greater is its resistance at a given temperature; it also means that the influence of composition on resistivity is greater the lower the temperature. With some exceptions, the values of A in Eqn 1 are found to vary between 1·5 and −4·5 while ΔH_{DC} varies from about 13 to 37 kcal/mol, or about 0·6–1·6 eV, for cationically conducting oxide glasses.

Some attempts have been made to interpret the values of activation energy in terms of glass structure. Most authors agree in distinguishing two contributions: one the coulombic energy of increasing the separation of positive and negative charges, and the other the elastic energy required to squeeze an ion through a restricted opening in the network. The electrostatic part would be easy to calculate in principle if all the surrounding ions remained exactly in place, but, as is well known for alkali halides, a considerable relaxation occurs amongst surrounding lattice ions when, for example, a vacancy and interstitial ion pair is formed. Anderson and Stuart (1954) obtained the expression $e^2[1/\overline{(r+r_0)} - (2/\lambda)]$ for the electrostatic energy required to move any singly charged ion of radius r from a position touching a singly charged bridging oxygen of radius r_0 to a position $\lambda/2$ away where λ is the total jump distance. For the elastic term they obtained the expression $4\pi G r_D(r - r_D)^2$ where r_D is the radius of the opening through which the ion $(r > r_D)$ must pass; r_D was estimated from rare gas diffusion data as 0·6 Å. They found good agreement with experimental values if the dielectric constant was inserted in the denominator of the electrostatic term, and they attributed this to a covalency parameter, but a more suitable explanation is that it represents the relaxation of the surrounding structure as the ion moves. The elastic term was about four times smaller than the electrostatic term.

For a few compositions, ionic migration rates in the glassy and crystalline forms of the same material have been compared. This has been done by melting glass of stoichiometric proportions and making measurements before and after devitrification. Unfortunately no simple experiment exists to determine the amount and the connectivity of residual glass content in ceramics, and it is not certain in any of these experiments that the measured ionic migration did not take place in a residual glass phase around the crystal grains. However, all the results agree in showing a higher activation energy for the devitrified material and it is therefore considered likely that this is a general rule as between crystalline and glassy phases. Frischat and Oel (1966) measured both diffusion and conductivities in crystalline and glassy $Na_2O . 2 CaO . 3 SiO_2$ with the results shown in Table I; the activation energies are only slightly higher in the crystal. Rather larger differences were found by Mazurin and Tsekhomskii (1964) for the compositions $Na_2O . 2 CaO_2 . 3 SiO_2$, $2 Na_2O . CaO . 3 SiO_2$ and $Na_2O . 3 CaO . 6 SiO_2$. The present authors (Isard, 1959) found that crystallized nepheline glass had an activation energy of 0·66–0·86 eV, depending on the temperature of crystallization, while the glass had a value of 0·56. Other data are given by Vargin and Antoneva (1956) and Foex (1944). Generally the temperature-independent terms differ little as between glass and crystal. Frischat and Oel (1966) found very similar values for the correlation coefficient (see Table I) in the glass and the crystal and concluded that very similar ion migration mechanisms occurred.

TABLE I. Activation energies and pre-exponential constants for sodium tracer diffusion and conductivity in vitreous and polycrystalline $Na_2O . 2 CaO . 3 SiO_2$ (after Frischat and Oel, 1966).

	Temp. Range (°C)	D_0	Q_D (kcal/mol)	σ_0	ΔH_{DC} (kcal/mol)
Vitreous	200–600	$3·67 \times 10^{-2}$	27·5		
,,	250–600			$6·98 \times 10^2$	25·9
Polycrystalline	500–900	$1·88 \times 10^{-2}$	29·9		
,,	470–900			89·9	26·2

The accurate comparison of cationic diffusion with conductivity has shown that the free migration model cannot be correct. If the cations migrate freely in a network with a large excess of ionic sites an exact agreement would be expected between the self diffusion coefficient, D_t, as measured by radio tracers, and the conductivity σ, according to the Nernst–Einstein equation:

$$\frac{D_t}{\sigma} = \frac{RT}{ne^2} . \tag{6}$$

However, if the process is controlled by a very small minority of vacant sites, as with the diffusion of vacancies in a crystal, the correlation co-efficient, f, must be inserted in the above equation, giving

$$\frac{D_t}{\sigma} = f\frac{RT}{ne^2} \tag{7}$$

f has been calculated for vacancy diffusion in various crystalline lattices and is, generally, a fraction between 0·5 and 1·0. Any process in which more than one ion changes its place in a given jump also requires $f \neq 1$; in particular $f \neq 1$ for the interstitialcy process in which two ions move to-gether. In general, f is smaller, the smaller the co-ordination number, i.e. the smaller the number of possible jump directions for any particular ion.

Haven and Stevels (1957) first considered the correlation coefficient in glass and they suggested that the cationic positions should be divided into two groups of different energy, corresponding to the lattice sites and interstitial positions in a crystal. If nearly all the lower energy sites are normally occupied, diffusion may proceed either by a vacancy mechanism, for which $f \neq 1$, or by ions being raised into the higher energy sites—as in the formation of Frenkel defects in a crystal. A few ions in the large number of higher energy sites could then migrate freely, as interstitials do in a crystal, and for such a process $f = 1$. However if they migrate by the interstitialcy process, in which an interstitial ion moves into a lattice site at the same time displacing the ion originally there into another interstitial site, values of $f \neq 1$ would be expected. Many determinations of f (e.g. Fitzgerald, 1952; Williams and Heckman, 1964; Heckman et al., 1967; Frischat, 1967; Terai, 1969) have given values of 0·3–0·7 for various compositions, apart from the work of Doremus who found values of unity for a complex commercial glass (1964) and for fused silica (1969). Haven and Verkerk (1965) have discussed possible structural models with low enough co-ordination to give the observed values of f with either vacancy or interstitialcy cationic migration, the latter being considered slightly more likely.

IV. Measurement of Transport Numbers

The electrolytic nature of electrical conduction in commercial soda glass was established by Warburg and Tegetmeier over the period 1884–1890. Their work and that of other early workers was reviewed by Littleton and Morey (1933). The essential feature was that rapid polarization occurred unless the anode could supply sodium ions to the glass as with sodium amalgam. Kraus and Darby (1922) electrolyzed silver into a glass tube from a fused silver nitrate anode bath and this also prevented polarization. They showed that the sodium released into a mercury cathode pool inside the tube corresponded with the total charge passed, according to Faraday's laws, and that the tube gained weight corresponding to the replacement of Na^+ by Ag^+.

The transport numbers for the cations in glass can be determined by the method of Tubandt (1932). A set of at least three discs of the glass are weighed before and after they are assembled in a pile and electrolyzed. It is convenient to use silver metal electrodes, since silver ions readily enter the glass in place of the alkali ions and the current is not blocked. Only the discs in contact with the electrodes should show a change in mass due to electrolysis. The sensitivity of the method depends on the repeatability in weighings of the central disc, or discs, before and after they are assembled in the pile and raised to temperature. In practice it is not realistic to expect this figure to be less than ± 0.1 mg for discs weighing a few grams. Hence the electrolytic deposition should be at least 10 mg to obtain 1% accuracy and for sodium this requires the passage of about 4 coulombs for example. Enough current can be passed in reasonable times only at elevated temperatures.

Evstropev and Pavlova (1958) used three ground glass discs clamped together with silver sheets for electrodes. At temperatures of 400–600°C up to 100 coulombs was passed in under 10 h. The weight of the central disc was unchanged to ± 0.4 mg and its resistance was not affected. For single alkali silicate glasses the transport number t_R for an alkali ion R^+ was found to be 1 ± 0.01, while the transport numbers of the separate alkali ions in glasses containing two alkalis were reproducible to 5%. Using similar methods Mazurin et al. (1957) found no weight changes in the alkali-free glass (mol%) 45 SiO_2 . 20 B_2O_3 . 5 Al_2O_3 . 20 CaO . 10 Fe_2O_3 and this glass was assumed to be an electronic conductor. Myuller and Prankin (1963, 1965) used this method to investigate soda aluminosilicate glasses which are of particular interest owing to their relatively high conductivity. They found that transport numbers could be calculated both from the weight loss of the silver plate used as anode, assuming Ag^+ ions leave for the glass, and also from the gain in weight of the anode glass disc owing to the replacement of Na^+ ions by Ag^+ ions. After the passage of about 20 coulombs at 260–300°C, the former gave $t_{Na} = 0.996 \pm 0.005$ while the latter gave $t_{Na} = 0.983 \pm 0.006$. Prankin (1964) determined t_{Na} for these glasses by measuring the alkali deposited at the cathode; the cathode products were dissolved in hot water and titrated. After the passage of 1–2 coulombs at 80–100°C he found $t_{Na} = 1.00 \pm 0.01$. It was concluded that there is no electronic current in these glasses.

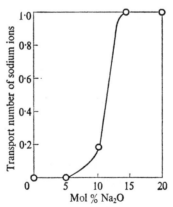

FIG. 4. Sodium ion transport number versus soda content for the series $xNa_2O . (1 \quad x)$ PbO . SiO_2 (after Hughes et al., 1968).

Hughes and Isard (1968) used the Tubandt method with silver electrodes fired on to the glass discs; the anode glass, together with its silver electrode, was weighed before and after electrolysis, and transport numbers determined from the weight loss. In glasses containing only one alkali, the transport numbers were 1.00 ± 0.01 with anode weight losses of 15–30 mg at temperatures about 40°C below the transformation range. It was found necessary to use polished glass surfaces, and to keep the field below about 500 V . cm^{-1} to prevent electrical breakdown occurring. Hughes et al. (1968) used similar techniques to determine transport number of Na$^+$ ions in the series $x\,\mathrm{Na_2O}$. $(1 - x)\,\mathrm{PbO}$. $1\mathrm{SiO_2}$, with the results shown in Fig. 4. The conductivity of the soda-free glass was about 10^{-7} ohm^{-1} cm^{-1} at the temperature of measurement and the current was as low as 10 μA so that electrolysis times of hundreds of hours were required to deposit at least 10 mg in the silver coulometer; this experiment showed that the current was either electronic or due to trace H$^+$ ion transport, as no weight change occurred in the anode glass to ± 0.1 mg. This evidently represents about the limit of measurement for this type of experiment and transport numbers could hardly be determined with any accuracy in glasses of lower conductivity.

If it is assumed that there is no anionic current and that secondary electrode reactions do not occur, transport numbers for the cations can be derived from analysis of the material deposited at the cathode. Lengyel et al. (1963) used flame photometry to analyze the cathode products from the electrolysis of tubes of experimental glasses. For glasses of good chemical resistance the inside of the tube was filled with alkali-free sulphuric acid as the cathode solution and immersed in an anode solution of potassium sulphate in sulphuric acid. For glasses of poorer chemical resistance, e.g. alkali disilicates, the cathode solution was distilled mercury and anode solution was potassium sulphate in glycerin. At high temperatures the inner wall was coated with silver by evaporation and the tube immersed in molten potassium nitrate. The total charge passed in each experiment was approximately three coulombs at temperatures of approximately 270°C and 420°C. The reproducibility was 3% at 270°C and 10% at 420°C.

Burt (1925) made use of the emission of electrons from a hot tungsten filament in an evacuated glass bulb to demonstrate the electrolysis of glass. The experiment can be readily carried out with a vacuum-filled incandescent electric lamp bulb. The bulb is partially immersed in a molten salt bath and a positive potential maintained between the bath and the filament. Electrons from the filament neutralize the alkali ions driven through the glass and alkali metal accumulates in the bulb. The transport number can be determined from the gain in weight of the bulb. The great difficulty in applying this to experimental glasses is to fabricate bulbs of the glasses and effect a vacuum seal to the filament; the difficulties in obtaining an expansion match are usually prohibitive. Lengyel (1940) however used the method on glasses in series $x . Na_2O . (1 - x) K_2O . 2 SiO_2$ and Hughes and Isard (1968) used it for a number of mixed alkali glasses of complex compositions designed to give a matching seal to a commercial glass. Both Lengyel (1940) and Hughes and Isard (1968) opened the bulb after electrolysis and washed out the alkali for flame photometric analysis. Although flame photometry is expected to be a much more sensitive method of determining the alkali than weighing the bulb both sets of authors found that its accuracy was limited; considerable alkali is picked up even without electrolysing the bulb. Danilkin et al. (1965) used a graphite coating to act as cathode on the inside surface of the evacuated bulb immersed in the fused salt; the alkali metal produced on electrolysis was condensed on to a cold finger of nickel, cooled by liquid air and sealed inside the bulb. Danilkin's apparatus was demountable and all fabricated from a single potash borosilicate glass. After electrolysis, argon was admitted and the cold finger was weighed in argon. The transport number for potassium ions was found to be unity to an accuracy of 0.3%.

There is a great interest in extending transport number measurement to glasses of lower conductivity, both to study known cationically conducting glasses at lower temperatures and to investigate glasses whose conductivity is less than 10^{-7} ohm^{-1} cm^{-1} even at the temperature where they begin to deform. In general, methods of directly analyzing electrode deposits are extremely sensitive and could be used, but the derivation of transport numbers from the results always involves the assumption that secondary electrode reactions do not take place. Hughes and Isard (1968) pointed out that when the Burt experiment is applied to mixed alkali glasses, it is possible that the proportions of different alkali atoms released at the surface are not identical with the proportions of the alkali ions carrying the current in the bulk of the glass; the proportions of the alkalis in the glass at the inner surface of the bulb may change during electrolysis if one is neutralized by the electrons more readily than the other. Certainly, it was shown by Hughes et al. (1968) that, although lead is deposited at the cathode on the electrolysis of a soda lead silica glass and grows into the glass as crystal trees, the current is carried by Na^+ ions; the lead is produced by a secondary reaction of the metallic sodium evolved on electrolysis of the lead glass.

V. Electrode Polarization Effects

If the metal electrodes which are applied to glass cannot readily supply ions to replace the alkali ions in the glass, the current will decay away when a steady potential is applied. Proctor and Sutton (1959, 1960) demonstrated the build-up of space charge at blocking electrodes by using a series of potential probes. For an alkali-containing glass, the potential distributions showed a build-up of space charge adjacent to the electrodes and the asymmetry showed a larger potential drop at the anode than at the cathode. A "steady state" was approached after 30 h, when the central region showed a small and nearly linear potential drop. The non-alkali glass showed a much smaller space charge development, the potential being almost linear across the specimen. This latter situation was not considered compatible with ionic conduction, although conduction due to alkali impurity was not discounted.

Following the above work, Sutton (1964) has reviewed the phenomena of space charge in silicates, discussing dielectric properties, conduction and polarization. A theoretical model was proposed, describing the distribution of space charge in a material with only a single mobile charge carrier, the dielectric absorption current being explained as a build up of a diffuse double layer or space charge at both electrodes. The experimentally observed potential distributions fitted the theory in a semi-quantitative way.

Electrode polarization has been the subject of investigation by a number of other workers (Mazurin and Brailovskii, 1966; Brailovskii et al., 1966; Kinser and Hench, 1969), in relation to its effect on resistivity measurements. Brailovskii et al. (1966) measured resistivity as a function of time for three different complex silicates with similar total alkali oxide contents of 15–16 wt %. Using inert graphite electrodes, it was found that after an initial period of constant resistivity which depended on the original glass composition and the temperature, there was a steady increase of resistivity with time, this being almost independent of composition and temperature, but dependent upon the applied voltage. The rise of resistivity was ascribed to the increasing thickness of an alkali-depleted layer adjacent to the anode which had similar properties for the three glasses investigated. For the glasses studied, at all temperatures below the transformation range the quantity of electricity passing through the specimen at 220 V was found to be about 1.5×10^{-3} coulombs/cm^2 for a current fall of 99.9% from the initial value. It was found that polarization effects become more pronounced with increase in temperature and ionic mobility, as might be expected.

Electrode polarization, if it occurs, will clearly limit the accuracy of conductivity measurements. However, the measurement of d.c. conductivity in glass is also affected by a slow dielectric polarization process, whatever electrodes are used, because this is an intrinsic property of the material. The dielectric relaxation in glass has the characteristics of a dipole reorientation process over a potential barrier and it is very closely related to the mechanism of d.c. conduction whether this be ionic or electronic. It is found (Isard, 1962a) that the peak of dielectric loss occurs when the quantity $\log (f\rho)$ is approximately 11, where f is the frequency of measurement and ρ the d.c. resistivity. When $\log (f\rho) < 10$ the dielectric relaxation contributes little to the measured conductivity and any substantial dispersion of conductivity at lower frequencies must be attributed to electrode polarization. For most metals in intimate contact with the glass there are several decades of frequency over which the conductivity is constant to, say, better than 1%. Similarly, if d.c. measurements were plotted against the time between application of the field and the reading of the current, three regions could be distinguished; at very short times the conductivity falls rapidly, owing to the dielectric relaxation process; it then levels out at a value of about $\frac{1}{4}$ to $\frac{1}{2}$ of the initial value, giving the true d.c. conductivity; at long times it falls away indefinitely owing to electrode polarization. The central constant region extends over several decades but the time scale of the whole graph depends critically on temperature. Figure 5 shows the results of Kinser and Hench (1969) on a lithium silicate glass; the glass as cast was homogeneous and the conductivity was constant over the time scale 10^{-5}–10^{-1}s; the heat-treated glass was phase separated and showed a more complex time dependence. Sodium metal, or sodium amalgam electrodes have been shown (Isard, 1962b) to give measurements free from electrode error and enable the dielectric relaxation to be measured accurately.

In the transformation range the conductivity is time dependent owing to the slow changes of the atomic structure of the glass after a sudden temperature change. Below the transformation range chilled glass has a lower resistivity than annealed glass because the atomic structure corresponding to a higher temperature is frozen in. The state of annealing should always be

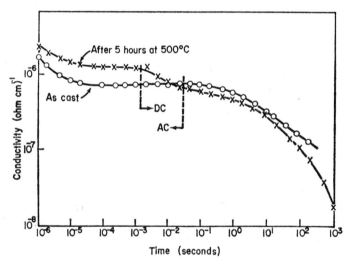

FIG. 5. Log conductivity versus log time for (mol %) 30 Li_2O. 70 SiO_2 glass at 80°C for as-cast and thermally treated glass (after Kinser and Hench, 1969).

reported along with any values of resistivity and it should be understood that the values discussed below for various compositions refer to glass cooled at approximately 1°C/min through the transformation range.

VI. Dependence of Cationic Conductivity on Composition

A. Silica Glass

Silica glass is manufactured either by melting crystalline quartz or by the hydrolysis of silicon tetrachloride in the flame. Amorphous thin films of silica are produced by the thermal oxidation of silicon or by the vacuum evaporation of silicon oxides; the insulating properties of these silica films are of critical importance in a large range of semi-conductor devices. Perfectly pure amorphous silica is expected to be an excellent insulator with a wide band gap and to show no ionic conduction. However, all forms contain varying levels of impurity introduced from the raw materials or by the methods of manufacture. Natural quartz crystals and fine quartz sands contain alkalies and alkaline earths together with aluminium, iron and other cations. These elements are incorporated if the fusion is carried out by electric heating. Flame fusion lowers the level of the more volatile impurities, such as alkalis, but causes hydroxyl to be incorporated in considerable amounts (up to 0·1 wt%). Chlorine may also be incorporated from flame hydrolysis of $SiCl_4$. Significant amounts of alkali contamination are difficult to avoid in the thermal oxidation of silicon.

The electrical properties of the various forms of silica glass are very dependent on the impurities present. The conductivity of fused quartz is attributed to the migration of cations, particularly the alkali ions. Owen and Douglas (1959) measured the resistivity of four different silica glasses with various impurity levels. Over the temperature range, room temperature to 800°C, two activation energies were found; all samples had a value of about 30 kcal/mol over the main part of the range, with a change to about 25 kcal/mol towards temperatures above about 408°C. A linear relationship was found between the logarithm of resistivity at 350°C and the logarithm of sodium concentration over the range 0·04–4 ppm. It was concluded that conductivity is due to the presence of impurities, particularly sodium. The presence of "water" appeared to have no significant influence on resistivity, despite its presence at levels of up to 10^5 times those of sodium. Frischat (1968) has also reported a similar lack of effect of "water" on sodium diffusion in silica. Veltri (1963) on the other hand found that after heating to 1800°C or above, the resistivity and activation energy at lower temperatures was raised considerably; the activation energy was initially 23·1 kcal/mol from 900–1650°C but was raised to 65–70 kcal/mol after heating to 1800°C, and a value of 86·7 kcal/mol was found over the range 1500–2500°C. He attributed the increase in activation energy to a loss of hydroxyl, implying that hydroxyl was involved in the initial conduction process with the low activation energy.

By means of suitable electrodes the original impurity ions can be electrolyzed out and replaced by other ions, including H^+. The most notable experiments are those of Hetherington et al. (1965) and Dunn et al. (1965) who also correlated their work with that of Sendt (1962) and of Garino-Carina and Priqueler (1962). Various types of silica were electrolyzed between 800° and 1300°C and under potential gradients of up to 1250 V/cm. Most results were obtained on a type manufactured by electric fusion of quartz crystal which contained 30–100 ppm. aluminium and 4 ppm. sodium as main impurities, but negligible "water". It was shown that, on electrolysis between platinum metal electrodes, alkali impurities moved towards the cathode to be replaced by protons produced at the anode from atmospheric moisture; the rate of introduction of protons was dependent upon the partial pressure of water vapour at the anode. A similar electrolysis mechanism was found by Kats et al. (1962) for quartz using graphite electrodes. The protons introduced by electrolysis into vitreous silica form OH groups which are unusually stable; they are not removed by heating in vacuo as are the OH groups introduced by the reaction of silica with water vapour. Hetherington et al. (1965) found that the number of OH groups introduced on electrolysis was about three times the number of alkali ions removed, and between $\frac{1}{3}$ and $\frac{1}{2}$ the number of aluminium atoms originally present.

Fused silica is permeable to molecular hydrogen, but the rate of permeation may be increased or decreased by the application of an electric field; the field-induced flow is due to the migration of H^+ ions which are formed at the electrodes and which replace the origin impurity ions. Jorgensen and Norton (1969) electrolyzed a pure vitreous silica formed by the pyrolysis of $SiCl_4$; they used platinum electrodes in pressures of hydrogen in excess of 0·1 torr. They found that 0·58 of the current was ionic, the rest being assumed to be electronic. The hydrogen introduced could be exchanged for deuterium and, when the deuterium content was measured subsequently by evolution into a mass spectrometer, it was found to be 8·2 ppm., in close agreement with the aluminium content of about 10 ppm. They therefore assumed that each proton electrolyzed into silica associated with an aluminium atom.

Hetherington's model of the electrolysis is shown in Fig. 6. Two kinds of centre are assumed: an interstitial alkali cation associated with a network substituent of lower valency than silicon, in this case aluminium; and an oxygen vacancy (V) as part of a chemically reduced centre of the form Si^{3+}–(V)–Al^{3+}, where the symbol Si^{3+} is used to indicate a localized chemical reduction, the exact nature of which is not known. In the electrolyzed silica, Na^+ has been replaced by H^+ to give hydroxyl groups, and the Si^{3+}

has been oxidized by migration of oxygen vacancies from the anode and the migration of oxygen from the cathode; this oxidation also involves proton migration from the anode, according to the model proposed, and accounts for the extra H introduced above the Na removed. It was found that for a given applied voltage the rate of electrolysis depended only on the electrical resistance of the anode region, and was independent of specimen thickness. Thus the determining factors were the mobility and concentration of the protons, except for small electrolytic penetration depths and short electrolysis times. The distances moved by the electrolysis boundary were shown up by the fluorescence in UV of the non-electrolyzed region due to the Si^{3+} centres; for a constant electrolysis time the logarithm of the distance was linear with the reciprocal temperature. The log resistivity in ohm . cm. of the electrolyzed region was found to be 9·5 at 1050°C compared with 5·5 for the non-electrolyzed material.

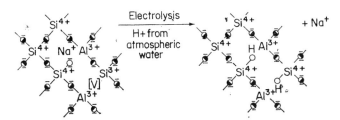

FIG. 6. Model of the electrolysis of vitreous silica (after Hetherington et al., 1965).

The platinum metal electrodes used in the above work were termed "inert" since they allowed only protons to enter the glass at the anode and this was termed "normal" electrolysis. Dunn et al. (1965) described further electrolytic phenomena, using the same vitreous silica, in which "active" electrodes were used. Lithium, gold, silver, copper and palladium ions were electrolyzed from metals or salts into the silica, replacing the alkali impurities. The metal cations, whose electrolysis rates were at least 10 times that of protons, were in turn displaced by protons as they migrated to the cathode; thus superimposed on the "active" electrolysis there is always a concurrent but slower "normal" electrolysis. The "active" electrolysis was described by the following:

$$-\overset{|}{\underset{|}{Si}}-O^-Na^+ + Au^+ \rightarrow -\overset{|}{\underset{|}{Si}}-O^-Au^+ + Na^+,$$

or

$$2(-\overset{|}{\underset{|}{Si}}-O^-Na^+) + Pd^{2+} \rightarrow -\overset{|}{\underset{|}{Si}}-O^-Pd^{2+}\,^-O-\overset{|}{\underset{|}{Si}}- + 2Na^+.$$

It was found that Li^+, K^+, Ag^+, Au^+, Cu^+, Mg^{2+}, Pd^{2+}, Cu^{2+} could be electrolyzed into the silica, but not trivalent ions or those with a radius greater than that of silver (1·37Å). A further characteristic of active electrolysis was that it occurred at different rates in different directions, i.e. the material behaved anisotropically. This was shown to be due to directional structural features resulting from a preferred orientation of the quartz crystals from which the vitreous silica was produced, i.e. along relics of the quartz crystal c-axis tunnels which are probable sites of the original impurity ions. The effect was not found with "normal" electrolysis, and this was attributed to the small size of the proton compared with that of the larger metal ions.

Doremus (1969) has investigated the mobilities of silver and alkali ions in vitreous silica by electrolyzing the ions into the glass from pure nitrate or eutectic melts. Silica glass tubes were initially electrolyzed between sodium nitrate electrodes until a constant conductivity was reached; they were then electrolyzed between lithium nitrate electrodes, for example, until the conductivity was again constant. The ratio of final conductivities was taken as the ratio of the ionic mobilities. The repeatability of the final conductivities for a given ion after several different electrolyses showed that complete ionic replacement took place. Two silica glasses were investigated: Glass 1 contained about 12 ppm alkali; Glass 2 contained less than 2·2 ppm metallic impurities but about 0·12 wt % hydroxyl. The relative mobilities of the ions are given in Table II, together with the activation energies of conduction.

TABLE II. Relative mobilities and activation energies for ions in fused silicas (after Doremus, 1969).

Ion	Relative mobility at 380°C		Activation energies (kcal/mol)		Temperature °C	
	Glass 1	Glass 2	Glass 1	Glass 2	Glass 1	Glass 2
Sodium	1	1	35	28	130–290	160–280
Lithium	0·15	0·03	35	35	180–400	270–350
Potassium	0·002	0·0007	30	32	190–470	360–440
Silver	0·08	—	—	—	—	—

The ionic mobilities are in the same sequence in both glasses, sodium ions being the most mobile, but neither the mobilities nor the activation energies are in the sequence of the ionic sizes. Frischat (1968) investigated the diffusion of sodium using a vitreous silica with a hydroxyl content of about 4×10^{-4} mol/litre and 0.01 wt % metallic oxides. Changes in slope of the diffusivity plot against reciprocal temperature were observed at about $573°$ and $273°C$; these are the temperatures at which $\alpha-\beta$ transitions occur in quartz and in cristobolite respectively and elements of the crystal structures were assumed to occur in the glass. Doremus (1969) however, showed that the resistance of fused silicas with either sodium or lithium conduction gave a slightly curved plot of log σ against I/T above about $280°C$, and he doubted the existence of definite breaks.

The rate of migration of polyvalent cations into silica is very much less than that of the monovalent cations, while anionic migration is negligible by comparison. Frischat (1969) has given the ratio of diffusion coefficients at $1000°C$ as $D_{Na} : D_{Ca} : D_{Al} : D_{0} = 1 : 2.5 \times 10^{-3} : 1.3 \times 10^{-8} : 1.1 \times 10^{-9}$. Stern (1968) found that silver ions exchanged with sodium ions in a fused quartz at $570°C$ on an atom for atom basis from chloride and bromide melts; no Cl or Br entered the silica and there was no exchange with Li or K. However, at $890°C$ there was a net diffusion of the cations Ag, Na and K into the silica from their chlorides, in spite of this temperature being well below the normal annealing point of $1020°C$ where structural changes could reasonably be expected; it was thought that the process was one of ion exchange with the protons in the original glass, which has a "water content" of 0.8 to 5×10^{-4} mol/mol SiO_2.

B. Effect of Alkali Content on Conductivity

The conductivity rises steeply with increasing alkali content in all composition systems containing at least 10–15 % alkali oxide. The rise in conductivity is due primarily to a decrease in activation energy. The pre-exponential term varies comparatively little with changes of composition, and A in eqn 1 is usually within the range 1–3, although Otto (1966) has reported values up to 8 for alkali borates of low alkali content. In the binary alkali silicate systems the conductivity rises steeply with initial alkali content, although there is little data in the range 0–10 % owing to the difficulty of preparing homogeneous glasses. In the binary alkali borates, Mazurin (1965) reported that the K, Rb and Cs glasses had conductivities independent of alkali content over the range 0–8 % approximately, after which the conductivity rose steeply; in the Li, Na, Ag and Tl glasses the conductivity rose steeply with alkali content from 2 % or less. In the $BaO–B_2O_3$, $BaO–SiO_2$, $PbO–B_2O_3$ and $PbO–SiO_2$ systems, additions of soda up to about 10 % cause either no change or even a slight decrease in conductivity, after which it increases steeply. In the $Na_2O–PbO–SiO_2$ system it is known (Hughes et al., 1968) that the conduction is not cationic in glasses containing 10 % or less Na_2O, and that the change in trend of conduction with Na_2O at 10–15% occurs where the conduction mechanism changes; in the range of composition showing cationic conduction the conductivity does increase with alkali content. It seems likely that the same may apply to other systems showing an alkali independent conductivity, since the conduction mechanism in most low alkali glasses has not been established experimentally. Evstropev and Ivanov (1963) and Ivanov *et al.* (1965), however, found a minimum in the molar conductivities of the Na_2O–GeO_2 glasses at an alkali concentration of about 0.7×10^{-2} atoms ml^{-1} with a corresponding minimum in the diffusion coefficient for Na (Evstropev *et al.*, 1965); they concluded that the minimum reflected a change in the structure as it concerns the mobility of the Na^+ ions.

In some glass-forming systems the occurrence of phase separation must be taken into account in interpreting conductivity data, particularly in the Li_2O–SiO_2 and Na_2O–SiO_2 systems (Charles, 1963, 1964, 1965, 1966). Near the edge of the dome of solute temperature against composition, glasses may be chilled without the disperse phase nucleating, but, within the spinodal, separation may take place very rapidly so that even chilled glasses are separated; in these circumstances the material is usually in the form of two continuous phases. After heat treatment of such material it develops into a system of disperse droplets in a continuum, as with phase separation by nucleation. Charles (1963) showed that lithia silica glass containing 6·7% Li_2O when chilled had an activation energy of 25·0 kcal/mol for d.c. conduction, but that this increased to 29·6 kcal/mol on heat treatment as a disperse high lithia phase was formed in a high silica continuum.

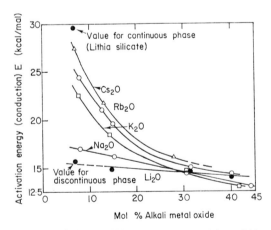

Fig. 7. Activation energies of d.c. condition versus composition of binary alkali oxide–silica glasses (after Charles, 1966).

This conducting disperse phase then gave rise to a Maxwell–Wagner dielectric loss peak with an activation energy of 15·6 kcal/mol approximately corresponding to the composition $Li_2O \cdot 2 SiO_2$. Glass of 15% Li_2O separated into a continuous phase of approximately $Li_2O \cdot 2 SiO_2$ composition and showed a d.c. conductivity with an activation energy 15 kcal/mol; see Fig. 7 after Charles (1966).[†] It is now known that soda silica glasses of less than

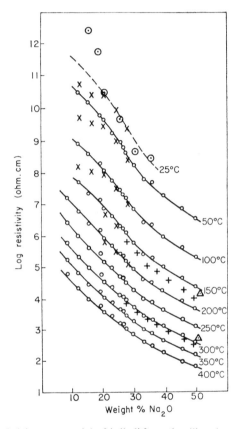

FIG. 8. Log d.c. resistivity versus weight % alkali for soda–silica glasses.

○ — Seddon *et al.* (1932).
⊙ — Fulda (1927).
× — Taylor (1959).
+ — Mazurin and Borisovskii (1957).
△ — Vargin and Antoneva (1956).

[†] Kuznetsov's data, used by Stevels (1967), shows a continuous trend of activation energy with lithia content in $Li_2O–SiO_2$ glasses, but this worker used fibres, drawn from the melt, which may have been so severely chilled as to have prevented phase separation.

20% Na_2O also separate into two phases and it is very probable that this explains many of the discrepancies between the data of various workers in the range 10–20% Na_2O; for 20% Na_2O and above there is very satisfactory agreement as shown in Fig. 8.

Seddon *et al.* (1932) suggested that the isotherms of resistivity against composition in the soda silica system show a sudden change of slope—or kink—at 33% Na_2O; in Fig. 8 it is seen however that smooth curves can be drawn through their data points. Kinks have also been suggested for other alkali silicate systems but they do not occur at the same % R_2O in all systems, and the results of various workers do not agree well—see Owen (1963). Charles (1966) represented the relation of activation energy to alkali content by smooth curves, apart from the lithia glasses as discussed above; his data are shown in Fig. 7. Milberg *et al.* (1966), and Otto and Milberg (1967, 1968) indicated a sharp kink at 25% R_2O (20% for Tl_2O glasses) as shown in Fig. 9, the kink being particularly marked for Rb_2O, Cs_2O and Tl_2O glasses. Otto and Milberg (1967) also found that the chemical shift of the nuclear magnetic resonance of the Cs and Tl ions showed sudden changes at 20 and 25% R_2O respectively, suggesting that a change in the environment of the ions occurs at these compositions. Milberg and Peters (1969) used X-ray diffraction to investigate the cation distribution in thallous silicate glasses; they found that the ions occur in clusters, rather than uni-

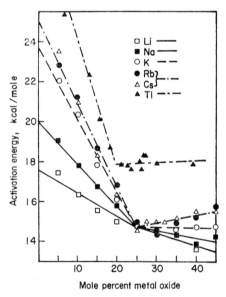

Fig. 9. Activation energy of d.c. conduction versus composition of binary alkali and thallous silicate glasses (after Otto and Milberg, 1968).

formally distributed throughout the network, but no direct evidence was found of a change in structure at 20% Tl_2O. A kink at $33\frac{1}{3}\%$ R_2O can be related to the glass structure; a glass containing more than $33\frac{1}{3}\%$ R_2O must have some silica tetrahedra with only two bridging oxygen ions while at lower alkali contents there must be some silica tetrahedra with no non-bridging oxygens. A marked change in the trend of alkali ion mobility might be expected therefore as this composition is passed. However no such simple structural interpretation can be given for the compositions 20% or 25% R_2O.

In the binary silicates of low (10%–20%) alkali content the activation energies are in order of ionic size. However, the activation energy decreases more steeply with alkali content the larger the ion, and at high alkali content the order tends to be reversed although there is then little difference. Stevels (1957) has suggested that the glasses of low alkali content have a rigid network with nearly all oxygens in bridging positions; the activation energy then has a large contribution from the elastic distortion of the network necessary to squeeze an ion through a restricted opening, and this contribution is larger the larger the ion. At high alkali contents, a large proportion of oxygens are in non-bridging positions and these can move aside relatively easily by bond bending to allow a cation to pass; the electrostatic term then predominates in the activation energy and Coulomb's law will give a term varying as $1/(r_{O^-} + r_{R^+})$ where r_{O^-} and r_{R^+} are the radii of non-bridging oxygen and cation respectively. Hence the order is the reverse of ionic size. Myuller (see Mazurin, 1965) has emphasized the importance of the non-bridging oxygen ions and the degree of electrostatic screening. At low alkali content, the migrating alkali ions must move away from a position close to one or more non-bridging oxygens into regions of the network with predominantly bridging oxygens and the activation energy is high; at high alkali content the ion migrates predominantly through regions with non-bridging oxygens but because these are largely screened by other alkali ions, the activation energy is low. Myuller (1960a) used an empirical relationship between dissociation energy ψ_ϕ and alkali concentration M of the form

$$\psi_\phi = \text{constant } M^{-b} \qquad (8)$$

where $b = \frac{1}{4}$ for alkali silicates and $\frac{1}{2}$ for alkali borates. ψ_ϕ is twice the measured activation energy, as for the temperature law for point defect formation in crystals.

C. Effect of Immobile Cations on Conductivity

The addition of divalent cations to the glass structure raises the activation energy and reduces the conductivity, owing to the migration of alkali ions.

The experimental data collected by Mazurin (1960) and by Mazurin and Brailovskaya (1960) for silicate glasses shows that:

  (i) The small divalent ions Be, Mg, Zn have little effect in amounts up to 20% RO but reduce the conductivity considerably in greater amounts.

 (ii) The larger divalent ions Ca, Sr, Pb, Ba raise the logarithm of resistivity (and the activation energy) in proportion to the % RO present; the effect increases systematically with size of the divalent ion.

(iii) The divalent ions have a larger effect in proportion on glasses of low alkali content than on glasses of high alkali content.

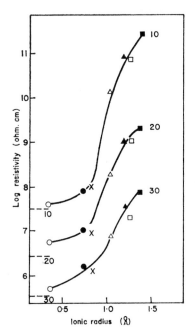

FIG. 10. Log d.c. resistivity at 150°C versus divalent ion radius of (mol %) xNa$_2$O. 20 RO. $(80 - x)$ SiO$_2$ glasses. Curves denoted by mol % Na$_2$O. Dashed lines represent resistivity of RO-free glasses (after Mazurin and Brailovskaya, 1960).

Symbol	Ion R
○	Be
●	Mg
×	Zn
△	Ca
□	Pb
▲	Sr
■	Ba

(iv) Similar effects are observed in glasses containing any of the alkali oxides.

Figure 10 shows the results of Mazurin and Brailovskaya (1960) for silicate glasses containing 20% RO and 10, 20, 30% Na_2O; the curves show the logarithum of resistivity at 150°C against the size of the divalent ion, and the dotted lines show the values for the binary soda silica glasses. Terai and Kitaoka (1968, 1969) reported similar divalent ion effects on both resistivity and diffusivity between 200° and 450°C for the Na_2O–R_2O–SiO_2 system containing oxides MgO, CaO, SrO, BaO, ZnO, CdO and PbO.

The action of the divalent ions may be partly accounted for by a blocking effect; the glasses containing RO oxides will have fewer interstices available for the alkali ions to jump into. However such an effect would not be expected to be appreciable for small amounts of RO as the alkali ions would be able to move round the blocked up interstices with little hindrance; but as noted above, the larger R^{++} ions have an effect proportional to % RO

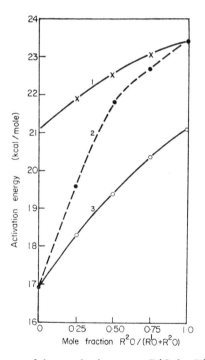

FIG. 11. Activation energy of d.c. conduction versus R^1O for R^2O substitution in series (mol %) 16 $(R^1O + R^2O)$. 16 Na_2O. 68 SiO_2 (after Lengyel and Boksay, 1961)

Curve 1 — R^1 = Ca, R^2 = Ba
Curve 2 — R^1 = Mg, R^2 = Ba
Curve 3 — R^1 = Mg, R^2 = Ca

even at low concentrations. Mazurin and Brailovskaya (1960), however, pointed out that the introduction of RO increased the concentration of non-bridging oxygens in the structure, and, because these are more polarizable than bridging oxygens, they increase the binding energy of the alkali ions to their sites and reduce their mobility. The small divalent ions polarize their associated non-bridging oxygens strongly and the latter therefore have less effect in holding the alkali ions to their sites: the larger divalent ions only polarize their associated non-bridging oxygens weakly so that the effect on the alkali ion mobility is greater. This effect is due to a decrease of field strength with increasing ionic radius and also to an increase of co-ordination number, and the larger the number of oxygens surrounding each R^{++} ion the less each will be polarized. In particular, it is probable that Be^{++} and possibly also Mg^{++} and Zn^{++} are co-ordinated by four bridging oxygens each with alkali ions in neighbouring interstices making up the balance of charge. These small divalent ions therefore act as network formers and do not increase the proportion of non-bridging oxygens. At RO concentrations in excess of the R_2O concentration however, this type of structure can no longer be formed.

Lengyel and Boksay (1961) made the interesting observation that the effect on the activation energy of two different divalent oxides together in a glass, is slightly greater than the sum of the effects of each separately. Figure 11 shows their results for the progressive substitution of BaO for CaO, of BaO for MgO and CaO for MgO in glasses containing constant soda; the curves are bowed slightly towards high activation energies.

D. Effect of Various Network Forming Ions on Conductivity

Oxides of trivalent ions, of formula R_2O_3, can form $[RO_4]^-$ groups in a glass when alkali ions are present to balance the negative charge. The $[RO_4]^-$ groups substitute for $[SiO_4]$ groups in the glass network. The pure oxide R_2O_3 may not itself form a glass but it can enter the glass structure as a network forming oxide. However when the mol % R_2O_3 exceeds the mol % alkali oxide, there is insufficient oxygen—and no balancing cations—for the formation of $[RO_4]^-$ groups from all the R_2O_3 and some other forms of co-ordination must be taken up.

B_2O_3 can be introduced into silicate glasses in any proportion; glasses can be formed at all compositions from a pure borate to a pure silicate. As B_2O_3 is substituted for SiO_2 in a series of glasses with constant alkali content $[BO_4]^-$ groups are formed until there are no non-bridging oxygens left, and then neutral BO_3 groups are formed as in pure boric oxide glass. Otto (1966) found that the activation energy for sodium and lithium borosilicate glasses increased linearly with B_2O_3 content over the whole range of substitution with no singularity at the composition where BO_3 groups first occur. Figure 12 shows his results for the soda glasses. Glasses in the upper line with 0·25 Na_2O can accommodate only up to 0·25 B_2O_3 in $[BO_4]^-$ groups and with higher mole fractions of B_2O_3, $[BO_3]$ groups must be formed; however there is no break in the line at this composition. Otto found that the effect of B_2O_3 content on activation energy decreased with increasing alkali content and that glasses with high alkali content (greater than 0·45 Na_2O or 0·43 Li_2O) had activation energies independent of B_2O_3 content. In the binary alkali borate glasses Bray and O'Keefe (1963) and Greenblatt and Bray (1967) have shown by NMR measurements that one $[BO_4]^-$ group is formed for each alkali ion up to about 50 mol % alkali oxide.

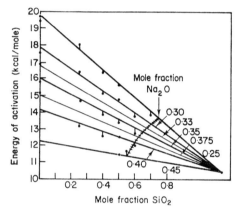

FIG. 12. Activation energy of d.c. condition versus mol fraction SiO_2 in the system Na_2O B_2O_3–SiO_2 (after Otto, 1966).

The substitution of Al_2O_3 for SiO_2 gives a quite sharp minimum of activation energy, and maximum of conductivity, at the composition $1Na_2O:1Al_2O_3$ where all oxygens are in bridging positions. In the series represented by $1Na.xAl.(2-x)Si$ and $1Na.xAl.(4-x)Si$ (with stoichiometric oxygen), Isard (1959) found minima of activation energy at the compositions with $x = 1$. Ivanov and Galant (1965) found minimum at $x = 13$ in the series $13 Na_2O.xR_2O_3.(87-x) SiO_2$ where R = Al, Ga or Fe, as shown in Fig. 13; for Al and Ga the minima are sharp but for Fe it is rather broad. It is generally agreed that aluminium must adopt four-fold co-ordination with oxygen to form $[AlO_4]^-$ groups when there is sufficient alkali oxide, but a number of different proposals have been put forward for its co-ordination when it is in excess. Isard (1959) suggested that the excess Al forms AlO_6

groups with bridging oxygens, the Al^{3+} ion entering the interstices of the
network as a network modifying ion. Lacey (1963) suggested the formation
of "triclusters" in which an oxygen is shared between three tetrahedral
groups, either one AlO_4 and two SiO_4 or two AlO_4 and one SiO_4.

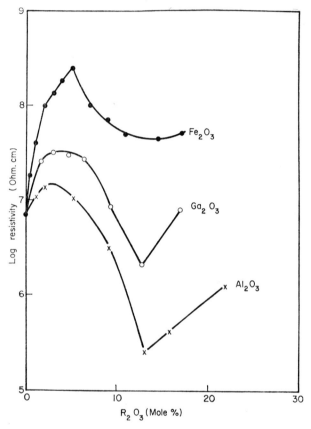

FIG. 13. Log d.c. resistivity at 150° versus R_2O_3 content in the series (mol %) 13 Na_2O.
xR_2O_3. $(87 - x)$ SiO_2 (after Ivanov and Galant, 1965).

The effect of Al_2O_3 on the activation energy can be explained qualitatively by the changes in the state of the oxygen ions. As Al_2O_3 is substituted
for SiO_2, non-bridging oxygens are replaced by less polarizable bridging
oxygens and the minimum of activation energy can be attributed to all the
oxygens being in bridging positions, and therefore being of low polarizability; with excess of Al_2O_3 some of the oxygens must be in a more
polarizable condition. The effect of B_2O_3, in giving a continuous rise of

activation energy with B_2O_3 content is, of course, contrary to this theory; the activation energy would be expected to *decrease* to a constant value at those compositions for which all the oxygens are in bridging positions, and the value would be expected to be lower in borate glasses than in silicate glasses. The difference between the effect of B_2O_3 and Al_2O_3 probably lies in the atomic densities of the glasses. The $[AlO_4]^-$ group is relatively large and the atomic concentration of oxygen hardly changes as Al_2O_3 is substituted for SiO_2; only the state of the oxygens changes. However both the BO_4 and BO_3 groups are small and the atomic concentration of oxygen increases as B_2O_3 is substituted for SiO_2; the change in oxygen density must over-ride the changes in the polarizability of the oxygens. It is not so much the average density of oxygens in the glass which is important but how closely they pack round the individual alkali ions. Mazurin (1960) supposed that an alkali ion associated with a $[BO_4]^-$ group is *more* tightly held than one associated with a non-bridging oxygen, in spite of the higher polarizability of the latter. Furthermore, the substitution of Al_2O_3 for B_2O_3 in a borosilicate glass lowers the activation energy while in a simple borate glass it has hardly any effect, as shown by Beekenkamp (1968) for K_2O glasses and by Otto (1966) for Li_2O glasses. The activation energy for ionic migration clearly depends on a number of factors and, unless the above theories can be placed on a quantitative basis, they must be regarded as very tentative.

Most other oxides of the form RO_2 can only be dissolved into silicate melts in limited quantities. In general, such oxides have only a very small effect on alkali ion migration; but this is to be expected if they enter the structure as network formers since there will be no changes in the co-ordination state of the oxygens, and, as most of the possible ions are relatively large the oxygen density of the glass will not increase.

E. The Mixed Alkali Effect

As one alkali is progressively substituted for another in a series of glass compositions containing more than about 10% total alkali, the electrical conductivity passes through a minimum. This is known as the "mixed alkali", "poly-alkali" or "neutralization" effect; it has been observed in many types of simple and complex glasses and for most pairs of alkalis. The minimum of conductivity is associated with a maximum of activation energy; the pre-exponential conductivity term generally shows a maximum. The magnitude of the mixed alkali effect increases systematically with increasing difference in size between the two alkali ions, as shown in the activation energy curves in Fig. 14 from the work of Hakim and Uhlmann (1967); the heights of the maxima increase in the order Rb < K < Na < Li when these alkalis are substituted for caesium. The partial substitution of a third alkali raises the activation energy still further, as shown by Mazurin (1965) in the system (Li, Na, K)$_2$ 0.2 SiO$_2$. The effect decreases with decreasing alkali concentration; Ivanov (1966) reported its disappearance in (Na$_2$O + K$_2$O)–GeO$_2$ glasses at about 10 mol % alkali oxide, i.e. approximately 10×10^{-3} mol/ml. Similar results have been reported for silicates (Leko, 1966, 1967a, b; Ipateva et al., 1967) and borosilicates (Ipateva et al., 1967) the critical alkali content at which the effect disappears being about 8×10^{-3} mol/ml.

The mixed alkali effect is only revealed in physical properties which depend primarily on structures associated with the alkali ion. In a recent review (Isard, 1969) it was shown that the molar volume follows a nearly ideal linear relation in a mixed alkali series. Expansion coefficient shows a considerable departure from linearity while chemical durability shows a pronounced maximum and viscosity a minimum. The linear variation of molar volume with alkali substitution means that the effect cannot be simply explained by a general compaction of the random network made possible by having ions of different sizes available to fill the interstices. Or, if such a compaction does occur around the alkali ions, it must be compensated by an equal opening up of the structure at places away from the alkali ions.

Myuller (1960a, b) introduced the idea of separated regions for each alkali; each kind of alkali ion can only migrate through a region where there are sites vacated by other ions of the same kind. The activation energy for a

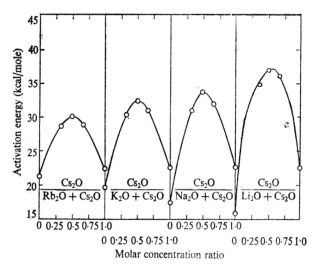

Fig. 14. Activation energy of d.c. condition versus molar concentration ratio for mixed alkali glasses of the series (mol %) 15 (Cs$_2$O + R$_2$O). 85 SiO$_2$ (after Hakim and Uhlmann, 1967).

given ion varies with its concentration as if the other ion was not present—i.e. as if the glass were a single alkali glass. Hence Eqn. 8 can be used for each ion; the total conductivity is given by

$$\sigma = \text{constant } [M_1] \exp \left(-\psi_{\phi_1}/2RT\right)$$
$$+ \text{constant } [M_2] \exp \left(-\psi_{\phi_2}/2RT\right) \quad (9)$$

where ψ_{ϕ_1} and ψ_{ϕ_2} depend on $[M_1]$ and $[M_2]$ as given in Eqn 8. However, for many mixed alkali glasses, the activation energy for conduction is even higher than that for either of the single alkali glasses containing the same mole fractions of the alkalis. Diffusion measurements lend some support to Myuller's theory. Evstropev (1960) found that, for single alkali glasses, sodium diffuses much more slowly into a potash glass than into a soda glass of the same molar composition; similarly potassium diffuses more slowly into a soda glass than into a potash glass. Evstropev and Pavlovskii (1966) obtained similar results with Na and Rb in germanate glasses. Figure 15 shows Evstropev's measurements on mixed alkali glasses. D_{Na} decreases

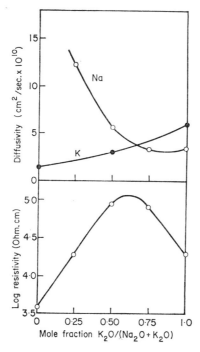

FIG. 15. Log d.c. resistivity and diffusivity at 415°C versus mole fraction $K_2O/(Na_2O + K_2O)$ for series (mol %) 20 $(Na_2O + K_2O)$. 80 SiO_2 (after Evstropev, 1960).

very steeply with substitution of K_2O for Na_2O reaching a minimum at about 0·8 mole ratio of K_2O to total alkali; D_K decreases less steeply as Na_2O is substituted for K_2O. If u indicates mobility, the minimum of conductivity then follows from the sum of terms $n_{Na} \cdot e \cdot u_{Na}$ and $n_K \cdot e \cdot u_K$ where u_{Na} decreases as n_{Na} decreases and u_K decreases as n_K decreases. Mazurin (1965) suggested that the relatively larger effect of substituting K for Na on D_{Na} than that of substituting Na for K on D_K is that polarizability of the non-polarizing oxygens increases as a larger alkali ion of lower field strength is substituted for a smaller ion. Thus in a potash glass, the non-bridging oxygen ions are less strongly polarized by the large K^+ ions, than they are in a soda glass of the same molar fraction of alkali; hence they provide a more polarizable medium for Na^+ ions and give a higher activation energy for Na^+ ion migration. However in the $Na_2O–Rb_2O–GeO_2$ glasses Evstropev and Pavlovskii found that D_{Na} passes through a minimum, and

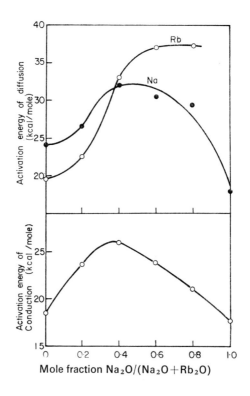

FIG. 16. Activation energies of d.c. condition and diffusion of sodium and rubidium versus mole fraction $Na_2O/(Na_2O + Rb_2O)$ for series (mol %) $25(Na_2O + Rb_2O)$. $75GeO_2$. (Evstropev and Pavlovskii, 1966).

the activation energy for sodium diffusion passes through a maximum, on substituting Rb for Na. Figure 16 shows the results of their measurements.

Myuller's theory does not require that observable phase separation occurs in mixed alkali glass, but only that distinct and separate structural groupings are associated with each kind of alkali ion. Some authors have suggested that phase separation does occur, but there is no evidence for this; on the contrary, the rate of phase separation in Li_2O–SiO_2 glasses decreases with partial substitution of K_2O, and no phase separation occurs in the alkali silicate glasses containing only K, Rb, and Cs, whereas the mixed alkali effect is very pronounced with these alkalis.

Lengyel and Boksay (1954, 1955) developed a mathematical theory for the mixed alkali effect based on the principle that the migration of the larger ion is blocked when it reaches a site vacated by a smaller ion. In its original form the theory was based on a number of assumptions that are hardly acceptable; the migration was assumed to be a vacancy diffusion process and diffusion was only allowed in one dimension—i.e. in the direction of the applied field. In a three-dimensional diffusion process, blocking effects are expected to be negligible until the blocking structures occupy an appreciable volume fraction of the material, whereas the mixed alkali effect is very marked for the first few percent substitution of one oxide for another. In a later paper (Lengyel and Boksay, 1963) the theory was modified to account for this and to explain the effect on activation energy.

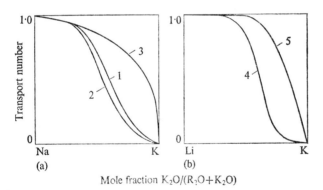

Mole fraction $K_2O/(R_2O + K_2O)$

FIG. 17. Transport numbers of (a) sodium and (b) lithium versus mol fraction $K_2O/(R_2O + K_2O)$ (after Pavlova, 1968)

Curve 1: $20(Na_2O + K_2O)$. $5 TiO_2$. $6 CaO$. $69 SiO_2$ at 400°C and $20(Na_2O + K_2O)$. $5 BaO$. $10 B_2O_3$. $65 SiO_2$ at 400°C.

Curve 2: $20 (Na_2O + K_2O)$. $80 SiO_2$ at 400°C and $30 (Na_2O + K_2O)$. $5TiO_2$. $6 CaO$. $59 SiO_2$ at 400°C

Curve 3: $10 (Na_2O + K_2O)$. $6 TiO_2$. $5 B_2O_3$ $79 SiO_2$ at 550°C.

Curve 4: $20 (Li_2O + K_2O)$. $5 TiO_2$. $6 CaO$. $69 SiO_2$ at 500°C.

Curve 5: $10 (Li_2O + K_2O)$. $6 TiO_2$. $5 B_2O_3$.$79 SiO_2$ at 550°C.

Theories of the mixed alkali effect mostly assume that conduction is predominantly due to a single ion except in glasses near the minimum; for example, in Eqn 9 one or other term will be by far the largest except over a narrow region of compositions. The relation of transport number for one ion to the mole fraction of that ion is expected to be a highly zigmodial curve with only a narrow range of compositions near the minimum of conductivity where both ions make a substantial contribution to the current. Experimental transport number measurements, however, suggest that mixed transport occurs over a wide range of compositions. Pavlova (1958) investigated Na_2O–K_2O glasses and Li_2O–K_2O glasses of complex compositions at 400–500°C with the results shown in Fig. 17; in all series mixed conduction occurred over a fairly wide range of compositions. Pavlova found that the minimum of conductivity occurred at the composition where the transport numbers of the two ions were equal; the series with larger total alkali contents gave deeper minima of conductivity and more sharply inflected transport number curves. Pavlova did not find a significant change in shape of the transport number curve with temperature. Lengyel et al. (1963) however, found sharper inflections at 270° than at 420° as shown in Fig. 18. If the two ions migrate independently with different activation energies, as suggested in Eqn 9, the transport number curve must become more sharply inflected as the temperature is lowered; for the minority ion gives the least contribution to the current and has the highest activation energy, and hence, this contribution must decrease more rapidly with decreasing temperature than that of the majority ion. On the other hand, if the conduction process is more like that suggested by Lengyel in which the migration of both ions is controlled by the limiting rate of a particular kind of ion jump, such as the large ions jumping into the small ion sites, the transport number for a given glass will be independent of temperature.

Hughes and Isard (1968), using the Tubandt method described earlier, measured transport numbers of two series of Na_2O–K_2O silicate glasses. Their results are shown in Fig. 19, with data from conductivity measure-

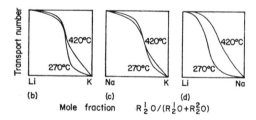

FIG. 18. Transport numbers of (a) lithium, (b) sodium and (c) lithium versus mol fractions in the series 16 $(R_2^1O + R_2^2O)$. 8 MgO. 8 BaO. 68 SiO_2 (after Lengyel et al., 1963).

ments. A few transport numbers were determined for one series using the method of Burt at a lower temperature. These agreed with those at the higher temperature. It was found that the maximum activation energy occurred at the molecular ratios at which $t_{Na} = t_K = 0\cdot5$. For the complex series the minimum conductivity also occurred close to this position but for the simple silicate series it was displaced toward a higher K_2O content. The temperature independent term of the conductivity equation varied comparatively little for the complex series, but showed a pronounced maximum for the simple series. In a further series the total alkali was varied, keeping the ratio of alkalis constant according to the formula $xK_2O \cdot xNa_2O \cdot (100-2x) SiO_2$, x being 7·5–15 mol %. It was found that t_{Na} increased with total alkali content; hence the molecular ratio $K_2O/(Na_2O + K_2O)$ at which $t_{Na} = 0\cdot5$ moves to high K_2O contents with the increase of total alkali content. By extrapolation it was concluded that t_{Na} would be 0·5 at the molecular ratio of 0·5 when the total alkali content is approximately 12·5 mol %.

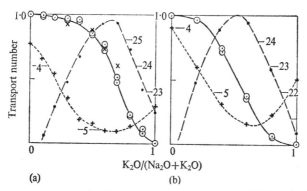

FIG. 19. Transport number of sodium versus mol fraction $K_2O/(K_2O + Na_2O)$ (after Hughes and Isard, 1968)

(a) Series (mol %) 13.53 $(K_2O + Na_2O)$. 5.54 MgO. 5.97 CaO. 1.22 Al_2O_3. 73.8SiO_2.

(b) Series (mol %) 15.25 $(K_2O + Na_2O)$. 84.75 SiO_2.

⊙   by Tubandt method.
×   by Burt method.
+----+ log conductivity (a) 510°C, (b) 410°C.
●——● activation energy (kcal/mol).

The results of the transport measurements of Hughes and Isard (1968) indicated that single alkali ion transport does not occur in any of the mixed alkali glasses, even though the curves are all definitely sigmoid in shape.

Assuming that all the ions of each type participated in conduction, ionic mobilities were derived from the equation

$$u_i = t_i . \sigma/F . N_i . d \qquad (10)$$

where i indicates the Na^+ or K^+ ion, N is the mole fraction of the ion per g of glass, d is density and F is the faraday. The resultant curves are shown in Fig. 20 and indicate that the mobility of the sodium ion decreases steeply as K_2O is substituted for Na_2O, but that the potassium ion mobility is not affected as critically. This is in general agreement with the diffusion measurements of Evstropev (1960), and of Sendt (1964). However, the potassium ion curve for the complex silicate shows a clear minimum in the mobility. If it is assumed that the transport number curve is the same shape at much lower temperatures, both the sodium and potassium ion mobilities must show minima.

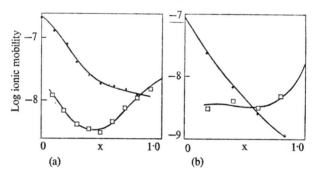

FIG. 20. Log ionic mobilities verus mol fraction $K_2O/(K_2O + Na_2O)$ (after Hughes and Isard 1968).
(a) Series (mol %) 13.53 ($K_2O + Na_2O$). 5.97 CaO.5.54 MgO. 1.22Al$_2$O$_3$. 73.8 SiO$_2$ at 510°C. (b) Series (mol %) 15.25 ($K_2O + Na_2O$) 84.75 SiO$_2$ at 410°C.● — Na$^+$ □ — K$^+$.

VII. Methods of Investigating Conduction Due to Other than Alkali Ions

A. The Nernst–Einstein Relation

As shown in Section IV, the direct determination of transport number in highly resistive glasses is extremely difficult. Electrode polarization may be difficult to distinguish from dielectric relaxation, as shown in Section V, and electronically conducting glasses exhibit similar dielectric relaxation effects to ionically conducting glasses (Isard, 1970). A considerable effort has therefore been devoted to indirect methods of inferring the conduction mechanism. None of these methods can be relied on entirely and conclusions based on indirect methods alone must be treated with reserve.

As discussed in Section III, order of magnitude agreement is expected between the measured conductivity of an ionic conductor and that calculated by the Nernst–Einstein relation from the self-diffusion coefficient of the conducting ion. The correlation coefficient may introduce a factor of about 0·2–1·0 so that exact agreement is not necessarily expected. Conversely, order of magnitude agreement between conductivity and diffusion experiments can be taken as strong evidence of a common ionic mechanism, especially if the temperature dependence is the same. Isotopic exchange diffusion measurements can be extremely sensitive and are often possible where electrode deposition cannot be measured by conventional means. Evstropev and Kharyuzov (1961) used the Nernst–Einstein relation to determine the charge carriers in barium silicate glasses. Conductivity was found to increase linearly with BaO content for glasses containing 40–60 mol % BaO and with an Na_2O impurity content not exceeding 0·02 wt %. It was assumed that the possible conducting species were either Na^+ or Ba^{2+} ions and the diffusion coefficients were measured on the 50 BaO . 50 SiO_2 glass at 655° using sodium -22 and barium -140 tracers. The diffusion coefficients were both $2(\pm 1) . 10^{-12} cm^2 . s^{-1}$ and the conductivities calculated for each ion were compared with the measured conductivity giving:

$$-\log \sigma_{Ba} \qquad -\log \sigma_{Na} \qquad -\log \sigma_{meas}$$

$$6·8 \pm 0·2 \qquad 10·3 \pm 0·3 \qquad 6·3 \pm 0·2$$

Even allowing for correlation effects, it was concluded that Ba^{2+} ions are the current carriers in this glass, and it was assumed that other divalent metal ions are the carriers in their respective alkali-free silicate glasses. The contribution of the sodium ion to conductivity was small due to its low concentration, although its mobility was of the same order of magnitude as that of the barium ion.

Indirect evidence for R^{++} ion migration has been adduced from the dependence of conductivity on composition. Myuller and Leko (1966) compared the activation energies of alkaline earth glasses with those of alkali glasses containing the same concentration of modifier ions. For borate glasses containing a metallic ion concentration of 14×10^{-3} mol . ml^{-1} the BaO–B_2O_3 glass had an activation energy of about 1·75 eV while the Na_2O–B_2O_3 glass had a value of about 0·9 eV: for silicate glasses containing ion concentrations of 24×10^{-3} mol . ml^{-1} the CaO–SiO_2 glass had a value of 1·4 eV while the Na_2O–SiO_2 glass had a value of 0·7 eV. They concluded that the divalent ions carry the current in alkali-free barium borate and calcium silicate glasses, since the electrolytic dissociation energy of the polar structural units, which controls the activation energy in their model, was expected to be proportional to the ionic charge. Schwartz and Mackenzie (1966) observed that, in $CaO-SiO_2$ glasses, the activation energy fell from 33·5 to 31·2 kcal mol^{-1} as the CaO content increased from 40 to 55 mol %; variations of the Na_2O impurity content in the range 0·01 to 1·30 mol % had little effect on conductivity for a constant mol % CaO. They concluded that Na^+ ions were not the current carriers, and that the likely carriers were the Ca^{2+} ions, their mobility increasing with CaO concentration as the network is broken up.

Milnes and Isard (1962) used the Nernst–Einstein relation to compare their measured conductivities of a lead silicate glass with lead diffusion data of Lindner et al. (1960) on glasses of the same composition. Although the temperature ranges of the two experiments barely overlapped, both gave very similar activation energies and the absolute magnitude of the measured conductivity agreed fairly closely at the same temperature with that calculated from diffusion. It was concluded that the Pb^{++} ion carries the current in alkali-free lead silicate glass. However, the transport measurements of Hughes et al. (1968) later gave direct proof that this could not be so; the lack of measurable electrode deposition in the Tubandt experiment required that only H^+ ions or electrons could carry the current, as shown in Fig. 4 above. The possibility of H^+ ion conduction in lead silicate glasses is supported by the dependence of the conductivity on the residual water content, which was observed by Milnes and Isard (1962). Recent unpublished measurements of lead diffusion and of conductivity on the same specimens have indicated that, indeed, the lead diffusion is too small to account for the conductivity. This shows the difficulty of identifying the current carriers by any means but direct transport measurements.

Even the Tubandt experiment can give conflicting results, as shown by Gough et al. (1969) on bismuth borate glass. Glass of composition 60 Bi_2O_3 . 40 B_2O_3 has about the same conductivity as 50 PbO . 50 SiO_2 glass and it should enable a detectable weight change to be observed in a similar experiment. The electrolysis of a pile of three discs of this bismuth borate glass at 340°C gave no detectable weight change to ±1·5 mg when 23 mg of silver was deposited in a series coulometer. However black dendrites were observed to have grown from the negative faces of each disc into the glass. It was concluded that the current was electronic at the points of contact where the field was high but cationic within the glass; the electrons entering the negative face of each disc would neutralize the cations and deposit metal, or if H^+ ions carry the current, the hydrogen released reduces the glass. However no dependence of conductivity on residual water content was observed in these glasses. Neither was any dependence on trace metal impurity observed when glasses were melted from oxides of different purity or when deliberate additions of up to 0·1% Na_2O, AgO and Fe_2O_3 were made. No difference was observed between melts bubbled with 100%, 10% and 1% O_2 in N_2. The activation energy decreases with increasing Bi_2O_3 content, but it seems unlikely that Bi^{3+} ions are mobile enough to give measurable conductivities.

Owen (1961) suggested that oxygen ions carry the current in the highly resistive $CaO-B_2O_3-Al_2O_3$ glasses. This conclusion was based on a comparison of the variation of activation energy with composition with a theoretical model of short range atomic structure; the activation energy increased as the proportion of non-bridging oxygens fell and had the same high value for all those compositions containing only bridging oxygens. Gough et al. (1969) using the data of Hirayama (1962) showed that very similar activation energies occur in all the $RO-B_2O_3-Al_2O_3$ glasses at the same molar compositions whatever the identity of the divalent ion R^{++} (except Pb^{++}). Hagel and Mackenzie (1964) measured oxygen diffusion in two $CaO-B_2O_3-Al_2O_3$ glasses and in a $CaO-Al_2O_3-SiO_2$ slag using oxygen-18 isotope exchange; diffusion coefficients were calculated from the measured conductivity by means of the Nernst–Einstein equation, and results are shown in Table III together with the activation energies of conductivity and oxygen diffusion, ΔH_{DC} and Q_D respectively.

TABLE III. The results of resistivity and oxygen diffusivity measurements on various glasses—after Hagel and Mackenzie (1964).

Composition	H_{DC} kcal/mol	Q_0 kcal/mol	$\dfrac{D \text{ calculated}}{D \text{ measured}}$
$42 \cdot 2\,CaO.15 \cdot 7\,Al_2O_3.42 \cdot 1\,B_2O_3$	$34 \cdot 1$	$35 \cdot 4$	Approx. 5
$25 \cdot 9\,CaO.12 \cdot 7\,Al_2O_3.61 \cdot 4\,B_2O_3$	$40 \cdot 9$	$46 \cdot 6$	Approx. 10
$45 \cdot 0\,CaO.13 \cdot 3\,Al_2O_3.41 \cdot 7\,SiO_2$	$36 \cdot 7$	$57 \cdot 7$	Approx. 10^3

Hagel and Mackenzie concluded that oxygen ion conductivity was highly improbable in any of these glasses but Owen (1965) considered that the results were in fact consistent with oxygen ion conduction in the $CaO-Al_2O_3-B_2O_3$ glasses, although in the silicate glass another conduction mechanism is present. However Gough et al. (1969) found that a 50% increase in the residual water content retained in the glass of composition $27\,BaO.13\,Al_2O_3.60\,B_2O_3$ resulted in a reduction of the activation energy from $44 \cdot 2$ to $40 \cdot 4$ kcal mol^{-1}. This is comparable to the effect of a large change in the major constitutents. It was therefore concluded that conduction was by H^+ or OH^- migration. The possibility of protonic conduction has also been suggested for barium phosphate glasses (Namikawa and Asahara, 1966), whose conductivity is dependent on water content.

The PbO glasses in the system $RO-B_2O_3-Al_2O_3$ are significantly more conducting than those containing other RO oxides and it is likely that a different conduction mechanism operates. Measurements of the diffusion of lead in the glass $PbO.2B_2O_3$ were made by De Luca and Bergeron (1969) over the range 400–480° using lead–207 isotope and analysis by mass spectrograph. The activation energy of diffusion was found to be 13·7 kcal mol^{-1}. The results of Gough et al. (1969) may be interpolated to give 34·9 kcal mol^{-1} for the activation energy of conduction at this composition. Although the conduction was measured over a somewhat lower temperature range, the difference is so large that conduction by Pb^{2+} ions in this system must be excluded.

B. Electrochemical Potentials

If reversible electrodes are applied to an ionic conductor for which the electrode reaction is known the transport number for ionic conduction can be determined, in principle, from the open circuit e.m.f. developed between the electrodes. If the electrode reaction involves n equivalents of a gas whose partial pressures are p_1, p_2 at the two electrodes, a purely ionic electrolyte will yield the full cell e.m.f. $V_0 = (RT/nF) \ln (p_1/p_2)$. Any electronic current can be regarded as a partial short circuit of the cell and if V is the e.m.f. actually developed, the transport number for ionic conduction, t_i, is given by V/V_0. Buchanan and Kingerey (1965) used platinum electrodes exposed to different partial pressures of oxygen on opposite sides of a disc of soda lime glass. They found values of $t_i = 0·99$ at 500°C for glass melted in air at atmospheric pressure, but the value decreased to 0·72 for glass of the same composition melted under oxygen pressures up to 12 atmospheres. They concluded that the current was partially electronic in the latter material, but it remains somewhat anomalous that melting under oxygen pressure caused conductivity to increase by the same factor over the whole temperature range so that the electronic contribution must have had the same activation energy as the ionic. Jorgensen and Norton (1969) used porous platinum electrodes on membranes of silica glass with different partial pressures of hydrogen on opposite sides. A prolonged heat treatment was used to remove hydroxyl and the membranes were electrolyzed to replace all the original alkali ions by hydrogen ions. E.m.f. measurements using hydrogen pressures of 0·1–100 torr then gave an ionic transport number of 0·6, in close agreement with that derived from the measured evolution of hydrogen with charge passed. Mackenzie (1964) was unable to obtain consistent values of electrochemical potential with known ionically conducting glasses but the values were of the correct order of magnitude; known electronically conducting glasses gave only very low potential in comparable experiments. A fuller investigation of this type of experiment seems called for, both to establish its validity with glasses whose transport number can be determined directly and to apply it to glasses of very high resistivity.

C. Dependence of Pre-Exponential Term on Activation Energy

Both electronically conducting glasses and ionically conducting glasses exhibit a temperature dependence below the transformation range governed by Eqn 1. Statistically there is a tendency for the temperature-independent term, A, to be lower in electronic glasses than in ionic (higher for the corresponding formula for resistivity). Figure 21 shows the graph of Zertzalova *et al.* (1965) in which the regions of electronic and ionic conduction are

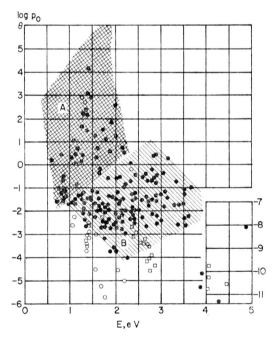

FIG. 21. Pre–exponential term (log ρ_0) versus activation energy of d.c. condition (E) for various glasses (after Zertzalova *et al.*, 1965).

A — region of glasses having proven or presumed electronic condition.
B — region of glasses having proven or presumed cationic condition.
○ — chalcogenide glasses.
□ — fluoride glasses.
● — other glasses.

shown on a plot of activation energy against temperature in independent terms of resistivity. A similar graph was produced by Evstropev et al. (1966). The two regions are continuous and the statistical distributions overlap; hence the position of a glass in this diagram cannot be regarded as "proof" of its conduction mechanism. Trap and Stevels (1963a, b) investigated the correlations between temperature independent term A and activation energy Q (in eV) of the form $A = mQ + n$. For groups of known ionic glasses they found m to lie between -5 and -9 and n between $+4$ and $+10$ with statistical correlation coefficients of 0·75–1·00. Complex silicate glasses both of the conventional and invert glass-forming compositions had values in this range. When increasing amounts of iron oxide were added to these compositions a sudden increase of conductivity by several decades was observed at a certain iron oxide content, depending on the state of reduction of the melt. The highly conducting glasses, which were considered to be electronic gave $m = +31·6$ and $n = 0·11$ with a statistical correlation coefficient of 0·85. They concluded that in specific groups of glasses, the values of m and n in the correlation of A with Q enabled electronic conduction to be distinguished from ionic.

The fluoride glasses shown on the diagram of Zertzalova et al. (1965) are based on BeF_2 although only complex mixtures of fluoride have a good glass forming tendency. Their conductivities are characterized by extremely high values of A in Eqn 1, combined with high activation energies, as illustrated in the data of Table IV.

TABLE IV.   Electrical parameters and compositions of some fluoride glasses—after Petrovskii et al. (1965).

Glass Composition	$\log A$	Activation Energy eV
60 BeF_2.10 AlF_3.20 CsF.	11·01	4·00
60 BeF_2.10 AlF_3.20 CsF.10 CaF_2.	10·69	4·45
60 BeF_2.10 AlF_3.20 CsF.10 SrF_2.	9·81	4·05
60 BeF_2.10 AlF_3.20 CsF.10 BaF_2.	10·40	4·05

Petrovskii et al. (1965) concluded that the current is carried by fluoride ions. Supporting evidence for this was that the conductivity of the glasses changed comparatively little on crystallization and some fluoride crystals are known to conduct by fluoride ion transport; furthermore the effects of adding alkali fluorides and alkaline earth fluorides is quite different from the effects of alkali and alkaline earth oxides in oxide glasses. Addition of alkali fluorides to the alkali-free composition 30 BeF_2 . 20 AlF_2 . 30 CaF_2 . 20 SrF_2 caused comparatively small increases in conductivity, the effect being largest for largest ion, Cs and less in the order Cs > K > Na > Li. The small effect of the addition of alkalis and the reversal of order compared with oxide glasses showing alkali ion conductivity suggest that conduction is not due to alkali ions. The addition of fluorides of divalent elements to the glass 60 BeF_2 . 10 AlF_2 . 20 CsF caused a decrease in conductivity in the order CaF_2 > SrF_2 > BaF_2 with MgF_2 about equal to BaF_2 but giving an anomalous combination of activation energy and temperature independent term. Thus the divalent ions do not have the same effect as oxide glasses with alkali ion conduction.

D. Characteristics of Electronic Conduction in Glasses

Two groups of glass composition are accepted as electronic conductors; the first group consists of oxide glasses containing relatively large concentrations of transition metal oxides, such as the vanadium phosphate glasses; the second group consists of sulphides, selenides and tellurides—the chalcogenide glasses. In both groups, the temperature dependence of conductivity is often represented by Eqn 1, at least over a wide range of temperature, and the conductivity is not critically dependent on trace impurities, as it is in the classical semi-conductors. However with the transition metal oxide glasses there is generally a dependence on the degree of reduction or oxidation during melting; the conductivity is generally at a maximum for a certain ratio of oxidized to reduced valence state of the transition metal ion (see Linsley *et al.*, 1970).

Electronically conducting glasses show at least some of the normal properties of semi-conductors but with characteristically very low mobilities. Direct transitions between localized electron levels are probably more important than conduction via bands of non-localized energy levels. Hence the Hall effect is small and difficult to observe. Thermoelectric e.m.f.s are readily observed (Mackenzie, 1964); however thermoelectric potentials can also be observed in ionically conducting glass (Oldekop, 1956). The optical absorption edge is broad but the energy corresponds approximately to the activation energy for conduction. Some vitreous semi-conductors show photoconduction. Raising the pressure generally increases the conductivity of electronic semi-conductors, though this is not an invariable rule. Mackenzie (1964) showed that the conductivity of vanadian phosphate glasses increases with pressure; Dolezalek and Spear (1970), however, found no effect of pressure on electron mobility in vitreous selenium. An increase of pressure always decreases the conductivity of ionic conductors. Charles (1962) has shown that the effect of hydrostatic pressure on an ionically conducting glass could be characterized by an activation volume Δv^* of 4·9 cc/mol in the equation

$$\rho = \rho_0 \exp(-p\,\Delta v^*/RT)$$

where p is the pressure, ρ the resistivity.

It must be concluded that none of the above properties of electronic conduction are sufficiently reliable to be applied as a test of conduction type, particularly in glasses of very low conductivity. Several such properties in combination may provide very strong evidence but ultimately it is necessary to demonstrate the presence or absence of electrolytic phenomena.

References

Anderson, O. L. and Stuart, D. A. (1954). *J. Am. Ceram. Soc.* **37**, 573.
Barton, J. L. (1970). *J. Non-Crystalline Solids* **4**, 220.
Beekenkamp, P. (1968). *Physics Chem. Glasses* **9**, 14.
Brailovskii, V. B., Rozenblyum, M. Ya. and Mazurin, O. V. (1966). *In* "The Structure of Glass' (E. A. Porai-Koshits, ed.) Vol, 7, p. 102. Consultants Bureau, New York.
Bray, P. J. and O'Keefe, J. G. (1963). *Physics Chem. Glasses* **4**, 37.
Buchanan, R. C. and Kingery, W. D. (1965), VII International Congress on Glass, Paper 368.
Burt, R. C. (1925). *J. opt. Soc. Am.* **11**, 87.
Charles, R. J. (1962). *J. Am. Ceram Soc.* **45**, 105.
Charles, R. J. (1963). *J. Am. Ceram. Soc.* **46**, 235.
Charles, R. J. (1964). *J. Am. Ceram. Soc.* **47**, 559.
Charles, R. J. (1965). *J. Am. Ceram. Soc.* **48**, 432.
Charles, R. J. (1966). *J. Am. Ceram. Soc.* **49**, 55.
Danilkin, V. I., Kudryavtsev, L. A. and Ivanov, V. A. (1965). *In* "The Structure of Glass" (O. V. Mazurin, ed.) Vol. 4, p. 106. Consultants Bureau, New York.
De Luca, J. P. and Bergeron, C. G. (1969). *J. Am. Ceram. Soc.* **52**, 629.
Dolezalek, F. K. and Spear, W. E. (1970). *J. Non-Crystalline Solids* **4**, 97.
Doremus, R. H. (1962). *In* "Modern Aspects of the Vitreous State" (J. D. Mackenzie, ed.) Vol. 2, p.1. Butterworth, London.
Doremus, R. H. (1964). *J. phys. Chem.,* Ithaca **68**, 2212.
Doremus, R. H. (1968). *J. electrochem. Soc.* **115**, 181.
Doremus, R. H. (1969). *Physics Chem. Glasses* **10**, 28.
Dunn, T., Hetherington, G. and Jack, K. H. (1965). *Physics Chem. Glasses* **6**, 16.
Evstropev, K. K. (1960). *In* "The Structure of Glass" (Proc. Third All-Union Conference on the Glassy State, Leningrad, 1959). Vol. 2, p. 237. Consultants Bureau, New York.
Evstropev, K. K. and Ivanov, O. A. (1963). *In* "Advances in Glass Technology" (F. R. Matson and G. E. Rindone, eds.) Part 2, p. 79. Plenum Press, New York.
Evstropev, K. K. and Kharyuzov, V. A. (1961). *Proc. Acad. Sci. USSR* **36**, 25.
Evstropev, K. K. and Pavlova, G. A. (1958). *Trudy leningr. tekhnol. Inst. im Lensoveta* **46**, 49.

Evstropev, K. K. and Pavlovskii, K. V. (1966). *In* "The Structure of Glass" (E. A. Porai-Koshits, ed.) Vol. 7, p. 103. Consultants Bureau, New York.

Evstropev, K. K., Pavlovskii, K. V. and Ivanov, A. O. (1965). *In* "The Structure of Glass" (O. V. Mazurin, ed.) Vol. 4, p. 110. Consultants Bureau, New York.

Evstropev, K. K., Kondrateva, B. S. and Petrovskii, G. P. (1966). *Soviet Phys. Dokl.* **169**, 457.

Fajans, K. and Kreidl, N. J. (1948). *J. Am. Ceram. Soc.* **31**, 105.

Fitzgerald, J. V. (1952). *J. chem. Phys.* **20**, 922.

Foex, J. V. (1944). *Bull. Soc. chim. Fr.* **11**, 456.

Frischat, G. H. (1967). *Glastech. Ber.* **40**, 382.

Frischat, G. H. (1968). *J. Am. Ceram. Soc.* **51**, 528.

Frischat, G. H. (1969). *J. Am. Ceram. Soc.* **52**, 625.

Frischat, G. H. and Oel, H. J. (1966). *Glastech. Ber.* **39**, 50.

Fulda, M. (1927). *Sprechsaal* **60**, 769, 789, 810. 831.

Garino-Carina, V. and Priqueler, M. (1962). *Physics Chem. Glasses* **3**, 37.

Gough, E., Isard, J. O. and Topping, J. A. (1969). *Physics Chem. Glasses* **10**, 89.

Greenblatt, S. and Bray, P. J. (1967). *Physics Chem. Glasses* **8**, 213.

Hagel, W. C. and Mackenzie, J. D. (1964). *Physics Chem. Glasses* **5**, 113.

Hakim, R. M. and Uhlmann, D. R. (1967). *Physics Chem. Glasses* **8**, 174.

Haven, Y. M. and Stevels, J. M. (1957). *In* "Proc. V[ie]. Conf. Int. du Verre. Paris, 1956" p. 343, International Commission on Glass.

Haven, Y. M. and Verkerk, B. (1965). *Physics Chem. Glasses* **6**, 38.

Heckman, R. W., Ringlien, J. A. and Williams, E. L. (1967). *Physics Chem. Glasses* **8**, 145.

Hetherington, G., Jack, K. H. and Ramsey, M. W. (1965). *Physics Chem. Glasses* **6**, 6.

Hirayama, C. (1962). *J. Am. Ceram. Soc.* **45**, 288.

Hughes, K. and Isard, J. O. (1968). *Physics Chem. Glasses* **9**, 37.

Hughes, K., Isard, J. O. and Milnes, G. C. (1968). *Physics Chem. Glasses* **9**, 43.

Ipateva, V. V., Borisova, Z. U. and Molchanov, V. S. (1967). *J. appl. Chem. USSR* **40**, 1373.

Isard, J. O. (1959). *J. Soc. Glass Technol.* **43**, 133T.

Isard, J. O. (1962a). *Proc. Instn elect. Engrs* **109B**, p. 440, Supplement No. 22.

Isard, J. O. (1962b). *J. scient. Instrum.* **40**, 403.

Isard, J. O. (1969). *J. Non-Crystalline Solids* **1**, 235.

Isard, J. O. (1970). *J. Non-Crystalline Solids* **4**, 357.

Ivanov, A. O. (1966). *In* "The Structure of Glass" (E. A. Porai-Koshits, ed.) Vol. 7, p. 100. Consultants Bureau, New York.

Ivanov, A. O. and Galant, E. I. (1965). *In* "The Structure of Glass" (O. V. Mazurin, ed.) Vol. 4, p. 84. Consultants Bureau, New York.

Ivanov, A. O., Evstropev, K. S. and Dorokhova, M. L. (1965). *In* "The Structure of Glass" (O. V. Mazurin, ed.) Vol. 4, p. 86. Consultants Bureau, New York.

Jones, G. O. (1956). "Glass". Methuen, London.

Jorgenson, P. J. and Norton, F. J. (1969). *Physics Chem. Glasses* **10**, 27.

Kaneko, H. and Isard, J. O. (1968). *Physics Chem. Glasses* **9**, 84.

Kats, A., Haven, Y. and Stevels, J. M. (1962). *Physics Chem. Glasses* **3**, 69.

Kinser, D. L. and Hench, L. L. (1969). *J. Am. Ceram. Soc.* **52**, 638.

Kraus, C. A. and Darby, E. J. (1922). *J. Am. chem. Soc.* **44**, 2783.

Lacey, E. D. (1963). *Physics Chem. Glasses* **4**, 234.

Leko, V. K. (1966). *In* "The Structure of Glass" (E. A. Porai-Koshits, ed.) Vol. 7, p. 96. Consultants Bureau, New York.

Leko, V. K. (1967a). *Inorg. Mater.* **3**, 1645.

Leko, V. K. (1967b). *Izv. Akad. Nauk. S.S.S.R.* **3**, 1224 From: (1969). *Ceramic Abstracts*, 337.

Lengyel, B. (1940). *Glastech. Ber.* **18**, 177.

Lengyel, B. and Boksay, Z. (1954). *Z. phys. Chem.* **203**, 93.

Lengyel, B. and Boksay, Z. (1955). *Z. phys. Chem.* **204**, 157.

Lengyel, B. and Boksay, Z. (1961). *Z. phys. Chem.* **217**, 357.

Lengyel, B. and Boksay, Z. (1963). *Z. phys. Chem.* **222**, 183.

Lengyel, B., Boksay, Z. and Dobos, S. (1963). *Z. phys. Chem.* **223**, 187.

Lindner, L., Hassenteuful, W. and Kotera, Y. (1960). *Z. phys. Chem.* Frankf. Ausg. **23**, 408.

Linsley, G. S., Owen., A. E. and Hayatee, F. M. (1970). *J. Non-Crystalline Solids* **4**, 208.

Littleton, J. T. and Morey, G. W. (1933). "The Electrical Properties of Glass". John Wiley, New York.

Mackenzie, J. D. (1960). *In* "Modern Aspects of the Vitreous State" (J. D. Mackenzie, ed.) Vol. 1, p. 1, 88. Butterworth, London.

Mackenzie, J. D. (1964). *In* "Modern Aspects of the Vitreous State" (J. D. Mackenzie, ed.) Vol. 3, p. 126. Butterworth, London.

Mazurin, O. V. (1960). *In* "The Structure of Glass.' (Proc. Third All-Union Conference on the Glassy State, Lenigrad, 1959) Vol. 2, p. 299. Consultants Bureau, New York.

Mazurin, O. V. (1965). *In* "The Structure of Glass" (O. V. Mazurin, ed.) Vol. 4, p. 5. Consultants Bureau, New York.

Mazurin, O. V. and Borisovskii, E. S. (1957). *Soviet Phys. tech. Phys.* **2**, 243.

Mazurin, O. V. and Brailovskaya, R. V. (1960). *Soviet Phys. solid St.* **2**, 1341.

Mazurin, O. V. and Brailovskii, V. B. (1966). *In* "The Structure of Glass" (E. A. Porai-Koshits, ed.) Vol. 7, p. 93. Consultants Bureau, New York.

Mazurin, O. V. and Tsekhomskii, V. A. (1964). *Izv. vȳssh. ucheb. Zaved. Fizika* **1**, 125.

Mazurin, O. V., Pavlova, G. A., Lev, E. Ia. and Leko, V. K. (1957). *Soviet Phys. tech. Phys.* **2**, 2511.

Milberg, M. E. and Peters, C. R. (1969). *Physics Chem. Glasses* **10**. 46.

Milberg, M. E., Otto, K. and Kushida, T. (1966). *Physics Chem. Glasses* **7**, 14.

Milnes, G. C. and Isard, J. O. (1962). *Physics Chem. Glasses* **3**, 157.

Morey, G. W. (1954). "The Properties of Glass", (American Ceramic Society Monograph). Reinhold, New York.

Myuller, R. L. (1960a). *Soviet Phys. solid St.* **2**, 1213, 1219. 1224.

Myuller, R. L. (1960b). *In* "The Structure of Glass" (Proc, Third All-Union Conference on the Glassy State, Leningrad, 1959) Vol. 2, p. 215. Consultants Bureau, New York.

Myuller, R. L. and Leko, V. K. (1966). *In* "Solid State Chemistry" (R. L. Myuller and Z. U. Borisova, eds.) p. 105. Consultants Bureau, New York.

Myuller, R. L. and Prankin, A. A. (1963). *J. appl. Chem. USSR* **36**, 144.

Myuller, R. L. and Prankin, A. A. (1965). *In* "The Structure of Glass" (O. V. Mazurin, ed.) Vol. 4, p. 93. Consultants Bureau, New York.

Namikawa, H. and Asahara, Y. (1966). *J. Ceram. Ass. Japan* **74**, 205.

Oldekop, W. (1956). *Glastech. Ber.* **29**, 73.

Otto, K. (1966). *Physics Chem. Glasses* **7**, 29.

Otto, K. and Milberg, M. E. (1967). *J. Am. Ceram. Soc.* **50**, 513.

Otto, K. and Milberg, M. E. (1968). *J. Am. Ceram. Soc.* **51**, 326.

Owen, A. E. (1961). *Physics Chem. Glasses* **2**, 87.

Owen, A. E. (1963). *In* "Progress in Ceramic Science" (J. E. Burke, ed.) Vol. 3, p. 77. Pergamon, London.

Owen, A. E. (1965). *Physics Chem. Glasses* **6**, 253.

Owen, A. E. and Douglas, R. W. (1959). *J. Soc. Glass Technol.* **43**, 159T.

Pavlova, G. A. (1958). *Trudy leningr. tekhnol. Inst. im Lensoveta* **46**, 56.

Petrovskii, G. T., Leko, E. K. and Mazurin, O. V. (1965). *In* "The Structure of Glass" (O. V. Mazurin, ed) Vol. 4. p. 88. Consultant Bureau, New York.

Porai-Koshits, E. A. (1958). *In* "The Structure of Glass" (Proc. Conference on the Structure of Glass, Lenigrad, 1953) p. 25. Consultants Bureau, New York.

Prankin, A. A. (1964). *J. appl. Chem. USSR* **37**, 887.

Proctor, J. M. and Sutton, P. M. (1959). *J. chem. Phys.* **30**, 212.

Proctor, J. M. and Sutton, P. M. (1960). *J. Am. Ceram. Soc.* **43**, 173.

Schwartz, M. and Mackenzie, J. D. (1966). *J. Am. Ceram. Soc.* **49**, 582.

Seddon, E., Tippet, E. J. and Turner, W. E. S. (1932). *J. Soc. Glass Technol* **16**, 450T.

Sendt, A. (1962). *In* "Advances in Glass Technology" (Compiled by the American Ceramic Society) Part 1, p. 307. Plenum Press, New York.

Sendt, A. (1964). *Glastech. Ber.* **37, 116.**

Stanworth, J. E. (1950). "The Physical Properties of Glass". Oxford University Press, London.

Stern, K. H. (1968). *J. phys. Chem. Ithaca* **72**, 2257.

Stevels, J. M. (1957). *In* "Handbuch der Physik" (S. Flügge, ed.) Vol. 20, p. 350. Springer–Verlag, Berlin.

Sutton, P. M. (1960). *In* "Progress in Dielectrics" (J. B. Birks and J. H. Schulman, eds.) Vol. 2, p. 113. John Wiley, New York.

Sutton, P. M. (1964). *J. Am. Ceram. Soc.* **47**, 188. 219.

Taylor, H. E. (1957). *J. Soc. Glass Technol.* **41**, 350T.

Taylor, H. E. (1959). *J. Soc. Glass Technol.* **43**, 126T.

Terai, R. (1969). *Physics Chem. Glasses* **10**, 146.

Terai, R. and Kitaoka, T. (1968). *J. Ceram. Ass. Japan* **76**, 393.

Terai, R. and Kitaoka, T. (1969). *Bull Govt Ind. Res. Inst. Osaka* **20**, 58.

Trap, H. J. L. (1964). *Sperchsaal* **97** 235.

Trap, H. J. L. and Stevels, J. M. (1959). *Glastech. Ber.* **32K**, (VI), 31.

Trap, H. J. L. and Stevels, J. M. (1960a). *Physics Chem. Glasses* **1**, 107.

Trap, H. J. L. and Stevels, J. M. (1960b). *Physics Chem. Glasses* **1**, 181.

Trap, H. J. L. and Stevels, J. M. (1963a). *In* "Advances in Glass Technology", (F. R. Matson and G. E. Rindone, eds.) Part 2, p. 70. Plenum Press, New York.

Trap, H. J. L. and Stevels, J. M. (1963b). *Physics Chem. Glasses* **4**, 193.

Tubandt, C. (1932). *In* "Handbuch der Experimentalphysik" Vol. XII, Part 1, p. 381. Akademische Verlagsgesellschaft, Leipzig.

Valenkov, N. and Porai-Koshits, E. A. (1936). *Z. Kristallogr. Kristallgeom.* **95**, 195.

Vargin, V. V. and Antoneva, E. A. (1956). *In* "Soviet Research in Glass and Ceramics, Part II: Glasses, Glazes and Enamels" p. 257. Consultants Bureau, New York.

Veltri, R. D. (1963). *Physics Chem. Glasses* **4**, 221.

Vermeer, J. (1956). *Physica, 's Grav.* **22**, 1247, 1257, 1269.

Warren, B. E. and Biscoe, J. (1938). *J. Am. Ceram. Soc.* **21**, 259.

Williams, E. L. and Heckman, R. W. (1964). *Physics Chem. Glasses* **5**, 166.

Zachariasen, W. H. (1932). *J. Am. Ceram. Soc.* **54**, 3841.

Zager, L. and Papanikolau, E. (1969). *Glastech. Ber.* **42**, 37.

Zertzalova, I. N., Fainberg, E. A. and Grechanik, L. A. (1965). *In* "The Structure of Glass" (O. V. Mazurin, ed.) Vol. 4, p. 74 Consultants Bureau, New York.

11. TRANSPORT PHENOMENA IN ION-EXCHANGE MEMBRANES

E. Riande

*Instituto de Pla´ticos y Caucho, Madrid, Spain**

I. Introduction

Membranes may be used chemistry and in chemical processes to control the flow of substances between two phases. The growth of polymer chemistry has made it possible to develop new membranes with evermore perfect structures, allowing different substances to be separated. The transport mechanism through a membrane depends on the membrane structure, which can be controlled by the preparation method. Membranes may be classified according to their structure.[1]

* Present Address: Mellon Institute, Pittsburgh, Pennsylvania, U.S.A.

Macroporous Membranes

The pores have a diameter of more than 50 Å and the transport mechanism through them is of convective type. They are very important for dialysis, ultrafiltration and osmotic processes.

Microporous Membranes

The pores have dimensions comparable with the thickness of the polymer chains and result from the irregularities in the packing of the almost randomly linked chain molecules. When the polymer chains are relatively bulky, as is the case with cellulose derivatives, the natural pores are large enough to let small molecules through. When the amorphous polymer is below its glass transition, the thermal movements of the chain segments are restricted in such a way that the pores actually exist. Strong interactions take place between the molecules and the pores as molecules move through these structures and the mechanism is of convective and diffusional type.

Membranes made of amorphous polymers above their glass transition

These membranes are characterized by the fact that the molecular diameter pores cannot have any real structure. The transport mechanism through these membranes is diffusive.

Membranes made up of crosslinked polymers

When the polymer is swollen by a liquid, a gel is formed through which liquid components may migrate by a mixed diffusion–convection mechanism. The substances dissolved in the liquid may be transported through the gel, but they interact with and are hindered by the interpenetrating polymer network. The transport mechanism is complex; diffusion and convection take place simultaneously.

Membranes made up of polymers crosslinked with ionic groups anchored in their structure

These membranes swell in water and ionic type substances may be transported through them. The interactions between the diverse flows in the membranes are determined by the distribution of substances in their structure and depend on the fixed ionic group concentration and the degree of crosslinking.

Ionic membranes may be either natural or synthetic. The former are found biologically and are structured such that polar groups are oriented towards the aqueous phase. The following man-made membranes may be distinguished:

1. Cation exchange membranes (with negative fixed groups)
2. Anion exchange membranes (with positive fixed groups)

3. Composite membranes: the anion and cation exchange membranes can be joined in various ways to form membranes of different configurations. Configurations which may be formed are.[2] (a) The cation and anion areas are so closely crosslinked, that they are physically indistinguishable; these are amphoteric membranes. (b) When the cation and anion areas are defined and distinguishable, these are called mosaic membranes. (c) A laminar combination of individual anionic and cationic membranes, either physically touching or separated by a porous spacer may be formed to give the bipolar array membrane.

Lakshminarayanaiah[2] has compiled an extensive bibliography on composite membranes, and phenomena on transport through these membranes have been studied by various workers.[3,4]

This study is divided into three parts. The preparation of simple ion exchange membranes is described in the first part. In the second part, major phenomena which occur when these membranes separate ionic solutions are dealt with. Thirdly, applications of ion exchange membranes are briefly mentioned.

II. Preparation of Ion Exchange Membranes

Meyer and Sievers [5] did the first work on membrane preparation; however this work was more important for showing that chemical preparation methods opened new and unsuspected possibilities than for the quality of the membranes they produced. Nevertheless, the Mayer Laboratories[6] showed little interest in the improving preparation methods and progress in this direction was slow. Several years went by before workers used the possibilities offered by polymer chemistry for membrane preparation.

Ion exchange membranes consist of polymer networks which have positive or negative charged fixed groups anchored in their structure. If the fixed groups are negative, the membrane is selective of cations, whereas positive fixed groups are selective of anions. The term selectivity may be explained as follows: counter-ions (those having the opposite sign from the fixed groups) have a transport number in the membrane phase which is higher than the co-ions, because the concentration of co-ions (ions with the same sign as the fixed groups) is low in the membrane due to Donnan exclusion. Electroneutrality is maintained by the fixed groups in the polymer matrix. A matrix may be obtained by addition or condensation polymerization reaction. Vinyl monomer polymerization, radical or ionic, is perhaps the simplest type of chain reaction as the only change is the increasing of the molecular size. Thus, high molecular weight linear macromolecules are obtained. There are three steps in radical addition polymerization (the most used for preparing membranes):

(A) *Initiation:* the decomposition of the initiator, by the action of heat or light, yields a pair of free radicals.

$$I \rightarrow 2R^{\cdot}$$

$$R^{\cdot} + M \rightarrow R - M^* \, (P).$$

(B) *Propagation:* new nomomer units are added to the growing free radical

$$P_n + M \rightarrow P_{n+1}.$$

(C) *Termination:* this process may be carried out by recombining the two growing radicals, by disproportionation, by transfer reactions to monomer, solvent, polymer, etc.

$$P_n + P_m \rightarrow M_{n+m}.$$

Another method of preparation is the condensation polymerization which takes place when monomers bearing two or more reactive groups may condense with the elimination of a by-product, for instance, water. When the functionality is greater than two, the condensation yields indefinitely large polymer structures. They may be considered as having infinite size and the occurence of a sharp gel point in these nonlinear condensations is very significant.

As ion groups make polymer chains soluble in water, crosslinking is necessary to prevent solution. In addition to polymerization, this is achieved by copolymerizing the vinyl monomers with monomers which have two double bonds, such as divinyl benzene (DVB).

In condensation polymerization, this is achieved by using monomers with more than two functional groups.

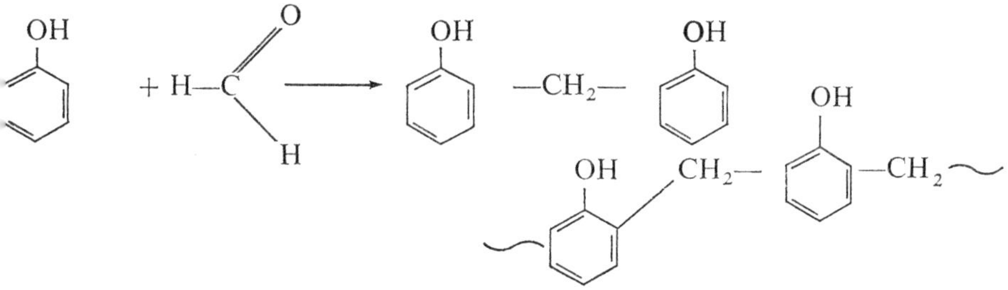

The following chart shows the fixed groups generally found in ion exchange membranes.

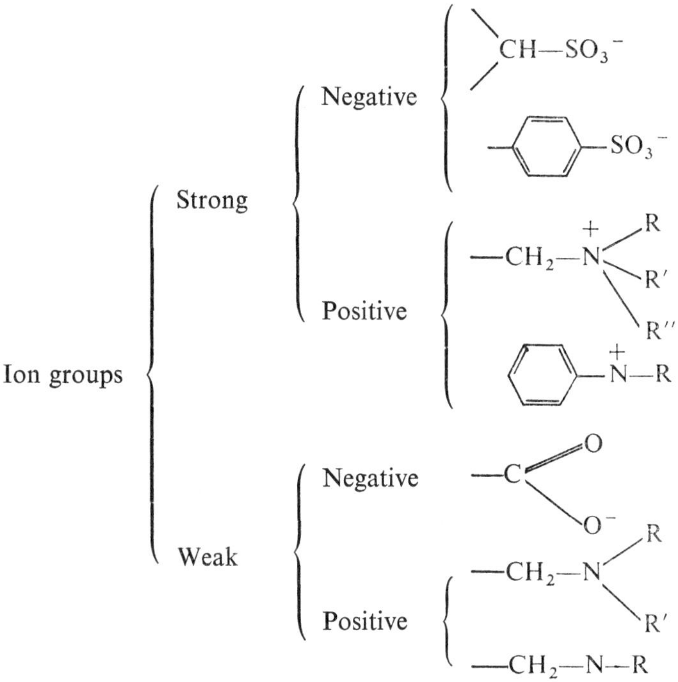

Sulphonate groups may be introduced by prior sulphonation of the monomer or else later sulphonation of the resin formed. Usually the polymer matrix is treated with chlorosulphonic or sulphuric acid for sulphonation.

However, if there are epoxy groups in the matrix, SO_3^- groups may be introduced with Na_2SO_3—$HNaSO_3$.

We must point out that an electronegative membrane in which the $-SO_3^-$ groups are joined to $-CH_2$ groups is weaker than when it is joined to a benzene group.

Electropositive fixed groups may be anchored in matrices with aromatic rings in their structure by chloromethylation using chlorodymethyl–ether with a catalyst ($ZnCl_2$) and then amination.

If there are epoxy groups:

Ionic groups may be introduced into membranes containing pyridine groups in their structure by quaternizing the pyridine rings with methyl sulphate or alkyl halides.

$$+ \, X\!-\!R \longrightarrow$$

N

$[N\!-\!R]^{+}$

Finally, we must point out that in order to prepare weak cation exchange membranes possessing carboxylic groups in their structure, it is necessary to polymerize methacrylic acid type monomers.

From a practical point of view, the membranes should have:

(A) High ion selectivity (Counterion transport number, approaching unity).

(B) Low permeability for free diffusion of electrolytes.

(C) High conductance.

(D) Chemical stability in use conditions (mainly in alkaline media)

(E) High mechanical resistance, high flexibility and good dimensional stability under various wetting conditions.

(F) Low electroosmosis.

Nevertheless, there are a number of incompatible optimum properties. For instance, high mechanical resistance requires thicker membranes, which is incompatible with (C) as this diminishes conductance. A high fixed group concentration in the membrane phase contributes to (A) and (C) but generally is a negative factor for (B), and (E). From a practical point of view, it is difficult to prepare membranes because it is necessary to reach a balance among incompatible properties. Bergsma and Krussink[7] point out for purposes of orientation that the exchange capacity of membranes (milli-equivalents of fixed ion groups/g of dry membrane) ranges between 1 and 2. Water content may range between 25–80% per gramme of dry membrane, and thickness varies between 100 and 500 µm. The following limits were established in work carried out in South Africa to prepare membranes useful in electrodyalysis of brackish water:[8]

Counter–ion transport number in NaCl, 03N solutions > 0.93

Conductance at 30°C in a 0·1% NaCl solution > 60m Ω^{-1} cm^{-2}

Free diffusion flux through a membrane separating a 1·5% NaCl solution and water $< 1.5 \times 10^{-6}$ meq/cm^2 sec.

It was found that these values were suitable for desalination of brackish water, with more than 80% current efficiency and without a high proportion of loss of the power used.

Since 1950 reports on research and patents for membrane preparation have appeared in chemical literature. Fortunately, over the years, reviews of preparation methods have been published. Among those that stand out by Morgan, [9] Bergsma and Krussink,[7] Hazenberg,[10] Krishnaswamy,[11] Carnell and Cassidy,[12] Lakshminarayanaiah[13,2] and Sollner.[6]

In general, membranes may be classified in two large groups[8] depending on their structure:

(1) Homogeneous membranes

(2) Heterogeneous membranes.

Types of heterogeneous membranes are: (a) reinforced membranes, (b) membranes made with chemical film treatment, (c) membranes made by placing a polymer inside a film, (d) membranes obtained by polymer matrix grafting, (e) interpolymer membranes and (f) membranes prepared by mechanical treatment.

A. Homogeneous Membranes

Homogeneous ion exchange membranes may be defined as those in which the ion exchange component is a continuous phase through the structure[14] (Fig. 1).

They may be classified according to how they are obtained:

(1) Membranes made by polycondensation reactions.

(2) Membranes made by addition reactions.

1. Membranes Prepared by Polycondensation Reactions

This is the oldest method used in preparing membranes. The base products of cation exchange membranes are generally phenolsulphonic acid and formaldehyde. Both condense in an acid medium, increasing the viscosity of the medium with the extent of the reaction. In the same way, in anion exchange membranes, polyamine–alkylene and formaldehyde are used.

Several authors have prepared membranes from phenolsulphonic acid (PSA).[15,16,17]

Lakshminarayanaiah and Subrahmanyan[17] used the following procedure: 58·5 g of phenol were treated with 73 g of H_2SO_4 at 80°C, thus obtaining phenolsulphonic acid. 16·8 g of this acid and 8·4 g of a 38% formaldehyde solution were dissolved in 5·65 g of water. The clear solution was transferred into glass formers which were sealed and heated in a water bath at 85° for 6 hours and left to cool overnight. The membranes were washed with distilled water in order to remove all traces of formaldehyde which had not reacted.

Onoue et al.[18] have prepared anion exchange membranes heating dimethyl 2–hydroxybenzeneamine, phenol and formic aldehyde, using H_2SO_4 and acetic acid as catalyst at 50–60°C. The viscous resin was spread on a glass plate and cured at 60–70°C.

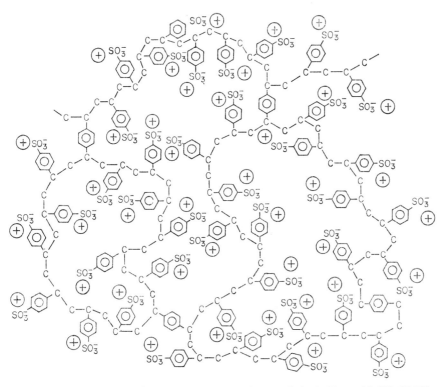

FIG. 1. Homogeneous membranes (H. P. Gregor, Pure and *Appl. Chem.,* **16**, 329 (1968)).

Membranes obtained by these procedures are characterized by high water uptake, high electroosmosis, low concentration of active groups and low electric resistance. The mechanical properties are poor. Selectivity is also low, at high concentrations.

2. Membranes Made by Addition Polymerization Reactions

Methacrylic acid (ethylene glicol dimethacrylate as a crosslinking agent) and styrene sulphonic acidester (DVB as crosslinking agent) were used to prepare, respectively, weak and strong cation exchange membranes. Vinyl pyridinium salts are used in anion exchange membranes.

Hills et al.[19] prepared an aqueous solution containing 50–60% methacrylic acid, 0·2% ammonium peroxydisulphate (which is the initiator of polymerization) and various amounts of dimethacrylate of ethylene glycol.

This solution was heated at 70°C and when it became viscous it was transferred to two glass plates separated 0·5 mm, sealed, and put into a 70°C bath. Later on the temperature was raised to 90°C, and held there for one or two hours. The membranes were washed with distilled water.

Spinner et al.[20] prepared sulphonic styrene acid propyl ester from β-bromoethyl benzene. Following the methods of Spinner et al., Graydon and Stewart[21] copolymerized the ester with DVB using BzO_2 as initiator. The mixture was placed in a Petri dish and sealed with masking tape, then heated at 110°C for 30 minutes in order to polymerize. Then the dish with the membrane was put into a boiling 5% NaOH solution and the ester was hydrolized until the maximum exchange capacity was reached. Hydrolysis may take a long time, but this was reduced by a few hours using dimethyl formamide in the polymerization mixture. Also using the methods of Spinner et al., other workers have prepared other esters from styrene sulphonic acid and have studied the ester alcohol group influence on some membrane properties such as permeability etc.[22, 23] Membranes made with aliphatic esters showed an increase in water uptake, permeability, and flexibility in direct relation to the increase of the size of the alcohol groups.

Lagos and Kitchener[24] and Zundel et al.[25] prepared homogeneous membranes by copolymeryzing styrene and DVB with benzoyl peroxide. Zundel et al. sulphonated the polymer matrixes with chlorosulphonic acid in anhydrous conditions and the excess acid was removed with water at 18° C. Hydrolysis took from six to eight weeks.

Nishimura et al.[26] obtained membranes from solution of polystyrene sulphonic acid and polyvinyl alcohol in water. The solution was spread on glass plate and dried for 48 hours at room temperature. Then, it was heated over 100°C which made the membrane insoluble.

Clark[27] patented a method for preparing strong anion exchange membranes. The preparation entailed polymerizing the quaternary ammonium salt of 2 vinyl-pyridine with divinylbenzene in a propanol solution. The membrane was cast between glass plates, heated at 80°C for three hours, leached with methanol and then with water. These membranes are not stable in alkaline solutions. Finally, it should be pointed out that the mechanical properties of homogeneous membranes prepared by addition methods are generally poor.

B. Heterogeneous Membranes

1. Reinforced Membranes

The mechanical properties of membranes may be improved by reinforcing them with suitable materials. The steps entailed in preparing these membranes are:[2]

(1) Dissolving the monomer in suitable solvents or preparing partially polymerized gels.

(2) Impregnation of a cloth with the monomer solution or with the partially polymerized gel.

(3) Curing until polymerization is complete, under or without pressure.

(4) Introduction of ionic groups by conventional methods, such as sulphonation or chloromethylation followed by amination.

Some reinforcements which have been used are glass fibre, orlon,[28] PVC fabric,[29] polypropylene screen,[30] nylon[31] etc. The impregnation products may polymerize either by condensation or by addition.

(a) *Reinforced membranes made by condensation reactions.* Kasper[32] prepared cation exchange membranes by impregnating Saran wrap (cloth) with aqueous solutions containing phenol sulphonate, resorcinol sulphonate or both, with formaldehyde. Condensation was carried out in place holding the impregnated cloth between two plates at 85°C for 3 hours. In the same way, using the same reinforcing material, Juda and Kasper[33] obtained anion exchange membranes condensing methylol forming phenols with alkyl polyamines and formaldehyde under acidic conditions.

By using orlon as a reinforcing material Oster and Fickett[28] made membranes by impregnating the cloth with a solution containing 200 g of PSA, 70 g of 32% formaldehyde and 20 g of paraformaldehyde. The impregnated orlon was kept between two plates and pressed in a mould at 70°C for two hours.

(b) *Reinforced membranes made by addition polymerization.* Styrene and divinylbenzene are generally the base polymerization materials used in these membranes.[34] Membranes have been obtained by putting two glass plates with a polypropylene net inside in the following solution: 50 parts ethylstyrene, 50 parts of DVB, 10 parts of epoxidized soya bean oil, 5 parts of polyoxypropilenglycol and 1 part of Bz_2O_2. The wet net was pressed between the glass plates, sealed and heated 8 hours at a 80°C. Then it was sulphonated with sulphuric acid in order to form a cation exchange membrane.

Reinforced cation[35] and anion[36] membranes have been prepared using FRS–203 rubber latex obtained by copolymerization of butadiene styrene and polyvinyl compounds. The latex was mixed with distilled water and potassium oleate and degassed with nitrogen. Then it was mixed with DVB and potassium persulphate (the initiator) was added. The mixture was stirred for 5 hours at 55°C. Latex with a viscosity grade of 85 cP was obtained and the mixture was spread on fibreglass to form membranes. Ionic groups were introduced by sulphonation in one case and chloromethylation and amination in the other.

2. Membranes Made by Chemical Treatment of a Film

As the membranes are sheet-type polyelectrolytes, an interesting way to prepare them is using commercial materials or materials which can easily be manufactured in sheet form, in order to introduce later on ionic groups into their structure. This procedure has been adopted by many workers in the membranes field and has led to various methods, classified according to the type of matrix, for giving ionic characteristics to the preformed matrices. The matrices used may be hydrophilic (cellophane[37] paper,[38] polyvinyl alcohol[39]) or hydrophobic (polyethylene films,[40] phenol–formaldehyde,[41] copolymers of styrene–butadiene and DVB with plasticizers[42] etc.).

(a) *Membranes based on hydrophylic matrices.* Hydrophylic matrices present certain advantages in preparing membranes, the most important being that activation procedures may take place in aqueous media. These materials swell in aqueous media and help diffusion of ion reagents into the interior of the sheet.

Both anion and cation membranes have been prepared by activation of regenerated cellulose film. This activation takes place when the cellophane sheet is impregnated with reagents containing at least one methylamide group and one ionic group or a group that can easily be replaced by an ionic one. The impregnated materials are heated until dry at 140°C.[43] A solution of hydroxy–methyl carbamide–methyl–trimethylammonium chloride is used for anion exchange membranes. Cation exchange membranes were obtained by reaction of regenerated cellulose with methylolchloroacetamide at 140°C and then immersing the sheet in a boiling sodium bisulphite aqueous solution. The difficulty of this method rests in the fact that impregnation must take place in an acid medium (pH 1·5–3), in order that ether unions form between the reagent and the matrix. This acidity contributes to the degradation of the cellulose.

Cooke *et al.*[44] used parchment paper as the matrix and impregnated it with alkaline solutions containing phenosulphonate, phenol and formaldehyde. Afterwards the papers were cured at 150°C. Along the same lines, Morgan and Schweigart[45] prepared anion exchange membranes using solutions containing guanidine salts, melamine and formaldehyde, as impregnation materials. It has been shown that the paper does not merely support these membranes, but combines chemically with the activation products.

Polyvinyl alcohol films have also been used.[46] In this case, activation was brought about by immersing the films in a solution of tertiary amines at 100°C for 2 hours followed by a subsequent crosslinking treatment with di–isocyanate.

(b) *Membranes based on hydrophobic matrices.* Polyethylene films have been used in numerous procedures to prepare cation exchange membranes. Chlorosulphonic acid is used to introduce ionic groups followed by NaOH solution treatment.[47,48,49] Sulphonation reactions of hydrophobic matrices are slow, as diffusion of chlorosulphonic acid to the inside of the matrix is not easy.

Sulphonation reactions are favoured using swelling agents as suggested by Hookway et al.[50] Thus, these authors prepared membranes by sulphonating PVC sheets plasticized with dioctyl phthalate.

Tsunoda and Seko[51] obtained matrices suitable for anchoring ionic groups. Partially polymerized styrene, divinylbenzene and ethylvinylbenzene, dissolved in styrene, were polymerized using benzoyl peroxide. The ionic groups were introduced by sulphonation with chlorosulphonic acid after swelling the sheet with tetrachloroethane. Tsunoda and et al.[52] prepared anion exchange membranes based on the above described, and based on vulcanized styrene butadiene copolymer films.[53]

3. Membranes Prepared by Deposition a Polymer Inside a Film

By this method the sheet is immersed in a solution containing the monomer, the crosslinking agent and the initiator. Generally the sheets swell in the solution in such a way that the monomers easily spread inside the sheet where they polymerize.[54, 55] Mizutani[56] has described how to prepare ion exchange membranes using polyvinylchloride, polyvinylidene chloride and polyethylene. DVB, styrene and solvent or vinyl pyridine, styrene DVB and solvent are used. Bz_2O_2 is used as initiator. The ion exchange groups are introduced by chlorosulphonation or chloromethylation followed by amination. This method has been used with cellulose type films. Cellulose[57] is put in contact with a 0.7% ferrous salt solution for 1 minute. Then it is washed until the washing water shows no sign of Fe^{+2}. Then it is refluxed for 15 min in 100 ml of 0.03 H_2O_2 solution containing 10 ml of 50% N N–dimethyl amino ethyl acrylate acetate ester salt. In the same way methacrylate acid may be settled (see ref. 58).

Hodgon and Boyack,[59] prepared membranes by submersing polyvinylidene fluoride, swollen in acetone, in a bath containing styrene and an initiator (benzoyl peroxide and cumene) at 0.1% concentration. When the membranes were removed from the bath, they were placed between two aluminium sheets and heated under pressure to 150°C for 51 minutes. This procedure was repeated until the weight increased by 15–20% of the original weight.

4. Membranes Made by Grafting Ionic Monomers or Monomers Susceptible to Turning into Ionic Monomers

Another method for obtaining membranes is by grafting to the films, polyelectrolyte chains or chains which easily turn into polyelectrolyte ones. A graft reaction consists in creating radical centres in a polymer matrix capable of growing other monomer units. Radicals may be created in various ways, the most important of which are interactions of the matrices with redox systems and high and low energy irradiation. Redox systems are sufficient to achieve a graft reaction when a hydrophilic type matrix, such as cellulose, is used. Thus the cellulose and the Ce^{IV} form a redox system such that in the presence of a monomer

$$1e^- + Ce^{IV} \longrightarrow Ce^{III}$$

$$R-CHOH \longrightarrow R\underset{\otimes}{C}OH + 1e$$

$$R-\underset{\otimes}{C}OH + M \longrightarrow R-\underset{\wr}{C}OH.$$

On the other hand, to graft vinyl monomers in hydrophobic matrices, high energy radiation (γ rays) and low energy radiation (ultraviolet rays) are sufficient. In these cases, the energy of a radiation quanta is enough to break the C—C or C—H bonds, thus creating a radical. The graft reaction may either be carried out irradiating the matrix before the monomer is added, thus forming little homopolymer, or with the monomer present. In the latter case a great deal of homopolymer is formed. Little work has been done on obtaining membranes by this procedure.

(a) *Grafts in hydrophilic matrixes.* Richards and White[60] grafted methyl acrylate–acrylic acid on parchment paper with Ce^{IV}. Riande et al.[61,62] obtained strong cation and anion exchange membranes grafting glycidil acrylate–co–methyl acrylate on parchment paper. The paper was treated with a diluted soda solution, favouring diffusion of monomers inside it. The graft reaction was carried out in a vacuum using Ce^{IV}, and 400 % graft percentages were obtained. The epoxy groups were opened with sodium sulphite–bisulphite and amines. Guzman and Riande[63] used another method to obtain membranes by grafting to paper. Their method consists in preparing cellulose allyl sheets and using a photosensitizer and ultraviolet light to graft suitable monomers. Thus cation exchange membranes were obtained by grafting methacylic acid and strong anion exchange membranes, by grafting 4–vinyl pyradine–co–acrylonitrile. The vinyl pyradine rings were quaternized with buthyl-bromide. These same workers obtained weak cation exhange membranes by grafting acrylic acid–co–methylacrylate on cellulose acetate.[64]

(b) *Grafts in hydrophobic matrices.* There is extensive work[65,66,67] on preparing membranes by grafting styrene in polyethylene films soaked in this monomer using ^{60}Co as a source of γ rays. The graft polymer is sulphonated, or chloroalkylated and aminated, depending on the ionic groups to be anchored. This technique was later changed to pre-irradiate the poly-ethylene sheets with γ-rays. The pre-irradiated films swell in suitable mono-mers (styrene, acrylonitrile) at very high temperatures.[68] By this method, weak cation exchange membranes have been obtained grafting methyl acrylate, ethyl acrilate or acrylonitrile to polyethylene films. Afterwards the grafts are hydrolized.[69] Also polyestyrene has been grafted in polythylene films, using ultraviolet radiation.[70]

Recently, grafts on teflon of acrylic acid,[71] 4–vinyl pyridine[72] and styrene[73] have been obtained. Ionic groups were introduced by the usual procedures.

5. Interpolymer Membranes

These membranes are prepared by dissolving a polymer and a polyelectrolyte in the same solvent or a mixture of solvents. Afterwards it is cast and the solvent evaporated. Gregor and Patzelt[74] considered that the polymer should be linear and insoluble in water. Vinyl and vinylidene polymers are the most suitable film formers. The membranes obtained were in the form of thin 0·05 mm films. There was between 15 and 30% polyelectrolyte concentration in the film and this should be mutually soluble with the film-forming polymer.

Neihof[75] and Gotolieb et al.[76] prepared cation exchange membranes by the dissolution technique, casting films of the required porosity from ether–alcohol solutions containing strong polyelectrolytes such as sulphonic polystyrene acid.

Gregor[77] obtained cation exchange membranes from a solution of sulphonic polystyrene acid and dynel (copolymer of acrulonitrile and vinyl chloride) in dimethylformamide. With poly (vinyl–benzil–trimethylammo-nium chloride) and Dynel,[8] anion exchange membranes have been obtained using cyclohexanone–methanol as the solvent. Cation exchange membranes may be prepared using this solvent.

6. Membranes Perpared by Mechanical Methods

A powdered ion exchange resin is mixed with a thermoplastic (binder) at a high temperature. Then the membrane is formed by pressure or calendering. These membranes generally have low conductivity, as the binder is an insulator and they are thicker than the membranes obtained by other methods. Polyethylene,[78] plasticized polyvinylchloride,[79] polyvinyl acetal plasticized with a 1–3 butadiene and acrylonitrile copolymer[80] etc. are generally used as binders.

There is usually more than 65% resin content, and it must be distributed in such a way that the membrane is not distorted, broken or disintegrated during swelling. In order to avoid tension due to the different reaction of the binder and the resin to water, ionic groups, similar to the fixed groups in the resin, have been added to the binder.

Another method is to bind the two thermoplastic polymers with mechanical pressure and then to add the ionic groups following the usual procedures.

There are many patents describing membrane preparation by the above described procedures and some of these will be given as examples. Thus, sulphonated polystyrene powder in sodium form[81] (75 parts) was mixed in a roller mill with branched polyethylene (17·5 parts) and linear polyethylene (17·5 parts) to form cation exchange membranes. In the same way,[82] 100 parts of polystyrene powder (2% intercross-linked with DVB), 30 parts of high pressure polyethylene were rolled out. An anion exchange membrane was obtained from the film by the usual methods. By another procedure,[83] a styrene–butadiene or methyl vinyl pyridine–butadiene co-polymer, was mixed with polyethylene and calendered into a membrane which may be converted to either electropositive or electronegative.

There is special interest in membranes containing inorganic salts and metallic oxides as ion exchange resins. Some salts such as phosphates, tungstates, vanadates, molybdates and chromates of thorium, titanium and zirconium, have been described as ion exchangers.[84] Furthermore, tetravalent metal oxides such as stannic, silicon, thorium, titanium and zirconium bioxides, act like anion exchangers. Therefore, membranes may be prepared with these compounds. Inorganic bonding agents such as sodium silicate, calcium aluminate cements, tetraethyl orthosilicate and silicone resins,[85, 86] or organic ones such as teflon[87] or polyvinylidene fluoride,[88] may be used. Their characteristics make these membranes useful at high temperatures. Nevertheless, such membranes are less selective than organic ones.

Finally we must point out that membranes have been prepared based on inorganic precipitates. The electric charge in these membranes depends not only on the precipitate, but is influenced by the nature of its surroundings as well. Several workers[89,90] have obtained membranes of this type absorbing salts such as barium sulphate, barium chromate, etc. in parafins.

III. Transport Phenomena in Membranes

When a membrane separates two solutions, a number of transport processes and related phenomena take place which depend on external conditions. The membranes are imperfect barriers through which solute and solvent flow due to the possible forces: gradients of concentration, of pressure, of temperature or electric potential.

Water flow may be caused by applying gradients of pressure (hydraulic permeability), of temperature (thermo-osmosis), of concentration (osmosis) or electrical potential (electro-osmosis). The solute flow may be caused by gradients of electric potential (conductance), or concentration (diffusion).

Another series of phenomena take place as well. Electrical potential are caused by differences in concentration on either side of the membrane, (concentration potential), or by different ions on either sides of the membrane (bi-ionic and multi-ionic potentials). A temperature difference may also cause electric potential (electrothermic potential), or a concentration difference (Soret effect). An electric potential is also obtained by maintaining a pressure difference (streaming potential).

Friedlander and Rickles[91] represent all of these phenomena in a circle (Fig. 2) where non-coupled phenomena are indicated by lines. The suggestion of coupled phenomena is implicit in the use of a circle.

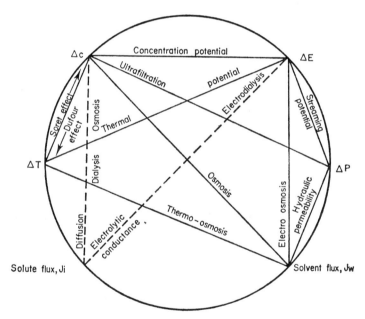

Fig. 2. Membrance circle (Friedlander H. Z. and Rickles R. N., *Chem. Eng.*, **73**, (5) 111 (1966)).

The main purpose of the theory is to correlate the various phenomena and find their characteristic magnitudes in such a way that membrane behaviour may be predicted.

Theories concerning transport through membranes may be divided into three groups, depending on the flow equation used in the treatment. The first group is based on the Nernst–Planck equation. Theories falling into the second group, use thermodynamic principles of irreversible processes and those, corresponding to the third group, use concepts of the theory of rate processes. Nevertheless, the ideal procedure for deriving relationships between transport phenomena is given by irreversible thermodynamic processes, though, unfortunately, many of the parameters contained in the resulting theories are at least unknown.

A. Nernst–Planck Flux Equation

The Nernst-Planck equation is basic to developing the theory of transport through membranes. In a viscous medium, the transport rate of component i, is proportional to the force X_i acting on that component. Thus,[92]

$$v_i = U_i X_i \tag{1}$$

where U is the mobility constant.† For diffusion type flows

$$X_i = - \text{grad } \mu_i \tag{2}$$

where μ_i is the chemical potential of the component i.

The flow, J_i, is expressed by the product of velocity and concentration

$$J_i = C_i v_i = C_i U_i X_i. \tag{3}$$

In the case of one-way flow of a non-electrolyte,

$$X_i = - \frac{d\mu_i}{dx} = - RT \frac{d \ln a_i}{dx} \tag{4}$$

because

$$\mu_i = \mu_i^0 + RT \ln a_i. \tag{5}$$

In the case of an ideal system and ideal chemical potential, eqn (4) takes on the following form

$$X_i = - \frac{RT}{C_i} \frac{dC_i}{dx}. \tag{6}$$

Substituting eqn (6) into eqn (3), eqn (7) is obtained:

$$J_i = - RT u_i \frac{dC_i}{dx} = - D_i \frac{dC_i}{dx} \tag{7}$$

where $D_i = RT U_i$. The above expression is the Fick equation. If an electrolyte is diffused, the electrochemical potential is given by

$$\hat{\mu}_i = \mu_i^0 + RT \ln a_i + z_i F\phi \tag{8}$$

† U denotes the diffusion mobility (mol cm^2 sec^{-1} joul^{-1}); the electrical mobility, u_i, has units (cm^2 sec^{-1} volt^{-1}). $U = u/(|z| F)$, where $|z|$ is the absolute valency of the ion.

where ϕ is the electric potential and Z_i the valence of component i and F the Faraday constant.

From eqns (8) and (2) it is possible to obtain the force X_i.

$$X_i = -\frac{RT}{C_i}\frac{dC_i}{dx} - RT\frac{d\ln\gamma_i}{dx} - z_iF\frac{d\phi}{dx}.$$ (9)

Finally, substituting eqn (9) into eqn (3), the Nernst–Planck equation is obtained

$$J_i = -D_i\left(\frac{dC_i}{dx} + C_i\frac{d\ln\gamma_i}{dx} + \frac{z_iC_iF}{RT}\frac{d\phi}{dx}\right).$$ (10)

In ideal systems, the activity coefficients, γ, are the unit with which eqn (10) takes on the form initially given by Nernst–Planck.[93,94] This expression was integrated by Goldman[95] and Teorell.[96,97] By applying an electrical field to the solution → membrane → solution system, the cations, move to the cathode while the anions move to the anode. If, for example, the membrane is cation-selective, the membrane phase will be enriched in cations which, when they move, will start up the surrounding water molecules in such a way that the water will flow in the same direction as the cations. In their movement, counter-ions will run up against less resistance than co-ions, so that if the membrane is the frame of reference, the counter-ions will move faster than if the pore liquid were standing still. As a result, the pore liquid convection will increase the cation flow and this convective flow is given by

$$J_i^* = \bar{C}_i v^*$$ (11)

where v^* is the velocity of the centre of gravity of the pore liquid. Total cation flow with respect to the membrane will be given by

$$J_i^\circ = \bar{C}_i v^* - \bar{D}_i\left(\frac{d\bar{C}_i}{dx} + \bar{C}_i\frac{d\ln\bar{\gamma}_i}{dx} + \frac{z_i\bar{C}_iF}{RT}\frac{d\phi}{dx}\right).$$ (12)

It is difficult to evaluate v^*, however Schlögl[98] and Helfferich[99] have estimated this parameter. $F\bar{X}$ represents the counter-ion charge in an electronegative membrane pore liquid, where $\bar{X}$ is the fixed charge concentration per unit pore liquid volume. If water permeability through the membrane (reciprocal to the specific resistance to the flow in the membrane) is represented by D_h, by a simple balance of energy eqn (13) is obtained.

$$v^* = D_h(F\bar{X})\left(-\frac{d\phi}{dx}\right).$$ (13)

Helfferich [99] expressed $v*$ by the equation

$$v* = \left(\frac{F\overline{X}}{\rho_0 \varepsilon}\right)\left(-\frac{d\phi}{dx}\right) \tag{14}$$

where ρ_0 is the specific flow resistance and ε the fraction pore volume/membrane volume.

In this case $\overline{X}$ is the fixed charge concentration per membrane volume unit.

Equation (12) may be considered a refined version of the Nernst–Planck equation. Schlögl[98] has expressed the Nernst–Planck equation in a broader sense, including the pressure factor and also approximately integrating the resulting expression. Lightfoot and Scattergood[100] also deduced an expression very like Schlögl's.

A serious limitation of the Nernst–Planck equation is that it considers flows through the membranes to be independent. Nevertheless, it has been shown that in electrokinetic experiments the flow of electricity, for instance, is accompanied by a volume flow while a volume flow, induced by mechanical pressure, results in a flow of electrical current. In other words, there are coupling phenomena between flows, which may profoundly change the transport pattern. It is therefore evident that a comprehensive theory of membrane transport should treat explicitly the coupling between flows and should provide a measure for the transport interactions.

A suitable theoretical introduction to the analysis of coupling phenomena is provided by the thermodynamics of irreversible processes. Although kinetics and statistical mechanic treatment are better suited for the visualization of the processes under consideration, the statistical mechanics of irreversible processes is still an inadequate tool for the treatment of condensed systems.

B. Irreversible Thermodynamics

1. Discontinuous Systems

In formal treatment of membrane permeability it has been assumed that the membrane is a geometric transition between two homogeneous subsystems, I and II, through which is established driving forces which cause different flows. The membrane is a black box whose characteristics may be derived by studying the neighbouring phases.

We will assume that the total system is closed. That is to say, no material is exchanged with its surroundings, only heat, energy and work. Subsystems I and II, however, are open systems so that matter may be transferred from one to the other. We admit the possibility of differences in the properties of the cells that almost discontinuously take place in the membrane. Thus we may have a difference in temperature ΔT, pressure ΔP, solute concentration k, ΔC_k, and electrical potential $\Delta \phi$; these are the forces that cause matter and heat flows. The forces and the flows are related by general type phenomenological equations[101]

$$J_i = \sum_k L_{ik} X_k \tag{15}$$

which assume that any flow is caused in part by all of the forces. L_{ik} ($i, k = 1$, $2 \ldots n$) coefficients are denominated phenomenological coefficients and according to Onsager's basic theorem, whenever an appropriate choice of flows J_i and forces X_i is made, the phenomenological coefficients matrix is symmetrical. That is to say

$$L_{ik} = L_{ki}.$$

The combined parameters J_i and X_i are chosen from the entropy production which takes place during the irreversible processes and which is related to said parameters by the equation

$$\sigma = T \frac{ds}{dt} = \sum_i J_i X_i. \tag{16}$$

The formulation of the basic point of the problem requires knowledge of the total entropy change which may be expressed as

$$dS = d_e S + d_i S \tag{17}$$

where $d_e S$ is the entropy variation due to energy exchange with the surroundings and $d_i S$ is the variation resulting inside the system from irreversible processes.

In order to determine the entropy balance we must know the law of conservation of masses, the energy equation and the second principle.

As the total system is a closed system, the conservation of masses is expressed by

$$dn_k{}^I + dn_k{}^{II} = 0 \tag{18}$$

where n_k are the moles of component k.

Internal energy change, dU^I, may be divided into energy exchanged with the surroundings, $d_e U^I$, and energy exchanged with the subsystem II, $d_i U^I$

$$dU^I = d_e U^I + d_i U^I, \quad dU^{II} = d_e U^{II} + d_i U^{II} \tag{19}$$

from which

$$d_i U^I + d_i U^{II} = 0. \tag{20}$$

Similarly we may separate the heat recieved by each subsystem:

$$dQ^I = d_eQ^I + d_iQ^I, \quad dQ^{II} = d_eQ^{II} + d_iQ^{II}. \tag{21}$$

The heat and energy recieved by the total system from the surroundings is

$$\begin{aligned} dQ &= d_eQ^I + d_eQ^{II} \\ dU &= d_eU^I + d_eU^{II}. \end{aligned} \tag{22}$$

Keeping in mind the first law of thermodynamics, we find the relationship

$$d_eQ^I + d_eQ^{II} = d_eU^I + d_eU^{II} + P^I dV^I + P^{II} dV^{II} \tag{23}$$

and considering that sizes I and II are independent

$$\begin{aligned} d_eQ^I &= d_eU^I + P^I \, dV^I \\ d_eQ^{II} &= d_eU^{II} + P^{II} \, dV^{II}. \end{aligned} \tag{24}$$

Applied to this system, the Gibbs equation takes the following form:

$$T \, dS = dU + P \, dV - \sum_k \hat{\mu}_k \, dn_k \tag{25}$$

where $\hat{\mu}_k$ is the electrochemical potential of component k. In subsystems I and II

$$\begin{aligned} T^I \, dS^I &= dU^I + P^I \, dV^I - \sum_k \hat{\mu}_k{}^I \, dn_k{}^I \\ T^{II} \, dS^{II} &= dU^{II} + P^{II} \, dV^{II} - \sum_k \hat{\mu}_k{}^{II} \, dn_k{}^{II}. \end{aligned} \tag{26}$$

The entropy variation in the total system will be

$$dS = dS^I + dS^{II} = (d_eU^I + P^I \, dV^I)/T^I + (d_eU^{II} + P^{II} \, dV^{II})/T^{II}$$

$$+ \, d_iU^I/T^I + d_iU^{II}/T^{II} - \frac{1}{T^I}\sum_k \hat{\mu}_k{}^I \, dn_k{}^I - \frac{1}{T^{II}}\sum_k \hat{\mu}_k{}^{II} \, dn_k{}^{II} \tag{27}$$

where eqn (26) has been used.

According to eqn (20), $d_iU^I = - \, d_iU^{II}$ and assuming T^I is close to T^{II}, eqn (27) takes the following form:

$$dS = \frac{d_eU^I + P^I dV^I}{T^I} + \frac{d_eU^{II} + P^{II}dV^{II}}{T^{II}} + \frac{\Delta T}{T^2}d_iU + \sum_k \Delta\left(\frac{\hat{\mu}_k}{T}\right) dn_k{}^I. \tag{28}$$

Expression (28) may be divided into two parts: one expresses the entropy received from the surroundings

$$d_e S = \frac{d_e U^I + P^I dV^I}{T^I} + \frac{d_e U^{II} + P^{II} dV^{II}}{T^{II}} = \frac{d_e Q^I}{T^I} + \frac{d_e Q^{II}}{T^{II}} \tag{29}$$

and the other expresses internal entropy production resulting from the action of irreversible processes within the system

$$d_i S = \frac{\Delta T}{T^2} d_i U^I + \sum_k \Delta\left(\frac{\hat{\mu}_k}{T}\right) dn_k^I. \tag{30}$$

With this equation it is possible to adequately chose the coupled forces and flows. In accordance with eqns (16) and (30) we obtain

$$\sigma = T\frac{ds}{dt} = J_u X_u + \sum J_k X_k \tag{31}$$

where energy and matter flows, J_u and J_k, are introduced respectively

$$J_u = -\frac{d_i U^I}{dt} = \frac{d_i U^{II}}{dt}$$

$$\tag{32}$$

$$J_k = -\frac{dn_k^I}{dt} = \frac{dn_k^{II}}{dt}$$

as well as the corresponding forces

$$X_u = T\Delta\left(\frac{1}{T}\right)$$

$$\tag{33}$$

$$X_k = -T\Delta\left(\frac{\hat{\mu}_k}{T}\right).$$

Phenomenological laws establish lineal relationships between flows and forces

$$J_i = \sum_k L_{ik} X_k + L_{iu} X_u \tag{34a}$$

$$J_u = \sum_k L_{uk} X_k + L_{uu} X_u \tag{34b}$$

in which the Onsager relationships are borne out

$$L_{ik} = L_{ki}, \quad L_{uk} = L_{ku}, \text{ etc.} \tag{35}$$

We may eliminate the L_{iu} coefficients by the magnitude U_k^*, which is defined by the equation[101]

$$L_{iu} = \sum_k L_{ik} U_k^*.$$ (36)

Thus, eqn (34a) may be written as follows:

$$J_i = \sum_k L_k (X_k + U_k^* X_u).$$ (37)

Multiplying both sides of eqn (37) by U_i^*, adding up all of the i's and subtracting from eqn (34b) we obtain

$$J_u - \sum_i U_i^* J_i = \sum_k \left(L_{uk} - \sum_i L_{ik} U_i^* \right) + \left(L_{uu} - \sum_{i,k} L_{ik} U_i^* U_k^* \right) X_u.$$ (38)

The first term on the right of eqn (38) is cancelled by applying the Onsager relationship to eqn (36). This leaves

$$J_u = \sum_i U_i^* J_i + \left(L_{uu} - \sum_{i,k} L_{ik} U_i^* U_k^* \right) X_u$$ (39)

Thus U^* represents the energy transferred per flow unit when T is constant. Introducing the forces given by eqn (33) in eqn (37) we find that

$$J_i = \sum_k L_{ik} \left\{ \left\{ - T\Delta \left(\frac{\hat{\mu}_k}{T} \right) + U_k^* T\Delta \left(\frac{1}{T} \right) \right\}.$$ (40)

For infinitesimal forces

$$J_i = \sum_k L_{ik} \left\{ - d\hat{\mu}_k + \frac{\hat{\mu}_k}{T} dT - U_k^* \frac{dT}{T} \right\}$$

$$= \sum_k L_{ik} \left\{ - d\hat{\mu}_k + (\hat{\mu}_k - U_k^*) \frac{dT}{T} \right\}.$$ (41)

However

$$d\hat{\mu}_k = - \bar{S}_k \, dT + \bar{V}_k d P + RT \, d \ln a_k + z_k F d\phi$$ (42)

where $\bar{S}_k$, $\bar{V}_k$, a_k and z_k are the partial molar entropy, partial molar volume, activity and valence of component k, and ϕ is the electrical potential.

Substituting eqn (42) into eqn (41) and keeping in mind that $\hat{\mu}_k = H_k^* - T\bar{S}_k$ the following expression for J_i is obtained:

$$J_i = \sum_k L_{ik} \left\{ -\bar{V}_k\, dP - RT\, d\ln a_k - z_k F\, d\phi + Q_k^* \frac{dT}{T} \right\} \quad (43)$$

where the difference between H_k^* and U_k^* is the transport heat Q_k^*.

2. Continuous Systems

In the previous section we have seen that the state variables were the same at any point in each of the subsystems, but varied widely between one side of the membrane and the other. Now we will study the behavious of a system, of which the membrane is one phase, and the state variables are continuous functions of the spatial coordinates.[101]

There are four components in an ion exchange membrane: the solvent, the counter-ions, the co-ions, and the fixed charges. If the membrane is in contact with an M^+A^- electrolyte, the electric charges of the membrane components will be respectively 0, $+1$, -1, and -1. Flows through the system may be caused by gradients of chemical potential, $\ln a_k$, of pressure, P, of temperature, T, or electrical potential, ϕ. Individual flows (in moles/unit of time . unit of area), relative to the centre of the gravity of the system, will be given by

$$J_i = \bar{C}_i(v_i - v) = J_i^{\circ} - \bar{C}_i v \quad (44)$$

where C_i is the molar concentration of component i, v_i is its velocity, v is the velocity of the centre of the gravity of the system, J_i° is the absolute flow and $C_i v_i$ is the convective flow.

The velocity vector of the centre of the gravity of the system may be expressed by

$$v = \frac{\sum_i \bar{C}_i v_i}{\sum_i \bar{C}_i} . \quad (45)$$

The absolute flow of the system's fixed charges is zero, because $v_x = 0$. However the flow relative to the centre of the gravity is $J_x \neq 0$. According to eqn (44),

$$J_x = -\bar{C}_x v. \quad (46)$$

Taking the centre of mass of the system as the frame of reference, we find the cation (J_+), anion (J_-), water (J_w) and fixed charges (J_x) flows.

In order to express the relationship between coupled forces and flows, it is necessary to calculate the dissipation function $\sigma = T\,dS/dt$. Evaluation of entropy production requires use of the Gibbs relationship[101]

$$T\frac{d\bar{S}}{dt} = \frac{d\bar{U}}{dt} + P\frac{d\bar{V}}{dt} - \sum_k \mu_k \frac{d\rho_k}{dt}. \tag{47}$$

In the above equation $\bar{S}$, $\bar{U}$ and $\bar{V}$ are the entropy, internal energy and volume per mol, respectively;

$$\rho_k = C_k \Big/ \sum_k C_k = \frac{C_k}{C}.$$

To evaluate dn_k/dt, dC_k/dt and dC/dt must be known

$$\frac{d\rho_k}{dt} = \frac{d(C_k/C)}{dt} = \frac{1}{C}\frac{dC_k}{dt} - \frac{C_k}{C^2}\frac{dC}{dt}. \tag{48}$$

These derivatives may be calculated considering that

$$\frac{dC_k}{dt} = \frac{\partial C_k}{\partial t} + v_k \operatorname{grad} C_k$$

$$\frac{dC}{dt} = \frac{\partial C}{\partial t} + v \operatorname{grad} C. \tag{49}$$

Furthermore the local derivation with respect to time may be expressed by

$$\frac{\partial C_k}{\partial t} = - \operatorname{div} C_k v_k \tag{50}$$

and adding this equation for the system's components ($k = 1, 2, ..., n$) we find

$$\frac{\partial C}{\partial t} = - \operatorname{div} Cv. \tag{51}$$

The k-component flow, with respect to the centre of gravity of the system is expressed by eqn (44), and considering eqn (45),

$$\sum_k J_k = 0 \tag{52}$$

that is to say, one flow is dependent on the rest.

From eqns (51), (50), (44) and (49), the following expressions are obtained:

$$dC_k/dt = - C_k \operatorname{div} v - \operatorname{div} J_k$$

$$dC/dt = - \bar{V}^{-2} d\bar{V}/dt = - C \operatorname{div} v \qquad (53)$$

$$d\rho_k/dt = - C^{-1} \operatorname{div} J_k.$$

Calculating the first term of eqn (47) requires previous knowledge of the system's energy equation, including kinetic energy of the centre of the mass, which is given by the following equation

$$d(\tfrac{1}{2}v^2 + \bar{U})/dt = - C^{-1} \operatorname{div} (P \cdot v + J_q) + \sum_k F_k \cdot v_k C_k \qquad (54)$$

where J_q is the heat flow and F_k is the external force applied on the component k. In order to obtain $d\bar{U}/dt$, it is necessary to subtract $v \, dv/dt$ from eqn (54). Considering that,

$$C \frac{dv}{dt} = - \operatorname{grad} P + \sum_k F_k C_k \qquad (55)$$

where P is pressure and using eqn (44) the following equation is obtained

$$\frac{d\bar{U}}{dt} = - P \frac{d\bar{V}}{dt} - C^{-1} \operatorname{div} J_q + C^{-1} \sum F_k J_k. \qquad (56)$$

Substituting eqns (53) and (56) into eqn (47), the entropy balance is left in the following form:

$$CT \frac{d\bar{S}}{dt} = - \operatorname{div} J_q + \sum_k F_k J_k + \sum_k \mu_k \operatorname{div} J_k \qquad (57)$$

which may also be written

$$C \frac{d\bar{S}}{dt} = - \frac{\operatorname{div}\left(J_q - \sum_k \mu_k J_k\right)}{T} + \frac{J_q X_u + \sum_k J_k X_k}{T} = - \operatorname{div} J_s + \frac{\sigma}{T} \qquad (58)$$

where

$$X_u = - (\operatorname{grad} T)/T; \quad X_k = F_k - T \operatorname{grad}\left(\frac{\mu_k}{T}\right). \qquad (59)$$

Equation (58) has the form of a balance equation. The entropy change has two causes: the negative divergence of entropy flow

$$J_s = \frac{J_q - \sum \mu_k J_k}{T} \qquad (60)$$

and the production of entropy with an intensity equal to

$$\frac{1}{T}\left(J_q X_u + \sum_k J_k X_k\right) \tag{61}$$

which is evidently the sum of the flow products J_q and J_k and the corresponding forces X_u and X_k.

According to the Onsager theory, it is assumed that linear relationships exist between flows and forces, leading to the phenomenological equations

$$J_i = \sum_k L_{ik} X_k + L_{iu} X_u$$
$$J_q = \sum_k L_{uk} X_k + L_{uu} X_u \tag{62}$$

in which the Onsager relationships are brought together. For example

$$L_{ik} = L_{ki}, \quad L_{iu} = L_{ui}, \quad L_{uk} = L_{ku}. \tag{63}$$

Substituting the magnitude Q_k^*, which is defined by

$$L_{iu} = \sum_k L_{ik} Q_k^* \tag{64}$$

for the L_{iu} coefficients, we obtain

$$J_i = \sum_k L_{ik}(X_k + Q_k^* X_u). \tag{65}$$

By the procedure followed in eqns (38) and (39), Q_k^* may be interpreted as the transport heat per mol at a constant temperature $(X_u = 0)$ and is called the transfer heat.

Substituting the values for the forces given in eqn (59), into eqn (65), the following expression is obtained for J_i:

$$J_i = \sum_k L_{ik}\left\{- e_k \operatorname{grad} \phi - T \operatorname{grad}\left(\frac{\mu_k}{T}\right) - Q_k^* \frac{\operatorname{grad} T}{T}\right\}. \tag{66}$$

where e_k is the electrical charge of the component k

Since:

$$\operatorname{grad} \mu_k = - \bar{S}_k \operatorname{grad} T + \bar{V}_k \operatorname{grad} P + RT \operatorname{grad} \ln a_k \tag{67}$$

then,

$$J_i = \sum_k L_{ik}\left\{- e_k \operatorname{grad} \phi - \bar{V}_k \operatorname{grad} P - RT \operatorname{grad} \ln a_k + \frac{\bar{H}_k - \bar{Q}_k^*}{T} \operatorname{grad} T\right\}$$

$$\tag{68}$$

which is the final expression of matter flow.

Equation (68) makes it possible to write the electrical parameters as functions of phenomenological coefficients.[102] Current density is given by

$$I = \sum e_i J_i^\circ = \sum{}'(e_i J_i + e_i C_i v) \tag{69}$$

in which the prime for Σ indicates that there is no X term. since $J_x^\circ = 0$. From the circumstance of electroneutrality and from eqn (46)

$$e_x C_x = -\sum e_i C_i, \quad \text{and} \quad e_x C_x v = J_x e_x. \tag{70}$$

By substituting eqns (70) into (69), it is possible to obtain the current density

$$I = \sum_i{}' e_i J_i - e_x C_x v = \sum_i e_i J_i$$

$$= \sum_{i,k} e_i L_{ik} \left\{ - e_k \operatorname{grad} \phi - \bar{V}_k \operatorname{grad} P - RT \operatorname{grad} \ln a_k + \frac{\bar{H}_k - \bar{Q}_k{}^*}{T} \operatorname{grad} T \right\} \tag{71}$$

Specific conductance is given by

$$\bar{K} = \left(\frac{I}{- \operatorname{grad} \phi} \right) = \sum_{i,k} e_i e_k L_{ik}$$

$$\operatorname{grad} P = 0$$
$$\operatorname{grad} T = 0$$
$$\operatorname{grad} \ln a_k = 0 \tag{72}$$

and the transport number of component k with reference to the centre of the mass is

$$t_k = \left(\frac{F J_k}{I} \right) = \frac{F \sum_i e_i L_{ik}}{\bar{K}}$$

$$\operatorname{grad} P = 0$$
$$\operatorname{grad} T = 0$$
$$\operatorname{grad} \ln a_k = 0. \tag{73}$$

The frame of reference in deducing the flow equation has been the plane perpendicular to the direction of flow passing through the centre-of-gravity of the system.[102] The value of the phenomenological coefficients, in this rigorous treatment, depends on the frame of reference chosen. Mackinley and Caplan[103] have discussed this aspect of the problem.

3. Treatment of Spiegler

Attempts have been made to convert the phenomenological coefficients into parameters independent of the frame of reference, in order to obtain a clearer idea of the membrane processes. Spiegler[104] and later other workers[105, 106, 107, 108] applied these concepts. Spiegler's treatment (described below) is based in the thermodynamics of irreversible processes and especially on the work of Staverman[109] and Lorenz.[110] It includes all transport phenomena through membranes, but not in such a general form, as the Staverman treatment; rather, certain simplifications allow calculation of transport data based on fewer measurements. Figure 3 shows a schematic model of Spiegler's proposed system. When a force, such as an electrical field, is applied to the ions, if these have no friction with the surroundings, they will accelerate up to high speeds. Nevertheless, a dynamic equilibrium is quickly established so that the forces applied to the ions are cancelled by friction forces. In this state, the ions move at a constant speed. In the model, friction is shown as though the particles were macroscopic. Obviously, the macroscopic concept of friction makes no sense with microscopic particles. The barrier impeding an ion to move in a straight line is collision with other particles, particularly water and solids molecules. Such collisions change the direction of the ions and cut down their speed. Nevertheless, the analogy between friction and these collisions may be observed, and in Spiegler's proposed treatment, he assumes that in both cases, when force is applied to a certain type of particle, its linear velocity is proportional to the force. The term "linear velocity" is understood as the macroscopic value, independent of the microscopic crooked paths.

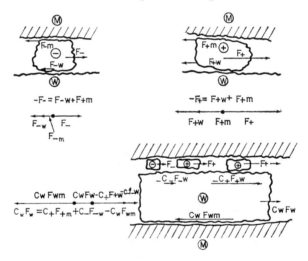

FIG. 3. Schematic representation of equilibrium forces in the Spiegler treatment (Spiegler (104)).

Many transport phenomena may be described in terms of this model. If a pressure gradient is applied through the system, the water moves faster than the ions. Thus, these are concentrated near the matrix and are subject to more friction. Self-diffusion for example, signifies a positional change of the ions without moving the water.

If a system is restricted in such a way that the migration of a single species is produced when several generalized forces act on the system, then the resultant flow is the algebraic sum of the flows caused by each of the forces independently. For example, if electrical potential, pressure and concentration gradients are applied through the membrane to positive ions, the resulting flow will be

$$J_+ = L_{++}\left(Z_+F\frac{d\phi}{dx} + \bar{V}\frac{d\rho}{dx} + RT\frac{d\ln\bar{a}_+}{dx}\right) = L_{++}F_+ \qquad (74)$$

However, if several components migrate simultaneously, they will exchange momentum; hence the migration of each species will be dependent upon the migration of all the other migrating species. In such a system, one can make a linear approximation and assume that the flow of each species is dependent upon each generalized force acting in the system. Then

$$J_i = \sum_k L_{ik}F_k; \quad i, k, = +, -, w. \qquad (75)$$

The molecular interaction of migrating species can be approximated by the simple friction model. We assume that there exists a molar friction coefficient, f_{ik}, which depicts the frictional interaction between components i and k per mole of i; hence the interaction between components i and k is given by

$$F_{ik} = -f_{ik}(v_i - v_k) \qquad (76)$$

If for example the cations move in a water mass, due to the action of a force, and if the movement is uniform, it is necessary that the friction force, proportional to the velocity of the cations with respect to the water, act on them

$$F_{+w} = -f_{+w}(v_+ - v_w) \qquad (77)$$

where f_{+w} is the friction coefficient between the water and the mobile cations. The negative sign indicates that the friction force acts in the opposite direction to the velocity vector of the particle which moves.

The f_{ik}'s are independent of the reference frame and are known to be more useful than the L_{ik}'s because they are less concentration-dependent.

In the system studied by Spiegler, consisting of sodium ion $(+)$, chloride ions $(-)$, water (w) and an ion matrix (m), there are six friction coefficients between the components. By assuming that in a highly selective negative ion exchange membrane, co-ions exist in insignificant amount so that it is not very probable that co-ions and counter-ions will collide (this is to say, $f_{+-} = 0$), Spiegler simplifies the number of coefficients, making five the number of friction coefficients in this system. The forces F_+, F_- and F_w, applied from the outside are offset by the viscous forces F_{+w}, F_{-w} and F_{ww} as is seen in Fig. 3. According to Newton's motion law, (to every action there is an equal and opposite reaction), the force of the ions on the water is equal and of the opposite sign to the viscous force the water puts on the ions. The equilibrium forces per mol of Na^+, Cl^-, and H_2O, respectively are

$$F_+ + F_{+w} + F_{+m} = 0; \qquad F_- + F_{-w} + F_{-m} = 0.$$

$$F_+ = - F_{+w} - F_{+m} = f_{+w} v_{+w} + f_{+m} v_+ \tag{78}$$

$$F_- = - F_{-w} - F_{-m} = f_{-w} v_{-w} + f_{-m} v_-.$$

In order to calculate F_w it is necessary to stipulate the $\bar{C}_+$, $\bar{C}_-$, and $\bar{C}_w$, moving particles concentrations. The forces acting in the opposite directions are $\bar{C}_w F_w$, $- \bar{C}_+ F_{+w}$, and $- \bar{C}_- F_{-w}$. These are opposed to $\bar{C}_w F_{wm}$ which has a negative value. From this

$$F_w = \left(\frac{\bar{C}_+}{\bar{C}_w}\right) F_{+w} + \left(\frac{\bar{C}_-}{\bar{C}_w}\right) F_{-w} - F_{wm}$$

$$= \left(\frac{\bar{C}_+}{\bar{C}_w}\right) f_{+w} v_{+m} + \left(\frac{\bar{C}_-}{\bar{C}_w}\right) f_{-w} v_{-m} + f_{wm} v_w \tag{79}$$

Considering that $J_i = \bar{C}_i v_i$ and eqns (75), (76), (78) and (79), the phenomenological coefficients are obtained as a function of the friction coefficients.

$$L_{++} = \frac{\bar{C}_+}{d} [(\bar{C}_+ f_{+w} + \bar{C}_w f_{wm})(f_{-w} + f_{-m}) + \bar{C}_- f_{-w} f_{-m}]$$

$$L_{--} = \frac{\bar{C}_-}{d} [(\bar{C}_- f_{-w} + \bar{C}_w f_{wm})(f_{+w} + f_{+m}) + \bar{C}_+ f_{+w} f_{+m}]$$

$$L_{ww} = \frac{\bar{C}_w{}^2}{d} (f_{+w} + f_{+m})(f_{-w} + f_{-m})$$

$$L_{+-} = L_{-+} = \frac{\bar{C}_+}{d} \bar{C}_- f_{+w} f_{-w} \tag{80}$$

$$L_{+w} = L_{w+} = \frac{\bar{C}_+}{d} \bar{C}_w f_{+w} (f_{-w} + f_{-m})$$

$$L_{-w} = L_{w-} = \frac{\bar{C}_-}{d} \bar{C}_w f_{-w} (f_{+w} + f_{+m})$$

where d is defined as

$$d = \bar{C}_+ f_{+w} f_{+m} (f_{-w} + f_{-m}) + \bar{C}_- f_{-w} f_{-m} (f_{+w} + f_{+m})$$
$$+ \bar{C}_w f_{wm} (f_{+w} + f_{+m})(f_{-w} + f_{-m}). \tag{81}$$

The Onsager relationships are borne out by the Spiegler treatment. That is to say, it does not violate the general principles of the thermodynamics of irreversible processes. Also, the following additional relationship is established:

$$L_{+w} L_{-w} = L_{+-} L_{ww}. \tag{82}$$

In an ideally selective negative membrane, the co-ion concentration is zero: $\bar{C}_- = 0$. From this, the phenomenological coefficients are reduced to

$$L_{+-} = L_{--} = L_{-w} = 0$$

$$L_{++} = \frac{\bar{C}_+}{d'} (\bar{C}_+ f_{+w} + \bar{C}_w f_{wm})$$

$$L_{+w} = \bar{C}_+ \bar{C}_w f_{+w}/d' \tag{83}$$

$$L_{ww} = \bar{C}_w{}^2 (f_{+w} + f_{+m})/d'$$

$$d' = \bar{C}_+ f_{+w} f_{+m} + \bar{C}_w f_{wm} (f_{+w} + f_{+m})$$

cutting down considerably on the friction coefficients.

In order to know all of the parameters it is necessary to measure diffusion, conductivity and transport numbers.[104, 111] The f_{ik} parameters have been evaluated since by other workers. [112, 113, 114, 1]

4. Elektrokinetic Phenomena

In the 19th century, Saxen[115] observed, for the first time, the electrokinetic effects caused by the current and solvent flows through membrane capillaries. The relationships derived by Saxen, based on a simple theory, were later deduced by Mazur and Overbeeck based on phenomenological equations of the thermodynamics of irreversible processes.[116]

Let us take a system consisting of two subsystems I and II separated by a porous membrane and assume that the concentrations and the temperature are the same throughout the system so that subsystems I and II differ only in pressure and electrical potential. Entropy produced when the components move from subsystem I to subsystem II is given, according to eqn (30), by

$$\frac{d_i S}{dt} = -\frac{1}{T} \sum_\gamma \hat{\mu}_\gamma \frac{dn_\gamma{}^I}{dt} \tag{84}$$

where

$$\hat{\mu}_\gamma = (\mu_\gamma{}^I - \mu_\gamma{}^{II}) + z_\gamma F \Delta\phi = \bar{V}_\gamma \Delta P + z_\gamma F \Delta\phi. \tag{85}$$

From eqns (84) and (85), it is possible to obtain:

$$\frac{d_iS}{dt} = -\frac{1}{T}\sum_\gamma \bar{V}_\gamma \frac{dn_\gamma^{\mathrm{I}}}{dt}\Delta P - \frac{1}{T}\sum_\gamma z_\gamma F \frac{dn_\gamma^{\mathrm{I}}}{dt}\Delta\phi. \qquad (86)$$

Introducing in eqn (86) the volume flow, J_v, and electrical current, I, given by

$$J_v = -\sum_\gamma \bar{V}_\gamma \frac{dn_\gamma^{\mathrm{I}}}{dt}$$

$$I = -\sum_\gamma z_\gamma F \frac{dn_\gamma^{\mathrm{I}}}{dt} \qquad (87)$$

eqn (88) is obtained:

$$T\frac{ds}{dt} = J_v\Delta P + I\Delta\phi. \qquad (88)$$

The phenomenological equations in this system are

$$J_v = L_{11}\Delta P + L_{12}\Delta\phi$$
$$I = L_{21}\Delta P + L_{22}\Delta\phi \qquad (89)$$

where the Onsager $L_{12} = L_{21}$ relationships are borne out.
The flow–forces relationships may also be expressed by

$$\Delta P = R_{11}J_v + R_{12}I$$
$$\Delta\phi = R_{21}J_v + R_{22}I \qquad (90)$$

where R_{ik} are the terms of the inverse matrix, L_{ik}^{-1}.

Twelve independent kinetic relationships may be obtained from the phenomenological equations, and Saxen's four relationships are deduced from these. Thus, for example, from eqn (89) it may be deduced that

$$(I/J_v)_{\Delta\phi=0} = L_{21}/L_{11}. \qquad (91)$$

On the other hand, the following may be deduced from eqn (89):

$$\left(\frac{\Delta P}{\Delta\phi}\right)_{J_v=0} = -\frac{L_{12}}{L_{11}}. \qquad (92)$$

Saxen's first relationship is obtained from eqns (91) and (92):

$$\left(\frac{I}{J_v}\right)_{\Delta\phi=0} = -\left(\frac{\Delta P}{\Delta\phi}\right)_{J_v=0}. \qquad (93)$$

Likewise, the rest of Saxen's relationships may be obtained:

$$\left(\frac{\Delta\phi}{\Delta P}\right)_{I=0} = -\left(\frac{J_v}{I}\right)_{\Delta P=0}; \quad \left(\frac{I}{\Delta P}\right)_{\Delta\phi=0} = \left(\frac{J_v}{\Delta\phi}\right)_{\Delta P=0}$$

$$\left(\frac{\Delta\phi}{J_v}\right)_{I=0} = \left(\frac{\Delta P}{I}\right)_{J_v=0}.$$

(94)

The phenomenological coefficients may be measured with a series of experiments (permeability, conductance, and electroosmosis). So long as $\Delta\phi = 0$, L_{11} may be obtained from $(J_v/\Delta P)$. While this measurement is made the electrical current is not zero. Its magnitude may be related with $(J_v/\Delta P)_{I=0}$. In fact, from eqn (89) we see that

$$\left(\frac{J_v}{\Delta P}\right)_{I=0} = L_p = L_{11} - \frac{L_{12}^2}{L_{22}}.$$

(95)

L_{22} may be obtained based on conductance measurements:

$$\left(\frac{I}{\Delta\phi}\right)_{\Delta P=0} = L_{22} = L_e'.$$

(96)

While L_e'† is being measured, electroconvective phenomena alter membrane conductance. If conductance is measured cancelling out these phenomena by applying a pressure, then,

$$L_e = \left(\frac{I}{\Delta\phi}\right)_{J_v=0} = \frac{1}{R_{22}}$$

(97)

and it is possible to establish a relationship between k and k' from eqn (89)

$$L_e = L_e' - \frac{L_{12}^2}{L_{11}}$$

(98)

from which we see that $L_e = L_e'$ when $L_{12} = 0$. Therefore L_{12}^2/L_{11}, is the part of electroconvection to the total conductance measurement. Knowing L_{22}, the L_{12} coefficient may be obtained from the electroosmotic permeability coefficients because

$$\beta = \left(\frac{J_v}{I}\right)_{\Delta P=0} = \frac{L_{12}}{L_{22}}.$$

(99)

Now we are able to find the flow–force relationships using practical parameters. Thus it is possible to obtain

$$J_v = L_p \Delta P + \beta I$$
$$I = L_e'\beta \Delta P + L_e' \Delta\phi.$$

(100)

† L_e is related to k (specific conductance) by

$$L_e = k\frac{A}{d}$$

where A is the area and d the thickness of the membrane.

Tombalakaian[117] and Kobatake *et al.*[118] using permeability and electroosmosis measurements, recently found the L_{ik} phenomenological coefficients.

C. Theory of Absolute Reaction Rates

The theory of transition states may be used to study the phenomena of transport through membranes. Danielli[119] thought of the membranes as a succession of potential barriers, so that the molecular emigration takes place by jumps of the molecules over such barriers. Danielli's approach was later extended by Zwolinsky *et al.*[120] in an excellent paper described below.

If $\bar{C}_i$ is the molecule concentration per cm^3 in the ith position, the number of particles per cm^2 of cross section is $\lambda \bar{C}_i$, where λ represents the distance between the positions of equilibrium. In accordance with the absolute velocity process theory, molecule jumps per second may be expressed as:

$$k_i = \chi \frac{RT}{Nh} \exp\left(-\frac{\Delta G_+^+}{RT}\right) \qquad (101)$$

where χ is the transmission coefficient or, in other words, the fraction of molecules which can reach the uplimit of the barrier and pass to the final state. RT/Nh is the frequency factor and ΔG_+^+ is the difference of free energy between the top and the foot of the barrier.

Assuming $k_i = k_{i+1} = k$ and $\lambda_i = \lambda_{i+1} = \lambda$, the number of molecules crossing cm^2 of cross section every second will be

$$J_i = k\lambda \bar{C}_i - k'\lambda \bar{C}_{i+1} = -k\lambda^2 \left(\frac{\bar{C}_{i+1} - \bar{C}_i}{\lambda}\right). \qquad (102)$$

But according to Fick's first law

$$J_i = -\bar{D}\frac{\bar{C}_{i+1} - \bar{C}_i}{\lambda} \qquad (103)$$

we see that

$$\bar{D} = k\lambda^2. \qquad (104)$$

Considering particle diffusion flow as a successive series of jumps, the final expression, of through-membrane flow, may be obtained. In a stationary state, and assuming equal distances between two equilibrium positions,

$$\begin{aligned} J &= k_0 \lambda \bar{C}_0 - k_1' \lambda \bar{C}_1 \\ J &= k_1 \lambda \bar{C}_1 - k_2' \lambda \bar{C}_2 \\ J &= k_n \lambda \bar{C}_n - k_{n+1}' \lambda \bar{C}_{n+1}. \end{aligned} \qquad (105)$$

From the previous system, the following expression is obtained for the flow:

$$
J = \frac{k_0 \lambda C_0 - \prod_{i=1}^{n} \left(\frac{k_i'}{k_i} \right) k_{n+1}' \lambda \bar{C}_{n+1}}{1 + \sum_{r=1}^{n} \prod_{i=1}^{r} \frac{k_i'}{k_i}}
\tag{106}
$$

When the distance between equilibrium positions differ,

$$
J = - \frac{k_0 \lambda C_0 - \prod_{i=1}^{n} \left(\frac{k_i' \lambda_i'}{k_i \lambda_i} \right) k_{n+1}' \lambda_{n+1}' \bar{C}_{n+1}}{1 + \sum_{r=1}^{n} \prod_{i=1}^{r} \frac{k_i' \lambda_i'}{k_i \lambda_i}} .
\tag{107}
$$

The following equation is obtained if we assume $x = 1$ in eqn (101) and substitute it into eqn (106)

$$
J = \frac{\dfrac{RT}{Nh} \lambda \left[C_0 \, e^{-\Delta G^+/KT} \exp \left[-\sum_{i=1}^{n} (\Delta G_i'^{+} - \Delta G^{i+}) + \Delta G_{n+1}'^{+}/RT \right] \bar{C}_{n+1} \right.}{1 + \sum_{r=1}^{n} \exp \left(-\sum \Delta G_i'^{+} - \Delta G_i^{+}/RT \right)} .
\tag{108}
$$

When an external force acts on a single unit process, an additional amount of work W is supplied which may help or hurt the process by raising or lowering the initial and final energetic positions (Fig. 4). Assuming a symmetrical potential barrier, the work is given by a force that acts only in the distance $\lambda/2$, between the initial and final states. The linear forward and reverse step is

$$
v = \lambda(k_f - k_b) = k_0 \lambda (e^{W/kT} - e^{-W/kT}) = 2\lambda k_0 \, sh \left(\frac{W}{kT} \right)
\tag{109}
$$

where k is the Boltzmann constant.

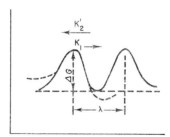

FIG. 4. Potential energy diagram.

Generally $W \ll kT$; therefore developing in series, $e^{W/kT}$, we see that

$$v = \lambda k_0 \frac{2W}{kT}. \tag{110}$$

As $W = f\lambda/2$, and generalizing diverse forces f_i, the following equation is obtained for v:

$$v = \frac{k_0 \lambda^2}{kT} \sum_i f_i = \frac{\bar{D}_0}{kT} \sum_i f_i. \tag{111}$$

Knowing v, the flow will be given by

$$J = vC. \tag{112}$$

Based on the above equations, we are able to find an expression for the flow of component i, when the driving forces are a concentration gradient

$$f_1 = -kT \frac{d \ln \bar{a}}{dx} \tag{113}$$

and an electrical potential gradient,

$$f_2 = -z_i F \frac{d\phi}{dx}. \tag{114}$$

In that case, from eqns (111), (112), (113), and (114):

$$J_i = -\bar{D}_0 \left(\frac{z_i F \bar{C}_i}{kT} \frac{d\phi}{dx} + \bar{C}_i \frac{d \ln \bar{a}_i}{dx} \right). \tag{115}$$

That is to say, the Nernst–Planck flow equation is obtained, which basically helps us to calculate the absolute diffusion coefficients.

D. Diffusion Across Membranes

1. Selfdiffusion

Selfdiffusion coefficients, in the membrane phase, depend on the size of the ion hydrated and are 1/5 to 1/20 lower than the corresponding coefficients in water. It has been seen that in the case of cation exchange membranes, in moderately concentrated electrolyte solutions, the cation self-diffusion coefficients increase considerably when the external concentration is increased, while co-ion selfdiffusion coefficients decrease slightly.[121, 122, 123,124]
Richman and Thomas[125] pointed out that cation diffusion coefficients, in cation exchange resins, increase slightly with the external electrolyte

concentration. However, when this concentration is around 0·03 M, these coefficients increase sharply, then remain practically uniform as concentration increases. The character of the diffusion coefficient–concentration curve, implies that there are at least two mechanisms responsible for transporting cations through the polymeric matrix. This effect was observed and discussed for the first time by Schlögl.[126] In the leached state, where co-ions are not found in the membrane phase, cation transfer must be an exchange between sufficiently separated fixed acid groups. This mechanism is characterized by a low diffusion coefficient. When anion content increases an easier route opens up for cation transfer given by presence of negative carriers. Assuming

$$\bar{D} = D_0 \exp\left(-\frac{E}{RT}\right).$$ (116)

Richman and Thomas[125] found that the activation energy, E, is around 10·3 kcal/mol for a 0·01 N external electrolyte concentration and 2·2 kcal/mol when the concentration is 0·07 N.

Lagos and Kitchener[24] looked into the influence of the degree of cross-linking and water content on cation selfdiffusion coefficients, in cation exchange resins. The experimental results of diffusion, in sulphonic polystyrene resins with a 2·33 and 4·5% divinyl–benzene content, show that in the first case, (moles of water/equiv = 8·94), the selfdiffusion coefficient of Na^+ is $3·86 \times 10^{-6}$ cm²/sec and in the second case, (moles of water/equiv = 6·93), this coefficient has the significantly lower value of $2·56 \times 10^{-6}$ cm²/sec. Nevertheless, if the cation selfdiffusion coefficients, in resins with different degrees of crosslinking, are plotted against the water content, we see that they are nearly on the same curve. These authors conclude that selfdiffusion coefficients are strongly dependent on water content in the membrane phase.

Spiegler[104] made a theoretical study of diffusion processes in electro-negative membranes separating two solutions, such as NaCl, with the same concentration, in which cations are marked on one side of the membrane. He assumes the co-ions are in static equilibrium since they do not take part in the diffusion processes. The generalized force acting on the ions is given by

$$F = -\frac{d\mu}{dx} = -RT\frac{d\ln\bar{a}}{dx} \simeq -\frac{RT}{C}\frac{d\bar{C}}{dx}.$$ (117)

As the total membrane concentration is constant,

$$\frac{d\bar{C}}{dx} = -\frac{d\bar{C}^*}{dx}$$ (118)

then

$$\frac{F_+}{F_+{}^*} = -\frac{\bar{C}_+{}^*}{\bar{C}_+} \tag{119}$$

where the asterisk refers to one of the isotopes. We should emphasize that $F_w = 0$, since no force is applied to the water molecules. For the isotopes $f_{+m} = f_{+m}{}^*$, and $f_{+w} = f_{+w}{}^*$.

From eqns (3), (78), (119) and (117) we find

$$J_+ = \frac{\bar{C}_+}{f_{+w} + f_{+m}} F_+ = -\frac{RT}{f_{+w} + f_{+m}} \frac{d\bar{C}}{dx}. \tag{120}$$

On comparing the above equation with the Fick's law

$$J_+ = -\bar{D}_+ \frac{d\bar{C}}{dx} \tag{121}$$

we find the following expression for the self-diffusion coefficient

$$\bar{D}_+ = \frac{RT}{f_{+w} + f_{+m}}. \tag{122}$$

It agrees with the Einstein law that postulates that the self-diffusion coefficient is equal to RT divided by the friction factor.

Caramazza et al.[127] obtained an expression for the self-diffusion coefficients which included the isotope interactions Spiegler did not take into account. Using the Laity[128,129] notation, the friction coefficients are defined by the following equation

$$F_i = \sum_k X_k r_{ik}(v_i - v_k) \tag{123}$$

where F_i is the total force exercised by all of the species on component i, X_k is the fraction of component k, and v_i and v_k are the respective velocity of components i and k. The r_{ii} coefficients do not appear in the above equation, but Laity[128,129] has shown that in a system where part of the components are radioactive and the tagged component transport is measured, these coefficients do appear. Applying Laity's treatment, the $^{35}Cl^-$ and $^{36}Cl^-$ coion selfdiffusion coefficients, through an electronegative membrane, are given by

$$\bar{D}_{--} = \frac{RT}{r_{+-}X_+ + r_{--}X_- + r_{-w}X_w + r_{-m}}. \tag{124}$$

Using the Donnan relationship

$$\bar{D}_{--}\bar{C} = \bar{D}_{(app)}C \tag{125}$$

where C is the electrolyte concentration inside the membrane, these authors calculate the true diffusion coefficients D_{--} (Table I). The phenomeno-logical coefficients, L_{--}, may be taken from D, using the equation

$$L_{--} = \bar{C}D_{--}/RT. \tag{126}$$

Dorst et al.[111] subjected Spieger's theory to a test by calculating the L_{ik} phenomenological coefficients from conductance, transport number of water and solute, and permeability and diffusive measurements. Their results do not confirm the theory, but neither is the conclusion definite.

TABLE I.   Apparent and corrected diffusion coefficients.

Molality of the external solution	$\bar{D}_{--(\text{app})} \times 10^7$	$\bar{D}_{--} \times 10^7 \,(\text{cm}^2/\text{sec})$
0·2092	1·95 ± 0·06	7·6
0·6059	2·82 ± 0·06	5·6
0·9490	3·91 ± 0·08	6·2
0·3922	4·34 ± 0·09	5·7
2·8277	4·48 ± 0·09	5·6

The membrane is made up of polyelectrolytic chains with water between them, and the main barrier to diffusion are these polymeric chains. Additionally, duffusing ions are submitted to electrostatic forces, so that the coions are repelled by the fixed ions in the polyelectrolytic chains. Mackay and Meares[106,130,131] studied the obstruction effect. They assumed that the diffusing particles were all the same size as the polymeric units.

They relate the counter-ion mobilities in the membrane phase and in free solution by the following expression

$$\frac{\bar{D}_+}{D_+{}^\circ} = \left(\frac{1 - v_p}{1 + v_p}\right)^2 \tag{127}$$

where v_p is the fraction in volume of the polymeric chains and $D_+{}^\circ$ is the diffusion coefficient in free solution. These authors compared the results obtained with equation (127) with experimental results and saw that eqn (127) is borne out when external electrolyte concentration is higher than 0·2 N.

Mackay and Meares,[106] using the Spiegler theory, calculated the friction coefficients f_{+w} in Permutit Zeo–Karb–315 membranes submerged in a

$0.05 \, \text{N}$ NaCl solution. They obtained the value of 4.93×10^8 joul sec. cm^{-2}. mol^{-1}. Keeping in mind that when $f_{+w} \gg f_{+m}$,

$$\bar{D}_+ = \frac{RT}{f_{+w}} \qquad (128)$$

and in free solution

$$D_+{}^\circ = \frac{RT}{f_{+w}{}^\circ} \qquad (129)$$

may be obtained

$$\frac{\bar{D}_+}{D_+{}^\circ} = \frac{f_{+w}{}^\circ}{f_{+w}} \qquad (130)$$

where $f_{+w}{}^\circ$ may be found from eqn (129) based on the free diffusion coefficients; its value is 1.863×10^8. According to this, $\bar{D}_+/D_+{}^\circ = 0.378$, a value which is close to the tortuosity coefficient $(1 - v_p)/(1 + v_p)$ which in this case is 0.341. This similarity points out that the particles follow a longer route diffusing through the membranes than for the same distance in free solution. This results in a proportional increase in the friction coefficients due to the additional collision of ions with water molecules.

Jakubovic et al.[132] found that the selfdiffusion coefficients obtained from the Mackie and Meares equation did not agree with experimental results except when $v_p > 0.4$. These authors find that in the $0 < v_p < 0.2$ interval, $\bar{D}_+$ increases with v_p, though the eqn (127) suggests the contrary. They discuss these discrepancies and postulate a diffusion mechanism in which, since an electric field may greatly influence outcome in a very swollen resin, counter-ions (in the absence of coions) move from a fixed group to another along the polymeric chain, following the most tortuous routes corresponding to them for purely geometric considerations. To jump from the ion atmosphere of one chain to the other, the corresponding potential barrier must be overcome. These authors denominate this process *diffusive volume*.

Andelman and Gregor[133] have compared the selfdiffusion coefficients, measured experimentally in an electropositive membrane, with those obtained from the Nernst–Einstein relationship

$$\bar{D}_i = 1000 \, RT \, \frac{\bar{\kappa}_i}{F^2 \bar{C}_i} \qquad (131)$$

based on the specific conductance measurements. They observed that the calculated values are 30% above the experimental ones. Despic and Hills[134] had noticed this discrepancy earlier and attributed it to the fact that the experimental values of $\bar{\kappa}_i$ are higher than they really should be, given the electro-osmotic flow of the solvent.

Recently McHardy et al.[135] carried out an interesting study of anion and counter-ion selfdiffusion in a homogeneous phenosulphonic Zeo Karb 315 membrane, using radio-tracers. We describe this briefly here. In the membrane phase the coions are electrostatically repelled by the fixed groups in the polymer matrix. Given Donnan's exclusion effect, they are concentrated wherever fixed charge density and counter-ion concentrations are lower than average. Thus, preferably, the coions are surrounded by water molecules, but because of blockage and the electrostatic potential of the matrix, they are forced to follow a more tortuous route than in free solution. These authors find that the Br$^-$ selfdiffusion coefficient, in an electro–negative membrane, increases slightly with the external electrolyte concentration. This contrasts with the results of Glueckauf et al.[136] who observed a stationary decrease.

MacHardy et al.,[135] observed that the Br$^-$ selfdiffusion coefficients depend on the cation form of the membrane and increase in the following sense:

$$Na^1 < Sr^{+2} < Cs^+.$$

It should be noted that though the sodic form of the membrane has greater volume and water content than the Cs$^+$ form, the Cs$^+$ is preferred for the polymeric matrix and is closer to it, offering less physical barriers to the coions which, as we know, tend to avoid the fixed charges. The activation energy for D_{Br}, with the sodic form membrane, is significantly greater than in the Sr^{+2} form (4·7 and 4·0 kcal/mol, respectively). They also measured diffusion coefficients for Na$^+$, Cs$^+$, and Sr^{+2} cations, observing that the respective values increase around three times in the interval of concentration 0–leq/l. The $\bar{D}_+/D_+^\circ$ relation where, D_+° is the free solution selfdiffusion coefficient, increases as coion concentration increases, and is highest when the counter-ion is least attracted by the membrane. These results bear out if one remembers that the diffusive volume, pointed out by Jakubovic et al.[132] preferably occurs with low charge ions and high hydration range. This process is accelerated by increasing the temperature and coion concentration in the membrane phase, so that they might act as electrical bridge in the diffusion stage. If the membrane is in heteroionic form, the Br$^-$ selfdiffusion coefficients decrease when the Na$^+$ fraction, of the thermodynamically non-preferred ion, increases.

2. Interdiffusion

If a membrane separates two electrolytic solutions having the same coion and different counter-ions, ionic interdiffusion takes place through the same. A quantitative description of this phenomenon has been made by Helfferich,[137] Helfferich and Ocker[138] and Mackay and Meares.[139,140]

Helfferich studied the problems of interdiffusion in systems where the external solution concentrations are very small, compared to the membrane's fixed ions, in such a way that the coions are excluded from the membrane phase. He assumes that the fixed ion concentration and the $\bar{D}_A/\bar{D}_B$ coefficient relationships are constants through the membrane; furthermore, he disregards the solvent transport. According to the Nernst–Planck flow equation, the counter-ion flows are given by

$$J_A = - \bar{D}_A \left(\frac{\partial \bar{C}_A}{\partial x} + \bar{C}_A \frac{\partial \ln \bar{\gamma}_A}{\partial x} + \bar{C}_A z_A \frac{F}{RT} \frac{\partial \phi}{\partial x} \right)$$

$$J_B = - \bar{D}_B \left(\frac{\partial \bar{C}_B}{\partial x} + \bar{C}_B \frac{\partial \ln \bar{\gamma}_B}{\partial x} + \bar{C}_B z_B \frac{F}{RT} \frac{\partial \phi}{\partial x} \right). \tag{132}$$

As the electroneutrality requires $\Sigma z_i J_i = 0$ and $z_A \bar{C}_A + z_B \bar{C}_B = $ constant $= \bar{X}$ (fixed ion concentration), from eqn (132) one obtains:

$$J_A = - \bar{D}_A \bar{D}_B \frac{\bar{C}_A z_A^2 + \bar{C}_B z_B^2}{\bar{D}_A \bar{C}_A z_A^2 + \bar{D}_B \bar{C}_B z_B^2} \cdot \frac{d\bar{C}_A}{dx} + \frac{\bar{D}_A z_A \bar{C}_A \bar{D}_B \bar{C}_B z_B}{\bar{D}_A \bar{C}_A z_A^2 + \bar{D}_B \bar{C}_B z_B^2}$$

$$\cdot \frac{d \ln (\bar{\gamma}_A{}^{z_B}/\bar{\gamma}_B{}^{z_A})}{dx} \tag{133}$$

If the solutions are ideal, the second term of eqn (133) is cancelled out and eqn (133) takes the following form:

$$J_A = - \bar{D}_A \bar{D}_B \frac{\bar{C}_A z_A^2 + \bar{C}_B z_B^2}{\bar{D}_A \bar{C}_A z_A^2 + \bar{D}_B \bar{C}_B z_B^2} \cdot \frac{d\bar{C}_A}{dx}. \tag{134}$$

A diffusion integral coefficient, dependent on counter-ion concentration in the membrane phase, may be defined by comparing eqn (134) with Fick's law,[137,138,141,142] which is given by:

$$\bar{D}_{AB} = \bar{D}_A \bar{D}_B \frac{\bar{C}_A z_A^2 + \bar{C}_B z_B^2}{\bar{D}_A \bar{C}_A z_A^2 + \bar{D}_B \bar{C}_B z_B^2}. \tag{135}$$

If $z_A = z_B$, this equation may also be expressed by

$$\frac{1}{\bar{D}_{AB}} = \frac{\bar{X}_A}{\bar{D}_B} + \frac{\bar{X}_B}{\bar{D}_A} \tag{136}$$

where $\bar{X}_A$ and $\bar{X}_B$ are, respectively, the molar fractions of A and B in the membrane phase.

From the above equations, the important conclusion that if $\bar{C}_A \ll \bar{C}_B$, then $\bar{D}_{AB} \gg \bar{D}_A$, is derived. That is to say, the diffusion in the membrane phase is controlled by the least concentrated component.

Helfferich and Ocker[138] integrated eqn (133), to obtain the counter-ion flows through the membranes when the solutions are not ideal. They also obtained the concentration profile in the membrane phase. If the conditions are ideal, the flow of component A is given by[137]

$$J_A = - \frac{(z_A - z_B)\bar{D}_A \bar{D}_B}{(\bar{D}_A z_A - \bar{D}_B z_B)d}$$

$$\left[\bar{C}_A'' - \bar{C}_A' + \frac{\bar{X} z_B (\bar{D}_A - \bar{D}_B)}{(z_A - z_B)(\bar{D}_A z_A - \bar{D}_B z_B)} \ln \frac{\bar{D}_A \bar{C}_A'' z_A^2 + \bar{D}_B \bar{C}_B'' z_B^2}{\bar{D}_A \bar{C}_A' z_A^2 + \bar{D}_B \bar{C}_B' z_B^2} \right]$$

$$(137)$$

where $\bar{C}'$ and $\bar{C}''$ are the component concentrations at the membrane interfaces (') and (''); d is the membrane thickness.

If $z_A = z_B$

$$J_A = - \frac{\bar{D}_A \bar{D}_B \bar{X}}{(\bar{D}_A - \bar{D}_B)d} \ln \frac{\bar{D}_A \bar{C}_A'' z_A^2 + \bar{D}_B \bar{C}_B'' z_B^2}{\bar{D}_A \bar{C}_A' + \bar{D}_B \bar{C}_B'}. \qquad (138)$$

Defining the integral diffusion coefficient as

$$\bar{D}_{AB} = \frac{d}{\bar{C}_A' - \bar{C}_A''} J_A$$

the values of $\bar{D}_{AB}$ in various extreme cases are given by

$$\bar{D}_{AB} = \begin{cases} \bar{D}_A \text{ for } \bar{C}_A \ll \bar{C}_B \\[2mm] \frac{\bar{D}_A \bar{D}_B}{\bar{D}_A - \bar{D}_B} \ln \frac{\bar{D}_A}{\bar{D}_B} \simeq (\bar{D}_A \bar{D}_B)^{1/2}, \\[1mm] \quad \text{for } \bar{C}_A' z_A = \bar{X}; \quad \bar{C}_A'' z_A = 0; \quad z_A = z_B \\[2mm] \frac{\bar{D}_A \bar{D}_B}{\bar{D}_A Z_A - \bar{D}_B z_B} \left[z_A - z_B + \frac{z_A z_B (\bar{D}_A - \bar{D}_B)}{\bar{D}_A Z_A - \bar{D}_B z_B} \ln \frac{\bar{D}_A z_A}{\bar{D}_B z_B} \right] \\[1mm] \quad \text{for } \bar{C}_A' z_A = \bar{X}, \quad \bar{C}_A'' z_A = 0; \quad z_A \neq z_B \\[2mm] \frac{2\bar{D}_A \bar{D}_B}{\bar{D}_A + \bar{D}_B}, \quad \text{for } (\bar{C}_A' - \bar{C}_A'') \ll \bar{X}, \quad \bar{C}_A z_A \simeq \bar{C}_B z_B \gg \frac{\bar{X}}{2}. \end{cases}$$

Mackay and Meares[139] also obtained the flow equations corresponding to interdiffusion processes in diluted and concentrated solutions, based on the Nernst–Planck equations: however, these authors kept in mind the movement of the solution's centre of mass in the membrane pores (see (139) and (140)).

If the integral interdiffusion coefficients are measured in the $A^+X^-|$ membrane $|B^+X^-$ and $A^+X^-|$ membrane $|C^+X^-$ systems, the apparent selfdiffusion coefficients may be derived from these integral coefficients. In effect, considering that $\bar{X}_B + \bar{X}_C + 2\bar{X}_A = 2$ in the membrane phase, from eqn (136) and the case in which $\bar{X}_A \ll 1$

$$\bar{D}_A = \frac{2\bar{D}_{AB}\bar{D}_{AC}}{\bar{D}_{AB} + \bar{D}_{AC}}. \tag{143}$$

The above equation was used by Ciric and Graydon[143] to calculate selfdiffusion coefficients from interdiffusion coefficients. In Table II, their results obtained for various polyestyrene sulphonic membranes crosslinked with divinylbenzene, are shown.

TABLE II.   Single ion diffusion coefficients[143]

| Ion | $\bar{D} \times 10^5$ for membranes | | | |
	1	2	3	4
H^+	28·0	11·0	7·0	3·70
K^+	5·50	2·20	1·40	0·77
Na^+	3·90	1·50	0·96	0·50
Li^+	2·32	0·86	0·57	0·29

It is seen that the ratio of single ion diffusion coefficient values are nearly independent from the degree of crosslinking and the exchange capacity of the membrane. Thus, for example, $D_{H^+}/D_{K^+} = 5$, $D_{H^+}/D_{Na^+} = 7·3$, and $D_{H^+}/D_{Li^+} = 12·5$, relationships similar to those of the equivalent conductances in free solution.

Worsely et al.[23] measured the interdiffusion coefficients of various electrolytes in different membranes and related them to those corresponding to the K—H system. They note that the sieve effect, as the consequence of crosslinking of the membrane, is small.

Recently Blaedel et al.[144] studied the mechanism of interdiffusion through ion exchange membranes, using tracers. They postulated the following processes

(a) Diffusion through the first Nernst layer next to the membrane.

(b) Heterogeneous exchange reaction on the surface of the film–membrane interface.

(c) Diffusion through the membrane.

(d) Heterogeneous reaction on the film–membrane interface.

(e) Diffusion through the second Nernst layer.

The flux, through the first and second Nernst layer and the membrane, is given by

$$J_i = D_i C_i \left(\frac{d \ln C_i}{dx} + \frac{d \ln \gamma_i}{dx} \right). \tag{144}$$

If the membrane is in the A form, and B flows from left to right, the following heterogeneous reaction takes place in the first film–membrane interface

$$B^b_{(aq)} + \frac{b}{a} A^a_{(memb)} \underset{k_b}{\overset{k_f}{\rightleftarrows}} B^b_{(memb)} + \frac{b}{a} A^a_{(aq)}$$

where B is a trace ion.

The fluxes of B through the films ($'$), ($''$) and the membrane are expressed by

$$J_{B[film(')]} = \frac{D}{\delta'} (C_B' - C_B{}^\circ); \quad J_{B[film('')]} = \frac{D}{\delta''} (C_B{}^d - C_B'')$$

$$J_{B(memb)} = \frac{\bar{D}}{d} (\bar{C}_B{}^\circ - \bar{C}_B{}^d). \tag{144'}$$

In the same way the fluxes of A may be obtained (see Fig. 5; assuming $C_B' > C_B''$, $C_A' < C_A''$). Exchange fluxes at membrane–solution ($'$) and ($''$) interfaces are expressed by

$$J_B = k_f(C_B{}^\circ)(\bar{C}_A{}^\circ)^{b/a} - k_b(\bar{C}_B{}^\circ)(C_A{}^\circ)^{b/a}$$
$$J_B = k_b(\bar{C}_B{}^d)(C_A{}^d)^{b/a} - k_f(C_B{}^d)(\bar{C}_A{}^d)^{b/a} \tag{145}$$

where k_f and k_b represent the rate constants of the heterogeneous reactions (forward and back), and D represents the diffusion coefficient of the transported species. In the stationary state, flows are equal and we can find J_B, eliminating $C_B{}^\circ$, $\bar{C}_B{}^\circ$, $C_B{}^d$, $\bar{C}_B{}^d$ and the corresponding values of C_A from the above equations. If the B concentration is much smaller than that of A, and we disregard the concentration gradient of A through the films next to the membrane, we find

$$J_B = \frac{\dfrac{C_B'}{(C_A')^{b/a}} - \dfrac{C_B''}{(C_A'')^{b/a}}}{\bar{D} \dfrac{d}{(k_f/k_b)(Q/a)^{b/a}} + \dfrac{D_2\delta'(C_A'')^{b/a} + D_1\delta''(C_A')^{b/a}}{D_1 D_2 (C_A')^{b/a}(C_A'')^{b/a}} + \dfrac{(C_A')^{b/a} + (C_A'')^{b/a}}{k_f(Q/a)^{b/a}(C_A')^{b/a}(C_A'')^{b/a}}}$$

where Q is the ion exchange capacity.

The above equation points out a very interesting phenomenon, which is the possibility of B transport from a region of low concentration to a region of high concentration solution, as has previously been observed by Blaedel *et al.*[145,146] These same workers partially proved the interdiffusion mechanism where $C_A' = C_A'' = C$, assuming $D_1 - D_2 = D$ and $\delta' = \delta'' = \delta$. In this case

$$\frac{C_B' - C_B''}{J_B} = \frac{d}{(k_f/k_b)\bar{D}(Q/a)^{b/a}} C_A^{b/a} + \frac{2d}{D} \frac{2}{k_f(Q/a)^{b/a}}. \tag{147}$$

Plotting the first term of eqn (147) against $C_A^{b/a}$, straight lines are obtained, which proves the adequacy of the equation and the ideal character of the mechanism from which it is derived. Nevertheless, it is not proven that all steps are necessary. This may be obtained from a mechanism including only diffusion stages and not ion exchange heterogeneous reaction rates. However, there are other considerations that indicate the importance of the ion exchange reaction (see ref. 144).

3. Multi-ionic Diffusion

When an electronegative membrane separates a solution containing AX, BX, and CX electrolytes, from another containing DX, EX, and FX electrolytes, all together this makes up a multi-ionic diffusion system. Making various simplifications, Helfferich calculated the flows and concentration profiles using the Nernst–Planck relationships.[99,147] According to these, the species flow is given by

$$J_A = -\frac{\bar{D}_A \bar{X} a_A}{z_i \bar{\gamma}_A d} \frac{M_k}{L_k M_j - L_j M_k} \ln \frac{L_k M_j}{L_j M_k} \tag{148}$$

where a_A is the activity of A in solution, j refers to the A, B, C, counter-ions and k refers to D, E, F, ones. At the same time

$$L_i = \sum_i (a_i/\bar{\gamma}_i)$$

and

$$M_i = \sum_i (\bar{D}_i a_i/\bar{\gamma}_i)$$

If there are only two counter-ions on the same side of a membrane, the equation is reduced to

$$\frac{J_A}{J_B} = \frac{\bar{D}_A a_A \bar{\gamma}_B}{\bar{D}_B a_B \bar{\gamma}_A} \tag{149}$$

an expression analogous to that obtained by Neihof and Sollner.[148]

4. Unstirred Layer

In diffusion processes, ion concentrations are not uniform near the membrane where unstirred layers are found whose thickness depend on stirring up the adjoining solution.

These layers may have a definitive effect on ion flows through the membrane, as well as on membrane potentials. The system consisting of a membrane separating two electrolytic solutions is made up of the following parts (Fig. 5).

1st compartment solution | film | membrane | film | 2nd compartment solution

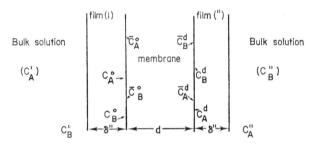

FIG. 5. Interdiffusion across a selective membrane.

The integral diffusion coefficients through the films and the membrane are defined by

$$\bar{D}_{AB} = J_A \frac{d}{\bar{C}_A{}^\circ - \bar{C}_A{}^d}; \quad D_{AB}{}' = \frac{\delta'}{C_A{}' - C_A{}^\circ} J_A; \quad D_{AB}{}'' = \frac{\delta''}{C_A{}^d - C_A{}''} J_A. \tag{150}$$

In a steady state,

$$\bar{D}_{AB} = J_A \frac{d}{\bar{C}_A{}^\circ - \bar{C}_A{}^d} = J_B \frac{d}{\bar{C}_B{}^d - \bar{C}_B{}^\circ}. \tag{151}$$

Furthermore, strong A and B counter-ion concentration discontinuity is found in the film–membrane interfaces. C_i and $\bar{C}_i$ are related by the partition coefficients K_i

$$K_i = \frac{\bar{C}_i}{C_i} \cdot \frac{C}{\bar{X}}. \tag{152}$$

The interfacial concentrations of component A may be obtained by Fick's law and eqn (152). If $z_A = z_B$, and $C' = C'' = C$ and $\delta' = \delta''$, one finds[149]

$$C_A^\circ = C - \frac{K_A^\circ C + \dfrac{D_{AB}'Cd}{\overline{D}_{AB}\overline{X}\delta}C_B' + K_A^d\dfrac{D_{AB}'}{D_{AB}''}C_B' - K_A^d C_A''}{\dfrac{D_{AB}'Cd}{\overline{D}_{AB}\overline{X}\delta} + K_A^d\dfrac{D_{AB}'}{D_{AB}''} + K_A^\circ}$$

$$C_A^d = \frac{K_A^\circ C + \dfrac{D_{AB}''Cd}{\overline{D}_{AB}\overline{X}\delta}C_A'' + K_A^\circ\dfrac{D_{AB}''}{D_{AB}'}C_A'' - K_A^\circ C_B'}{\dfrac{D_{AB}''Cd}{\overline{D}_{AB}\overline{X}\delta} + K_A^\circ\dfrac{D_{AB}''}{D_{AB}'} + K_A^d}$$

$$(153)$$

When the diffusion characteristics of A and B counter-ions are identical $(D_A = D_B = D)$, the flows through the films are given by

$$J_A'' = \frac{D}{\delta}(C_A^d - C_A'') = \frac{D}{\delta}\left[\frac{C}{\dfrac{DCd}{\overline{D}\overline{X}\delta} + 2} - C_A''\right]$$

$$J_A' = \frac{D}{\delta}(C_A' - C_A^\circ) = \frac{D}{\delta}\left[C_A' - C\left(1 - \frac{1}{\dfrac{DCd}{\overline{D}\overline{X}\delta} + 2}\right)\right]$$

$$(154)$$

The $(DCd)/(\overline{D}\overline{X}\delta)$ amount is a basic parameter for controlling flow in the system. It indicates the relationship between the maximum flow obtained in the films and in the membrane.[149, 137] For $(DCd)/(\overline{D}\overline{X}\delta) \gg 1$ film resistance is much less than membrane resistance; in this case, $C_A^\circ = C_B^d = C$ and $C_A^\circ = C_B^\circ = 0$. That is to say, concentration gradients are entirely localized within the membrane (ideal membrane control). On the other hand, for $(DCd)/(\overline{D}\overline{X}\delta) \ll 1$, membrane flow is much greater than that in the films. In this case $C_A' \gg C_B'$, $C_B'' \gg C_A''$, and $C_A^\circ = C/2$. Here the concentration gradients are localized completely within the films (ideal film control). Finally, if $(DCd)/(\overline{D}\overline{X}\delta)$ takes intermediate values, diffusion is controlled by both the films and the membrane.

Various workers[149, 150, 151] have evaluated the limiting layer thickness. Thus Peterson and Gregor[149] calculated the thickness of the films in interpolymer membranes as a function of the stirring of the compartment solutions.

They used the system

$$0{\cdot}001 \text{ M ClK} \mid \text{Cation selective membrane} \mid 0{\cdot}001 \text{ M NH}_4\text{NO}_3.$$

The flux for each time interval was evaluated, and by extrapolation to zero time, they calculated the flux, J^*, under the initial conditions when $C_B' = C_A'' = 0$.

Initial flux values were obtained from the following general expression for the case where a coupled mechanism prevails.

$$J_{K^+} = \frac{D(C_{K^+}' - C_{K^+}°)}{\delta}. \tag{155}$$

At the zero time, under steady conditions

$$C_{K^+}° = C\left[1 - \frac{1}{\dfrac{DCd}{\overline{D}\overline{X}\delta} + 2}\right] \tag{156}$$

$$C_{K^+}' = C, \quad K = 1.$$

Then, the general expression becomes

$$J_{K^+}^* = \frac{D}{\delta}\left(\frac{C}{\dfrac{DCd}{\overline{D}\overline{X}^\delta} + 2}\right) \tag{157}$$

or

$$\delta = \frac{DC}{2}\left(\frac{1}{J^*} - \frac{d}{\overline{D}\overline{X}}\right).$$

Peterson and Gregor calculated D_+ from conductance measurements, using the Nernst–Einstein equation, and calculated $J_{K^+}^*$ from flow measurements at different times and extrapolating for $t = 0$. They noted that the δ values are a function of stirring, varying between 1 and 30 μ at 1200 to 200 rev/min stirring interval.

Mackay and Meares[150] evaluated δ, using two membranes with the same characteristics, but different thicknesses. In the theoretical development of flow equations in the interdiffusion processes they found

$$\delta = \frac{C\overline{D}(X_A' - X_A'')(J_a d_a - J_b d_b)}{2J_a J_b (d_a - d_b)} \tag{158}$$

where X_A' and X_A'' are the molar fraction of A in compartment solutions on either side of the membrane. J_a and J_b are the A and B component flows, in the d_a and d_b thick membranes. Mackay and Meares' work shows that film thickness does not tend toward zero but rather toward $4\cdot7 \times 10^{-3}$cm at high stirring speeds.

Similar studies of δ were made by Peers,[151, 152] using electrodialysis, in C–10 Permutit electronegative membranes. In steady state, univalent cation flow through the films and the membrane is given by

$$\bar{J}_+ = t_+ \frac{I}{F} - D\frac{\partial C}{\partial x} = \bar{t}_+ \frac{I}{F} - \bar{D}\frac{\partial \bar{C}}{\partial x} \tag{159}$$

where the overbar refers to the membrane phase. If the solvent transfer is disregarded, $-\partial C/\partial x$ is independent of x and may be replaced by $\Delta C_d/\delta$, where ΔC_d is the concentration difference between the compartment solution and the surface of the membrane. The salt diffusion coefficient inside the membrane may be replaced by $\bar{P}_s\Delta\bar{C}_s$, where $\bar{P}_s$ is the permeability constant for a given salt and $\Delta\bar{C}_s$ is the concentration difference between the two faces of the membrane. It is very easy to show that

$$\Delta C_s = C'' - C' + 2\Delta C_d; \qquad C' < C''. \tag{160}$$

As a result, cation flow is given by

$$\bar{J}_+ = t_+ \frac{I}{F} + \frac{D\Delta C_d}{\delta} = \bar{t}_+ \frac{I}{F} - \bar{P}_s\Delta\bar{C}_s \tag{161}$$

and from eqn (161)

$$\Delta C_d = \frac{(\Delta t_+)(I/F) - \bar{P}_s(C'' - C')}{D/\delta + 2\bar{P}_s} \tag{162}$$

where

$$\Delta\bar{t}_+ = \bar{t}_+ - t_+.$$

If the current density through the system, solution $(C') \to$ membrane $\to$ solution (C''), increases, ΔC_d increases to a limiting value of C' (i.e. concentration at the membrane surface is zero); the corresponding current density is called the "limiting current density," I_{lim}. From eqn (162) one finds

$$I_{lim} = \frac{F}{\Delta\bar{t}_+}\left[\frac{DC'}{\delta} + \bar{P}_s(C' + C'')\right]. \tag{163}$$

In a highly selective membrane that is very thick, immersed in a highly stirred up system, where C'' is very small, $\bar{t}_+ = 1$ and $\bar{P}_s \gg D/\delta$. Therefore, eqn (163) becomes

$$I_{lim} = \frac{FDC'}{(1 - t_+)\delta}.$$

Equation (164) was also derived by Rosenberg and Tirrell.[153] All of the parameters found in eqn (164) are known. I_{lim} may be found with the Peers procedure. As a result, δ, may be evaluated. Finally substituting eqn (162) into (161) and arranged terms, cations flow net, as a function of current density, is found.

$$J_+ = \frac{t_+ I}{F} + \frac{D}{\delta}\left[\frac{\Delta t_+(I/F) - \bar{P}_s(C'' - C')}{(D/\delta) + 2\bar{P}_s}\right].\tag{165}$$

This equation on rearrangement gives

$$\frac{J_+ F}{I} = t_+ + \frac{D}{\delta}\left[\frac{\Delta t_+}{(D/\delta) + 2\bar{P}_s}\right] - \frac{DF}{\delta I}\left(\frac{\bar{P}_s}{(D/\delta) + 2\bar{P}_s}\right)(C'' - C').\tag{165}$$

We will use this expression later.

5. Electrolyte Flux

When the membrane separates the same solution but in different concentration, the electrolyte migrates from the concentrated to the diluted solution. The membrane remains electroneutral because if an ion moves faster than another bearing the opposite charge, an electrical field is created which slows down the faster ion and accelerates the slower one. Several workers have treated electrolyte flow through ion exchange membranes, basing their work on the Nernst–Planck flow equations. Helfferich,[99] disregarding convective flow, calculated ion flows and internal concentration profiles.

Schlögl[154] resolved the flow equations for the case of univalent electrolytes and assumed that diffusion coefficients, as well as active group concentration through the membrane, were constants. Oel[155] left out the activity coefficients, disregarded convective flux and assumed mobility constants in the membrane phase.

Mackie and Meares[156] derived an equation for a univalent salt flux through a membrane, taking convection into account, but assuming mobility and fixed group concentration were constant. Ion flux referent to the membrane is given by Nernst–Planck (eqn (10)). Eliminating $d\phi/dx$ between J_+ and J_-, assuming that $z_+ dC_+ = z_- dC_-$ and using the following empiric re-relationship for the activity coefficient

$$\ln \bar{\gamma}_\pm = A \ln (\bar{C}_+ \bar{C}_-) + B\tag{166}$$

where A and B are constants, Mackay and Meares obtained the following expression for the net electrolyte flux (1:1) through a cationic membrane:

$$J_+ = \frac{\bar{D}}{d}\left[(\bar{C}_+' - \bar{C}_+'') - \frac{\bar{X}(\bar{U}_+ - \bar{U}_-)}{2(\bar{U}_+ - \bar{U}_-)}\ln S\right] + \frac{A\bar{D}}{d}\left[2(\bar{C}_+' - \bar{C}_+'')\right.$$

$$\left. - \frac{\bar{X}(\bar{U}_+ - \bar{U}_-)}{(\bar{U}_+ + \bar{U}_-)}\ln S\right]\left[\frac{\bar{D}}{d}(\bar{C}_+' - \bar{C}_+'') + \frac{v^*(\bar{C}_-'M - \bar{C}_-'')}{1 - M}\right]$$

where

$$\bar{D} = \frac{2RT\,\bar{U}_+\bar{U}_-}{\bar{U}_+ + \bar{U}_-}$$

$$\ln S = \ln\frac{\bar{U}_+\bar{C}_+' + \bar{U}_-\bar{C}_-'}{\bar{U}_+\bar{C}_+'' + \bar{U}_-\bar{C}_-''} \tag{167}$$

$$M = \exp(v^*d/D)$$

and $\bar{C}_+$ and $\bar{C}_+''$ represent cation concentrations on either side of the membrane (just in the membrane phase).

$\bar{U}_+$ and $\bar{U}_-$ may be calculated by the relationship

$$\bar{U} = U\frac{1 - v_p}{1 + v_p} \tag{168}$$

and $\bar{C}_+'$ and $\bar{C}_+''$ may be found by measurement of sorption. v^* is calculated using the equation

$$v^* = -\frac{dml}{1 - v_p} \tag{169}$$

where ml is the ml flow per second, through a hydrogen type membrane separating HCl 1 M and conductivity water.

Mackay and Meares tested this equation using Zeo Karb membranes and saw the calculated flows were always somewhat larger than those observed. They noted that the equation provided the closest predictions for moderately concentrated electrolyte solutions rather than for diluted ones.

Meares and Ussing[157] calculated, theoretically and experimentally, the flows through the membrane in either direction when the same substance is found on either side of the membrane, but in different concentrations. For the theoretical calculations they used Ussing's[158] relationships. It is briefly described below.

If a membrane of area A separates two electrolyte substances a and b, the flow of substance a will be given by

$$J_a = A \overline{U}_a \overline{C}_a \left(- \frac{d \hat{\bar{\mu}}_a}{dx} + \frac{1}{A} \sum_{i=a}^{k} J_i \overline{V}_i f_i^a \right) \tag{170}$$

where $\overline{U}_a$ is a's mobility when all the J_i, except J_a, are zero; $\overline{C}_a$ and $\hat{\bar{\mu}}_a$, are the concentration and electrochemical potential on plane x and f_a^i is the force in the x direction equivalent to the frictional drag exercised on a by a flow of i at unit velocity, relative to a in the x direction. The electrochemical potential may be expressed by

$$\hat{\bar{\mu}}_a = \mu_a^\circ + RT \ln \overline{C}_a + RT \ln \bar{\gamma}_a + P_a \overline{V}_a + z_a F \phi. \tag{171}$$

By defining a magnitude a_a given by

$$\ln a_a = \frac{\hat{\bar{\mu}}_a - \mu_a^\circ}{RT} - \frac{1}{RT} \int_0^x \left(\frac{\sum_{i=a}^{k} J_i \overline{V}_i f_i^a}{A} \right) dx \tag{172}$$

from eqns (170), (171) and (172), one obtains

$$J_a = - RT \, A \overline{U}_a \overline{C}_a \frac{d \ln a_a}{dx} \tag{173}$$

and

$$\overline{C}_a = \frac{a_a}{\bar{\gamma}_a} \exp - \left\{ \frac{P \overline{V}_a}{RT} + \frac{z_a F \phi}{RT} - \frac{1}{RT} \int_a^x \left(\frac{\sum_{i=a}^{k} J_i \overline{V}_i f_i^a}{a} \right) dx \right. \tag{173b}$$

Substituting $\overline{C}a$ into eqn (173) we find the flow, J_a. In the same way, the flow of component b may be found. If the substances on either side of the membrane are isotopic, then $\overline{U}_a = \overline{U}_b$, $z_a = z_b$, $\overline{V}_a = \overline{V}_b$ and $f_i^a = f_i^b$. In this case, considering that

$$\frac{J_a}{J_b} = \frac{da_a/dx}{da_b/dx} \tag{174}$$

in steady conditions, the following equation is obtained

$$J_a \int_0^d \left(\frac{da_b}{dx} \right) dx = \int_0^d \left(\frac{da_a}{dx} \right). \tag{175}$$

Since isotope a is found on one side of the membrane and isotope b on the other, the limits are

$$x = 0 \begin{cases} a_a = a_a' \\ a_b = 0 \end{cases}$$

$$x = d \begin{cases} a_a = 0 \\ a_b = a_b''. \end{cases} \tag{176}$$

Then, from eqns (175) and (176) we find that

$$-\frac{J_a}{J_b} = \frac{a_a'}{a_b''}. \tag{177}$$

Finally, using eqns (177) and (173b), the relationship between isotopic flows is found.

$$\ln\left(-\frac{J_a}{J_b}\right) = \ln\frac{\bar{C}_a'}{\bar{C}_b''} + \ln\frac{\bar{\gamma}_a'}{\bar{\gamma}_b'} + \bar{V}\left(\frac{P' - P''}{RT}\right) + \frac{zF(\phi' - \phi'')}{RT}$$

$$+ \frac{1}{RT}\int_0^d \left(\sum_{i=a} \frac{J_i \bar{V}_i f_i^a}{A}\right) dx. \tag{178}$$

The net flow will be the difference between the flows given in the above equation.

Behn[159] and Teorell[160] derived an equation identical to eqn (178), which consists of only the first four terms. To do so, they used quasi thermodynamic procedures. The same was done by Hoshiko and Lindley,[161] using phenomenological equations of irreversible thermodynamic processes. The equation (178) may be simplified to take the following form

$$\ln\left(-\frac{J_a}{J_b}\right) = \ln\frac{\bar{C}_a'}{\bar{C}_b''} + \ln\frac{\bar{\gamma}_a'}{\bar{\gamma}_b''} + \bar{V}\left(\frac{P' - P''}{RT}\right) + \frac{zF(\phi' - \phi'')}{RT} + \frac{v^*d}{D_b}.$$

Meares and Ussing used this equation to calculate flow relationships with different concentrated ClNa solutions, using ^{24}Na and ^{36}Cl for the experimental measurements. It was observed that theoretical were larger than experimental values, but these values became closer if activity coefficients were disregarded.

Other workers[162, 163] have measured electrolyte diffusion through membranes at different temperatures and have evaluated the activation energy of the process.

E. Donnan Equilibrium

The importance of electrochemistry in the field of electrobiology has been declared by many biologists[164, 165, 166] during the first third of this century. Membrane electrochemistry may be dated from 1935. Physicists and chemists showed little interest in this field except for Donnan who in 1911 established the theory of ion distribution and the electromotive effects that occur in electrolytic systems separated by semipermeable membranes which may be permeated by two or more species, though a single ion species may not pass across it. Donnan derived his theory[167] on a thermodynamic base, from classical electrochemistry of solutions principles. Donnan's work marks a stage in the development of membrane electrochemistry.

Following Donnan, we may assume an ion exchange membrane as a binary polyelectrolyte with complete dissociation R^-Na^+, in which the colloidal anion may not be diffused. If this type of polyelectrolyte comes into contact with a solution of small, diffusible M^+A^- ions, a Donnan type equilibrium will be reached. Unequal ion distribution, osmotic pressure, and a difference in potential between the two phases will result. In equilibrium, the chemical potential will be the same in both phases

$$\bar{\mu}_i = \mu_i \tag{180}$$

where the terms with overbars refer to the membrane phase and the terms without overbars refer to the solution. From eqn (180) the following equation is deduced:

$$RT \ln \frac{a_i}{\bar{a}_i} + z_i F(\phi - \bar{\phi}) = (\bar{P} - P)\, \bar{V}_i \tag{181}$$

where $\phi - \bar{\phi}$ is the Donnan potential and $\bar{P} - P = \pi$ is the difference between the swollen membrane pressure and the hydrostatic pressure in the solution.[168] Whether or not the potential difference may be evaluated depends on whether or not the two solutions inside and outside of the membrane are sufficiently diluted for the $\bar{\gamma}_i$ values (activity coefficients) to be calculated in the usual way. In any case, for the ij electrolyte, in the equilibrium, $\bar{\mu}_{ij} = \mu_{ij}$ and from eqn (181) it is possible to obtain

$$\ln \frac{a_{ij}}{\bar{a}_{ij}} = \pi \frac{\bar{V}_{ij}}{RT} \tag{182}$$

where $\bar{V}_{ij}$ is the partial molar volume of ij. If ij dissociates in ∂_i and ∂_j ions, eqn (182) takes the form of

$$\ln \frac{m_i^{\nu i} m_j^{\nu j} \gamma_\pm{}^\nu}{\bar{m}_i^{\nu i} \bar{m}_j^{\nu j} \bar{\gamma}_\pm{}^\nu} = \pi \frac{\bar{V}_{ij}}{RT}. \tag{182'}$$

The above relationship may be related with the condition of electro-neutrality, in order to obtain the counter-ion, and the coion molalities, in the membrane phase. For a membrane with X molal-concentration of negative fixed groups, in equilibrium with a single (1:1) electrolyte solution, the following are borne out:

$$\bar{m}_+ = \bar{X} + \bar{m}_- \tag{183}$$

and

$$\frac{m_+ \gamma_\pm^2}{\bar{m}_+ \bar{m}_- \bar{\gamma}_\pm^2} = \exp\left(\frac{\pi \bar{V}}{RT}\right). \tag{184}$$

Finding $\bar{m}_-$ and $\bar{m}_+$ from eqn (184) and substituting into eqn (183), we find, respectively, that

$$\bar{m}_+ = \frac{\bar{X}}{2}[1 + (1 + \xi^2)^{1/2}]$$

$$\bar{m}_- = -\frac{\bar{X}}{2}[1 - (1 + \xi^2)^{1/2}] \tag{185}$$

where

$$\xi = \frac{2a_\pm}{\bar{X}\bar{\gamma}_\pm \exp(\pi \bar{V}/RT)}. \tag{186}$$

Ion activities inside of the membrane are given by

$$\bar{a}_+ = \bar{m}_+ \bar{\gamma}_+; \quad \bar{a}_- = \bar{m}_- \bar{\gamma}_- \tag{187}$$

where $\bar{a}$ and $\bar{a}_+$ are the coion and counter-ion activities in the membrane phase. If we disregard the pressure term of eqn (186) and assume the electro-lyte coefficient in the membrane phase is equal to the unit, the equations coincide with those of Meyer and Sievers[169] and Teorell.[170, 196, 97]

Furthermore, cancelling out the pressure term for eqn (186), the Donnan potentials are obtained, where $a_+/\bar{a}_+ = \bar{a}_-/a_- = r$, is known as the Donnan relationship. The equations are entirely rigorous, but cannot be used unless the activity coefficients $\bar{\gamma}_\pm$ in the membrane phase are known. These coefficients may be evaluated with the equation (184)[171, 172, 173, 174, 175] considering that the term $\exp(\pi V/RT) = 1$. From counter-ion and coion concentrations, it is easy to find $\bar{\gamma}_\pm$. The values, calculated in this way by Lakshminarayanaiah[17] are shown in the Table III. It is seen that the activity coefficient, opposite in aqueous solutions, increase with the con-centration. Thus, in highly diluted solutions, in which the activity coefficients in free solution approximate to the unit, in the membrane phase they are close to zero. Some workers[176,136,177] have attributed this anomaly to the electrolyte occlusion in the membrane surface and the coion sorption by the resin impurities. Making the necessary corrections for the colloid electrolyte, it was found[174] that it slowly but surely did decrease, with the concentration. All of these facts have resulted in criticism of quantitative studies based on the Donnan theory and other theories have been suggested as alternatives by Glueckauf.[177] Nevertheless, the meticulous work of Boyd and Bunzyl[173] recently carried on, supports Donnan's theory.

TABLE III. Equilibrium water content W, Fixed charge molality—and the activity coefficient term $\bar{\gamma}_\pm \exp(\pi \bar{V}/2RT)$ in a PSA membrane as functions of activity of external solutions.[17]

Molality $m_\pm$	Activity $a_\pm$	Water content, g H$_2$O/g wet resin	$\bar{m}_-$ (molality)	$\bar{X}^-$ (molality)	$\bar{\gamma}_\pm e^{\pi \bar{V}/2RT}$	ζ
0·001004	0·000969	0·633	0·006	1·263	0·011	0·138
0·09115	0·00907	0·633	0·010	1·291	0·079	0·177
0·1006	0·0781	0·622	0·034	1·372	0·357	0·319
1·024	0·6738	0·602	0·675	1·372	0·573	1·714
5·700	5·444	0·540	5·213	1·481	0·921	7·980

F. Membrane Potentials

1. Concentration Potentials

The e.m.f. resulting when an ion exchange membrane separates two identical electrolyte solutions, but of distinct concentration, is well studied. Usually the e.m.f. is different than that resulting between the solutions in the absence of a membrane, that is, in a state of free diffusion.

The e.m.f. may be measured with reversible electrodes, such as calomel or silver chloride electrodes. The e.m.f. obtained using the former is the same as the membrane concentration potential if the liquid junction potential is discounted (bridge solution); this is a negligible factor in dilute solutions. Nevertheless, it becomes more significant the more the concentration of the solution increases. A more exact measurement of the e.m.f. may be obtained using Ag–AgCl electrodes. In this case, the measurement differs from the membrane potential by the potential between the electrodes and the solution.

Using a calomel electrode, the measurement cell is made up of the following components:

$$Hg_2Cl_2 \quad KCl(sat) \quad M^+A^-(C_1) \quad memb. \quad M^+A^-(C_2) \quad KCl(sat) \quad Hg_2Cl_2.$$

The sign and magnitude of the potential depend on the characteristics of the electrolyte, its concentration on either side of the membrane and the characteristics of the membrane. In fact, this potential may vary between the liquid union potential resulting from free diffusion and given by the Henderson equation, and that resulting if the membrane is replaced by a pair of specific reversible electrodes for the permeable ions.

The transport of electrical current through the membrane is carried out by anions and cations in a proportion differing from transport numbers of these ions in free solution. If there is an electronegative and selective membrane, a very high fraction of electrical current is transported by cations. In this case, the transport number of cations, in the membrane phase, is higher than in free solution and the transport number of anions in the membrane phase is lower than in free solution.

In the membrane phase and in free solution

$$\bar{t}_+ + \bar{t}_- = t_+ + t_- = 1.$$

From the Nernst equation, for the diffusion potential, it is possible to establish a correlation between the concentration potentials and the transport numbers. For the case of a single (1:1) electrolyte and a negative membrane[16]

$$E = \frac{\bar{t}_+ - \bar{t}_-}{\bar{t}_+ + \bar{t}_-} \cdot \frac{RT}{F} \ln \frac{a^{II}}{a^{I}}. \tag{189}$$

If the membrane is ideally selective, $\bar{t}_- = 0$ and $\bar{t}_+ = 1$, and the concentration potential may therefore be given as

$$E = \frac{RT}{F} \ln \frac{a^{II}}{a^{I}} \tag{190}$$

which is the same as the Donnan equation for the membrane potential. Furthermore, this is the maximum concentration potential a permselective membrane may have.

Though eqn (189) does not take into account the effect of the water transport, it allows discussion of the relationship between the concentration potential and the membrane structure.[6]

One may consider the membrane made up of pores and with fixed positive or negative charges in their walls. However, the pore diameter and length are not uniform. Due to thermal fluctuations of the polymer segments, the diameter of the pore walls varies with time.

The fixed charges cannot move and are unable to take part in diffusion or in transport of electrical current through the membrane, If the diameter of the pores is small and there is a high concentration of fixed charge, the coions are repelled by the fixed ions and only the counter-ions take part in the phenomena of transfer through the membrane (Fig. 6); but repulsion decreases as porosity increases, and coions may take part in the transport phenomena in the membrane phase. When the external electrolyte concentration is increased, there is an increase in the amount of electrolyte entering the pores. This decreases the superficial action of the pores and therefore the membrane selectivity. At sufficiently high concentrations, some electrolytes may penetrate the tightest pores (Fig. 6), which then lose their optimal ion selectivity. The macromolecules of the pores are generally crosslinked forming more or less irregular networks. The degree of irregularity depends on the components of the membrane as well as the preparation method used.

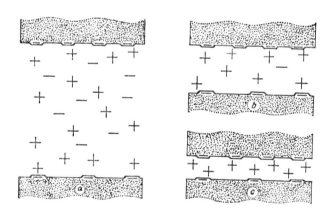

FIG. 6. Distribution of ions in three pores of different diameter at the same concentration of the outside electrolyte solution (Sollner, K., *Macromol. Sci.*, A3, 1 (1969)).

The transport of non-electrolytes through the membrane is determined by the size of the pores they pass through. The diffusion path of electrolytes depends on a geometric factor and an electric factor due to the fixed charge repulsion of ions of the same sign. Figure 7 shows, how the location of fixed charges in geometrically identical pores, may determine ion permeability and therefore the electrical characteristics of the pore. In the figure, the solid circles around the signs + or − represent the size of the hydrated ions and the broken lines represent the effective range of the repulsion.

Precise localization of ionic processes or processes which start the electromotive forces of membrane cells is a problem in membrane electrochemistry. Luther,[178] Nernst[179] and Haber[180] were the pioneers in this work. However, it was Sollner,[181] basing his work on that of these authors, who concluded that the potentials are made up of three parts; the two potentials originated in the membrane–solution interface and the diffusion potential in the inside of the membrane, though this author did not quantitatively express these ideas. Teorell,[170, 182] using a kinetic procedure and a little later Meyer and Sievers,[169] using a thermodynamic procedure, independently and with a great deal of detail, presented theoretic approximations of the three-part origin of membrane potential. These workers established an equation relating the concentration potential with external concentrations, ion mobility inside the membrane and fixed ion concentration. These authors simplified the problem by assuming that:

(1) the electrolyte solutions are ideal.

(2) the relation of ion mobility and fixed ion concentration is constant at any point of the membrane

(3) the water transfer effects are insignificant.

(4) the ion distribution in the membrane interface–liquid may be expressed by the Donnan equation.

Given the concentration discontinuity found in the membrane interface–solution, there is a different Donnan potential on either side of the membrane

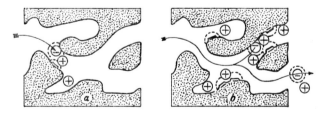

FIG. 7. The influence of the location of fixed charges at the pore walls upon the blockage of ions of the same sign (Sollner[6]).

and a diffusion potential inside it. The electrical potential of a membrane is measured in cells of the type.

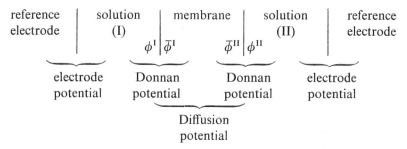

The concentration potential is given by

$$\phi^{II} - \phi^{I} = (\phi^{II} - \bar{\phi}^{II}) - (\phi^{I} - \bar{\phi}^{I}) + (\bar{\phi}^{II} - \bar{\phi}^{I}). \qquad (191)$$

The following is a reformulation of the TMS theory (Hill *et al.*[102]). Let us consider a cation exchange membrane separating two different solutions of the same single (1:1) electrolyte. The difference between the Donnan potentials may be obtained from eqn (181).

$$(\bar{\phi}^{II} - \bar{\phi}^{II}) - (\phi^{I} - \bar{\phi}^{I}) = \frac{RT}{F} \ln \frac{\bar{a}_{+}^{II}}{a_{+}^{II}} - \frac{RT}{F} \ln \frac{\bar{a}_{+}^{I}}{a_{+}^{I}} + \frac{1}{F}(\pi^{I} \bar{V}_{+}^{I} - \pi^{II} \bar{V}_{+}^{II})$$

$$= \frac{RT}{F} \ln \frac{a_{-}^{II}}{\bar{a}_{-}^{II}} - \frac{RT}{F} \ln \frac{a_{-}^{I}}{\bar{a}_{-}^{I}} + \frac{1}{F}(\pi^{I} \bar{V}_{-}^{I} - \pi^{II}V_{-}^{II}); \qquad (192)$$

where $\bar{a}_{+} = \bar{m}_{+}\bar{\gamma}_{+}$ and $\bar{a}_{-} = \bar{m}_{-}\bar{\gamma}_{-}$; and $\bar{m}_{+}, \bar{m}_{-}, \bar{\gamma}_{+}$ and $\bar{\gamma}_{-}$ are respectively, the molal concentrations and the activity coefficients inside the membrane. In the Meyer and Siever's theory, the diffusion potential $\bar{\phi}^{II} - \bar{\phi}^{I}$ was equated to that of the liquid junction and evaluated by the Planck method. In order to integrate the flow equation, Planck assumed that the total ion concentration varied linearly through the diffusion zone. Teorell used the following expression:

$$\bar{\phi}^{II} - \bar{\phi}^{I} = \frac{\bar{u}_{+} - \bar{u}_{-}}{\bar{u}_{+} + \bar{u}_{-}} \frac{RT}{F} \ln \frac{\bar{u}_{+}\bar{m}_{+}^{I} + \bar{u}_{-}\bar{m}_{-}^{I}}{\bar{u}_{+}\bar{m}_{+}^{II} + \bar{u}_{-}\bar{m}_{-}^{II}} \qquad (193)$$

where $\bar{u}_{+}$ and $\bar{u}_{-}$ are cation and anion mobilities and $\bar{m}_{+}^{I}, \bar{m}_{+}^{II}, \bar{m}_{-}^{I}$ and $\bar{m}_{-}^{II}$ are the ion molalities in points I and II.

The diffusion potential is obtained by substituting eqn (185) into eqn (193)

$$\bar{\phi}^{II} - \bar{\phi}^{I} = \frac{u_{+} - u_{-}}{u_{+} + u_{-}} \cdot \frac{RT}{F} \ln \frac{\bar{X}^{I}\{U + (1 + \xi^{I2})^{1/2}\}}{\bar{X}^{II}\{U + (1 + \xi^{II2})^{1/2}\}} \qquad (194)$$

in which $\bar{U} = (\bar{u}_{+} - \bar{u}_{-})/(\bar{u}_{+} + \bar{u}_{-})$, and $\bar{X}$ is the concentration of fixed ions.

Using reversible anion electrodes, the contribution of the two electrodes to the total e.m.f. is given by

$$E = \frac{RT}{F} \ln \frac{a_-{}^{I}}{a_-{}^{II}}. \tag{195}$$

From eqns (192), (194) and (195), the following expression, for the membrane cell electromotive force, is obtained:

$$E = \frac{RT}{F} \ln \frac{\bar{\gamma}_-{}^{I} \bar{X}^{I}\{-1 + (1 + \xi^{I2})^{1/2}\}}{\bar{\gamma}_-{}^{II} \bar{X}^{II}\{-1 + (1 + \xi^{II2})^{1/2}\}} + \frac{1}{F} (\pi^{I} \bar{V}_-{}^{I} - \pi^{II} \bar{V}_-{}^{II})$$

$$+ \frac{\bar{U}RT}{F} \ln \frac{\bar{X}^{I}[\bar{U} + (1 + \xi^{I2})^{1/2}]}{\bar{X}^{II}[\bar{U} + (1 + \xi^{II2})^{1/2}]}. \tag{196}$$

The only values in eqn (196) which may be obtained experimentally are X and ξ, while $\bar{\gamma}_-$ and $\pi V/RT$ remain undetermined. Hills et al.[171] and later on Lakshminarayanaiah and Subrahmanyan,[17] discussed this problem as well as the admissable approximations, testing the TMS rigorously and keeping in mind factors often overlooked. Using chemical analysis, they calculated the ion concentration in the membrane phase as well as the fixed ion concentration.

They also evaluated U from the equation

$$\bar{U} = \frac{\bar{t}_+ \bar{m}_- - \bar{t}_- \bar{m}_+}{\bar{t}_+ \bar{m}_- + \bar{t}_- \bar{m}_-}$$

where $\bar{t}_+$, $\bar{t}_-$, $\bar{m}_+$, $\bar{m}_-$, may be determined as functions of the external concentration.

Disregarding $I/F (\pi^{I} \bar{V}_-{}^{I} - \pi^{II} \bar{V}_-{}^{II})$ in eqn (196), they calculated the difference between the potential obtained using the TMS theory and that obtained experimentally (Table IV). It was found that for external concentrations less than 0·015 N the results obtained theoretically and experimentally agree reasonably well. However, over 0·015 N values calculated according to the theory are higher than those actually observed. Adding in eqn (196) the e.m.f. due to water transfer, calculated[17] using the equation

$$\phi_w = -\frac{RT}{F} \int_{I}^{II} t_w \, d \ln a_w \tag{197}$$

the results are more satisfactory.

TABLE IV.   Differences between the membrane cell EMF exptl. and calculated from the TMS theory and from the Scatchard equation, in PSA membranes.[17]

m^{I}	m^{II}	TMS theory $(E' - E_{\mathrm{obs}})\,\mathrm{mV}$	$-\phi\, l_W\,(\mathrm{mV})$	Scatchard theory $(E - E_{\mathrm{obs}})\,\mathrm{mV}$
0·002004	0·001004	0·58	0·32	0·50
0·01005	0·005005	−0·07	0·54	0·24
0·05006	0·02005	2·30	1·56	−0·49
0·1006	0·05006	1·91	1·94	−0·94
0·5066	0·2026	9·91	6·77	−0·55
1·024	0·5066	8·21	6·86	−0·27
2·089	1·024	6·84	7·80	−0·09

Assuming all the single ion activity coefficients to be unity, the pressure volume term to be negligible and X to remain constant at all the values of the external electrolyte concentrations, eqn (196) becomes[13]

$$E = \frac{RT}{F}\left[\overline{U}\ln\frac{(4a'^2 + \overline{X}^2)^{1/2} + \overline{U}\overline{X}}{(4a''^2 + \overline{X}^2)^{1/2} + \overline{U}\overline{X}} + \ln\frac{a''}{a'}\cdot\frac{(4a'^2 + \overline{X}^2)^{1/2} + \overline{X}}{(4a''^2 + \overline{X}^2)^{1/2} + \overline{X}}\right]. \quad (198)$$

When $a \gg \overline{X}/2$, eqn (198) reduces to

$$E = \frac{RT}{F}(\bar{t}_+ - \bar{t}_-)\ln\frac{a'}{a''}. \quad (199)$$

When $a \ll \overline{X}/2$, then eqn (198) reduces to the Nernst equation

$$E = \frac{RT}{F}\ln\frac{a'}{a''}. \quad (200)$$

Finally when $a \simeq \overline{X}/2$, a simplification is difficult, but eqn (199) is often used. By eqn (196) it is possible to obtain the transport numbers. Keeping in mind that $\bar{t}_+ + \bar{t}_- = 1$, eqn (199) may be rearranged to

$$E = \frac{RT}{F}(2\bar{t}_+ - 1)\ln\frac{a'}{a''}. \quad (201)$$

From eqns (200) and (201), $\bar{t}_+$ may be obtained. Equation (198) was also used by several workers[183,184,185] to determine the fixed charge capacity in membranes, the values of which are too low to determine by the usual methods.

Using the equation proposed by Scratchard,[186] the concentration potential may be expressed as a function of experimentally measurable values

$$\phi^{II} - \phi^{I} = -\frac{RT}{F} \int_I^{II} \sum_i \bar{t}_i \, d \ln a_i \tag{202}$$

where $\bar{t}_i$ is the transport number in the membrane phase of the component i. The fixed ion transport number in the membrane is zero, so the equation takes the following form:

$$\phi^{II} - \phi^{I} = -\frac{RT}{F} \int_I^{II} [\bar{t}_+ d \ln a_+ + \bar{t}_- d \ln a_- + \bar{t}_w \, d \ln a_w]. \tag{203}$$

By using the Gibbs–Duhem relationships, $d \ln a_w$ may be obtained by the following equation

$$d \ln a_w = - 0{\cdot}036 \, m_\pm \, d \ln a_\pm. \tag{204}$$

On the other hand

$$\bar{t}_+ + \bar{t}_- = 1. \tag{205}$$

Combining the eqns (203,) (204) and (205) one may find the membrane cell e.m.f. measured with reversible anion electrodes

$$E = -\frac{2RT}{F} \int_I^{II} (\bar{t}_+ - 10^{-3} \, \text{M} \, m_\pm t_w) \, d \ln a_\pm \tag{206}$$

where $m_\pm$ is the average molal concentration of the external (1:1) electrolyte with activity $a_\pm$, t_+ and t_w correspondent to cation transport number and that for water and M is the molecular weight of the solvent.

Hills et al.[102] derived the Scatchard's equation from irreversible thermodynamic procedures. Taking the case of a single (1:1) electrolyte solution, they obtained from eqns (71), (72) and (73)

$$- \text{grad} \, \phi = \frac{I}{\kappa} + \frac{I}{F} \sum_k t_k \left\{ \frac{Q_k^{**}}{T} \text{grad} \, T + \bar{V}_k \, \text{grad} \, P + RT \, \text{grad} \ln a_k \right\}. \tag{207}$$

When membrane potentials are determined, $I = 0$. Assuming one dimensional flux (perpendicular to the membrane) and experimental isothermic and isobaric conditions, eqn (207) becomes

$$- \frac{F \Delta \phi}{RT} = \int_I^{II} \sum_k \bar{t}_k \, d \ln a_k.$$

In Hills et al's.[102] treatment, the fixed charge transport number is not zero, because they flow in relation to the mass centre of the system. The e.m.f. of the cell, measured with reversible anion electrodes, will be

$$- E = \frac{RT}{F} \left\{ \ln \frac{a^{II}}{a^{I}} + \int_{I}^{II} [\bar{\imath}_+ \, d \ln a_+ + \bar{\imath} \, d \ln a_- + \bar{\imath}_{\bar{x}} \, d \ln a_{\bar{x}}] \right. \tag{208}$$

Taking into account that

$$\bar{\imath}_+ - \bar{\imath}_- - \bar{\imath}_{\bar{x}} = 1 \tag{209}$$

the electrical neutrality condition $(C_+ = C_- + \bar{X})$ and the Gibbs–Duhem relation $C_i \, d\mu_i = 0$ eqn (208) becomes

$$- \frac{FE}{RT} = 2 \int_{I}^{II} \bar{\imath}_+^{\,\circ} \, d \ln a_{\pm} + \int_{I}^{II} \bar{\imath}_w \, d \ln a_w \tag{210}$$

where

$$\bar{\imath}_+^{\,\circ} = \bar{\imath}_+ + \frac{\overline{m}_+}{\overline{m}_w} \bar{\imath}_w \tag{211}$$

and

$$\bar{\imath}_w = - \frac{\overline{m}_x}{\overline{m}_w} \bar{\imath}_{\bar{x}} . \tag{212}$$

Equation (210) coincides with Scatchard's. In calculating eqn (210) it is assumed that the centre of the mass of the system coincides with that of the solvent. In this case, $J_w = 0$. When the true centre of mass is used, the expression obtained for the e.m.f. of the cell, differs from eqn (210) in the term[187]

$$\frac{RT}{F} \int_{I}^{II} (2\bar{\imath}_+ - 1) \, d \ln a_w. \tag{213}$$

Membrane potentials have been quantitatively studied using irreversible thermodynamic processes.[102, 171, 17, 188] This approach does not supply information on the actual mechanism bringing about the observed membrane potentials. Kobatake et al.[189, 190, 191] developed a line of work relating concentration potentials with the molal concentration of ions in the membrane phase. Taking a capillary type membrane as their model, Kobatake and co-workers calculated the ion fluxes through an electronegative membrane. The fluxes are produced by the forces, $\partial \hat{\mu}_+/\partial x$, $\partial \hat{\mu}_-/\partial x$ and $\partial \mu_w/\partial x$ in which $\hat{\mu}$ and μ are electrochemical and chemical potentials, respectively. If C_+, C_- and C_w represent average ion concentrations and the relationship

$$\sum_{i=+,-,w} C_i (\partial \hat{\mu}_i/\partial x) = 0$$

is kept in mind, absolute ion flows are found

$$J_k = -\left(L_{kk} - \frac{\bar{C}_k}{\bar{C}_w}L_{kw}\right)\frac{\partial \hat{\mu}_k}{\partial x} - \left(L_{kj} - \frac{\bar{C}_j}{\bar{C}_w}L_{jw}\right)\frac{\partial \hat{\mu}_j}{\partial x} + \bar{C}_k v^* \quad (214)$$

where $k, j = +, -$ and $k \neq j$. v^* is the velocity of the centre of the mass and the phenomenological coefficients are in reference to the centre of the mass.

These authors simplified eqn (214) disregarding the final term $C_k v^*$ as well as the factors $(\bar{C}_k/\bar{C}_w)L_{kw}$, as c_k, $C_j \ll c_w$. Then

$$J_+ = -L_{++}\left(\frac{\partial \hat{\mu}_+}{\partial x}\right) - L_{+-}\left(\frac{\partial \hat{\mu}_-}{\partial x}\right)$$

$$J_- = -L_{-+}\left(\frac{\partial \hat{\mu}_+}{\partial x}\right) - L_{--}\left(\frac{\partial \hat{\mu}_-}{\partial x}\right) \quad (215)$$

which fulfill the $L_{+-} = L_{+-}$ relationships of Onsager.

From the reduced current density $I^* = I/F = J_+ - J_-$ and reduced density of flow $J_s = 1/2(J_+ + J_-)$, they obtained for the steady state $(dI^*/dx = 0, dJ_s/dx = 0)$ and when $I^* = 0$, the electrochemical potentials and J_s as a function of the phenomenological coefficients. For isothermic and isobaric conditions

$$\frac{d\hat{\mu}_+}{dx} = -\frac{(L_{+-} - L_{--})J_s}{2(L^2_{+-} - L_{++}L_{--})} = F\frac{d\phi}{dx} + RT\frac{d\ln a_+}{dx} \quad (216)$$

$$\frac{d\hat{\mu}_-}{dx} = \frac{(L_{++} - L_{+-})J_s}{2(L^2_{+-} - L_{++}L_{--})} = -F\frac{d\phi}{dx} + RT\frac{d\ln a_-}{dx}. \quad (217)$$

Finally, from eqns (216) and (217) the final expression of concentration potential is obtained

$$\Delta\phi = -\frac{RT}{F}\int_{-\infty}^{\infty}\frac{\bar{u}_+\bar{C}_+ - \bar{u}_-\bar{C}_-}{\bar{u}_+\bar{C}_+ + \bar{u}_-\bar{C}_-}\frac{d\ln a}{dx}dx \quad (218)$$

where ion mobility has been defined with respect to the centre of mass of the system, by the following equations

$$\bar{u}_+\bar{C}_+ = F(L_{++} - L_{+-})$$

$$-\bar{u}_-\bar{C}_- = F(L_{+-} - L_{--}) \quad (219)$$

and the fact that

$$a_+a_- = a^2 \quad (220)$$

has been taken into account.

Toyoshima et al.[191] solved eqn (218), keeping in mind the effect of the liquid layer remaining on the membrane surface. Average activity is related to concentration on the membrane surface by

$$a^2 = a_+ a_- = \gamma_+ \gamma_- C_+ C_-. \tag{221}$$

The equilibrium phenomena in aqueous solution of a flexible and linear polyelectrolyte which contains an externally added single valence external electrolyte, are very well expressed by the ion activity role, so long as the concentration of the added electrolyte is not too low. For a polyelectrolyte dissociated in the same positive ion as the added single valence electrolyte:

$$\bar{\gamma}_+ = \frac{\gamma_+{}^\circ(C_-)(\bar{C}_- + \theta\bar{X})}{(\bar{C}_- + \bar{X})}; \qquad \bar{\gamma}_- = \gamma_-{}^\circ(C_-) \tag{222}$$

where $\bar{X}$ and $\bar{C}_-$ are the fixed ion and coion concentrations in the membrane phase. $\gamma_+{}^\circ(C_-)$ and $\gamma_-{}^\circ(C_-)$, the activity coefficient values, for the C_- concentration, in the polyelectrolyte-free solution of the added electrolyte; and θ is a characteristic constant for the polyelectrolyte–electrolyte pair. The $\theta\bar{X}$ quantity is called the thermodynamically effective concentration of the counterion of polyelectrolyte. Katachlsky et al.[191] consider that only a small fraction of the counterions, dissociated from the polyelectrolyte molecules, are able to take part in the flow of electricity. The mobility of such hydrodynamically effective ions is the same as that in a free solution containing no polyelectrolytes. In this case, for a single valence polyelectrolyte

$$\bar{u}_+ \bar{C}_+ = u_+{}^\circ(\bar{C}_- + \theta'\bar{X}); \qquad u^- \bar{C}_- = u_-{}^\circ \bar{C}_- \tag{223}$$

where $u_+{}^\circ$ and $u_-{}^\circ$ represent positive and negative ion mobility in the free solution. $\phi'X$ is the molar concentration of the hydrodynamically effective counterion of the polyelectrolyte.

From eqn (223) the following is derived

$$\bar{u}_+ = \frac{\bar{u}_+{}^\circ(C_+)(\bar{C}_- + \theta'\bar{X})}{\bar{C}_- + \bar{X}}. \tag{224}$$

Substituting eqns (221), (222), (223), (224) into (218) (noting that $\bar{X} = 0$, outside the membrane and neglecting the variation of $u_+{}^\circ$, $u_-{}^\circ$ and $\gamma_+{}^\circ$, $\gamma_-{}^\circ$ with concentration) it is possible to obtain (Fig. 8):

$$\Delta\phi_r = \frac{F\Delta\phi}{RT} = -(2\alpha - 1)\ln\frac{C_2}{C_1} + \frac{1-\alpha}{\alpha\beta - 1}\left\{ 2(1-\alpha\beta)\ln\frac{\bar{C}_d}{\bar{C}_0} \right.$$

$$\theta + (2\alpha\beta - 1)\ln\frac{Z(\bar{C}_{d1}, \theta\bar{X}) + (2\alpha\beta - 1)\theta\bar{X}}{Z(\bar{C}_{01}, \theta\bar{X}) + (2\alpha\beta - 1)\theta\bar{X}} - \ln\frac{Z(\bar{C}_{d1}, \theta\bar{X}) + \theta\bar{X}}{Z(\bar{C}_{01}, \theta\bar{X}) + \theta\bar{X}} \right\} \tag{225}$$

where

$$\alpha = \frac{u_+{}^\circ}{u_+{}^\circ + u_-{}^\circ}$$

$$\beta = \frac{\theta'}{\theta}$$

(226)

$$Z(C_1\theta X) = (4C^2 + \theta^2 \overline{X}^2)^{1/2}.$$

As the salt flow is the same through the layer limit and the membrane surface, C_0 and C_d may be obtained as functions of C_1 and C_2 (see ref. 191)

$$\overline{C}_0 = C_1 + vf(C_1, C_2) + O(\partial^2)$$
$$\overline{C}_d = C_2 - vf(C_1, C_2) + O(\partial^2).$$

(227)

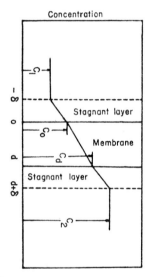

FIG. 8. Schematic diagram of the system (Toyoshima *et al.*[191]).

Then, $\Delta\phi_r$ may be obtained as a function of C_1, C_2, θ, θ' and X. This fucntion at high concentration of electrolyte may be expressed in powers of $1/C_1$

$$\Delta\phi_r = -(2\alpha - 1)\ln\gamma - [2\alpha\beta(1 - \alpha)(1 - \gamma^{-1})] \cdot$$

$$[1 - 2\partial(\gamma + \gamma^{-1})]\left(\frac{\theta\overline{X}}{C_1}\right) + O(C_1^{-2})$$

(228)

where

$$\gamma = \frac{C_2}{C_1}.$$

Combining eqn (228) and $-\Delta\phi_r = (1 - 2t_-)\ln\gamma$, these authors obtained an expression for t_-. Expanding $1/t_-$, as a power series in $1/C_1$, it is possible to obtain the different parameters of eqn (228).

If $\theta = 0$, $\theta' = 1$ and $\partial = 0$, eqn (225) reduces to

$$\Delta\phi_r = -\ln\frac{C_2}{C_1} + 2(1 - \alpha)\ln\frac{C_2 + \alpha\overline{X}}{C_1 + \alpha\overline{X}} \qquad (229)$$

which coincides with the findings of these authors previously. Kobatake and colleagues have tested their theories and have found differences between them and experimental values, mainly where concentrations are very low.

2. Bi-ionic Potential

When a membrane separates two electrolyte solutions with different counterions but at the same concentration, the counterions freely pass through the membrane causing a progressive degradation in the system so that the amount of B in 1 and A in 2 increases until finally a Donnan membrane equilibrium is reached.

Solution 1	Cation	Solution 2
Electrolyte AX	Selective	Electrolyte BX
C_1	Membrane	C_1

The resulting potential is called bi-ionic potential and is measured in undegraded stationary cells. Michaelis[192,193,194] pointed out that the sign and magnitude of bi-ionic potential must depend on the ease with which both counter-ions pass through the membrane. This worker related the bi-ionic potential with ion mobilittes ($\bar{u}_A$ and $\bar{u}_B$) and using the Planck–Henderson equation obtained the following one:

$$E_{BI} = \pm\frac{RT}{F}\ln\frac{\bar{u}_A}{\bar{u}_B}. \qquad (230)$$

Gregor and Sollner[195,196] have shown that the bi-ionic potential is a function of the fraction of current transferred through the membrane by the counter-ions. This is to say, it is a function of their transport numbers which, in turn, depend on the ion mobilities and concentrations in the membrane phase. As a result, the equation for an ideally selective membrane is

$$E_{BI} = \pm\frac{RT}{F}\ln\frac{\bar{t}_A^{\,\circ}}{\bar{t}_B^{\,\circ}}. \qquad (231)$$

Using this equation it is possible to find the relationship $\bar{\imath}_A^{\,\circ}/\bar{\imath}_B^{\,\circ}$, which may be considered the quantitative measurement of counter-ion permeability through the membrane when both are present in the same system.

TABLE V. Bi-ionic potentials, E_{BI}, through a cation-selective collodion membrane[6].

Solution 1 0·0100 M	Solution 2 0·0100 M	E_{BI}(mV)	$\dfrac{t^0_{B*(2)}}{t^0_{K*(1)}}$
KCl	CsCl	−8·7	1·41
KI	NH$_4$I	−6·8	1·30
KCl	RbCl	−5·6	1·25
KCl	KCl	0·0	1·00
KI	NaI	35·4	0·252
KCl	NaCl	35·5	0·251
KCl	LiCl	63·7	0·084
KI	(CH$_3$)$_4$NI	81·6	0·042
KI	(C$_2$H$_5$)NI	110·0	0·014

If the transfer number relationship is replaced by the relationship of the mobilities products and concentrations, the above equation may be written as follows:

$$E = \pm \frac{RT}{F} \ln \frac{\bar{u}_A \bar{C}_A}{\bar{u}_B \bar{C}_B} \qquad (232)$$

where $\bar{C}_A$ and $\bar{C}_B$ are the corresponding molal concentrations in the membrane phase. The selectivity coefficient $K_B^{\,A}$ is given by

$$K_B^{\,A} = \frac{\bar{C}_A C_B}{C_A \bar{C}_B} \qquad (233)$$

where C_A and C_B are the ion concentrations in the solution. When $C_A = C_B$ we have

$$E = \pm \frac{RT}{F} \ln \frac{\bar{u}_A}{\bar{u}_B} K_B^{\,A}. \qquad (234)$$

Neither Donnan's interface potentials nor concentration gradients in the membrane phase have been taken into account in deriving this equation. Based on Marshall's[197] work, Wyllie[198] derived a more complete equation for the bi-ionic potential, using the Henderson equation and adding the Donnan interface potentials.

Helfferich[137] developed a more rigorous bi-ionic potential theory which considered that the different ion fluxes, through the membranes and solution membrane interfaces, are constant in a stationary state. In an ideal electronegative membrane, anion flux is zero, and the electric neutrality principle requires that

$$\sum_i z_i J_i = 0. \tag{235}$$

From the Nernst–Planck flux equations (eqn 132) and taking into account eqn (235), the membrane diffusion potential is obtained:

$$E_{\text{dif}} = \frac{RT}{F} \left\{ \frac{\bar{D}_B - \bar{D}_A}{\bar{D}_A z_A - \bar{D}_B z_B} \ln \frac{X \bar{D}_B z_B + \bar{C}_A'' z_A (\bar{D}_A z_A - \bar{D}_B z_B)}{X \bar{D}_B z_B + \bar{C}_A' z_A (\bar{D}_A z_A - \bar{D}_B z_B)} \right.$$

$$\left. - \int_{\prime}^{\prime\prime} [\bar{t}_A \, d \ln \bar{\gamma}_A + \bar{t}_B \, d \ln \bar{\gamma}_B] \right. \tag{236}$$

where

$$\bar{t}_i = \frac{\bar{D}_i z_i \bar{C}_i}{\bar{D}_A \bar{C}_A z_A{}^2 + \bar{D}_B \bar{C}_B z_B{}^2}.$$

The bi-ionic potential is considered to be composed of two Donnan potentials, ϕ' and ϕ'', at the two solution–membrane interfaces, (') and (''), and three diffusion potentials arising from inequal concentration through the membrane phase and through both films

Bulk solution (α)	film (1)		membrane	film (II)		Bulk solution (β)
	←Diff pot.→			←Diff pot.→		
		ϕ' (Don)		ϕ'' (Don)		

The Donnan potentials are expressed by eqn (188)

$$E = \pm \frac{RT}{z_i F} \ln \frac{\bar{a}_i}{a_i}$$

(negative for the side α and positive for the β).

For ideal membrane control, the diffusion potential in the films vanish and the limit conditions for the diffusion potential in the membarne are $\bar{C}_A'z_A = \bar{X}$ and $\bar{C}_A''z_A = 0$. In that case, from eqns (236) and (188), the bi-ionic potential may be obtained

$$E_{BI} = \frac{RT}{F}\left\{ \frac{\bar{D}_A - \bar{D}_B}{z_A\bar{D}_A - z_B\bar{D}_B} \ln\frac{\bar{D}_A z_A}{\bar{D}_B z_B} + \frac{z_A - z_B}{z_A z_B}\ln\frac{\bar{X}}{C} - \int_I^{II} [\bar{t}_A \, d\ln\bar{\gamma}_A \right.$$

$$\left. + \bar{t}_B \, d\ln\bar{\gamma}_B] + \ln\frac{(\bar{\gamma}_B'')^{1/z_B}}{(\bar{\gamma}_A')^{1/z_A}} + \ln\frac{(\gamma_A')^{1/z_A}}{(\gamma_B'')^{1/B_z}} \right\}$$

where $C = z_A C_A + z_B C_B$.

The bi-ionic potential may also be expressed by[137]

$$E_{BI} = \frac{RT}{F}\left\{ \frac{\bar{D}_B - \bar{D}_A}{\bar{D}_A z_A - \bar{D}_B z_B} \ln\frac{\bar{D}_B z_B}{\bar{D}_A z_A} + \ln\frac{\bar{\gamma}_B^{1/z_B}}{\bar{\gamma}_A^{1/z_a}} + \frac{z_A - z_B}{z_A z_B}\ln\frac{\bar{X}}{C_A'} \right.$$

$$\left. + \frac{1}{z_B}\ln\frac{C_A'}{C_B''} + \ln\frac{(\gamma_A')^{1/z_A}}{(\gamma_B'')^{1/z_B}} \right\}. \qquad (238)$$

If $z_A = z_B$, it is reduced to

$$E_{BI} = \frac{RT}{zF} \ln\frac{\bar{D}_A a_A' \bar{\gamma}_B}{\bar{D}_B a_B'' \gamma_A} = \frac{RT}{zF} \ln\frac{\bar{D}_A a_A'}{\bar{D}_B a_B''} K_B^{'A}; \qquad (239)$$

If one neglects activity coefficient in the membrane, the formula of Marshall is obtained.

For ideal film control, the diffusion potentials in the membrane vanish. If we assume $\bar{X}_x = $ constant, the sum of the Donnan potentials also is cancelled out and the following expression is obtained

$$E_{BI} = \frac{RT}{F} \frac{D_A - D_B}{D_A z_A + D_B z_B} \ln\frac{D_A z_A}{D_B z_B} - \int_\alpha^\beta (t_A \, d\ln\gamma_A + t_B \, d\ln\gamma_B). \qquad (240)$$

Without assuming $\bar{D}_A/\bar{D}_B$ constant, Bergsma[7] obtained, for the case of single valence ions, the following equation:

$$E_{BI} = \frac{RT}{F} \ln\frac{a_A' \bar{D}_A^\alpha \bar{\gamma}_B^\beta}{a_B' \bar{D}_B^\beta \bar{\gamma}_A^\alpha} + \int_\alpha^\beta t_A \, d\ln\frac{\bar{D}_A}{\bar{\gamma}_A} + \int_\alpha^\beta t_B \, d\ln\frac{\bar{D}_B}{\bar{\gamma}_B}. \qquad (241)$$

This last equation differs from Scatchard's bi-ionic potential[186] equation in that it leaves out water and coion transfer.

Based on Scatchard's procedures, Andelman and Gregor[133] obtained the following expression for the bi-ionic potential of positive membranes

$$E_{BI} = \frac{RT}{F} \left\{ \ln \frac{\bar{D}_B a_B''}{\bar{D}_A a_A'} K^A_B - \int_I^{II} [\bar{t}_A \, d \ln \bar{\gamma}_A + \bar{t}_B \, d \ln \bar{\gamma}_B] \right.$$

$$= \frac{RT}{F} \ln \frac{\bar{D}_B a_B''}{\bar{D}_A a_A'} K^A_B + \int_I^{II} \bar{t}_A \, d \ln K^A_B$$

(242)

where A and B represent both anions, one on the left and the other one on the right of the membrane. In developing eqn (242) it has been assumed that $\bar{t}_w = 0$ and that the membrane phase mobility relationships are constant as well as the fixed ion concentration across it. They applied eqn (242) to the system, $Cl^- \left| \begin{array}{c} \text{membrane} \\ \text{positive} \end{array} \right| I^-$ and the results obtained agree with the observed.

Mackay and Meares[139,140] have carried out a detailed treatment of bi-ionic potential which takes into account the effects of simultaneous transfer of coins and of water. These same authors developed equations for bi-ionic potentials in systems with unstirred diffusion layers. In their treatment they consider flow effects, as well as variations in ion mobilities and activity coefficients within the membrane. In the majority of cases, the experimental and calculated bi-ionic potentials were the same.

Little work has been done on the effect of the nature of the functional groups on bi-ionic potential. Sollner and colleagues[199] found differences in the behaviour of sulphonic and carboxylic acid membranes toward Li^+/K^+ ions. Gregor et al.[200,201] also noticed the bi-ionic potentials are higher with Li^+/K^+ systems in carboxylic acid membranes than in sulphonic acid membranes. Nevertheless Bergsma and Staverman[202] found the bi-ionic potentials were nearly the same for phosphonic and sulphonic acid membranes with the Na^+/K^+ system. These last results do not agree with those obtained recently by Hale and Govindam[203] with the same type of membranes.

3. Polyionic Potentials

Dray and Sollner[204,205] extended the treatment of bi-ionic potentials polyionic systems in which a membrane separates two solutions containing counter-ions whose activity is different on either side of the membrane. The system may be represented by the following scheme

Solution 1   Solution 2

| Activity: | Cation
Selective
Membrane | Activity: |

$$\left.\begin{array}{l} a_1\ A^+ \\ a_2\ B^+ \\ a_3\ C^+ \end{array}\right\} Y^- \qquad \left.\begin{array}{l} a_4\ A^+ \\ a_5\ B^+ \\ a_6\ C' \end{array}\right\} Y^-$$

The simplest case of polyionic potential results from the system

$$a_1(A^+ Y^-)\,|\,\text{membrane}\,|\,a_2(B^+ Y^-).$$

The following equation is obtained for this system's potential by applying the Planck–Henderson equation

$$E = \pm \frac{RT}{F} \ln \frac{\bar{t}_A}{\bar{t}_B}. \tag{243}$$

Dray and Sollner assume that the ratio of counter-ion transport numbers is equal to the ratio of the counter-ion transport, in the corresponding bi-ionic system, multiplied by the activities ratio. As a result

$$E_{2IP} = \pm \frac{RT}{F} \ln \frac{a_{A^+(1)}\,\bar{t}_{A^+}{}^{\circ}}{a_{B^+(2)}\,\bar{t}_{B^+}{}^{\circ}}. \tag{244}$$

The same authors, for the following systems

$$a_{A^+(1)}, \qquad a_{B^+(1)}|\text{membrane}|a_{A^+(2)}, \qquad a_{B^+(2)}$$

have obtained the following equation

$$E_{2IP} = \frac{RT}{F} \ln \frac{a_{A^+(1)}\,\bar{t}_{A^+}{}^{\circ} + a_{B^+(1)}\,\bar{t}_{B^+}{}^{\circ}}{a_{A^+(2)}\,\bar{t}_{A^+}{}^{\circ} + a_{B^+(2)}\,\bar{t}_{B^+}{}^{\circ}}. \tag{245}$$

The theoretical values obtained through the eqn (245) and the experimental values agree satisfactorily.[6]

4. Electro-thermal Potential

When a membrane separates two electrolytic solutions of equal composition, an electrostatic potential difference arises if a different temperature is maintained on either side of the membrane. It is important to study these thermal potentials because these phenomena often come up in physiology, electrodialysis, and desalinisation. Nevertheless, little attention has been paid to them.

Hills et al.[102] made predictions of these potentials based on irreversible thermodynamic processes. They related them with ion transport heat. In fact, from eqn (207) considering $\Delta P = 0$, $\Delta a_k = 0$, $I = 0$, the following equation may be obtained

$$F \frac{\Delta \phi}{\Delta T} \simeq - \sum_k \bar{\imath}_k \frac{Q_k^{**}}{T}. \tag{246}$$

Ikeda[206] studied the thermal potentials in oxidized collodion membranes. He eliminated the potential difference between the electrodes using athermo-cell made up of the following components:

$g \,|\, ClAg, ClK_{(aq)} \,|\, ClK\text{--agar}(c) \,|\, ClKaq(c) \,|\, membrane \,|\, ClKaq(c) \,|\, ClK\text{--agar}(c) \,|\, ClKaq(c), ClAg(s) \,|\, Ag.$
$\quad\quad\quad T \quad\quad\quad\quad T \quad\quad\quad\quad T \quad\quad\quad\quad\quad T+\Delta T \quad\quad\quad T$

According to Ikeda, the potential of thermal diffusion, through a cation selective membrane, is expressed by[206]

$$F \frac{d\phi}{dT} = - \left[\frac{(t_- Q_-^* - t_+ Q_+^*)}{T} + \frac{\bar{Q}_+^*}{T} \right] \tag{247}$$

where t_+, t_- and Q^* are the transport numbers and transport heat in the solution. $\bar{Q}_+^*$ is the transport heat in the membrane phase.

From the diffusion value for the Soret effect, $S = - (Q_+^* + Q_-^*)/2RT^2$, and assuming $\bar{Q}_+^* \simeq Q_+^*$ the following equation is found:

$$\frac{d\phi}{dT} = \frac{2t_- RTS}{F}. \tag{248}$$

A value of 0.045 mV/°C was found for $d\phi/dT$ ($t_+ = 0.51$ and $S = 0.17 \times 10^{-2}$ for ClK 0.1). Afterwards this value was rejected by this researcher[207] who found it to be 0.024 mV/°C.

Ikeda et al.[208] found that $d\phi/dT$ does not increase linearly with t_-, though according to the theory, if $\bar{Q}_+^*$ is constant, it should vary linearly. Consequently, $\bar{Q}_+^*$ should depend on the membrane properties and the assumption that $\bar{Q}_+^* = Q_+^*$ is not well founded.

Kobatake[209] also studied this phenomenon and derived an equation in which the thermal potential is a function of the ion mobilities and transport heat.

Tasaka et al.[210] derived an expression different than that of Hills et al.[102] which does not take ionic transport heat into account. This is described below. In a negative membrane with a temperature and a concentration gradient, the dissipation function is given by

$$- \sigma = J_s \operatorname{grad} T + \sum_{i=w,+,-} J_i \operatorname{grad} \hat{\mu}_i \tag{249}$$

where J_s is the entropy flow, $\hat{\mu}$ the electrochemical potential, and J_i the mass flow. The solvent (water) flow, J_w, can be considered a function of cation (J_+) and anion (J_-) flows, since

$$\sum_{i=+,-,w} w_i J_i = 0 \tag{250}$$

where w_i is a weight factor.

On the other hand, current density I is given by

$$I = F \sum_{i=+,-} z_i J_i. \tag{251}$$

Therefore we are able to express J_- as a function of current density and of cation flow. Based on these assumptions, the dissipation function takes the following form

$$- \sigma = J_s \, \mathrm{grad} \, T + J_+ \, \mathrm{grad} \left(\mu_+' - \frac{z_+}{z_-} \mu_-' \right) + I \, \mathrm{grad} \left(\frac{\mu_-'}{z_- F} + \phi \right) \tag{252}$$

where

$$\mu_i' = \mu_i - \frac{w_i}{w_w} \mu_w.$$

The relationships between flows and forces may be expressed by

$$- J_i = \Omega_{ij} \frac{dX_j}{dx} \tag{253}$$

where Ω_{ij} is a symmetrical matrix, $i, j = s, +, I$, and $X_s = T$,

$$X_+ = \left(\mu_+' - \frac{z_+}{z_-} \mu_-' \right), \quad X_I = \left(\frac{\mu_-'}{zF} + \phi \right).$$

From eqn (253),

$$\frac{dX_j}{dx} = - R_{ij} J_i \tag{254}$$

where

$$R_{ij} = \Omega_{ij}^{-1} = \frac{|\Omega|_{ij}}{|\Omega|}. \tag{255}$$

If we assume the flows are constant, the equation may be integrated:

$$- \Delta X_j = \int_0^d (R_{ij} dx) J_i = \gamma_{ji} J_i \tag{256}$$

Multiplying both sides by $\gamma_{ij}^{-1} = \omega_{ij}$ we find

$$- J_i = \omega_{ij} \Delta X_j. \tag{257}$$

According to eqn (257), current density through the membrane is given by

$$- I = \omega_{Is} \Delta T + \omega_{I+} \Delta \left(\mu_+' - \frac{z_+}{z_-} \mu_-' \right) + \omega_{II} \Delta \left(\frac{\mu_-'}{z_- F} + \phi \right). \quad (258)$$

Placing this equation equal to zero, substituting chemical potentials for their value, and keeping in mind that

$$t_i = \left(\frac{z_i F J_i}{I} \right)_{\substack{\Delta T = 0 \\ \Delta \mu_i = 0}} \quad (259)$$

and

$$\tau_i = \frac{t_i}{F} \quad (260)$$

the electrochemical potential is obtained:

$$- \Delta \phi = \eta \Delta T + \sum_{i = +, -} \frac{\bar{t}_i}{z_i F} \Delta \mu_i' = (2\bar{t}_+ - 1) \frac{RT}{F} \ln \frac{a_\pm^{II}}{a_\pm^{I}}$$

$$+ (2\bar{t}_+ - 1) R \frac{\Delta T}{F} \ln a_\pm^{II} + (\bar{t}_+ \alpha_+ + \bar{t}_- \alpha_-); \quad (261)$$

where, considering activity coefficient of water $= 1$,

$$\eta = \frac{\omega_{Is}}{\omega_{IJ}}, \qquad \alpha_+ = \eta - \left(\frac{S_+^\circ}{F} + \tau_w \right)$$

$$\alpha_- = \eta + \left(\frac{S_-^\circ}{F} - \tau_w S_w^\circ \right)$$

$$S_i^\circ = \frac{\partial \mu_i^\circ}{\partial T}.$$

If $(a_\pm)_1 = (a_\pm)_2$, the eqn (261) takes the following form:

$$- \frac{\Delta \phi}{\Delta T} = 2 \cdot 303 \, (2\bar{t}_+ - 1) \left(\frac{R}{F} \right) \log (a_\pm) + (\bar{t}_+ \alpha_+ + t_- \alpha_-). \quad (262)$$

When $\bar{t}_+ = 1$, a straight line will be obtained, to represent $\Delta \phi / \Delta T$ versus $\log (a_\pm)_2$, with a slope given by $2 \cdot 303 \, R/F$ and an intercept given by α_+. For cation and anion exchange membranes. Tasaka et al.[210] observed that the potentials increased linearly with the temperature and that the slope agrees with the theoretical one.

5. *Streaming Potential*

A pressure gradient through a membrane separating the same solution with the same concentration causes flows of solute J_s and solvent J_w.

When the saline solution is pressed through the membrane, the liquid moves in the membrane pores developing an electric potential called the streaming potential. This delays the counter-ion movement and accelerates coion movements, so that the pore liquid electroneutrality is maintained.

An equation relating the streaming potential with the applied pressure difference, may be obtained based on the thermodynamics of irreversible processes. For instance, when $\Delta T = 0$ and $\Delta a_k = 0$ from eqn (207) one obtains[102]

$$\frac{\Delta \phi}{\Delta P} = -\frac{1}{F}\sum_k \bar{\imath}_k \bar{V}_k. \tag{263}$$

The difficulty of this equation is that $\bar{\imath}_k$ must be known in order to evaluate eqn (263). Assuming that neither concentration gradients in the membrane phase nor mobile-ion–fixed-ion interactions exist, Schmid[211] found a new expression which we briefly describe. In an ideally selective membrane, the coions are excluded in the membrane phase. Due to a pressure gradient, the counter-ion contained in the pore liquid moves through the membrane causing an electrical current. If the fixed ion concentration is $\bar{X}$ and the current density is I, then

$$I \, dt = F\bar{X} \, dV \tag{264}$$

where dV is the element of liquid volume that moves in time dt.

As a consequence of ionic migration, a potential difference which tends to cancel out the pressure gradient effects, develops in the membrane, cancelling the current, I. That is to say

$$\bar{\kappa}\Delta\phi = F\bar{X}\frac{dV}{dt} \tag{265}$$

where $\bar{\kappa}$ is membrane conductivity.

Since membrane permeability is proportional to the pressure gradient

$$\frac{dV}{dt} = D_h \, \Delta P \tag{266}$$

the following expression is obtained for the streaming potential

$$\Delta\phi = D_h \frac{F\bar{X}}{\bar{\kappa}} \Delta P. \tag{267}$$

The streaming potentials may be measured placing electrodes in the two solutions on either side of the membrane. If the two electrodes short circuit, an electric current, called the streaming current, passes through the circuit.

The streaming potential has small values. Brun[212] found a value of around 0·18 mV/at. in fenolsulphonate membranes. Brun and Vaula[213] studied concentration changes on the surfaces of the membrane (salt accumulation on the high pressure surface and depletion on the low pressure surface) effects, on the streaming potential. Such changes cause concentration potentials which significantly alter the experimental streaming potential values. These authors found that the average potential in time t, may be related to the real streaming potential by the following equation

$$E = \Delta\phi + A \sqrt{\frac{D}{\Pi}} t \tag{268}$$

where A is a constant. Therefore, if $t = 0$, $E = \Delta\phi$

The pressure effect on bi-ionic cells has been studied by Henderson.[214] He found it to be less than 1 mV/100 at. However, this effect is important in bi-polar membranes.[215]

G. Ion Fluxes Under an Electric Field

Equations for individual fluxes of counter-ions, resulting to establish an electric field through the system

| Counter-ion $a(c)$ | membrane | Counter-ion $b(c)$ |
| (iostope) | | (iostope) |

were derived by quasithermodynamic methods by Meares and Ussing.[216] For simplicity zero hydrostatic pressure difference between the solutions, is assumed. An electric current of I A/cm^2 flows through the membrane, as consequence of the electric field. The flux of isotope a may be written

$$J_a = - \bar{U}_a \bar{C}_a \left(RT \frac{d \ln \bar{C}_a}{dx} + RT \frac{d \ln \bar{\gamma}_A}{dx} + z_a F \frac{d\phi}{dx} \right) + \bar{C}_a v^* \tag{269}$$

where $\bar{C}_a$, $\bar{\gamma}_a$ and ϕ refer to the plane x. Bearing in mind the chemical similarity between a and b, we have

$$\bar{U}_a = \bar{U}_b; \quad z_a = z_b; \quad \bar{C}_a + \bar{C}_b = \text{const}; \quad d\bar{\gamma}_a/dx = d\bar{\gamma}_b/dx. \tag{270}$$

On the other hand, according to eqn (13)

$$v^* = \frac{\varepsilon' F \omega \bar{X} \Delta\phi}{d} \tag{271}$$

where ε' is a network constant with the character of a permeability to liquid flow.

and $\omega = -1$ for membrane cation selectives and $+1$ for membrane anion selectives. From eqns (269), (270), (271), the fluxes of a and b in the x direction may be expressed, in the case of ideal solution by

$$J_a = -\bar{U}_a RT \frac{d\bar{C}_a}{dx} + \bar{C}_a F(\varepsilon'\omega\bar{X} - z_a\bar{u}_a)\frac{\Delta\phi}{d}$$

$$J_b = +\bar{U}_a RT \frac{d\bar{C}_a}{dx} + (\bar{C} - \bar{C}_a) F(\varepsilon'\omega\bar{X} - z_a\bar{u}_a)\frac{\Delta\phi}{d}$$

(272)

where, they assumed

$$\frac{d\phi}{dx} = \frac{\Delta\phi}{\Delta x}.$$

Considering that in the steady state $dJ_a/dx = 0$ from eqn (272), it is possible to obtain

$$\bar{U}_a RT \frac{d^2\bar{C}_a}{dx^2} + F(z_a\bar{U}_a - \varepsilon'\omega\bar{X})\frac{\Delta\phi}{d} \cdot \frac{d\bar{C}_a}{dx} = 0. \qquad (273)$$

Solving the differential eqn (273) bearing in mind that boundary conditions

$$x = 0, \quad \bar{C}_a = C; \qquad x = d, \quad \bar{C}_a = 0$$

one easily obtains an expression for dC/dx, with which may be obtained, J_a. In the same way it is possible to evaluate J_b. The ratio of both quantities may be expressed by

$$\ln\left(\frac{J_a}{J_b}\right) = -\frac{F\Delta\phi(z_a\bar{U}_a - \varepsilon'\omega\bar{X})}{\bar{u}_a RT}. \qquad (274)$$

Replacing $\bar{u}_a RT$ by $\bar{D}_a$ and $\varepsilon'\omega\bar{X}$ by $(v*d/F)\,\Delta\phi$ eqn (274) becomes

$$\ln\left(-\frac{J_a}{J_b}\right) = \frac{z_a F(\phi° - \phi^d)}{RT} + \frac{v*d}{\bar{D}_a}. \qquad (275)$$

Finally, the net flux of the substance a and b is

$$J_a + J_b = -\frac{(z_a\bar{U}_a - \varepsilon'\omega\bar{X})\,F\Delta\phi C}{d}. \qquad (276)$$

The agreement between the fluxes calculated according the above equations and the observed was poor. However, when the conductance term,

$$\lambda_a = \frac{z_a F^2 (z_a \overline{U}_a - \varepsilon' \omega \overline{X})}{|z_a|} \qquad (277)$$

was introduced into the flux equation, the corresponding fluxes were

$$J_a = \frac{|z_a| \lambda_a \, \Delta \phi \, \overline{C} \, L}{z_a F d (1 - \overline{L})}; \qquad \text{etc.,} \qquad (278)$$

where

$$\overline{L} = \exp \quad -\frac{\lambda_a |z_a| \Delta \phi}{z_a F \overline{D}_a} \qquad (279)$$

then, the agreement was good. This behaviour was discussed by Meares and Ussing.[216]

H. Conductance

Dry membranes are poor conductors of electricity, but are highly conductive when submerged in an electrolytic solution. The conduction mechanism, in swollen membranes, has hydrolytic characteristics; the counter-ions and coions, present in the membrane phase, take part in electricity transport. It is evident that the specific conductivity of a membrane depends on the external electrolyte concentration and on the concentration of fixed ions in the membrane. This dependency may be established by the fixed charges theory. Let us consider a cation selective membrane in equilibrium with a solution of the uni-univalent electrolyte $M^+ A^-$. The specific conductance of the liquid in the membrane is given by[96]

$$\overline{\kappa} = 0 \cdot 001 \, F (\overline{u}_+ \overline{C}_+ + \overline{u}_- \overline{C}_-) \qquad (280)$$

where $\overline{u}_i$ and $\overline{C}_i$ represent the mobilities (cm^2 sec^{-1} volt^{-1}) and ion concentrations, respectively, in the membrane phase. Using the Donnan relationships, the following expression is obtained, disregarding the osmotic effects:

$$\overline{\kappa} = 0 \cdot 001 \, F \left\{ \overline{u}_+ \left(\sqrt{\left(\frac{\overline{X}}{2}\right)^2 + C^2} + \frac{\overline{X}}{2} \right) + \overline{u}_- \left(\sqrt{\left(\frac{\overline{X}}{2}\right)^2 + C^2} - \frac{\overline{X}}{2} \right) \right.$$

$$= 0 \cdot 001 \, F \left\{ (\overline{u}_+ + u_-) \sqrt{\left(\frac{\overline{X}}{2}\right)^2 + C^2} + \frac{\overline{X}}{2} (\overline{u}_+ - \overline{u}_-) \right\}. \qquad (281)$$

This equation shows that for membranes with high charge density, immersed in highly diluted solutions, $\bar{X} \gg C$, and $\bar{\kappa} = 0{\cdot}001\, F\bar{u}_+ \bar{X}$. If this value is compared with the external solution conductivity,

$$\kappa = 0{\cdot}001\, FC(u_+ + u_-) \tag{282}$$

we see that situations may arise in which the pore liquid conductivity is higher than in free solution.[217,218,219]

When the external solution concentration increases, $\bar{\kappa}$ slowly increases at first, then increases sharply. At high concentrations $(C \gg X)$ the pore liquid composition differs little from the composition of the external solution and the conductivity increases linearly with the concentration as in the case of a free solution.

Ion conductance through a membrane is a function of various factors, the most important of which are ion size and the formation of ion-pairs with the fixed groups. Ion size is important because the pore diameters in these systems are so small that there is considerable hydrodynamic drag. Peterson and Gregor[149] found that these diameters ocsillate between 9 and 13 Å. Conductivity measurements do not let us find out whether ion-pairing is caused by culombian or van der Wals type forces.

Andelman and Gregor (see ref. 149) measured electropositive membrane conductance in various ion states, noting the following conductivity sequence:

$$Cl^- > CH_3COO^- > IO_3^- > I^- > SCN^- > ClO_4^- > CH_3\text{--}C_6H_4\text{--}SO_3^-$$

Also, Gregor et al.[220] estimated ion-pair formation in this type of system, finding this generally happened in the following order:

$$ClO_4^- > CH_3\text{--}C_6H_4\text{--}SO_3^- > SCN^- > I^- > Cl^- > CH_3\text{--}COO^- > IO_3^-$$

Specific conductance is one of the values necessary for evaluating friction coefficients according to Spiegler's[104] theory. This value is equal to the electricity flow under a potential unit gradient. According to this, for a single (1:1) electrolyte

$$\bar{\kappa} = F(J_+ - J_-). \tag{283}$$

In measuring conductance, the membrane is between two solutions with the same characteristics and the same concentration. In this case, from eqns (75) and (283) the specific conductance is given by

$$\bar{\kappa} = F^2 \left[L_{++} - 2\,(L_{+-})(L_{--})\right]. \tag{284}$$

Equation (284) is finally obtained, where $F = 96500$ Coul/mol. Replacing L_{ik} by its corresponding values (eqn (80)), conductance as a function of f_{ik} is obtained.

Toyoshima et al.[221] studied the membrane resistance of oxidized collodion membranes. When a membrane of thickness, d, and area, A, separates two aqueous solutions of a single (1:1) electrolyte of the same concentration, C, disregarding the contribution of the mass flow, the membrane resistance, R, is given by

$$R = \frac{d}{FA[\bar{u}_+(\bar{C}_- + \bar{X}) + \bar{u}_-\bar{C}_-]} \tag{285}$$

where $\bar{u}_+$ and $\bar{u}_-$ are the ion mobilities in the membrane with reference to the centre of mass, $\bar{C}_-$ and $\bar{X}$, are the coion and fixed groups concentrations in the membrane phase. Disregarding the osmotic pressure effect between the membrane and the solution, applying the Donnan equation and taking into account eqn (224), it is possible to obtain $\bar{C}_-$ as a function of external electrolyte concentration and fixed charge density. The $\bar{C}$ value is substituted into eqn (285), and R is obtained by the following equation

$$R = \frac{2}{KF\Lambda^\circ(C)\{[4C^2 + (\theta X)^2]^{1/2} + (2\alpha\beta - 1)\theta X\}} \tag{286}$$

where

$$K = A/d \quad \text{and} \quad \Lambda^\circ(C) = u_+^\circ(C) + u_-^\circ(C).$$

R may be expressed in powers of $1/C$. Thus

$$\frac{1}{F\Lambda^\circ(C)RC} = K + \tfrac{1}{2}K(2\alpha\beta - 1)\theta\bar{X}\left(\frac{1}{C}\right) + O\left(\frac{1}{C}\right)^2. \tag{287}$$

All values for the first side of the equation may be found: plotting $1/(F\Lambda^\circ(C)RC)$ versus $1/C$ may be obtained K and $(2\alpha\beta - 1)\theta\bar{X}$. The equation's terms may be rearranged in the following way

$$\left\{\frac{1}{C}\left[\frac{1}{FKR\Lambda^\circ(C)} - \tfrac{1}{2}(2\alpha\beta - 1)\theta X\right]\right\}^2 = 1 + \frac{(\theta\bar{X})^2}{4C^2}. \tag{288}$$

If K and $(2\alpha\beta - 1)\theta\bar{X}$ are known, the first side of eqn (288) may be represented against $1/C^2$, and $\theta\bar{X}$ may be taken from the slope. Knowing $\theta\bar{X}$ and α, β may be obtained.

Toyoshima *et al.*[221] have observed that their theory agree with experimental data and the values of different parameters of various collodion membranes as shown in the Table VI.

TABLE VI. Numerical values for the parameters K, $\theta \bar{X}$ and $\theta' \bar{X}$ for various electrolytes and membranes.[221]

Membrane (oxidized collodion)	Electrolyte	$K \times 10^3$	$\theta \times 10^2$	$\theta' \times 10^2$	θ'/θ	α
1	LiCl	0·645	0·44	0·49	1·1$_2$	0·311
	KCl	0·628	0·39	0·41	1·0$_5$	0·489
	KIO$_3$	0·622	0·42	0·42	1·0$_4$	0·645
2	LiCl	0·874	1·3$_1$	1·4$_2$	1·0$_8$	0·311
	KCl	0·887	1·2$_0$	1·2$_3$	1·0$_2$	0·488
	KIO$_3$	0·887	1·1$_2$	1·1$_3$	1·0$_1$	0·645
3	LiCl	0·725	1·9$_7$	2·2$_4$	1·1$_4$	0·311
	KCl	0·734	1·9$_1$	2·0$_4$	1·0$_7$	0·489
	KIO$_3$	0·728	1·8$_5$	1·8$_7$	1·0$_1$	0·645

Recently Fadley and Wallace[222] studied the influence of water absorption on acid form membrane conductance. These authors assume that membrane phase conductance occurs with a counter-ion (hydrogen ions) passing over an energy barrier existing between two points of the membrane, separated by the distance λ. Using the Nernst–Einstein equation, which relates conductivity and diffusion, they find that

$$\bar{\kappa} = \frac{Cq^2\lambda^2}{h} \exp\left(-\frac{\Delta G^{\ddagger}}{RT}\right) \qquad (289)$$

where $\bar{\kappa}$ = specific conductance ($\Omega^{-1}\ cm^{-1}$): C = charge carrier concentration (cm^{-3}): q = electronic charge (C): λ = effective jump distance (cm): h = Planck constant (J. seg.): G = free activation energy: R and T have the usual meaning.

Since $\Delta G^{\ddagger} = \Delta H^{\ddagger} - T\Delta S^{\ddagger}$ and assuming $\Delta H^{\ddagger} \simeq E$, $\bar{\kappa}$ may be expressed by

$$\bar{\kappa} = \bar{\kappa}_0 \exp\left(-\frac{E}{RT}\right) \qquad (290)$$

where E is the activation energy and κ_0 is a constant that includes the entropy term.

The $\Delta G^{\ddagger}$ dependance of the amount of water absorbed may be established if we consider the reaction

1 equiv. dry memb + n moles of water → 1 equiv. wet memb.

Then, a reasonable assumption proves to be that

$$\Delta G^{\ddagger} = \Delta G_D{}^{\ddagger} + \beta \Delta G_A \tag{291}$$

where $\Delta G_D{}^{\ddagger}$ is the free energy in the dry state and ΔG_A is the free energy change in the hydration reaction. Usually this value is negative, and β is a constant larger than 1.

From eqns (289) and (291) we find that

$$\bar{\kappa} = \bar{\kappa}_D \left(\frac{C}{C_D} \right) \exp \left(- \frac{\beta \Delta G_A}{RT} \right). \tag{292}$$

In the above equation, κ_D is membrane conductivity in a dry state.

Fadley and Wallace relate ΔG_A with the water moles n absorbed by the membrane, by the equation

$$\Delta G_A = \Delta G_A^{\circ} \left[1 - \exp \left(\frac{n}{n_0} \right) \right] \tag{293}$$

where n_0 is a constant and ΔG_A° is the asymptotic free absorption energy, at high n. From eqns (292) and (293), one obtains

$$\bar{\kappa} = \kappa_D \left(\frac{C}{C_D} \right) \exp \left\{ - \beta \Delta G_A^{\circ} \left[1 - \exp \left(- \frac{n}{n_0} \right) \right] \bigg/ RT \right\}. \tag{294}$$

This theory agrees with experimental results when $0 < n < 5$, but the theoretical predictions are too low around a factor of 10, when $n > 10$. These authors explain such discrepancies pointing out that this theory does not take into account possible abnormal conduction. To support their thesis, they point out that in sodic-type membranes, the measurements approximate to the theoretical values.

I. Counter-ion Transport Number

The counter-ion transport number may be found by measuring concentration potentials or by Hirtoff's analytical procedure. The first procedure requires a cell in which the membrane separates two solutions with different concentrations (for example, NaCl). The cell e.m.f. may be calculated quasi-thermodynamically, looking at the changes taking place in the cell when passing a

Faraday of current under the action of its own potential. In the system[8]

$$Ag^- \,|\, AgCl \,|\, NaCl(a_1) \,|\, \text{Electronegative membrane} \,|\, NaCl(a_2) \, AgCl \,|\, Ag^+$$

t_+ equiv. of NaCl pass from solution 1 to solution 2 and electrons pass through the external connecting wire from the electrode on the left to that on the right. If the process is reversible and we remember that the free energy change ΔG is equal to $-EF$, we see that

$$E = \bar{t}_{+(ap)} \frac{RT}{F} \ln \frac{a_1}{a_2} = 2\bar{t}_{+(ap)} \frac{RT}{F} \ln \frac{(a_\pm)_1}{(a_\pm)_2} \tag{295}$$

given that $a = (a_\pm)^2$.

The e.m.f. maxima is found when the cation transport number is equal to the unit; this is to say

$$E_{(max)} = \frac{2RT}{F} \ln \frac{(a_\pm)_1}{(a_\pm)_2}. \tag{296}$$

Finally from eqns (295) and (296) the cation transport number is obtained through the following relationship

$$t_{+(ap)} = \frac{E}{E_{max}}. \tag{297}$$

The transport numbers obtained according to eqn (297) are apparent because the liquid is their reference point and it also moves with respect to the membrane.[186] If the real transport numbers with reference to the membrane are wanted, it is necessary to correct for water transport as we will see later.

By Hirttoff's method,[223, 17, 224] the salt concentration variation in the cathode and anode compartments is measured when a known amount of electrical current passes through the membrane by the use of reversible electrodes. The transport number is given by

$$\bar{t}_i = z_i F \frac{J_i}{I} \tag{298}$$

where J is the i component flow and I is the current density. As several workers in the membrane field have pointed out, it is difficult to measure transport numbers using this technique. If anion reversible electrodes are used, the electrolyte concentration on either side of the membrane (initially the same) changes in such a way that it increases in the cathode compartment and decreases in the anode chamber. With cation exchange membranes a large change of concentration occurs, which can lead to errors in the determination of $\bar{t}_+$, due to back diffusion. The resulting transport numbers are significantly lower than the actual ones. The more concentrated the solution in contact with the membrane, the more marked is this diffusion; this is unimportant in highly diluted solutions. Transport numbers also depend on current density. When external concentration is less than 0·1 N, transport numbers decrease as current density increases, due to polarization effects in the anode compartment solution–membrane interphase.[226,17,225]

Various ways of eliminating back diffusion effects have been suggested for when transport numbers, in concentrated solutions, are being measured. One such is to use a high density current for a short time.[17] Another is to begin the experiment with a concentration difference between the two compartments in such a way that this difference would be of the opposite sign at the end of the experiment.[227,228] Recently Meares and Sutton[229] developed a technique using tracers to measure transport numbers without changing the concentration on either side of the membrane.

Finally, Hale and McCauley[227] measured transport numbers of univalent cations basing their work on the treatment of Peers and Patridge.[152] This procedure requires using various membranes with the same selectivity but different permeability. Plotting J_+F/I against $C'' - C'$ (eqn (155a)), they obtained straight lines for each membrane, which intersected at the point for which the values of the abscissa ($C'' - C'$) and the ordinate (J_+F/I) are the same. By applying eqn (165) to the two membranes and solving the two simultaneous equations we obtain

$$C'' - C' = - (2\Delta t_+ I\delta/DF)$$
and
$$\frac{J_+F}{I} = \bar{t}_+$$

where $\bar{t}_+$ is the transport number with respect to the membrane.

The transport numbers, obtained by the Hirttoff method or by electrochemical means, are apparent transport numbers with respect to the liquid moving in the membrane phase. Comparing eqns (206) and (295), the relationship of real and apparent transport numbers is seen through the equation

$$\bar{t}_+ = \bar{t}_{+(ap)} + 0·018\, m_{\pm}\bar{t}_w. \tag{299}$$

Various workers tested this relationship.[17,230,188] They found that the t_+ values, obtained using said equation were somewhat higher than those obtained experimentally. Nevertheless, McCauley[227] and other workers [231,8] observed that eqn (299) was satisfactory.

Oda and Yawataya[232] related real and apparent transport numbers considering that electrolyte conduction, in a porous membrane, is of an electrolytic and convective type as pointed out Schmid.[233] A membrane with a fixed charge density X, in equilibrium with an electrolyte solution, contains $\bar{X}(1 + s)$ counter-ion equivalents, where s is the co-ion equiv. per equivalent of fixed groups, present in the membrane due to the Donnan electrolyte uptake.

Due to water, counter-ion and coion interactions, the counter-ions and water move in the same direction while the coions and water move in the opposite direction. Consequently, the counter-ion and coion mobilities, under a potential gradient ($cm^2 \ sec^{-1}V^{-1}$) in an electronegative membrane, are given by

$$\bar{u}_+' = \bar{u}_+ + \bar{u}_w; \qquad \bar{u}_-' = \bar{u}_- - \bar{u}_w \qquad (300)$$

where $\bar{u}_+$ and $\bar{u}_-$ represent, respectively, the counterion and co-ion mobilities with respect to water.

Taking into account the electro-osmotic effects, membrane conductance is given by the equation

$$\bar{\kappa}' = F[\bar{X}(1 + s)\bar{u}_+' + s\bar{X}\bar{u}_-'] = F\bar{X}[\bar{X}(1 + s)\bar{u}_+ + s\bar{u}_- + \bar{u}_w]. \qquad (301)$$

In the absence of these phenomena, conductance will be

$$\bar{\kappa} = F\bar{X}[(1 + s)\bar{u}_+ + s\bar{u}_-]. \qquad (302)$$

From eqns (301) and (302) we see that

$$\bar{\kappa}' - \kappa = F\bar{X}\bar{u}_w. \qquad (303)$$

Since the real and apparent transport numbers are given by

$$\bar{t}_+ = \frac{(1 + s)\bar{u}_+'}{(1 + s)\bar{u}_+' + s\bar{u}_-'}$$

$$\bar{t}_{+(ap)} = \frac{(1 + s)\bar{u}_+}{(1 + s)\bar{u}_+ + s\bar{u}_-} \qquad (304)$$

from the above equation one may obtain the following expression

$$\bar{t}_+ - \bar{t}_{+(ap)} = [\bar{t}_{-(ap)} + s]\frac{F\bar{X}u_w}{\bar{\kappa}'}. \qquad (305)$$

Oda and Yawataya related $\bar{u}_w$ to the electro-osmotic volume β_e that flows through the membrane under a unit potential gradient

$$\beta = \beta_e \bar{\kappa}' = \bar{u}_w S \tag{306}$$

where S is the total area of the membrane pores.

Finally, substituting eqn (306) into (305) one finds that

$$\bar{t}_+ = \bar{t}_{+(ap)} + [\bar{t}_{-(ap)} + s] A_s \beta F \tag{307}$$

where A_s is the fixed ion content in the membrane phase per volume unit of interstitial solution. Recently Lakshminarayanaiah[231] developed this same equation. Remembering that the number of water moles per ion exchange point is

$$W_e = \frac{1}{18 \bar{X}_v}$$

he obtains

$$\bar{t}_+ = \frac{\bar{t}_w}{W_e} (1 + s) + \bar{t}_{(ap)} \left(1 - \frac{\bar{t}_w}{W_e} \right) \tag{308}$$

Lakshminarayanaiah[231] measured the parameters $\bar{t}_w$, W_e, $\bar{t}_{(ap)}$ and $\bar{s}$ in phenosulphonic membranes and calculated $\bar{t}_+$ using eqn (308). This worker saw that these values coincided satisfactorily except in the $0 \cdot 1 - 0 \cdot 05$ N interval in which the real transport numbers calculated are slightly higher than those observed. Arnold and Swift[234] calculated $\bar{t}_+$ assuming that the mobility relationships are the same in both free solution and the membrane phase

$$\frac{\bar{u}_+}{\bar{u}_-} = \frac{u_+}{u_-} \tag{309}$$

therefore

$$\bar{t}_{+(ap)} = \frac{t_+(1 + s)}{t_+ + s}$$

where

$$t_+ = \frac{u_+}{u_+ + u_-}. \tag{310}$$

The $\bar{t}_+$ values calculated coincide satisfactorily with experimental values as can be seen from the following Table VII.[234]

TABLE VII. Water and hydrogen-ion transport through membranes in SO_4H_2 solutions.[234]

Membrane	Acid normality	W_e	$\dfrac{S\text{ equiv}}{\text{(equiv.)}}$	$\dfrac{W_e}{(1+s)}$	$\bar{t}_W$	$\bar{t}_+$	$(\bar{t}_+)$ calc.
ACI	0·1	20	0·004	19·9	2·1	1·00	1·00
ACI	1·0	19·3	0·009	17·7	1·5	1·00	0·99
ACI	5·0	15·7	0·81	8·7	1·0	0·99	0·96
AZL	0·1	18·3	0·007	18·2	4·4	1·00	1·00
AZL	1·0	18·1	0·16	15·6	2·9	0·99	1·00
AZL	5·0	16·9	1·01	8·4	1·1	0·95	0·96
DYG	0·1	11·7	0·002	11·7	1·0	1·00	1·00
DYG	1·0	11·5	0·04	11·0	1·0	1·00	0·99
DYG	5·0	10·5	0·405	7·5	1·0	0·99	0·98
C313/100	1·0	46	0·35	34·1	4·0	0·99	0·97

J. Electro-osmosis

If an ion membrane separates two electrolyte solutions and a potential difference through it is established, a net flow of water from one solution to the other is the result. In the case of a cation selective membrane most of the current is carried by cations. As the cations are hydrated, part of the water flow comes from the hydration water. Nevertheless, other water flow is made up of that water carried along by the interaction of moving ions with the water molecule around them. It has been agreed to use the term electro-osmotic for the total amount of water flow regardless of the transport mechanism. This flow is represented by t_w, that is to say, mole of transported water per Farady of current.

Electro-osmotic phenomena were observed and studied early this century.

Great advances in theoretical interpretation were made by Helmholtz[235] and Smoluchowski[236] who introduced the concept of a double electric layer in the area separating the two phases. Applying these theories to membranes, it may be postulated that in a system consisting of capillaries with fixed charges in their walls, there is a second diffusion layer of the opposite charge which neutralized the first. When an electric field is applied parallel to the pore walls, this second layer begins to move and move the water molecules around it somewhat.

If the ζ potential (potential difference between the double layer fixed part and the solution altogether) is represented by ξ, viscosity by η and the dielectricity constant by ε, the liquid volume per second passing through the capillary is given by

$$V = \frac{\varepsilon \xi r^2 E}{4l} \tag{311}$$

where E is the potential difference applied, r the capillary radius and l its length.

The pressure that must be applied at the ends of the capillaries to prohibit electro-osmotic flow, is called electro-osmotic pressure and is given by

$$P_e = \frac{2\varepsilon \xi E}{\pi r^2}. \tag{312}$$

The main problem arising when this theory is tested lies in the fact that the parameters η, ε and ξ cannot be found without making some assumptions.

The theories of Helmholtz and Smoluchowski only successfully apply to uncharged membranes with relatively large pores. Schmid and Schwarz[217, 211] studied the electroconvection phenomena in fine membrane capillary systems. Given the fact that counter-ions move in the same direction as the solvent in the presence of an electrical field, the intensity of the current through a membrane, i, is higher than if were the same electrical field applied in a situation with no solvent flow. These authors related the electroconvection current i, to the fixed ion concentration and membrane pore radius by the equation

$$\frac{i - i'}{i} = \frac{\Delta i}{i} = \frac{F^2 \overline{X}^2 r^2}{8 \eta \bar{\kappa}_i} \tag{313}$$

where $\bar{\kappa}_i$ and η are the specific conductance and viscosity of the interstitial solution.

Despic and Hills[134, 237] used the above equation in the following form

$$\bar{\lambda} - \bar{\lambda}' = \frac{10^3 F^2 \overline{X} r^2}{8\eta} \tag{314}$$

where $\bar{\lambda}$ is the electrically measured equivalent conductance and $\bar{\lambda}'$ is the conductance calculated, using the Nernst–Einstein relationship

$$\overline{D} = \frac{RT}{zF^2} \bar{\lambda}'. \tag{315}$$

Based on the equations derived by Bjerrum and Manegold[238] and Manegold and Solf,[239] Schmid developed a theory of electro-osmosis using the pore model. This author showed that electro-osmosis permeability per ampere is given by

$$D_i = \frac{F\bar{X}D_h d}{\kappa} \tag{316}$$

where D_h is the permeability defined as the volume of solution transferred through a membrane area unit in a unit of time under a unit of pressure change, d is the membrane thickness and κ is the specific membrane conductance. Recently Lakshminarayanaiah[240] has checked Schmid's theory in ion exchange membranes with various water content. This author found that Schmid's theory may be applied to tight membranes whose water content is around 14%. The capillary model seems realistic enough for evaluating electroconvection and total water transport.

Several workers have studied electro-osmotic phenomena based on irreversible process thermodynamics.[3, 96, 104, 109, 118, 241] Spiegler[104] found an equation for water flow through a membrane caused by interaction between the moving ions and the water around them. This equation does not include the ion hydration of water. From eqns (75), (76), (80) and assuming $\bar{C}_- = 0$, $L_{--} = L_{+-} = L_{-w} = 0$, he obtains

$$\frac{J_w}{J_+} = \frac{L_{+w}}{L_{++}} = \frac{\bar{C}_w}{\bar{C}_+} \left(\frac{1}{1 + \dfrac{\bar{C}_w f_{wm}}{\bar{C}_+ f_{+w}}} \right). \tag{317}$$

In very porous membranes many water molecules are far from the pore walls, thus cutting down on friction between the water molecules and the matrix. In this case $f_{wm} = 0$ and

$$\frac{J_w}{J_+} = \frac{\bar{C}_w}{\bar{C}_+}. \tag{318}$$

That is to say, the counter-ions and the water move through the membrane at the same velocity. Helmholtz[235] and McBain[242] assume that this is possible only when the double layer thickness is much less than the pore radius. This is not generally the case in most membranes and $J_w/J_+ < C_w/C_+$. Therefore the second term of the denominator of eqn (317) may not be disregarded.

Spiegler[104] compares $\bar{C}_w/\bar{C}_+$ and J_w/J_+ in various membranes with different degrees of crosslinking (Table VIII). This shows that J_w/J_+ is always smaller than $\bar{C}_w/\bar{C}_+$ except in membranes with a high degree of crosslinking. This does not mean that water in high cross-linked membranes moves faster than ions but, given the association between fixed ions and counterions, the real concentration of the latter is less than that obtained by chemical analysis. Furthermore, it is noted that most of the results show that $(J_W/J_+)/(C_W/C_+) \simeq 1/2$. it seems that nearly half of the water molecules move with the ions. Using reduced friction coefficients:

$$Y_{+w} = \frac{f_{+w}}{\gamma_w}, \qquad Y_{+m} = \frac{f_{+m}}{\gamma_m}, \qquad Y_{wm} = \frac{f_{wm}}{\gamma_m}$$

(Y_{ij} represents the friction between 1 mol of i particles and the volume unit j), the ion hydration numbers given by Glueckauf[243] and Stewart and Graydon's results,[244] Spiegler finds that prediction based on theory and experimental results are satisfactorily alike. Picking up Spiegler's theory, Mackay and Meares[106] calculated the friction coefficients for various concentrations in cation membranes, assuming $f_{-m} = 0$ and $f_{-+} = 0$. In Table IX, it may be seen that as external electrolyte concentration increases, the f_{-w} values increase considerably.

TABLE VIII.   Comparison of water content and electroosmotic water transport in Cation exchange membranes (sodium form).[104]

Membrane	Type	Water content C_W/C_+ (mol H$_2$O/ equiv cap)	Water transport, W (mol H$_2$O/Far)	$\dfrac{W}{(C_W/C_+)}$
Nepton CR–51	Phenol sulphonic	31·4	16·6	0·53
Permaplex 110	sulphonic	11·9	6·7	0·56
PV–51	Phenol sulphonic	18·5	7·8	0·42
A (4%.DVB)	Polyestyrene sulphonic, Hetrogeneous	19·5	10·5	0·54
B'' (8.5 DVB)	,,	10·8	9·0	0·83
C'' (15 DVB)	,,	6·6	7·5	1·13

Recently Scattergood and Lightfoot[245] went over the work of Spiegler[104] and Mackay and Meares,[106] taking into account the isotope interactions disregarded by them.

TABLE IX.   Frictional coefficients as a function of concentration.[106]

External NaCl concentration	f_{+W} joul. sec.	f_{+-} cm^{-2}. mol^{-1}	f_{-W} $\times 10^8$
0·01	8·10	2·53	0·06
0·02	6·00	2·34	0·40
0·05	4·94	2·10	3·48
0·10	4·63	2·03	2·75

Oda and Yawataya have carried a rather complete treatment of the electro-osmotic phenomena.[232,246,247] According to these authors, part of the water existing in the membrane phase is carried by the ions like hydration water; another fraction is dragged along by the counter-ions, but slower than them. A third fraction does not move at all as they are physically joined to or trapped in the membrane phase. Accordingly,

$$\bar{t}_w = h_+ \bar{t}_+ - h_- \bar{t}_- + \frac{f}{1+s} \bar{t}_+ \frac{\bar{u}_w}{\bar{u}_+} \tag{319}$$

where h_+ and h_- are the hydration numbers of the counter-ions and of the coions; $\bar{t}_+$ and $\bar{t}_-$ are the transport numbers in the membrane phase; f is the number of moles of water per ion exchange place, s is the total amount of the electrolyte absorbed; $\bar{u}$ is the cation and water mobility in the membrane phase.

The water transport numbers are inversely related to the external solution concentration, decreasing to the extent that the latter increases. Winger *et al.*[228] found that $\bar{t}_w$ decreases with the concentration because the counter-ion transport numbers also decrease. Kressman *et al.*[248] observed that the transfer number, $\bar{t}_w$, of the membranes they studied, corresponded to the absence of fixed water in the membrane phase. In this case

$$\bar{t}_w = \bar{m}_w \bar{t}_+ - \bar{t}_- h_- \tag{320}$$

where m_w is the number of water moles per counter-ion equiv. in the membrane.

Arnold and Swift[234] show that several authors' discoveries of a limit value for the transfer number conflict with Oda and Yawataya's equation. According to eqn (319), as external electrolyte concentration increases, electrolyte absorbtion may increase without limit, causing a continuous fall in t_w. Arnold and Swift considered f as free water. The modified equation is as follows

$$\bar{t}_w = h_+\bar{t}_+ - h_-\bar{t}_- + \frac{f - sh}{1 + s}\,\bar{t}_+\,\frac{\bar{u}_w}{\bar{u}_+} \tag{321}$$

where $h = h_+ + h_-$.

As the amount of electrolyte absorbed increases, the third term might be cancelled out or even become negative; in the latter case, t_w will decrease sharply. However, since this does not happen it can only be because the semi-hydrated counter-ions are held in place by the fixed charges and current is transported by the ions in the membrane phase which have been completely hydrated.

There is still another factor, not yet firmly established, that may influence electro-osmotic flow besides the membrane water content and external electrolyte concentration. This is current density, Mackay and Meares[106] Carr *et al.*[249] and other workers[250,251] have found that t_w does not depend on current density. On the other hand, however, Lakshminarayanaiah [252,253,254] observed the electro-osmotic flow depends on current density in very diluted solutions. According to the latter authors, at under 0·1 N concentrations, electro-osmotic flow gradually decreases to the extent that current density increases, until a limit is reached. However, at over 0·1 N concentrations, t_w is not dependent on current density. The change in water transfer with current density may be attributed to conditions in the solution–membrane interphase or within the membrane. Interphase phenomena such as polarization concentration were eliminated by Lakshminaray-anaiah and Subrahmanyan[253] by efficient stirring and by using low density currents. As a result, $\bar{t}_w$ variations depend on the fact that friction coefficients have different effects depending on current density.

From the Table XI it may be seen that $\bar{t}_w$ has for Li^+ a value of 72·6 and a value of 62·1 for Na^+ at a 0·32 mA/cm^2 current density.

TABLE X.   Exchange capacity and water content of a phenol–sulphonic membrane.[253]

	Li^+	Na^+	K^+	Rb^+	Cs^+
Capacity, meq/g wet membrane	0·61	0·70	0·52	0·53	0·49
$\bar{M}_w$, mol of H_2O/g equiv ion	55·6	46·7	65·1	57·9	57·9

TABLE XI. t_w in the phenol–sulphonic membranes described in the above table.

Current density (mA/cm²)	Li⁺	Na⁺	K⁺	Rb⁺	Cs⁺
0·32	72·6	62·1	55·5	45·5	46·9
1·58	42·6	39·3	34·2	33·4	30·8
3·15	36·9	32·9	27·7	26·2	25·8
15·75	27·6	24·7	20·3	19·5	19·6

These values in order exceed the interstitial water (Tables X, and XI) by 17 and 15 moles. This may be because not all of the counter-ions in the membrane phase take part in the transfer or because the transfer is through uncharged or only slightly charged pores, in which case C_w/C_+ would be a high number. Lakshminarayanaiah and Subrahmanyan conclude that the latter is more likely the case.

Brun and Vaula[213] arrived at the conclusion that t_w values experimentally obtained with diluted solutions might be incorrect, even though they are not dependent on current density, due to polarization effects. They obtained the following equation

$$\bar{t}_w{}' = \bar{t}_w + \frac{4RTt_- \sigma}{dD} = \bar{t}_w + A\delta \tag{322}$$

where $\bar{t}_w$ is the actual water transport number, $\bar{t}_w{}'$ the experimental one, σ specific membrane permeability, t_- is the anion transport number, D is the salt diffusion coefficient, d the membrane thickness and δ the thickness of the Nernst film on either side of the membrane. The correction term may be about a 30% in the case of natural convection ($\delta = 0·035$ cm) and around 1–10% for stirred solutions ($\delta = 0·001$–$0·01$ cm).

There is little available in membrane literature on the temperature effect on electro-osmotic phenomena. Yawataya's equation,[232] later modified by Arnold,[234] shows that of all of the variables affecting $\bar{t}_w$, the $\bar{u}_w/\bar{u}_+$ relationship is the one most affected by temperature. A temperature increase will cause a drop in interactions and rupture the water structure. As a result, $\bar{u}_w/\bar{u}_+$ will decrease causing a drop in t_w. On the other hand, according to the eqn (317), transfer numbers depend on f_{+w} and f_{wm}. As temperature increases, both coefficients decrease. However, in membranes with a high water content, the f_{+w} decrease is more marked than the f_{wm} one, as the ion–water interaction is the most important. It is to be expected, then, that $\bar{t}_w$ decreases as temperature increases.

Nevertheless, temperature effects on electro-osmotic processes are not clearly established in the case of ordinary ions. For instance, George and Courant[255] took electro-osmotic measurement at different temperatures in cation exchange membranes and observed that $\bar{t}_w$ decreased as temperature increased, while Leitz[256] found $\bar{t}_w$ independent of temperature. Finally, Bejerano and Forgacs[257] saw that $\bar{t}_w$ increased as temperature increased from 30 to 90°C. The aforementioned authors took electro-osmotic measurements using alkaline metals as counter-ions.

TABLE XII.   Electro-osmotic transfer numbers in 5N sulphuric acid, corrected for anion transport.[258]

ACI Membrane Temperature, °C	$\bar{t}_w$	DYG Membrane Temperature, °C	$\bar{t}_w$
1·5	0·98	2·6	0·92
3·4	1·00	15	0·96
24	1·02	25	1·01
40	1·10	39	1·10
55	1·00	54	1·22

Recently Arnold[258] studied water transport in acid membranes and postulated that in this case part of the current is transported by proton-jumping. As this process does not include water transport, only the fraction of current transported by ordinary movement is responsible for water transport. If eqn (321) is given the form

$$t_w = \bar{t}_+ T_w - \bar{t}_- h_-$$ (323)

according to Arnold's model

$$T_w = (h + f')\beta$$ (324)

where

$$f' = \frac{f - sh}{1 + s} \cdot \frac{\bar{u}_w}{\bar{u}_+}$$

and

$$\beta = \frac{\lambda_m}{\lambda_m + \lambda_j}.$$

This last equation includes λ_m and λ_j which are the hydrogen ion mobilities in migration and proton-jumping, respectively.

The temperature effect on β has to be determined by the activation energy (ΔE) difference between movement and proton-jumping processes. Accordingly

$$\ln \frac{\lambda_j}{\lambda_m} = \ln \left(\frac{1 - \beta}{\beta}\right) = \text{const} + \frac{\Delta E}{RT}. \tag{325}$$

To measure electro-osmotic effects as a function of temperature, Arnold used polystyrene sulphonic acid membranes supported by a DYG fibreglass net and unsupported homogeneous membranes. ΔE may be obtained by plotting $\ln[(1 - \beta)/\beta]$ against $1/T$, assuming $(h + f')$ constants. The resulting graphs are straight lines in SO_4H_2 1 N solutions and slightly curved in SO_4H_2 5 N. The ΔE values obtained fluctuate between 0·8 and 1·4 kcal/mol.

K. Anomalous Osmosis

When a membrane separates an electrolyte solution and pure water or two electrolyte solutions of different concentration, the rate of osmotic movement of liquid across the membrane may be greater than that caused by non electrolytes of equal concentration. This effect is called anomalous positive osmosis. If the flow of solvent is in the opposite direction to that expected on the basis of concentration difference, this effect is called anomalous negative osmosis.

This phenomenon was first described by Dutrochet[259] during the 19th century and has warranted the attention of numerous workers in the membrane field.[260,261,262,263] However, there is still no convincing theory for this phenomenon.

Graham[264] suggested that anomalous osmosis is an electro-osmotic process. This has been upheld by other distinguished workers.[260,261,262,265,266,267,268] These researchers based their theories on the idea that electro-osmotic flux caused by electrostatic potential differences on both sides of the membrane, superimposes to pure osmotic flow caused by the chemical potential difference between both. Nevertheless, no quantitative theory to explain this phenomenon in accordance with these ideas has been established.

Kedem and Katchalsky[108] as well as Dorst et al.[269] attribute anomalous osmosis to the crossed factors in the phenomenological flow equations. In other words, solvent flow is not caused only by chemical gradients of solvent but by the chemical gradient of the solute as well. In this way, solvent flow may be altered considerably by the action of viscous forces between the shifting solute and the solvent. Based on these ideas, Tasaka et al.[270] showed that if a membrane separates two differently concentrated chemical solutions, the water flux observed is the difference between the ordinary osmotic water flow and the water flow due to friction between the water and the ions that move due to the concentration difference. In the case of a charged membrane, the solute velocity decreases due to Donnan exclusion; hence, the solute retards the solvent to a lesser degree if there are fixed charges in the membrane phase. Tasaka et al.,[270] established J_+, J_- J_w as flows in this system, and grad $\hat{\mu}_+$, grad $\hat{\mu}_-$, grad μ_w, as forces, where electrochemical potential is given by

$$\hat{\mu}_i = \mu_i + z_i F\phi + \bar{V}_i \Delta P.$$

The phenomenological relationships, in matrix form, are given by

$$J_i = L_{ik}\frac{dX_k}{dx}; \quad i, k = +, -, w; \quad X_k = \hat{\mu}_+, \hat{\mu}_-, \mu_w \qquad (326)$$

Multiplying both sides of eqn (326) by r_{ik}, the matrix inverse of L_{ik},

$$r_{ik} = \frac{|L|_{ik}}{|L|}.$$

The following equation is obtained

$$\frac{dX_k}{dx} = r_{ki}J_i. \qquad (327)$$

From here,

$$\Delta X_k = \int_0^d (r_{ki}dx)J_i = R_{ki}J_i \qquad (328)$$

in which constant flows have been assumed. Multiplying eqn (328) by the matrix inverse of R_{ik}, $\lambda_{ik} = |R|_{ik}/|R|$ the following expression is found

$$J_i = \lambda_{ik}\Delta X_k. \qquad (329)$$

We can eliminate $\Delta\hat{\mu}_+$ and $\Delta\hat{\mu}_-$ from the relationship between J_i and ΔX_k which leaves water flow in the following form

$$J_w = A\Delta\mu_w + BJ_+ + CJ_- \qquad (329a)$$

where $A = 1/R_{ww}$; $B = -R_{w+}/R_{ww}$; $C = R_{w-}/R_{ww}$.

Making a number of assumptions ($L_{+-} = L_{-+}$ as insignificant and considering L_{ww} independent of concentration), Tasaka et al.[270] find A, B and C constant. Furthermore, R_w, R_{w+} and R_{w-} are given according to Kedem and Katchalsky's[108] theory by:

$$R_{ww} = -\frac{1}{C_w}\left(f_{wm} - \frac{C_+f_{+w} + C_-f_{-w}}{C_w}\right); \quad R_{w+} = \frac{f_{+w}}{C_w}; \quad R_{w-} = \frac{f_{-w}}{C_w} \quad (330)$$

where C_w and f_{iw} are the concentration and friction coefficient between the i component and the water.

The A, B and C coefficients bear a positive sign and the $J_+ = J_- = J_s$ flows, bear the sign opposite to $\Delta\mu_w$ if no external electrical field is applied. As a result, if B and C are large, J_w may be opposite to $\Delta\mu_w$ that is to say, negative anomalous osmosis might result if the friction between the water and the ions is high.

Solvent flow due to osmotic phenomena is given by

$$A\Delta\mu_w = J_w^w = J_w - (B + C)J_s \qquad (331)$$

keeping in mind that

$$\Delta\pi = -\frac{\Delta\mu_w}{V_w} = \frac{\partial RTM}{1000\,V_w}\phi C_1\left(\frac{C_2}{C_1} - 1\right) \qquad (332)$$

where $\Delta\pi$ is the osmotic pressure difference, M is the solvent's molecular weight and ϕ is the osmotic coefficient. It is possible to calculate J_w^w from the experimental values of J_w and J_s, and the plot log J_{ww} versus log C_1 must be linear with unit slope. The value of A may be calculated from the intercept when log $C_1 = 0$.

From the relationships

$$I = F\sum_{i=+,-} z_i J_i, \quad t_i = \left(\frac{z_i J_i}{\displaystyle\sum_{i=+,-} z_i J_i}\right)_{\substack{\Delta T=0 \\ \Delta P=0 \\ \Delta\mu_w=0}} \qquad (333)$$

and eqn (331) the following equation is obtained, when $\Delta\mu_w = 0$

$$\left(\frac{J_w}{I/F}\right)_{\substack{\Delta T=0 \\ \Delta P=0 \\ \Delta\mu_w=0}} = \frac{B}{z_+}t_+ + \frac{C}{z_-}t_-. \qquad (334)$$

In the case of an ideal cation exchange membrane $t_- = 0$ and B may be obtained from electro-osmotic measurements. The J_w^w versus log C_1 curve has the N-form similar to those previously reported by Sollner,[263] Loeb[260] and Toyoshima et al.[191] Sollner,[271,272] comparing anomalous osmotic phenomena in collodion membranes, observes that the more fixed groups there are the greater are the anomalous osmotic effects as well. Tasaka et al.[270] also compare the experimental data for membranes with varying charge density. They compare a sulphonic polystyrene type membrane (C1) with 0·253 meq/g dry membrane (exchange capacity) and 1·96 g water (water uptake) with another (C2) of the same type with CC 1·24 meq/g dry membrane, and 0·975 g H_2O/g dry membrane. Experimental results show that there is more flow in (C1) than in (C2), though the charge density is greater in (C2) than in (C1). This is because the (C2) membrane is more porous than the (C1) one and the purely osmotic flow, is 8·6 times higher in the first than in the second. There are a number of theories[155, 273, 274] which assume that when a membrane separates two equally concentrated electrolyte solutions a pressure gradient is established inside the membrane though the solutions stay at the same pressure and temperature on both sides of the membrane. It is assumed that in addition to the electrostatic potential variation, this pressure gradient causes local movement of the centre of the mass. That is to say, it accelerates solution flow through the membrane. These theories either disregard interactions between moving ions and the solvent or interpret them in terms of local movement of the centre of the mass. Based on these ideas Kobatake *et al.*[191, 274, 275] recently brought to light a theory briefly described below. Liquid flow[14] passing through the membrane, taking the cell as frame of reference, is

$$(J_v)_c = \sum \bar{V_i}(J_i)_c \tag{335}$$

where $i = +, -, w$, and $\bar{V_i}$ is the partial molar volume of the i component. Furthermore

$$(J_i)_c = J_i + C_i v^* \tag{336}$$

and $\Sigma M i(J_i) = 0$ (M_i is the molecular weight of the i component)(337).
  Assuming that $L_{+-} = L_{-+} = 0$ and that the electrical current is zero (whereby $J_+ - J_- = 0$) it is possible from eqns (215), (335), (336), (337) to obtain $(J_v)_c$ in low charge density membranes separating two single (1:1) electrolytes:

$$(J_v)_c = -\frac{RT}{F}\left(\bar{V_s} - \frac{M_s}{M_w}\bar{V_w}\right)\int_{0+}^{d-} \frac{\bar{u}_+\bar{u}_-\bar{C}_-\bar{C}_+}{\bar{u}_+\bar{C}_+ + u_-C_-}\cdot\frac{d\ln a^2}{dx} + \frac{1}{d}\int_{0+}^{d-}\bar{V}^*dx \tag{338}$$

where d_- and 0_+ are, respectively, $\lim_{\delta\to 0} d - \delta$ and $\lim_{\delta\to 0} + \delta$.
  All volume elements in the membrane phase are submitted to two types of external force: a mechanical force given by $- dp/dx$ and another electrical force caused by the potential gradient given by $-F\psi\bar{X}\,d\phi/dx$, where ψ is a variable depending on the freedom of counter-ion in the membrane phase. In a stationary state, the sum of these forces and viscous forces tend to cancel each other out. Therefore,

$$\frac{v^*}{K} = -\frac{dP}{dx} - F\psi\bar{X}\frac{d\phi}{dx}. \tag{339}$$

From eqns (338) and (339) they finally obtain

$$(J_v)_c = \frac{D_0}{2}\left(\overline{V}_s - \frac{M_s}{M_w}\overline{V}_w\right)\left[Z(C_2,\theta\overline{X}) - Z(C_1,\theta\overline{X}) - (2\alpha - 1)\theta\overline{X}\right.$$

$$\left. + \ln\frac{Z(C_2,)\theta\overline{X} + (2\alpha - 1)\theta\overline{X}}{Z(C_1,\theta\overline{X}) + (2\alpha - 1)\theta\overline{X}}\right] - \frac{k}{d}[(P)_{x=d-} - (P)_{x=0+}]$$

$$+ \left[\frac{K\psi\overline{X}}{d}[(\phi)_{x=d-} - (\phi)_{x=0+}]\right] \qquad (340)$$

in which $Z(C, \theta\overline{X})$ are given in eqn (226) and

$$D_0 = \frac{2RT}{F}\frac{u_+{}^\circ u_-{}^\circ}{u_+{}^\circ + u_-{}^\circ}$$

The first term of eqn (340), which represents the bulk liquid flow caused by water electrolyte interdiffusion, is thermodynamic. The second and third terms represent flows caused by a pressure gradient and an electrical potential gradient; consequently they are caused mechanically and electrically, respectively.

Toyoshima *et al.* calculate the various parameters of eqn (340) and observe that experimental and theoretical results are satisfactorily alike. Theory predicts satisfactorily the maximum and minimum position of the curves J_v versus log C.

IV. Applications

Electrodyalisis through membranes has many applications. Some of these applications are already commercialized and others are in the developmental stage.[276,277,278]

Demineralization, is the most promising field of electrodyalisis; and two cases may be distinguished.

(a) Demineralization of solutions containing only electrodialysable electrolyte solutes.

(b) Demineralization of solutions containing an electrolyte and a non-dialysable electrolyte (for example, a protein) which are to be separate from the electrolyte electrodialysable.

Meyer and Strauss[279] suggested demineralization be tried out in electrolytic cell groups separating each cell with an anion exchange membrane and another cation exchange one as shown in the figure. Assuming both membranes are ideally selective, for every X of current Faradays that pass through, X equivalents of Cl^- will pass from cell C to cell B, and X equivalents of Na^+ will pass from cell C to cell D, thus leaving cell C demineralized (Fig. 9). In the same way, cell D will be concentrated when X equivalents of

Cl⁻ pass from cell E to cell D. Thinking along these lines it is easy to see that alternate cells are demineralized and concentrated, thus alternating the brine and dialysate compartments.

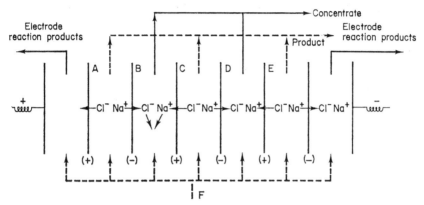

FIG. 9. Conventional electrodaliysis.

Wilson[8] looked into demineralization plant design. The slow but continuous progress in this field has been reviewed by Kunin.[280] Among the most important electrodyalisis applications are[91]

Applications in commercial stage

Water treatment
Concentration of NaCl
Removal of salts from whey
Ion balancing in milk.

Applications in laboratory or pilot plant stages

Recovery of steel pickle liquor
Concentration of radioactive solutions
Demineralization of proteins and clays
Production of conductivity water
Reduction of uranyl to uranous ions
Demineralizarion of dextrose and sucrose solutions
Preparation of photographic emulsion
Treatment of spent sulphite liquor to recover pulping liquors
Decitrification of fruit juices
Demineralization of gelatins.

Electrodialitic processes for ion separation by competing ion transfer across ion selective membranes have been studied. Thus Di Benedetto and

Lightfoot[281] studied the relative transfer of Cl^- and glycine while research on other amino acids has been reported by Peers.[282] Glueckauf and Kitt[283] have suggested an interesting procedure for separating uni- di- and trivalent ions. This method is based on the principle of ion-exclusion and in placing a double acid-base membrane in such a way that the anion exchange side faces the anode and the cation exchange side faces the cathode. Therefore, the ions may pass through the membrane and they go part way as coions. They separate because the concentration of the various coions in the membrane phase are generally different.

Rare earth mixtures may be separated by forming complexes.[284] If the stability constant of the complexes is different, separation may be by electrodialysis. In this case, the positive metalic ions are removed through the negative membrane and the negative complexes are removed through the positive membrane.

Reactions of the type

$$M^+Y^- + N^+X^- \rightarrow M^+X^- + N^+Y^-$$

type may take place if salts according to the following scheme are available:

In this way, NaOH and NH_4Cl have been prepared from NaCl and NH_4OH;[285] Uranyl fluoride has been obtained from uranyl nitrate[286] and weak acids[287] from esters.

Perm-selective membranes may be used as membrane electrodes, at least in diluted solutions.[288, 289] An ideally selective membrane separating two solutions develops a potential that is given by

$$E = \frac{RT}{F} \ln \frac{a_2}{a_1}.$$

If one of the activities is known, the other may be found from the potential. Nevertheless, this procedure is only limited because the membranes have little specific selectivity.

Finally we will point out that electroosmotic transport may be used also to separate solvents.[290] Marinsky and Katz separated H_2O and D_2O using this method.

Another Application

A promising field for using ion exchange membranes is as electrolytes in low temperature fuel cells, mainly in H_2–O_2 fuel cells.[291, 292] As solids, non-leached electrolytes, allow cells to be built requiring the fewest possible outer and control components. The favourable geometry is another important advantage. The consequent cell thinness compensates the lower current density these cells have in comparison to Bacon's. Gases containing significant amounts of CO_2 may also be used.

Figure 10 shows a diagram of cell structure. It is made up of an electrolyte in the form of a membrane in which the layers of the electrode material (for example, platinum or palladium black) were bonded on the surfaces of the membrane.

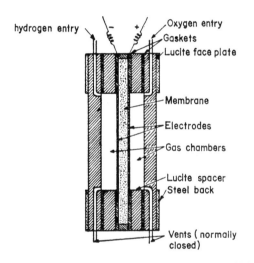

FIG. 10. Schematic diagram of a fuel cell (Niedrach[294]).

Organic membranes such as acidic cation exchange membranes obtained by mechanical procedures using ion exchange resins set in an inert binder such as polyethylene or teflon, or inorganic membranes, for example zirconium phosphate, may be used in fuel cells. Gregor[293] has discussed the main methods for preparing membranes for use in fuel cells.

Hydrogen has been the fuel used in most cases. However, Niedrach[294] has studied the behaviour of these cells using propane, propylene, ethylene, methane, and CO as fuel.

Grubb and Niedrach[295] have obtained the polarization curves of various electrodes noting that higher current densities are obtained when platinized screen electrodes rather than foil type ones are used. With these there was a smaller area of contact with the electrolyte than with those and the internal resistance of the cell was greater. Grubb obtained very low current densities, but these increased as cell design was perfected.

Thus Cairns et al.[296] using ion exchange membranes of the phenol sulphonic acid–formaldehyde type, and Pt, Pd, Ir and Rh as electrodes, obtained open circuit voltages of 0·9–1·1 V in H–O fuel cells. The performance of the cells fluctuated between 30 mA/cm^2 and 80 mA/cm^2 at 0·5 V and cell life was about 40 A h/cm^2 when working with from 8·5 to 230 Ω/cm^2 loads. Cell performance is optimal at 55°C. Using electropositive organic membranes as polyelectrolytes, Miller et al.[297] designed cells which operating on H–O at room temperature gave 140 mA/cm^2 at 0·70 V for 190 hours; at 80°C, performance was about the same (0·67 V) for 20 hours.

Lurie et al.,[298] designed a dual cell with the gas electrodes in contact with two membranes separated by electrolytic liquid. These cells have the following advantages: (a) prevention of accidental mixing of the H and O through pinholes in the membrane; (b) cooling of the cell when the electrolyte evaporates or rather as this circulates through the external heat exchangers; (c) finally, it is possible to work at higher currents due to efficient cooling.

As examples of the use of inorganic perm-selective membranes we cite the works of Berger and Strier.[299] These researchers, using zirconium phosphate membranes, in the range of temperature from ambient to 150° C, as polyelectrolytes, obtained performances of 30 mA/cm^2 at 0·77–0·78 V and 151° C.

Ion exchange membranes also are used in ion exchange batteries. These are galvanic cells in which the electrolyte is a partially hydrated solid.

Grubb[300] studied the behaviour of systems

Zinc foil | partially hydrated membrane | Silver foil.

Phenol sulphonic (Nepton type) and polyesterin sulphinic (Am–berplex type) membranes were used. The boundary between ionic forms is not sharp as Fig. 11 shows, but becomes smeared out by cross diffusion. Little charge

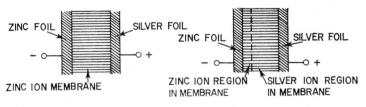

FIG. 11. Schematic diagram of silver–zinc cell. Left, uncharged cell; right, charged cell (Grubb[300]).

can be recovered from cells which were charged and then allowed to stand for 24 hours before discharging, because the silver ions eventually reach the Zn electrode and deposit because of the diffusion.

Lovreck et al.[301] managed to rectify alternating current by passing it through systems in which the ion exchange membrane separated hydroxyl ions and protons. These authors attibuted the rectification property to the combination of H and OH to form water in one cycle, and to ionization of the water in the other cycle. [Also see refs (302)(303)(304)]. Current amplification was also noted in systems made up of two pairs of cation and anion exchange membranes connected to a source of alternating current and a source of continually pulsating current.[305]

References

1. Meares, P., Dawson, D. G., Sutton, A. H. and Thain, J. F. (1967). *Ber Bunsenges. Physik. Chem.* **71**, 765.
2. Lakshminarayanaiah (1969). "Transport Phenomena in Membranes". Academic Press New York and London.
3. Kedem, O. and Katchalsky, A. (1963). *Trans. Far. Soc.* **59**, 1918, 1931, 1941.
4. Läuger, P. (1969). *Angew. Chem.* **81**, 56.
5. Meyer, K. H. and Sievers, J. F. (1936). *Helv. Chim. Acta.* **19**, 649.
6. Sollner, K. J. (1969). *Macromolecular Sci.* A3, (1) 1.
7. Bergsma, F. and Krussink, Ch. A. (1961). *Fortschr. Hochpolym. Forsch.* **2**, 307
8. Wilson, J. (Ed.). (1960). "Demineralization by Electrodyalysis". Butterworths, London.
9. Morgan, T. D. (1960). "Demineralization by Electrodyalysis" J. Wilson (Ed.).
10. Hazenberg, J. F. A. (1962). *Dechema Monograph* **47**, 487.
11. Krishnaswamy, N. (1958). *J. Sci. Ind. Res. (India)* **17A**, 328; *Ibid.* **20A**, 656 (1961); **24A**, 244 (1965).
12. Carnell, P. H. and Cassidy, H. G. (1961). *J. Polymer Sci.* **55**, 233.
13. Lakshminarayanaiah, N. (1965). *Chem. Rev.* **65**, 548.
14. Gregor, H. P. (1968). *Pure and Appl. Chem.* **16**, 329
15. Manecke, G. (1952). *Z. Physik. Chem.* **201**, 193.
16. Jakubovic, A. O. (1960). *J. Chem. Soc.* 4820.
17. Lakshminarayanaiah, N. and Subrahmanyan, V. (1964). *J. Polymer Sci.* **Part A**, 4491.
18. Onoue, Y., Mizutani, T. and Izumi, Y. (1965). *Chem. Abs.* **62**, 6627.
19. Hills, G. J., Kitchener, J. A. and Ovenden, P. J. (1965). *Trans. Faraday Soc.,* **51**, 719.
20. Spinner, I. H., Ciric, J. and Graydon, W. F. (1954). *Can. J. Chem.* **32**, 143.
21. Graydon, W. F. and Stewart, R. J. (1955). *J. Phys. Chem.* **59**, 86.
22. Rosenblum, P., Tombalakaian, A. S. and Graydon, W. F. (1966). *J. Polmer Sci.* **Part A**, 1703.
23. Worsely, M., Tombalakaian, A. S. and Graydon, W. F. (1965). *J. Phys. Chem.* **69**, 883.
24. Lagos, A. E. and Kitchener, J. A. (1960). *Trans. Faraday Soc.* **562**, 1245.
25. Zundel, G., Noller, H. and Schwab, G. M. (1961). *Naturfosch* **16**, 716.
26. Nishimura, M., Yabu, M. and Sugihara, M. (1967). *Kogyo Kagaku Zasshi* **70**, 393.

27. Clark, J., (Ionics Inc.). U.S. Pat. 2,731,411.
28. Oster, E. A. and Fickett, A. P. U.S. Pat. 3,207,708.
29. Yamane, R., Mizutani, Y., Motomura, H. and Izuro, R. (1964). *Denki Kagaku* **32**, 277.
30. Asahi Electrochemical Co. Ltd. Japan Pat. 21635.
31. Natarajan, R. and Rajawat, M. S. (1966). *J. Appl. Polymer Sci.* **10**, 1975.
32. Kasper, A. A. (Ionics Inc.). U.S. Pat. 2,702,272.
33. Juda, W. and Kasper, A. A. (Ionics Inc.). U.S. Pat. 2,731,425.
34. Asahi Electrochemical Co. Ltd. Japan Pat. 16673.
35. Asahi Glass Co., Ltd. Japan Pat. 5271.
36. Hani, H., Nishihara, A. and Hifaga, H. U.S. Pat. 3,276,992.
37. Farbenfabriken Bayer, A. G. Ger. Pat. 1,020,600.
38. South Africa Council for Scientific and Industrial Research, Fr. Pat. 1163010.
39. Motozato, Y., Egawa, H., Meagaki, H. and Kunitake, K. (1956). *Kogyo Kagaku Zasshi,* **59**, 479.
40. Hani, H. Japan Pat, 2695.
41. Farbenfabriken Bayer A. G. Ger Pat. 958,458.
42. Asahi, Chem. Ind. Co. U.S. Pat. 2,864,776.
43. Roebersen, H. G. and Bochove, V. (T.N.O.) C.S.A. Pat. 17,366.
44. Cooke, B. A. *et al.* (S.A.C.S.I.R.) S.A/Pat. 23396.
45. Morgan, T. D. and Schweigart, H. (S.A.C.S.I.R.) S.A. Pat. 2530.
46. Ross, S. *et al.* (Sprague Elect. Co.) U.S. Pat. 2,648,717.
47. Hani, H. Japan Pat. 2695.
48. Karshi, F. Israel Pat. 14720.
49. Hani, H. and Komo, K. (1962). *Asahi Garasu Kenkyu Hokoku* **12**, 157.
50. Hookway, H. T. *et al.* (Nat. Res. Dev.) Brit. Pat. Appl. 336/57.
51. Tsunoda, Y. and Seko, M. (Asahi Chem. Ind. Co.). Brit Pat. 794,426.
52. *Ibid.* Brit, Pat. 795,379.
53. Asahi Garasu Kabushiki Kaisha. Brit. Pat. 793,212.
54. Hazenberg, J. F. A. and Knol, B. P. South Africa Application No. 1754/58.
55. ICI Australia Application No. 43088/58.
56. Mizutani, Y. (1962). *Kogyo-Kagaku Zasshi,* **65**, 1124.
57. Bridgeford, D. J. (1962). *Ind. Eng. Chem. Prod. Res. Dev.* **1**, 45.
58. Baldwin, W. H., Holcomb, D. L. and Johnson, J. S. (1965). *J. Polymer Sci. Pat.* **A,** 833.
59. Hodgon, R. B. Jr. and Boyack, J. R. (1965). *J. Polymer Sci.* **Part. A,** 1463.
60. Richards, G. N. and White, E. F. T. (1964). *J. Polymer Sci.* **C4,** 1251.
61. Riande, E., Mateos, A. M. and Guzman, G. M. (1970). *Eur. Poylmer J.* **6,** 437.
62. Riande, E., Mateos, A. M. and Guzman, G. M. (1970). *Ibid.* **6,** 1247.
63. Guzman, G. M. and Riande, E. (1969). *J. Polymer Sci.* **Part C** (22), 887.
64. Riande, E. and Guzman, G. (1969). *Anales de Quimica,* **65,** 483.
65. Mesorbian, R. B. (1958). *Proc. Second U.N. International Conference on the Peaceful Uses of Atomic Energy. Geneva* **29,** 196. United Nations, New York.
66. American Machine and Foundry Co. Brit., Pat. 872217.
67. Sporkenbach, E., Langner, H. and Wuckel, (1964). *Ber. Deut. Akad. Wiss. Berlin,* **6,** 57.
68. Rozenblyum, N. D., Kocherginskaya, L. L., Zhitkova, L. G., Breger, A. Kh., Goldin, V. A., Chepel, L. V., Voropaev, Yu. V. and Stasyuk, Kh. A. (1964). *Radiats Khim. Polim. Mater. Simp., Moscow,* p. 179 *Nauka.*

69. Yanagita, M., Kawabe, H., Shinohara, K. and Takamatsu, T. (1962). *Sci. Papers Inst. Phys. Chem. Res.* (*Tokyo*) **56**, 218.
70. American Machine and Foundry Co. Brit. Pat. 988,516.
71. Centre National de la Recherche Scientifique, French Pat. 1,371, 843.
72. Chapiro, A. and Seidler, P. *Eur. Polymer J.* **1**, 189.
73. Dobo, J., Somogyi, A. and Czvikovsky, T. (1964). *J. Polymer Sci.* Pt C, 1173.
74. Gregor, H. P. and Patzelt, H. I. (Nat. Aluminate Corp.) S.A. Pat. 622.
75. Neihof, R. (1954). *J. Phys. Chem.* **58**, 916.
76. Gotolieb, M. H., Neihof, R. and Sollner, K. (1957). *J. Phys. Chem.* **61**, 154.
77. Gregor, H. P. and Wetstone, D. M. (1956). *Discuss. Far. Soc.* **21**, 162.
78. Asahi Glass Co, Japan Pat. 3213.
79. Honey, E. M. O. and Hardy, Ch. R. U.S. Pat. 2,810,932.
80. Kressman, T. R. E. and Smith, S. C. British Pat. 810391.
81. VEB. Farbenfabriken Wolfen. Ger. Pat. 1,201,055.
82. Bachmann, R., Krauss, U., Reuter, H., Schwachula, G., Warkecke, D., Wehlend, W., and Wolf, F. E. Ger. Pat. 42616.
83. Hani, H., Nishihara, A., and Oda, Y. U.S. Pat. 3,276,991.
84. Amphlet, C. B. (1964). "Inorganic Ion Exchangers". Elsevier Amsterdam.
85. Bregman, J. I. and Braman, R. S. (1956). *J. Colloid Sci.* **20**, 913.
86. Bregman, J. I. (1966). Res. Develop. Progr, Rept. No. 184. OSW, U.S. Dept. of Interior, Washington D.C.
87. Dravnieks, A. and Bregman, J. I. (1961). *Chem. Eng. News.* **39**, October 42.
88. Rajan, K. S., Boies, D. B., Casol, A. J. and Bregman, J. I. (1966). *Desalination*, **1**, 231.
89. Fischer, R. B. and Babcock, R. F. (1958). *Anal. Chem.* 1732.
90. Tendeloo, H. J. C. and Krips, A. (1957). *Rec. Trav. Chim.* **76**, 703, 946.
91. Friedlander, H. Z. and Rickles, R. N. (1966). *Chem. Eng.* **73**, (5) 111.
92. Katchalsky, A. (1968). *Pure Appl. Chem.* **16**, 229.
93. Nernst, W. (1888). *Z. Physik. Chem.* **2**, 613.
94. Planck, M. (1890). *Ann. Physic. u. Chem.* **39**, 161.
95. Goldman, D. E. (1945). *J. Gen. Physiol.* **27**, 37.
96. Teorell, T. (1953). *Progr. Biophys. Chem.* **3**, 305.
97. Teorell, T. (1951). *Z. Elektrochem.* **55**, 460.
98. Schlögl, R. (1966). *Ber. Bunsenges., Physik. Chem.* **70**, 400.
99. Helfferich, F. (1962). "Ion Exchange". McGraw Hill, N.Y.
100. Lightfoot, E. N. and Scattergood, M. A. (1962). *I. Chem. E. J.* **11**, 175.
101. De Groot, S. R. (1952). "Thermodynamics of Irreversible Processes". Interscience N. Y.
102. Hills, G. J., Jacobs, P. W. M. and Lakshminarayanaiah, N. (1961). *Proc. Royal Soc.*, **A262**, 246.
103. Mckinley, D. C. and Caplan, S. R. (1966). *J. Phys. Chem.* **70**, 3049.
104. Spiegler, K. S. (1958). *Trans. Far. Soc.* **54**, 1408.
105. Meares, P. (1959). *Trans. Far. Soc.* **55**, 1970.
106. Mackay, D. and Meares, P. (1959). *Ibid.* **55**, 1221.
107. Wills, G. B. and Lightfoot, E. N. (1966). *Ind. Eng. Chem.* (*Fund*). **5**, 114.
108. Kedem, O. and Katchalsky, A. (1961). *J. Gen. Physiol.* **45**, 143.
109. Staverman, A. J. (1952). *Trans. Far. Soc.* **48**, 176.
110. Lorenz, P. B. (1952). *J. Phys. Chem.* **56**, 775.
111. Dorst, W., Polak, P. L. and Staverman, A. J. (1962). *Gazz. Chim. Ital.* **92**, 1241.

112. Dorst, W. and Staverman, A. J. (1967). *Rec. Trav. Chim.* **86,** 61.
113. Tombalakaian, A. S., Worsely, M., and Graydon, W. F. (1966). *J. Amer. Chem. Soc.* **88,** 661.
114. Dawson, D. G., Dorst, W. and Meares, P. J. (1969). *Polymer Sci.* C(22) 901.
115. Saxén, U. (1892). *Ann. Physik. Chem.* **47,** 46.
116. Mazur, P. and Overbeek, T. G. (1951). *Rec. Trav. Chim.* **70,** 83.
117. Tombalakaian, A. S. (1968). *J. Phys. Chem.* **72,** 1566.
118. Kobatake, Y., Yuasa, M. and Fujita, H. (1968). *J. Phys. Chem.* **72,** 1752.
119. Danielli, J. F. (1943). "The Permeability of Natural Membranes, "McMillan, N.Y.
120. Zwolinski, B. J., Eyring, H. and Reese, C. (1949). *J. Phys. Chem.* **52,** 1426.
121. Schlögl, R. (1953). *Z. Elektrochem.* **57,** 195.
122. Soldano, B. A., Boyd, G. E. (1953). *J. Am. Chem. Soc.* **75,** 6107.
123. Tetembaum, M. and Gregor, H. P. (1954). *J. Phys. Chem.* **58,** 1156.
124. Meares, P. (1958). *J. Chim. Phys.* **55,** 273.
125. Richman, D. and Thomas, H. C. (1956). *J. Phys. Chem.* **60,** 273.
126. Schlögl, R. (1952). *Z. Electrochem.* **57,** 195.
127. Caramazza, R. Dorst, W. Hoeve, A. C. and Staverman, A. J. (1963). *Trans. Far. Soc.* **59,** 2415.
128. Laity, R. W. (1959). *J. phys. Chem.* **63,** 80.
129. Laity, R. W. (1959). *J. Chem. Phys.* **30,** 682.
130. Mackay, D. and Meares, P. (1955). *Proc. Roy. Soc.* **A232,** 498.
131. Mackay, D. and Meares, P. (1956). *J. Polymer. Sci.* **20,** 507.
132. Jakubovic, A. O., Hills, G. J., and Kitchener, J. A. (1958). *J. Chim. Phys.* **55,** 263.
133. Andelman, J. B. and Gregor, H. P. (1966). *Electrochim. Acta.* **11,** 869.
134. Despic, A. and Hills, G. J. (1956). *Discuss Faraday Soc.* **21,** 50.
135. MacHardy, W. H., Meares, P. and Thain, J. F. (1969). *J. Electrochem. Soc.* **116,** 920.
136. Glueckauf, E. and Wats, R. E. (1962). *Proc. Royal Soc.* **A268,** 339.
137a. Helfferich, F. (1956). *Discuss. Faraday Soc.* **21,** 83.
137b. Helfferich, F. (1959). "Ionenaustauscher". Vol. 1. Ch. 8. Verlag Chemie, Weinheim.
138. Helfferich, F. and Ocker, H. D. (1957). *Z. Physik. Chem. Frankfurt,* **10,** 213.
139. Mackay, D. and Meares, P. (1960). *Kolloid Z.* **171,** 139.
140. Mackay, D. and Meares, P. (1961). *Ibid.* **176,** 23.
141. Helfferich, F. (1960). *J. Colloid Sc.* **15,** 483.
142. Helfferich, F. and Plesset, M. S. (1958). *J. Chem. Phys.* **28.** 418.
143. Ciric, J. and Graydon, W. F. (1962). *J. Phys. Chem.* **66,** 1549.
144. Blaedel, W. J., Haupert, T. J. and Evenson, M. A. (1969). *Analyt. Chem.* **41,** 583.
145. Blaedel, W. J. and Haupert, T. J. (1966). *Anal. Chem.* **38,** 1305.
146. Blaedel, W. J. and Christensen, E. L. (1967). *Ibid.* **39,** 1262.
147. Helfferich, F. and Schlögl, R. (1956). *Discuss Faraday Soc.* **21,** 133,
148. Neihof, R. and Sollner, K. (1956). *Ibid.* **21,** 94.
149. Peterson, M. A. and Gregor, H. P. (1959). *J.Electrochem. Soc.* **106,** 1051.
150. Mackay, D. and Meares, P. (1959). *Kolloid Z.,* **167,** 31.
151. Peers, A. M. (1956). *Discuss. Faraday Soc.* **21,** 124.
152. Patridge, S. M. and Peers, A. M. (1958). *J. Appl. Chem.* **8,** 49.
153. Rosenberg, N. W. and Tirrell, C. E. (1957). *Ind. Eng. Chem.* **49,** 780.
154. Sclhögl, R. (1955). *Z. Physik. Chem.* **3,** 73.
155. Oel, J. H. (1958). *Ibid.* **15,** 280.

156. Mackie, J. S. and Meares, P. (1955). *Proc. Royal. Soc.* **A232**, 485.
157. Meares, P. and Ussing, H. H. (1959). *Trans. Far. Soc.* **55**, 142.
158. Ussing, H. H. (1952). *Advances in Enzymology,* **15**, 21.
159. Behn. (1897). *Ann. Phys. Chem.* **62**, 54.
160. Teorell, T. (1949). *Arch. Sci. Physiol* **3**, 205.
161. Hoshiko, T. and Lindley, B. D. (1964). *Biochim. Biophis. Acta.* **79**, 301.
162. Bauge, K. and Brun, T. S. (1959). *Arbok. Univ. Bergen. Mat. Nat. Ser.* No. 10.
163. Brun, T. S. and Meisingseth, E. A. (1960). *Ibid.* No. 13.
164. Loeb, J. (1932). "Proteins and the Theory of Colloidal Behavior". McGraw Hill, New York,
165. Michaelis, L. and Fujita, A. (1925). *Biochem. Z.* **158**, 28.
166. Höber, R. and Hoffmann, F. (1928). Pfluegers. *Arch. Ges Physiol.* **194**, 558.
167. Donnan, F. G. (1911). *Z. Electrochem.* **17**, 572.
168. Gregor, H. P. (1948). *J. Am. Chem. Soc.* **70**, 1293.
169. Meyer, K. H. and Sievers, J. F. (1936). *Helv. Chim. Acta.* **19**, 649, 665, 987.
170. Teorell, T. (1935). *Proc. Soc. Explt. Biol. Med.* **33**, 282.
171. Hills, G. J., Jacobs, P. W. M. and Lakshminarayanaiah, N. (1961). *Proc. Roy. Soc.* **A262**, 257.
172. Lakshminarayanaiah, N. (1963). *J. Pol. Sci.* **Pt A 139**.
173. Boyd, G. E. and Bunzl. K. (1967). *J. Am. Chem. Soc.* **89**, 1776.
174. Gustafson, R. L. (1963). *J. Phys. Chem.* **67**, 2549; (1966), **70**, 957.
175. Freeman, D. H., Patel, V. C. and Buchanan, T. M. (1965). *Ibid.* **69**, 1477.
176. Freeman, D. H. (1960). *J. Phys. Chem.* **64**, 1048.
177. Glueckauf, E. (1962). *Proc. Roy. Soc.* **A268**, 350.
178. Luther, R. (1896). *Z. Physik. Chem.* **19**, 529.
179. Nernst, W. and Riesenfeld, E. H. (1902). *Ann. Phys.* **8**, 600.
180. Haber, F. and Klemensiewicz. (1909). *Z. Physik. Chem.* **67**, 385.
181. Sollner, K. (1930). *Z. Electrochem.* **36**, 36.
182. Teorell, T. (1935). *Proc. Nat. Acad. Sci. Wash.* **21**, 152.
183. Kumins, C. A. and London, A. (1960). *J. Polymer Sci.* **46**, 395.
184. Laksminarayanaiah, N. (1966). *J. Appl. Polymer Sci.* **10**, 687.
185. Riande, E. and Guzman, G. M. (1969). *Anales de Quimica* **65**, 483.
186. Scatchard, G. (1953). *J. Am. Chem. Soc.* **75**, 2883.
187. Riande, E., Guzman, G. M. and Dominguez, M. (1970). *Anales de Quimica* **66**, 57.
188. Lorimer, J. W., Boterenbrood, E. I. and Hermans, J. J. (1956). *Discuss. Faraday Soc.* **21**, 141.
189. Kobatake, Y., Takeguchi, N., Toyoshima, Y. and Fujita, H. (1965). *J. Phys. Chem.* **69**, 3981.
190. Kobatake, Y., Toyoshima, Y. and Takeguchi, N. (1966). *Ibid.* **70**, 1187.
191. Toyoshima, Y., Kobatake, Y. and Fujita, H. (1967). *Trans. Faraday Soc.* **63**, 2814.
192. Michaelis, L. and Fujita, A. (1925). *Biochem Z.* **161**, 47.
193. Michaelis, L. (1929). *Bull. Natl. Res. Council,* **69**, 119.
194. Michaelis, L. (1933). *Kolloid Z.,* **62**, 2.
195. Gregor, H. P. and Sollner, K. (1946). *J. Phys. Chem.* **50**, 53.
196. Gregor, H. P. and Sollner, K. (1955). *Biochim. Biophys. Acta,* **18**, 341.
197. Marshall, C. E. (1948). *J. Phys. Chem.* **52**, 1284.
198. Wyllie, M. R. J. (1954). *J. Phys. Chem.* **58**, 67.

199. McClintock, R., Neihof, R. and Sollner, K. (1960). *J. Electrochem. Soc.* **107,** 315.
200. Gregor, H. P., Jacobson, H., Shair, R. C. and Wetstone, D. M. (1957). *J. Phys. Chem.* **61,** 147.
201. Gregor, H. P. and Wetstone, D. M. (1957). *Ibid.* **61,** 147.
202. Bergsma, F. and Staverman, A. J. (1956). *Discuss Faraday Soc.* **21,** 61.
203. Hale, D. K. and Govindam, K. P. (1969). *J. Electrochem. Soc.* **116,** (10), 1373.
204. Dray, S. and Sollner, K. (1956). *Biochim. Biophys. Acta* **22,** 213.
205. Dray, S. and Sollner, K. (1956). *Ibid.* **22,** 220.
206. Ikeda, T. (1958). *J. Chem. Phys.* **28,** 166.
207. Ikeda, T. (1959). *J. Chem. Phys.* **31,** 267.
208. Ikeda, T., Tsuchiya, M. and Nakano, M. (1964). *Bull. Chem. Soc. Japan* **37,** 1482.
209. Kobatake, Y. (1959). *Bull. Tokyo Inst. Technol. Serv. B.p.* 97.
210. Tasaka, M., Morita, S., and Nagasawa, M. (1965). *J. Phys. Chem.* **69,** 4191.
211. Schmid, G. and Schwarz, H. (1952). *Z. Electrochem.* **56,** 35.
212. Brun, T. S. (1957). *Univ. Bergen Naturvitenskap. Rekke No.* 8.
213. Brun, T. S. and Vaula, D. (1967). *Ber. Bunsenges, Physik Chem.* **71,** 824.
214. Henderson, R. M. (1966). *J. Phys. Chem.* **70,** 2694.
215. Ishibashi, N. and Hirano, K. (1959). *J. Electrochem. Soc. Japan. Overseas Ed.,* **27,** E–195.
216. Meares, P. and Ussing, H. (1959). *Trans. Faraday Soc.* **55,** 2144.
217. Schmid, G., Schwarz, H. (1951). *Z. Electrochem.* **55,** 295.
218. Juda, W., Rosenberg, N. W., Marinsky, J. A. and Kasper, A. A. (1952). *J. Am. Chem. Soc.* **74,** 3736.
219. Kawabe, H., Jacobson, H., Miller, I. F. and Gregor, H. P. (1959). *J. Colloid Sci.*
220. Gregor, H. P., Belle, J. and Marcus, R. A. (1955). *J. Am. Chem. Soc.* **77,** 2713.
221. Toyoshima, Y., Yuasa, M., Kobatake, Y. and Fujita, H. (1967). *Trans. Faraday Soc.* **63,** 2803.
222. Fadley, C. S. and Wallace, R. A. (1968). *J. Electrochem. Soc.* **115,** 1264.
223. Rosenberg, N. W., George, J. H. B. and Poter, W. D. (1967). *J. Electrochem. Soc.* **104,** 111.
224. Tombalakaian, A. S. and Graydon, W. F. (1966). *J. Phys. Chem.* **70,** 3711.
225. Kressman, T. R. E. and Tye, F. L. (1956). *Discuss. Faraday Soc.* **21,** 185.
226. Gregor, H. P. and Peterson, M. A. (1964). *J. Phys. Chem.* **68,** 2201.
227. Hale, D. K. and McCauley, D. J. (1961). *Trans. Far. Soc.* **57,** 135.
228. Winger, A. G., Ferguson, R. and Kunin, R. (1956). *J. Phys. Chem.* **60,** 556.
229. Meares, P. and Sutton, A. H. (1968). *J. Colloid Interface Sci.* **28,** 118.
230. Subrahmanyan, V. and Lakshminarayanaiah, N. (1962). *J. Sci. Ind. Res. (India),* **21B,** 229.
231. Laksminarayanaiah, N. (1969). *J. Phys. Chem.* **73,** 97.
232. Oda, Y. and Yawataya, T. (1956). *Bull. Chem. Soc. Japan* **29,** 673.
233. Schmid, G. and Schwarz, H. (1951). *Z. Elekrochem.* **55,** 295, 684.
234. Arnold, R. and Swift, D. A. (1967). *Australian J. Chem.* **20,** 2575.
235. Von. Helmholtz, H. (1879). *Wied. Ann.* **7,** 337.
236. Smoluchowski, M. (1951). *Bull. Engng Res. Inst. Univ. Mich.* No. 33.
237. Despic, A. and Hills, G. J. (1955). *Trans. Faraday Soc.* **51,** 1260.
238. Bjerrum, N, and Manegold, E. (1927). *Kolloidz.* **43,** 5.
239. Manegold, E. and Solf, K. (1931). *Kolloid Schr.,* **25,** 273.

240. Laksminarayanaiah, N. (1969). *J. Electrochem. Soc.* **116**, 343.
241. Manning, G. S. (1967). *J. Chem. Phys.* **46**, 4976.
242. McBain, (1924). *J. Phys. Chem.* **28**, 706.
243. Glueckauf, E. (1955). *Trans. Far. Soc.* **51**, 1235.
244. Stewart, R. J. and Graydon, W. F. (1957). *J. Phys. Chem.* **61**, 164.
245. Scattergood, E. M. and Lightfoot, E. N. (1968). *Trans. Far. Soc.* **64**, 1355.
246. Oda, Y. and Yawataya, T, (1955). *Bull Chem. Soc. Japan* **28**, 263.
247. Oda, Y. and Yawataya, T. (1957). *Ibid* **30**, 213.
248. Kressman, T. R. E., Stanbridge, P. A., Tye, F. L. and Wilson, A. G. (1963). *Trans. Far. Soc.* **59**, 2133.
249. Carr, C. W., McClintock, R., and Sollner, K. (1962). *J. Electrochem. Soc.* **109**, 251.
250. Tombalakaian, A. S., Barton, H. J. and Graydon, W. F. (1962). *J. Phys. Chem.* **66**, 1006.
251. Kressman, T. R. E., Stanbridge, P. A. and Tye, F. L. (1963). *Trans. Far. Soc.* **59**, 2129.
252. Lakshminarayanaiah, N. (1967). *Desalination* **3**, 97.
253. Lakshminarayanaiah, N. and Subrahmanyan, V. (1968). *J. Phys. Chem.* **72**, 1253.
254. Lakshminarayanaiah, N. (1959). *Current Sci.* **28**, 321.
255. George, J. H. B. and Courant, R. A. (1967). *J. Phys. Chem.* **71**, 246.
256. Leitz, F. B. (1968). *J. Electrochem. Soc.* **115**, 86C.
257. Bejerano, T., Forgacs, C., and Rabinowitz, J. (1967). *Desalination* **3**, 129.
258. Arnold, R. (1969). *J. Phys. Chem.* **73**, 1414.
259. Dutrochet, M. (1855). *Ann. Chim. Phys.* **60**, 337.
260. Loeb, J. J. (1922). *Gen. Physiol.* **4**, 463, 621.
261. Bartell, F. F. and Madison, O. E. (1920). *J. Phys. Chem.* **24**, 444, 593.
262. Sollner, K. (1930). *Z. Elektrochem.* **36**, 234.
263. Sollner, K. (1954). *J. Phys. Chem.* **49**, 47, 171, 265.
264. Graham, T. (1854). *Phil. Trans. Roy. Soc. London,* **144**, 177.
265. Sollner, K. and Grollman, A. (1932). *Z. Electrochem.* **38**, 274.
266. Grollman, A. and Sollner, K. (1932). *Trans. Electrochem. Soc.* **61**, 487.
267. Carr, C. W. and Sollner, K. (1964). *Nature,* **204**, 878.
268. Grim, E. and Sollner, K. (1957). *J. Gen. Physiol.* **40**, 887; (1960) *Ibid* **44** ,381.
269. Dorst, W., Staverman, A. J. and Caramazza, R. (1964). *Rec. Trav. Chim.* **83**, 1329.
270. Tasaka, M., Kondo, Y. and Nagasawa, M. (1969). *J. Phys.* **73**, 3181.
271. Sollner, K. and Abrams, I. (1940). *J. Gen. Physiol.* **24**, 1.
272. Sollner, K., Abrams, I. and Carr, C. W. (1941). *J. Gen. Physiol.* **25**, 7.
273. Kobatake, Y. (1952). *J. Chem. Phys.* **28**, 442.
274. Kobatake, Y., Fujita, H. (1964). *Kolloid Z.* **196**, 58.
275. Fujita, H. and Kobatake, Y. (1968). *J. Colloid Interface Sci.* **27**, 609.
276. Sanders, B. H., Parsi, E. J. (1963). "Symposium on the Less Common Means of Separation". Inst, Chem. Eng., London.
277. Katz, W. E. (1960). "Preliminary Evaluation of Electric Membrance Processes for Chemical Processing Applications". Presented at 8th Annual All-Day Meeting, Philadelphia-Wilmington Section, A.I.Ch.E. and U. of Pa, Philadelphia. March, 29.
278. Dubey, G. A., McElhanney, T. R. and Wiley, A. J. (1965). *Tappi* **48**, 95.
279. Meyer, K. H. and Strauss, W. (1940). *Helv. Chim. Acta.* **23**, 795.

280. Kunin, R. (1966, 1967, 1968, 1969). *Ind. Eng. Chem.*
281. Di Benedetto, A. T. and Lightfoot, E. N. (1958). *Ind. Eng. Chem.* **50,** 691.
282. Peers, A. M. (1958). *J. Appl. Chem.* **8,** 59.
283. Glueckauf, E. and Kitt, G. P. (1956). *J. Appl. Chem.* **6,** 511.
284. Bril, K. S., Bril, S. and Krumholz, P. (1959). *J. Phys. Chem.* **63,** 256.
285. Ishibashi, N. and Emura, H. (1957). *Denki Kagaku,* **25,** 625.
286. Schulz, W. W., Neuvar, E. W., Carroll, J. L. and Burns, R. E. (1958). *Ind. Eng. Chem.* **50,** 1768.
287. Rohm and Haas Co., B.P. 967,103.
288. Chaussidon, J. (1957). *Compt. Rendu,* **244,** 2798.
289. Basu, A. S. (1958). *J. Indian Chem. Soc.* **35,** 451.
290. Marinsky, J. A. ,and Katz W. E. (1953). U.S.A.C.C. Rep. No. AECD–3556.
291. Mitchell, W., Jr. (Ed.) (1963). "Chemical Technology". Academic Press.
292. Berger, C. (1965). *Advan. Chem. Serv.* **47,** 188.
293. Gregor, H. P. (1961). *Proc. Ann. Powers Sources Conf.,* **15,** 4.
294. Niedrach, L. W. (1961). *J. Electrochem. Soc.* **109,** 1092.
295. Grubb, W. T. and Niedrach, L. W. (1960). *J. Electrochem. Soc.* **107,** 131.
296. Cairns, E. J., Douglas, D. L. and Niedrach, L. W. (1961). *A.I.Ch.E. J.* **7,** 55.
297. Miller, M. L., Skogman, J. and Sutherland, J. U.S. Pat. 3,265,536.
298. Lurie, R. M., Shuman, R. J. and Wiklund, H. I. (1961). U.S. Dept. Com. Office Tech. Serv. AD, 266,036.
299. Berger, C. B. and Strier, M. P. (1967). *Advances Chem. Serv.* No. 64, 17.
300. Grubb, W. T. (1959). *J. Electrochem. Soc.* **106,** 275.
301. Lovreck, B., Despic, A. and Bockris, J. O. M. (1960). *J. Phys. Chem.* **63,** 750.
302. Katchalsky, A. and Kedem, O. (1962). *Biophys. J.* **2,** 53.
303. Kolf, G. (1967). *Ber Bensunges. Physik. Chem.* **71,** 877.
304. Bahr, G. (1967). *Ibid.* **71,** 881.
305. Forgacs, C. and Stein, G., (1964). *Israel J. Chem.* **2,** 209.

Author Index

The numbers in brackets are the reference numbers and those in italic refer to the Reference pages where the references are listed in full. Absence of page number indicates a general reference.

A

Abbink, H. C. 179, 180, 181, 182, 183, 193, *201*, 274, *292*, 1068, *1069*, 1115 (Ab1), 1123(Ab1), *1151*

Abdullaev, G. B. 1146(Ak1), 1147(Ku1), *1152*, *1157*

Abey, A. E. 1115(Ab2), 1123(Ab2), 1126(Ab2), 1127(Ab2), *1151*

Abraham, K. P. 575, 582, *614*, *619*, *621*

Abraham, M. 801, 802, *806*

Abrams .I. 502(271, 272), *515*

Ackermann, R. J. 578, *614*

Ackermann, W. 557, 575, *616*

Adachi, A. 607, *614*

Adam-Benveniste, M. 1121(Be9), *1153*

Adda, Y. 201, *201*, 206(4), 213, 231, 244, 254, *291*, *292*, 700, *743*, *1149*

Adler, R. B. *1150*

Airokli, G. 86, 98, 99, 100, *126*

Airoldi, G. 290, *295*

Akerstroem, A. 1142(Li5, Li6), 1143 (Li11), 1144(Li7), *1158*

Akhundov, G. A. 1146(Ak1), *1152*

Alcock, C. B. 331, 332, 336, *344*, *346*, 553, 575, 576, 581, 587, *614*, *615*, *618*, *621*, 684, *698*, 749, *759*, 852, *865*, 998(26), 1011(48), *1046*, *1047*, 1134 (St1), 1135(St1), 1145(Al1), *1152*, *1162*

Allen, C. A. 220, 283, *292*, *294*, *297*, *298*

Allen, R. L. 1145(Al2), *1152*

Allen, R. R. 1112(Al3), 1121(Al3), *1152*

Alles, J. J. 1034(97), *1049*

Allnatt, A. R. 174, 179, *201*, 204, 284, *292*, *297*, 699, 700, 703, 704, 705, 706,

709, 711, 715, 716, 717, 734, 737, 738, 739, 740, 742, *743*, *745*, 825, 828, 830, 833, *836*, 1113(Al4), 1121(Al4, Al5), *1152*

Amata, C. D. 569, *621*, 1134(Sm1), 1143(Sm1), *1161*

Amphlet, C. B. 416(84), *511*

Amsel, G. 127, 128, 130, 132, 134, 135, 137, 139, 140, 141, 142, 145, 146, 147, *149*

Andelman, J. B. 442(133), 475(133), *512*

Anderegg, F. O. 931, *956*

Anderson, J. S. 1147(An1), *1152*

Anderson, O. L. 359, *396*

Andes, R. V. 955, *956*, 981, *985*

Ando, R. 1118(As2), 1119(As2), *1152*

Ansell, G. S. 697, *697*

Anthony, A. M. 1129(An2), *1151*, *1152*

Antoneva, E. A. 360, 373, *399*

Antonsen, O. 1020(71), *1048*

Antropoff, A. V. 1118(An3), *1152*

Aoki, H. 610, *617*

Aoyama, H. 1011(51), 1020(51), *1047*

Arai, G. 278, *292*, *297*, *1152*

Arbarenkov, V. 60, *77*

Archer, D. A. 327, 328, *344*

Archer, D. H. 1020(72), 1031(85, 86), 1034(97), 1037(72), 1045(104), 1046 (104), *1048*, *1049*

Arends, J. 1079, 1080, *1090*, 1114(Ar2, Ar3), 1122(Ar2), *1152*

Argue, G. R. 41, *77*, 336, 340, 342, *345*, 932, 936, 946, *956*, 967, 968, 977, 983, 985, *985*, *987*, 1116(Ow1), *1160*

Arkhangelskaya, V. A. 1116(Ar4),, 1117 (Ar4), *1152*

Arkharov, V. I. 1147(Ar5), *1152*

Armstrong, G. *928*

xv

Pointud, Y. 857, 858, 859, 860, 861, *865*, 868, 869, 872, 873, 893, 894, 897, 898, 914, 916, 917, 922, *929*, *930*
Polak, P. L. 433(111), 441(111), *511*
Polikarpova, I. P. *298*
Pond, G. R. 340, *346*, 1116(Su2), *1162*
Pool, M. 577, 578, 579, 612, *619*
Porai-Koshits, E. A. 355, *399*
Porter, J. T. 326, 328, 329, *344*, 1129 (Di1), *1154*
Poter, W. D. 488(223), *514*
Pourbaix, M. 753, *798*
Pourbaix, M. J. 748, *798*
Powell, B. E. 331, 333, 335, 338, 340, *346*, 679, *698*
Powell, H. M. 816, *837*
Powers, R. A. 973, *986*
Prankin, A. A. 362, *398*, *399*
Prasad, K. K. 582, *619*
Pratt, G. W. Jr. *78*
Pratt, P. L. 170, 172, 176, 177, *202*, 264, *293*, 1112(St7), 1121(Ki3, St7), 1138 (St7), *1157*, *1162*
Preis, H. 541, *615*, 993(2), *1046*
Pretzel, F. E. 1112(Pr1), 1121(Pr1), *1160*
Preuner, G. 534, *538*
Price, J. B. 1144(Pr2), *1160*
Pringle, J. P. S. 147, *149*
Priqueler, M. 368, *397*
Proctor, J. M. 364, *399*
Pröve, G. 329, 330, *345*
Pryor, A. W. 1128(Pr3), *1160*
Ptashnik, V. B. 258, *294*, *298*

R

Rabinowitz, J. 499(257), *515*
Raccah, P. M. 1031(90), *1048*
Radzilowski, R. H. 827, *837*
Rahlts, P. 811, *837*
Rajan, K. S. 416(88), *511*
Rajawat, M. S. 411(31), *510*
Raleigh, D. O. 655, *675*, 810, 811, 828, 831, 832, *837*, 902, 903, *930*, 983, *987*
Ramasastry, C. 1118(Ra1, Ra2), 1124 (Ra2), *1160*
Ramsey, M. W. 368, 369, *397*
Rand, M. H. 679, *697*

Randall, M. 178, *202*
Randsalu, A. 719, *745*
Ranford, R. E. 583, *619*
Rank, E. G. 578, *614*
Ranny, M. W. 1031(81), *1048*
Ranon, U. 101, 102, *126*
Rao, C. N. R. 286, 287, 288, 290, *294*, 1129(Me1), 1130(Me1), 1134(Me1), *1159*
Rao, K. J. 286, 287, 288, 290, *294*
Rapoport, E. 1127(Ra3), 1139(Ra3), *1160*
Rapp, R. A. 327, 331, 332, 335, 336, 339, *345*, 545, 553, 554, 555, 556, 567, 576, 581, 587, 588, 594, 595, 597, 598, *618*, *619*, *621*, 679, *698*, 814, 820, *836*, 851, 852, 854, *865*, 903, 904, 925, 926, 927, 928, *930*, 1129(La3), 1134(Pa6), 1135(La3, Pa6, Ra4), *1158*, *1160*
Rasch, 299, *318*
Ratchford, R. J. 520, 526, *538*, 660, 663, *675*
Rautenfeldt, von. 299, *318*
Rayleigh, Lord. 210, *294*
Raynor, G. V. 875, *929*
Reachter, H. L. 1020(69), *1048*
Reade, R. F. 283, *294*, *298*, 1139(Re1), *1160*
Rector, C. W. 89, 112, *126*
Redfield, A. G. 1111(Ei2), *1155*
Redington, R. W. 1142(Re2), *1160*
Reed, C. A. 258, *294*, *298*
Reese, C. 436(120), *512*
Reid, A. F. 816, *837*
Reilley, C. N. *930*
Reilly, M. H. 106, 118, *125*, 174, 194, *202*, 267, 268, 270, 286, 287, 288, 290, *293*, 316, *317*, 337, *344*, 1113(Fu3, Fu4), 1114(Fu3), 1138(Fu3), *1155*
Reinhold, H. 304, 306, 307, 308, *318*, 521, *538*, 650, 655, *675*, 676, 699, *745*, 811, 821, *837*, 855, *865*, 962, 975, *987*, 1000(27), *1046*, 1071, *1091*, 1136(Re3), *1160*
Reinhold, J. 314, *318*
Reinmuth, W. H. *930*
Reisfeld, R. 258, 283, *294*, *298*
Rembaum, A. 809, 810, *836*, 977, 978, *986*
Renz, C. 1070, *1090*

Subject Index

A

Acanthite, 43
Activation energy, 2, 266, 269, 287, 359, 360, 367, 370, 439, 456, 486
Activity coefficient, 456, 457, 479
Aluminate, 343
Aluminium,
  anodic oxidation of, 148
  oxide film, 147
Amorphous,
  electrolytes, 51
  polymer, 402
  solids, 2
Analcite, 46
Anions,
  divalent, 171
  polyatomic, 138
Anode,
  dissolving, 302, 304
  silver, 302, 304
Anodic oxide films, 132
Arrhenius,
  activation energy, 324
  law, 238, 252, 269, 284, 289, 290
Association, Coulomb energy of, 85
Atomic,
  wave functions, 16
  radius, 58
Auger electron spectroscopy, 127

B

Band,
  structure, 64
  conduction, 30
  electronic energy, 62, 65
  forbidden energy, 9
  p-band, 19, 66
  s-band, 16
  valence, 32

Batteries, 508
Bloch functions, 6, 9, 16
Boltzmann constant, 357
Borate glasses, 355
Born-Haber cycle, 72
Bragg equation, 24
Brillouin zones, 11, 24
Bromides, 40

C

Cathode, platinum, 302
Cathodic reaction, 122
Cations, see also Impurity, Vacancy
  divalent, 171
  impurity, 82
  interstitial, 156
  polyvalent, 371
  trivalent impurity, 90
Cell, silver-zinc, 508
Chabazite, 46
Chloride,
  potassium, 64
  sodium, 66
Chloromethylation, 406
Clathrate, 51
Cohesive energy, 66, 72, 75
Colour centres, 49
Complex ions, 42
Concentration,
  defect, 158, 180
  Frenkel defect, 159
  isotopic, 142
  potential, 459
  profiles, 130
Conduction,
  anionic, 38, 304, 308
  band, 2
  cationic, 38, 308
  electronic, 307, 319, 395
  ionic, 307, 323, 392

Compound Index